WORLD ATLAS

Rand M⚆Nally & Company

Chicago   New York   San Francisco

CONTENTS

EARTH: THE LIFE-SUPPORTING PLANET pages 4A-75A
inclusive copyright © 1972 by Mitchell Beazley Limited.

Library of Congress Catalog Card Number: 73-3377
Copyright © MCMLXXV by Rand McNally & Company.
Copyright © MCMLXXIV, MCMLXXIII, MCMLXXI by Rand McNally & Company.
Copyright © MCMLXVIII, MCMLXVI, MCMLXV, MCMLXIV
    by Rand McNally & Company.
Copyright © MCMLXVIII under International Copyright Union
    by Rand McNally & Company. All rights reserved.
Printed in the United States of America.

The Sun is the controlling body of the solar system and is far more massive than all its planets combined. Even Jupiter, much the largest of the planets, has a diameter only about one-tenth that of the Sun. The solar system is divided into two main parts. The inner region includes four relatively small, solid planets: Mercury, Venus, the Earth and Mars. Beyond the orbit of Mars comes a wide gap in which move many thousands of small minor planets or asteroids, some of which are little more than rocks. Further out come the four giants: Jupiter, Saturn, Uranus and Neptune. Pluto, on the fringe of the system, is a curious little planet; it appears to be in a class of its own, but at present very little is known about it and even its size is a matter for conjecture. Maps of the solar system can be misleading in that they tend to give a false idea about distance. The outer planets are very widely separated. For example, Saturn is further away from Uranus than it is from the Earth.

The contrasting planets

The inner, or terrestrial, planets have some points in common, but a greater number of differences. Mercury, the planet closest to the Sun, has no atmosphere and that of Mars is very thin; but Venus, strikingly similar to the Earth in size and mass, has a dense atmosphere made up chiefly of carbon dioxide, and a surface temperature of over 400°C. The giant planets are entirely different. At least in their outer layers they are made up of gas, like a star; but, unlike a star, they have no light of their own and shine only by reflecting the light of their star, the Sun. Several of the planets have moons. The Earth has one (or it may be our partner in a binary system), Jupiter has 12, Saturn 10 (discounting its rings), Uranus five and Neptune two. Mars also has two satellites but these are less than 15 mi (24 km) in diameter and of a different type from the Earth's Moon. The Earth is unique in the solar system in having oceans on its surface and an atmosphere made up chiefly of nitrogen and oxygen. It is the only planet suited to life of terrestrial type. It is not now believed that highly evolved life can exist on any other planet in the Sun's family, though it it still possible that some primitive life forms may exist on Mars.

Observing the planets

Five of the planets, Mercury, Venus, Mars, Jupiter and Saturn, were known to the inhabitants of the Earth in very ancient times. They are starlike in aspect but easy to distinguish because, unlike the stars, they seem to wander slowly about the sky whereas the true stars appear to hold their position for century after century. The so-called proper motions of the stars are too slight to be noticed by the naked eye, but they can be measured by modern techniques. Mercury and Venus always appear to be in the same part of the sky as the Sun. Mercury is never prominent but Venus is dazzlingly bright, partly because its upper clouds are highly reflective and partly because it is close; it can come within 25,000,000 mi (40,000,000 km), only about 100 times as far as the Moon. Jupiter is generally very bright, as is Mars when it is well placed. Saturn is also conspicuous to the naked eye, but Uranus is only just visible and Neptune and Pluto are much fainter.

The Sun's active surface *right*

The structure of a star, such as the Sun, is immensely complex. The very concept of its surface is hard to define, and the size of the Sun depends on the wavelength of the light with which it is viewed. Using the 'hydrogen alpha' wavelength the bright surface of the Sun, known as the photosphere, appears as shown right, above. The surface, at about 6000 °C, is dotted with light and dark patches as a result of the violent upcurrents of hotter gas and cooler areas between them. Larger, darker regions are sunspots (right), temporary but very large disturbances.

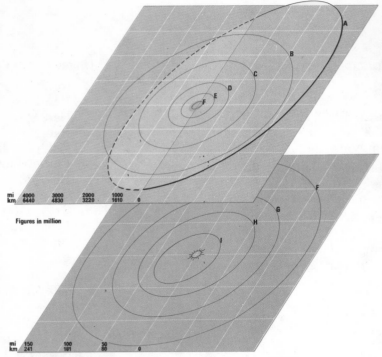

mi 4000 3000 2000 1000 0
km 6440 4830 3220 1610 0

Figures in million

mi 150 100 50 0
km 241 181 80 0

Orbits around the Sun *above*
The Sun's nine known planets, and the asteroids, describe heliocentric orbits in the same direction. But some planetary orbits are highly eccentric, while some asteroids are both eccentric and steeply inclined. The outermost planet, Pluto, passes within the orbit of Neptune, while one asteroid reaches almost to the radius of Saturn. Over 350 years ago Johannes Kepler showed that the planets do not move in perfect circles, and found that the line joining each planet to the Sun sweeps out a constant area in a given time. so that speed is greatest close to the Sun.

A	Pluto
B	Neptune
C	Uranus
D	Saturn
E	Jupiter
F	Mars
G	Earth
H	Venus
I	Mercury

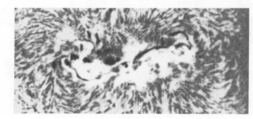

The Sun's structure *right*

The Sun is made up of highly dissimilar regions. This narrow sector includes the inner part of the corona (A) which, though very diffuse, has a temperature of some 1,000,000 °C. Into it leap solar prominences, 'flames' thousands of miles long which arch along the local magnetic field from the chromosphere (B), the outer layer of the Sun proper, which covers the visible photosphere with a layer of variable, highly mobile and rarefied gas about 6000 mi (10000 km) thick. Inside the Sun the outer layer (C) of gas is in constant movement and transfers heat from the interior. Inner region D is thought to transfer energy mainly by radiation. The innermost zone of all (E), the conditions of which can only be surmised but are thought to include a temperature of some 14,000,000 °C, sustains the energy of the Sun (and its planets) by continuous fusion of hydrogen into helium.

1,250
2,000

432
695
400,
640,
350
560
300,
480,
250,
400,
200,
320,
150,
240,
100,
160,

mi 50
km 80

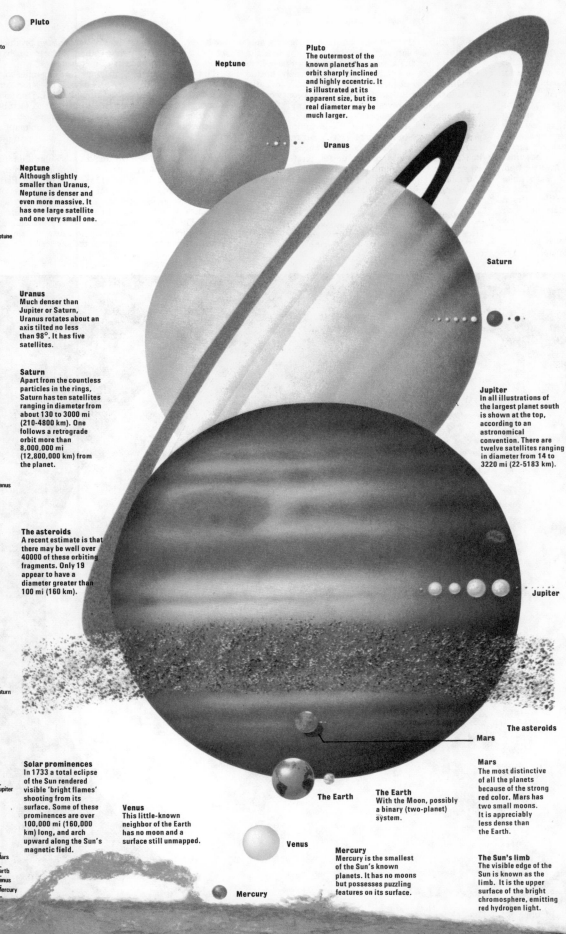

Pluto

Neptune

Pluto
The outermost of the known planets has an orbit sharply inclined and highly eccentric. It is illustrated at its apparent size, but its real diameter may be much larger.

Uranus

Saturn

Neptune
Although slightly smaller than Uranus, Neptune is denser and even more massive. It has one large satellite and one very small one.

Uranus
Much denser than Jupiter or Saturn, Uranus rotates about an axis tilted no less than 98°. It has five satellites.

Saturn
Apart from the countless particles in the rings, Saturn has ten satellites ranging in diameter from about 130 to 3000 mi (210-4800 km). One follows a retrograde orbit more than 8,000,000 mi (12,800,000 km) from the planet.

Jupiter
In all illustrations of the largest planet south is shown at the top, according to an astronomical convention. There are twelve satellites ranging in diameter from 14 to 3220 mi (22-5183 km).

The asteroids
A recent estimate is that there may be well over 40000 of these orbiting fragments. Only 19 appear to have a diameter greater than 100 mi (160 km).

Jupiter

The asteroids

Mars

Solar prominences
In 1733 a total eclipse of the Sun rendered visible 'bright flames' shooting from its surface. Some of these prominences are over 100,000 mi (160,000 km) long, and arch upward along the Sun's magnetic field.

Venus
This little-known neighbor of the Earth has no moon and a surface still unmapped.

The Earth

Venus

Mercury

Mars
The most distinctive of all the planets because of the strong red color. Mars has two small moons. It is appreciably less dense than the Earth.

The Earth
With the Moon, possibly a binary (two-planet) system.

Mercury
Mercury is the smallest of the Sun's known planets. It has no moons but possesses puzzling features on its surface.

The Sun's limb
The visible edge of the Sun is known as the limb. It is the upper surface of the bright chromosphere, emitting red hydrogen light.

The solar system *left*
The Sun is the major body in the solar system. It lies 30000 light-years from the center of our galaxy and takes 225 million years to complete one journey around it. There are nine planets and their satellites in the system, as well as comets and various minor bodies such as meteoroids. The diagram on the left shows the upper limb of the Sun (bottom) and the main constituent members of the solar system very greatly condensed into a smaller space. To indicate the amount of the radial compression, the limb of the Sun is drawn for a near-sphere of 5 ft (1.52 m) diameter. On this scale the Earth would be about 420 ft (127 m) away and the outermost planet Pluto, no less than 3 mi (4.9 km) distant.

Pluto, discovered in 1930, has a very eccentric orbit, with a radius varying between 2766 and 4566 million mi (4500 and 7400 million kilometers). Being so far from the Sun, it is extremely cold, and probably has no atmosphere.

Neptune, discovered in 1846, has a diameter of 31500 mi (50700 km) and is made up of gas, although little is known of its interior. It orbits the Sun once in 164¾ years. Seen through binoculars it is a small bluish disk.

Uranus, discovered in 1781, is apparently similar to Neptune, but less massive. Although faintly visible to the naked eye, even large telescopes show little detail upon its greenish surface

Saturn is the second largest planet, its equatorial diameter being 75100 mi (122,300 km). Visually it is unlike any other heavenly body, because of its equatorial system of rings made up of particles of various sizes. The planet itself is less dense than water and at least its outer layers are gaseous.

Jupiter, the largest planet, has an equatorial diameter of 88700 mi (142,750 km), but its rapid spin, once every 9¾ hours, makes it very flattened at the poles. It appears to have cloud belts, possibly of liquid ammonia, and various spots, of which the great red spot seems to be semi-permanent.

The asteroids, a mass of apparent planetary material ranging in size from dust up to one lump about as large as the British Isles, orbit mainly between Mars and Jupiter, though some have eccentric orbits which approach the Earth.

Mars is about 4200 mi (6760 km) in diameter. It has a thin atmosphere, mainly of carbon dioxide, and its surface is pitted with Moon-like craters. It is not thought today that the planet contains any life.

The Earth/Moon system is today regarded as a double planet rather than a planet and satellite. The Moon has an average distance from Earth of 239,000 mi (385,000 km) and it is now known that it has never contained life.

Venus is almost the twin of the Earth in size and mass. It is too hot to contain life, and its very dense atmosphere is mainly carbon dioxide. It has a year' of 224¾ Earth days, and it spins on its axis once every 243 Earth days.

Mercury, the innermost planet, is only about 3000 mi (4800 km) in diameter, and has lost whatever atmosphere it had. Like Venus it shows phases, but it is always close to the Sun when viewed from the Earth and cannot be seen clearly.

EARTH'S COMPANION: THE MOON

The Moon is our companion in space. Its mean distance from the Earth is less than a quarter of a million miles – it varies between 221,460 miles (356,410 km) and 252,700 miles (406,685 km) – and it was the first world other than our Earth to come within the range of man's space probes. At first mere masses, these then became instrument packages and finally spacecraft carrying men. With their aid our knowledge of the Moon has been vastly increased in the past decade. Astronauts Neil Armstrong and Edwin Aldrin made the first human journey to the lunar surface in July 1969, and the Moon has since been subjected to detailed and direct investigation.

The mean diameter of the Moon is 2158 miles (3473 km), and its mass is 1/81st as much as that of the Earth. Despite this wide difference the ratio is much less than that between other planets and their moons, and the Earth/Moon system is now widely regarded as a double planet rather than as a planet and satellite. The Moon's mean density is less than that of the Earth, and it may lack a comparable heavy core. Escape velocity from the lunar surface is only 1.5 mi/sec (2.4 km/sec), and this is so low that the Moon has lost any atmosphere it may once have had. To Earth life it is therefore an extremely hostile world. Analysis of lunar rock brought back to Earth laboratories and investigated by Soviet probes on the Moon has so far revealed no trace of any life. The Moon appears to have always been sterile.

Much of the surface of the Moon comprises large grey plains, mis-called 'mare' (seas), but most of it is extremely rough. There are great ranges of mountains, isolated peaks and countless craters which range from tiny pits up to vast enclosures more than 150 miles (240 km) in diameter. Many of the craters have central mountains or mountain-groups. Some of

Full Moon *below*
This striking photograph was taken by the *Apollo 11* astronauts in July 1969. It shows parts of both the Earth-turned and far hemispheres. The dark plain near the center is the Mare Crisium.

the larger craters show signs of having been produced by volcanic action, while others appear to have resulted from the impacts of meteorites.

The Moon rotates slowly, performing one complete turn on its axis every 27.3 days. This is the same as its period of revolution around the Earth, so it always presents the same face to us. But in October 1959 the Soviet probe *Lunik 3* photographed the hidden rear hemisphere and it has since been mapped in detail. It contains no large 'seas'. The appearance of the lunar surface depends strongly on the angle at which it is viewed and the direction of solar illumination. In the photograph on the right, taken from a height of about 70 miles (115 km) with the Earth having once more come into full view ahead, the lunar surface looks deceptively smooth; in fact, there is practically no level ground anywhere in the field of vision. The lunar horizon is always sharply defined, because there is no atmosphere to cause blurring or distortion. For the same reason, the sky seen from the Moon is always jet black.

Earthrise *above*
This view of the Earth rising was visible to the crew of *Apollo 10* in May 1969 as they orbited the Moon 70 miles (115 km) above the surface. They had just come round from the Moon's rear hemisphere.

Eclipses

Once regarded as terrifying actions of angry gods, eclipses are today merely useful. They provide a different view of the Sun and Moon that opens up fresh information. In a lunar eclipse the Earth passes directly between the Sun and Moon; in a solar eclipse the Moon passes between Sun and Earth. Both the Earth and Moon constantly cast a shadow comprising a dark inner cone surrounded by a region to which part of the sunlight penetrates. A body passing through the outer shadow experiences a partial eclipse, while the inner cone causes a total eclipse in which all direct sunlight is cut off.

A total solar eclipse is magnificent. The bright star is blocked out by a black Moon, but around it the Sun's atmosphere flashes into view. The pearly corona of thin gas can be seen extending a million miles from the Sun. Closer to the surface huge 'prominences' of red hydrogen leap into space and curve back along the solar magnetic field. In a partial solar eclipse these things cannot be seen, while in a total eclipse caused by the Moon at its greatest distance from Earth a ring of the Sun is left visible. As the Moon's orbit is not in the same plane as the Earth's, total solar eclipses occur very rarely, on occasions when the tip of the Moon's dark shadow crosses the Earth as a spot 169 miles (272 km) wide.

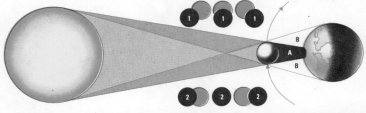

Eclipses *left and below*
When the Moon passes in front of the Sun as in sequence 1 its shadow B causes a partial solar eclipse (below, left, taken 21 November 1966).
But in the case of sequence 2, shadow cone A gives a total eclipse (below, right, 15 February 1961).

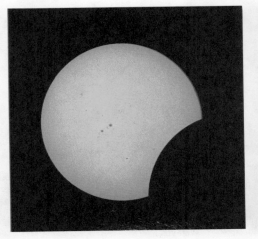

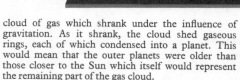

3 The gas cloud begins to assume the form of a regular disk. The infant Sun begins to shine - by the energy from gravitational shrinkage.

4 Material is thrown off from the Sun to join that already in the solar cloud, whose condensations have become more noticeable.

1 According to the most widely accepted theory, (the 'accretion' theory) the solar system originally consisted only of a mass of tenuous gas, and dust. There was no true Sun, and there was no production of nuclear energy. The gas was made up chiefly of hydrogen, with occasional random condensations.

2 Gravitational forces now cause the cloud to shrink and assume a more regular shape. Its density and mass near the center increase, but there are still no nuclear processes.

How did the Earth come into existence? This question has intrigued mankind for centuries but it was not until the start of true science that plausible theories were advanced. Although some theories held sway for many years, they were eventually deposed by the discovery of some fatal flaw. Even today, it is impossible to be sure that the main problem has been solved, but at least some concrete facts exist as a guide. It is now reasonably certain that the age of the Earth is of the order of 4550-4700 million years. The other planets are presumably about the same age, since they were probably formed by the same process in the same epoch.

Several centuries ago Archbishop Ussher of Armagh maintained that the world had come into being at a definite moment in the year 4004 BC. This estimate was made on purely religious grounds, and it soon became clear that the Earth is much older. In 1796 the French astronomer Laplace put forward the famous Nebular Hypothesis, according to which the Sun and the planets were formed from a rotating cloud of gas which shrank under the influence of gravitation. As it shrank, the cloud shed gaseous rings, each of which condensed into a planet. This would mean that the outer planets were older than those closer to the Sun which itself would represent the remaining part of the gas cloud.

The Nebular Hypothesis was accepted for many years, but eventually serious mathematical weaknesses were found in it. Next came a number of tidal theories according to which the Earth and other planets were formed from a cigar-shaped tongue of matter torn from the Sun by the gravitational pull of a passing star. The first plausible theory of this kind came from the English astronomer Sir James Jeans, but this too was found to be mathematically untenable and the idea had to be given up.

Most modern theories assume that the planets were formed by accretion from a rotating solar cloud of gas and finely-dispersed dust. If the Sun were originally attended by such a cloud, this cloud would, over a sufficiently long period of time, become a flat disk.

If random concentration had become sufficiently massive, it would draw in extra material by virtue of its gravitational attraction, forming 'proto-planets'. When the Sun began to radiate strongly, part of the mass of each proto-planet would be driven off due to the high temperatures, leaving a solar system of the kind that exists today.

The fact that such an evolutionary sequence can be traced emphasizes that in talking about the origin of the Earth we are considering only a small part of a continuous story. What will become of the Earth in the far future? The Sun is radiating energy because of the nuclear process within it: hydrogen is being converted into helium causing mass to be lost with a resulting release of energy. However, when the supply of hydrogen begins to run low, the Sun must change radically. It will move towards a red giant stage swelling and engulfing the Earth. Fortunately, this will not happen for at least another 6000 million years, but eventually the Sun which sustains our planet will finally destroy it.

Alternative theories

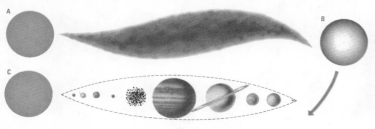

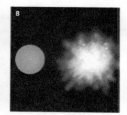

Contracting nebula *above*
Laplace suggested that a contracting nebula might shed gas which then condensed.

Tidal theories *above*
In 1901 Sir James Jeans postulated that Sun A was attracted to another star B which passed at close range. A cloud of matter was drawn off by their gravitational attraction. Star B moved on while the cloud condensed to form planets circling our Sun at C.

A violent beginning *above*
One of the theories of how the solar system came to be formed assumes that the Sun once had a binary companion star. This exploded as a supernova (above) and was blown off as a white dwarf

16 As the 'fuel' runs out, the radiation pressure falls, and under internal gravity the Sun will collapse inwards changing in only 50000 years from a red giant into a super-dense white dwarf.

17 As a white dwarf, the Sun will continue to radiate feebly for an immense period. At last all radiation must cease, and the Sun will remain as a dead, dark globe - a black dwarf.

15 By now all the inner planets will have long since been destroyed. The Sun will become unstable, reaching the most violent stage of its career as a red giant, with a vast, relatively cool surface and an intensely hot, dense core.

14 When the center of the Sun has reached another critical temperature, the helium will begin to 'burn' giving the so-called 'helium flash'. After a temporary contraction the Sun will then swell out to a diameter 400 times that at present.

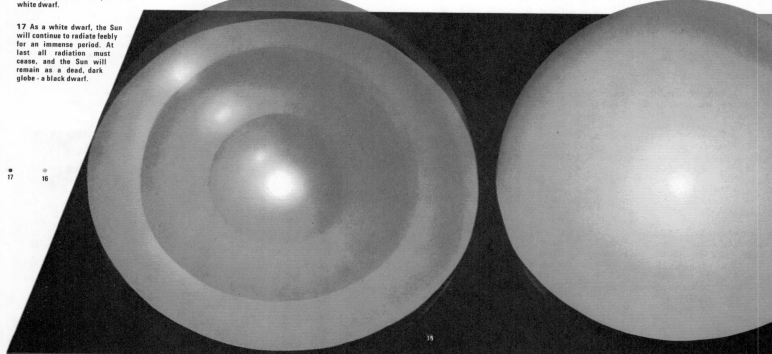

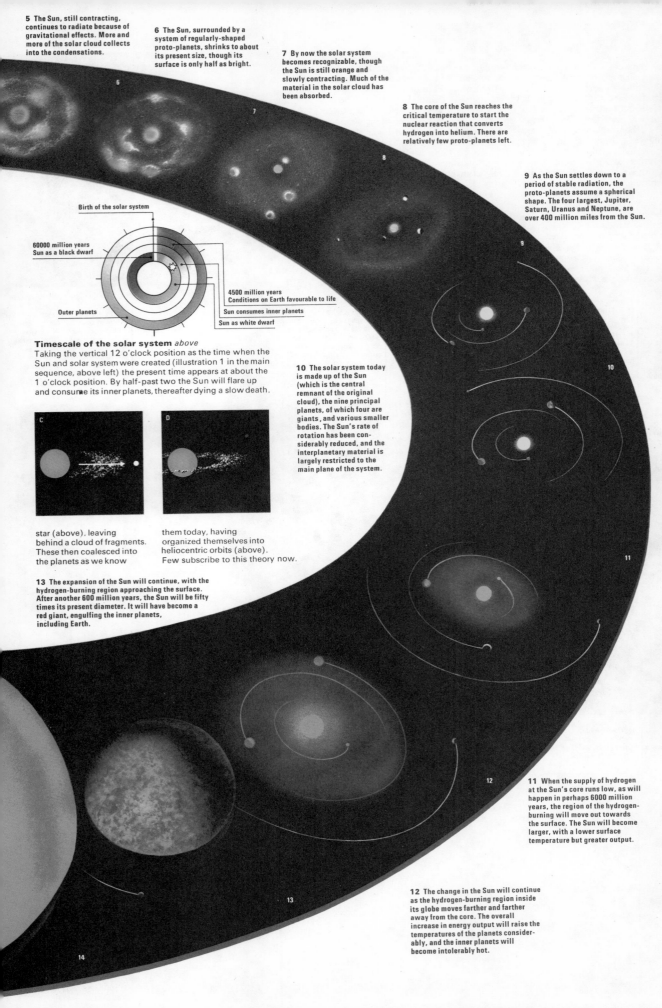

5 The Sun, still contracting, continues to radiate because of gravitational effects. More and more of the solar cloud collects into the condensations.

6 The Sun, surrounded by a system of regularly-shaped proto-planets, shrinks to about its present size, though its surface is only half as bright.

7 By now the solar system becomes recognizable, though the Sun is still orange and slowly contracting. Much of the material in the solar cloud has been absorbed.

8 The core of the Sun reaches the critical temperature to start the nuclear reaction that converts hydrogen into helium. There are relatively few proto-planets left.

9 As the Sun settles down to a period of stable radiation, the proto-planets assume a spherical shape. The four largest, Jupiter, Saturn, Uranus and Neptune, are over 400 million miles from the Sun.

Birth of the solar system

60000 million years
Sun as a black dwarf

Outer planets

4500 million years
Conditions on Earth favourable to life

Sun consumes inner planets

Sun as white dwarf

Timescale of the solar system *above*
Taking the vertical 12 o'clock position as the time when the Sun and solar system were created (illustration 1 in the main sequence, above left) the present time appears at about the 1 o'clock position. By half-past two the Sun will flare up and consume its inner planets, thereafter dying a slow death.

C

D

star (above), leaving behind a cloud of fragments. These then coalesced into the planets as we know

them today, having organized themselves into heliocentric orbits (above). Few subscribe to this theory now.

10 The solar system today is made up of the Sun (which is the central remnant of the original cloud), the nine principal planets, of which four are giants, and various smaller bodies. The Sun's rate of rotation has been considerably reduced, and the interplanetary material is largely restricted to the main plane of the system.

13 The expansion of the Sun will continue, with the hydrogen-burning region approaching the surface. After another 600 million years, the Sun will be fifty times its present diameter. It will have become a red giant, engulfing the inner planets, including Earth.

11 When the supply of hydrogen at the Sun's core runs low, as will happen in perhaps 6000 million years, the region of the hydrogen-burning will move out towards the surface. The Sun will become larger, with a lower surface temperature but greater output.

12 The change in the Sun will continue as the hydrogen-burning region inside its globe moves farther and farther away from the core. The overall increase in energy output will raise the temperatures of the planets considerably, and the inner planets will become intolerably hot.

The lifespan of the Earth

The Earth was produced from the solar cloud (1-6 on main diagram). It had no regular form, but, as more and more material was drawn in, it began to assume a spherical shape (7-8).

When it had reached its present size (9), the Earth had a dense atmosphere; not the original hydrogen atmosphere but one produced by gas from the interior. Life had not started.

The Earth today (10), moving in a stable orbit, has an equable temperature and oxygen-rich atmosphere, so that it alone of all the planets in the solar system is suitable for life.

When the Sun nears the red giant stage (11-13), the Earth will be heated to an intolerable degree. The atmosphere will be driven off, the oceans will boil and life must come to an end.

As the Sun reaches the peak of its violence (14-15), it will swell out until the Earth is engulfed. Its natural life is probably no more than 8000 million years : its end is certain

Man's most powerful nuclear weapons pale into insignificance beside the violence of an earthquake or the destructive and indiscriminate force of a volcano. These cataclysmic phenomena frequently occur along the same belts of instability in the Earth's crust and are often only different manifestations of the same fundamental processes. About 800 volcanoes are known to have been active in historical times, and many are extremely active today. All the mid-ocean ridges are volcanic in origin, and many underwater eruptions occur along these submarine mountain ranges. Spectacular volcanic eruptions sometimes break the ocean surface, such as during the formation in 1963 of the island of Surtsey, south of Iceland (photograph, right). Some islands, such as Iceland itself, are the products of continued outpourings of lava along the crest of the mid-ocean ridge.

Oceanic earthquakes caused by sudden sea-floor displacements may result in tsunamis or giant sea waves. About 80 per cent of the shallow earthquakes and almost all deep ones take place along the belt around the Pacific. Clear evidence of the large scale movements of the mantle are provided by the zones within which earthquake shocks are generated along some Pacific island arc systems. These zones plunge down from sea-floor level to depths of 440 miles (700 km) beneath the adjacent continents and mark the positions of downward flow of the mantle convection currents (page 15A). The corresponding upwelling regions lie along the mid-ocean ridges, where new basic volcanic material is continually being added to the ocean crust as outward movement takes place away from the ridges.

These sea-floor spreading movements act as 'conveyor belts' for the continents, and constitute the basic mechanism for the large displacements involved in continental drifting. Geological data confirm the former close fits of the margins of the reassembled continental jig-saw puzzle, and also corroborate the detailed paleomagnetic evidence visible in today's rocks of the movements of the continents relative to the geographic poles.

Geysers
Ground water and mud heated by volcanic activity can lie on the surface as puddles and hot springs, rendered colorful by dissolved minerals, or be pumped out in the form of geysers. The latter are connected to extensive underground reservoirs in which steam pressure builds up above the hot water. Intermittently the system discharges high into the air.

Fissure eruption
In this type of eruption freely flowing molten basaltic material exudes from apertures forced in the crust. The surface crack may be several miles in length and the more or less horizontal flow has on occasion covered more than 200 square miles (500 km²).

Hawaiian-type eruption
In this case large, shallow cones, often containing lakes of molten lava, generally release gas and vapor in a relatively passive way. But sometimes glowing lava is expelled as a fine spray which in a high wind can be drawn out into fine threads called Pelée's hair.

Emissions
Incandescent lava issues from the main cone or from side vents, while dense vapors pour from every crevice. Water vapor is the main gaseous component, but nitrogen and sulphur dioxide are also important.

Layering
Most volcanoes have a history extending back thousands or even millions of years. Over this time the main cone has built up in many stratified layers, sometimes of contrasting types of lava. Each fresh eruption produces at least one additional layer.

Underground water
Heated beyond normal boiling point, the pressurized water issues in a rush when pressure is relieved.

Magma chamber
Underlying every volcano is a volume of intensely hot fluid under high pressure.

Laccolith
Above the pipes and sills of the hot magma lies a giant lens-shaped intrusion of cold rock.

Metamorphic rock
The strata adjacent to the fiery magma are physically and chemically altered by the heat.

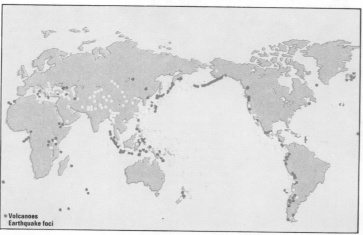

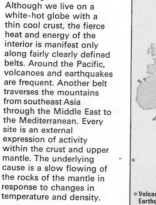

Where the Earth seems active *right*
Although we live on a white-hot globe with a thin cool crust, the fierce heat and energy of the interior is manifest only along fairly clearly defined belts. Around the Pacific, volcanoes and earthquakes are frequent. Another belt traverses the mountains from southeast Asia through the Middle East to the Mediterranean. Every site is an external expression of activity within the crust and upper mantle. The underlying cause is a slow flowing of the rocks of the mantle in response to changes in temperature and density.

• Volcanoes
  Earthquake foci

Types of eruption *above*
Volcanic cones differ in both shape and activity. The Strombolian (1) erupts every few minutes or hours; the Peléan form (2) gives a hot avalanche; the Vesuvian (3) is a fierce upward expulsion, while the Plinian (4) is the extreme form.

A caldera *left*
Expulsion of lava (A) from the magma chamber (B) may leave the central core (C) without support. A collapse results in a large, steep-sided caldera (D). The magma chamber may cool and solidify (E), and water may collect inside the caldera (F).

Earthquake *right*

Along lines of potential movement, such as fault planes, stresses may build up over many years until the breaking strength of some part of the rock is exceeded (A). A sudden break occurs and the two sides of the fault line move, generating shockwaves which travel outward in all directions from the focus at the point of rupture (B). The point on the surface directly above the focus is the epicenter (C). While the fault movement reaches its fullest extent, the shockwaves reach the surface (D). Far right the aftermath of an earthquake.

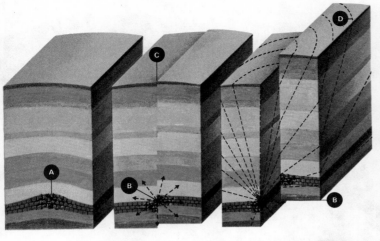

Destructive waves *right*

The Japanese, who have suffered severely from them, have given the name tsunami to the terrifying waves which follow earthquakes. Their character depends on the cause. In the case of a sudden rift and slump in the ocean bed (A) the wave at the surface is initially a trough, which travels away to both sides followed by a crest and subsequent smaller waves (B). A fault causing a sudden changed level of sea bed (C) can generate a tsunami that starts with a crest (D). Travelling at 400 miles (650 km) per hour or more the tsunami arrives at a beach as a series of waves up to 200 feet (60 m) high (E), the 'trough first' variety being heralded by a sudden withdrawal of the ocean from the shore. Warning stations ring the Pacific (far right) and the concentric rings show tsunamic travel time from an earthquake site to Hawaii at the center.

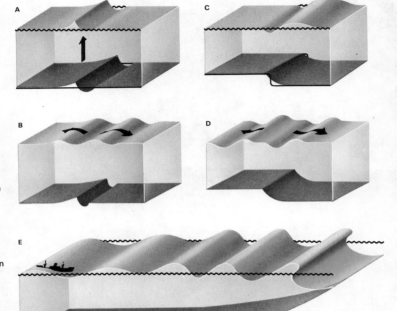

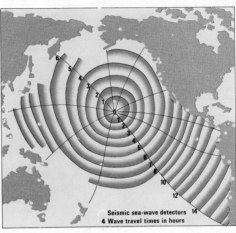

Seismic sea-wave detectors
4 Wave travel times in hours

Tsunami warning *above*

Numerous seismographic warning stations around the earthquake belt of the Pacific Ocean maintain a continuous alert for earthquake shocks and for the tsunami waves that may follow it. Possible recipients of such waves plot a series of concentric rings, such as these centered on the Hawaiian Islands, which show the time in hours that would be taken for a tsunami to travel from any earthquake epicenter. Aircraft and satellites are increasingly helping to create a globally integrated life-saving system.

Seismic waves *right*

An earthquake caused by a sudden movement in the crust at the focus (A) sends out a pattern of shock waves radiating like ripples in a pond. These waves are of three kinds. Primary (P) waves (full lines) vibrate in the direction of propagation, and thus are a rapid succession of high and low pressures. Secondary (S) waves (broken lines), which travel only 60 per cent as fast, shake from side to side. Long waves (L) travel round the crust. In a belt around the world only waves of the L-type occur, giving rise to the concept of a shadow zone (B and shaded belt in inset at lower right). But intermittent records of P waves in this zone led seismologists to the belief that the Earth must have a very dense fluid core (D, lower drawing) capable of strongly refracting P waves like a lens. Seismic waves are almost man's only source of knowledge about the Earth's interior.

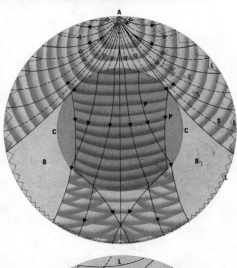

Seismology *right*

Seismic waves of all three types (P, S and L) are detected and recorded by seismographs. Usually these contain a sprung mass which, when an earthquake shock passes, stays still while the rest of the instrument moves. Some seismographs detect horizontal waves (A) while others detect vertical ones (B). The pen in the instrument leaves a distinctive trace (P-S-L). P (primary) waves are a succession of rarefactions and compressions, denoted by the packing of the dots; S (secondary) waves are a sideways shaking, shown here in plan view.

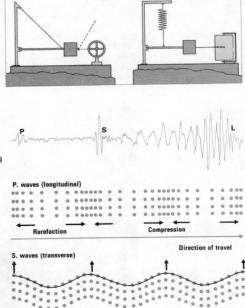

P   S   L

P. waves (longitudinal)

← Rarefaction   Compression →

Direction of travel →

S. waves (transverse)

A fundamental mystery that still confronts science even today is the detailed internal structure of the planet on which we live. Although Jules Verne's intrepid Professor Otto Lindenbrock was able to journey to the center of the Earth, this is one scientific fantasy that will never be achieved. The deepest boreholes and mines do little more than scratch the surface and so, deprived of direct observation, the geologist is forced to rely almost entirely on indirect evidence (pages 12A-13A) to construct his picture of the Earth's anatomy. In spite of these drawbacks, he can outline with some confidence the story of the planet's development from the time of its formation as a separate body in space some 4550 million years ago.

Since that time the Earth has been continuously evolving. The crust, mantle and inner core developed during its first 1000 million years, but there is only scant evidence of how they did so. Probably the original homogenous mass then partly or completely melted, whereupon gravitational attraction caused the densest material to form a part-liquid, part-solid central core overlaid by the less dense mantle. The extremely thin outermost layer of 'scum' began to form at an early stage and as long ago as 3500 million years parts of it had reached almost their present state. But most of the crust evolved in a complex way through long-term cyclic changes spanning immense periods of time. The evidence of today's rocks can be interpreted in different ways; for example, the core, mantle and crust could have separated out quickly at an early stage or gradually over a longer period.

Today's restless Earth

Many of the changes which have taken place in the Earth's structure and form have been very gradual. For example, although it may well be that our planet has been getting larger (as illustrated below), the rate of increase in radius has been no more rapid than $2\frac{1}{2}$ inches (65 mm) per century. But this does not alter the fact that the Earth is very far from being a mere inert sphere of matter. Although it is not possible faithfully to portray it, almost the whole globe is at brilliant white heat. If the main drawing were true to life it would contain no color except for a thin band, about as thick as cardboard, around the outer crust in which the color would change from white through yellow and orange to red. With such high temperatures the interior of the Earth is able to flow under the influence of relatively small differences in density and stress. The result is to set up convection currents which are now believed to be the main driving force behind the formation of mountain ranges and the drifting apart of continents. But the fact remains that our knowledge of the interior of our planet is derived almost entirely from indirect evidence, such as the passage of earthquake shock waves through the mantle (see page 13A). Direct exploration is confined to the surface and to boreholes which so far have never penetrated more than about five miles (8 km) into the crust. It is difficult to imagine how man could ever devise experiments that would greatly enhance and refine his knowledge of the Earth's interior. Indeed, he knows as much about the Moon and other much more distant heavenly bodies as he does about the Earth below a depth of a mere 20 miles (32 km).

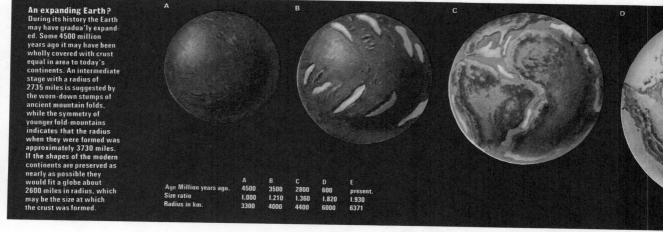

The crust (A)
This varies in thickness from 25 miles (40 km) in continental regions, where it is largely granitic, to 3 miles (5 km) under the oceans, where it is basaltic.

The upper mantle (B, C)
From the crust down to 375 miles (600 km), this layer is divided into upper and lower zones with differing P wave speeds (see page 39).

The lower mantle (D¹, D²)
Made of peridotite, as is the upper mantle, this zone extends down to a depth of 1800 miles (2900 km). P wave speeds increase still further.

The outer core (E, F)
Largely iron and nickel, this molten zone reaches to 2900 miles (4700 km). Dynamo action of convection currents may cause the Earth's magnetic field.

Not a true sphere *below*
The Earth's shape is controlled by equilibrium between inward gravitational attraction and outward centrifugal force. This results in the average radius at the equator of 3963 miles (6378 km) slightly exceeding that at the poles of 3950 miles (6356 km).

An expanding Earth?
During its history the Earth may have gradua'ly expanded. Some 4500 million years ago it may have been wholly covered with crust equal in area to today's continents. An intermediate stage with a radius of 2735 miles is suggested by the worn-down stumps of ancient mountain folds, while the symmetry of younger fold-mountains indicates that the radius when they were formed was approximately 3730 miles. If the shapes of the modern continents are preserved as nearly as possible they would fit a globe about 2600 miles in radius, which may be the size at which the crust was formed.

	A	B	C	D	E
Age Million years ago.	4500	3500	2800	600	present.
Size ratio	1.000	1.210	1.360	1.820	1.930
Radius in km.	3300	4000	4400	6000	6371

Temperature *left*

Temperature inside the Earth increases with depth, initially at a rate of 48°C per mile (30°C/km) so that 60 miles (100 km) down it is white hot. The rate of increase then falls, and the shaded area indicates how uncertain is man's knowledge of great depths.

Pressure *left*

This likewise increases with depth. Only 200 miles (320 km) down it reaches 100,000 atmospheres, 1200 times the pressure at the deepest point in the ocean. A change of state at the discontinuity between the mantle and core shows as a kink on the graph.

Crust   Mantle   Core

O₂	OXYGEN
Si	SILICON
Al	ALUMINUM
Fe	IRON
Ni	NICKEL
Co	COBALT
Mg	MAGNESIUM
Ca	CALCIUM
Na	SODIUM
K	POTASSIUM

(Note: O₂ = O_2)

Chemical composition *above*

The crust is made of mainly light elements and has relatively low density. Towards the base of the crust the composition is probably richer in iron and magnesium. The mantle is composed of heavier elements and the core is probably of iron and nickel.

The inner core (G)

The pressure of 3½ million atmospheres (35000 kg/mm²) keeps this a solid ball of 750 miles (1200 km) radius. Its density varies from 14 to about 16.

Density *left*

Virtually all man's knowledge of the interior of the Earth stems from measuring the transit of earthquake waves. The resulting data indicate sharp increases in density at the boundaries of both the outer core and the 'solid' inner core, with several intermediate zones.

Convection currents

The fundamental pattern of movement in the mantle (A) is modified by the Earth's rotation (B) and also by friction between adjacent cells as shown in the main figure, below, in which core (X) and mantle (Y) are shown but crust (Z) is removed.

X Core
Y Mantle
Z Crust

Convection theory

Geologists and geophysicists are not unanimous on the question of whether there are convection currents present in the Earth's mantle or not, nor on the part these could play in providing the driving mechanism for major movements of the continents. Slow movement of 'solid' rocks can occur over long periods of time when the temperature is high and only relatively small density differences would be required to trigger them. Another matter for debate is whether convection is confined to the upper mantle or is continuous throughout the whole. It is not certain whether changes of physical state at different levels would constitute barriers to mantle-wide convection. The convection cells above are highly schematic but could largely explain the formation of some of the major geosynclinal fold mountains in the crust over the past thousand million years. Large-scale convection current systems in the mantle could also be the driving force for sea floor spreading and the associated continental drift.

The watery Earth *below*

Almost three-quarters of the Earth is covered by water. Basically the continents are rafts of relatively light crust 'floating' on generally denser oceanic crust. They comprise not only the visible land but also the adjacent continental shelves covered by shallow water. Oceanic crust underlies the deep sea platforms and ocean trenches. The areas of the major lands and seas (below, left) do not take into account the continental shelves but are the gross areas reckoned in terms of the land and water distribution at mean sea level. Extra area due to terrain is not included.

The watery Earth *right*
Key to numbered areas.

Oceans	Area (×1000)	
	Sq mi	km²
1 Arctic	5541	14350
2 Pacific	63986	165750
3 Atlantic	31530	81660
4 Indian	28350	73430

Continents		
5 Americas	16241	42063
6 Europe (excluding USSR)	1903	4929
7 Asia (excluding USSR)	10661	27611
8 USSR	8649	22402
9 Africa	11683	30258
10 Oceania	3286	8510
11 Antarctica	5500	14245

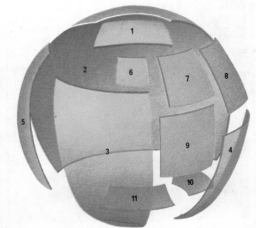

Measured against the time standards of everyday life, the major forces that shape the face of the Earth seem to act almost unbelievably slowly. But in geological terms the erosion of rock formations by river, marine or ice action is in fact rather rapid. Indeed in isolated locations, on coasts or below waterfalls, visible erosion can take place in a period of months or even days.

Over large regions of the Earth the rates of river erosion, expressed as the mass of material removed from each unit of land area in a given time, range between about 30 and 6000 tons per square mile per year (12–2300 tonnes/km²/year). The main factor determining the rate at any place is the climate. The average rate of erosion for Eurasia, Africa, the Americas and Australia, a land area of some 50 million square miles (130 million km²), has been calculated to be of the order of 350 tons per square mile per year (135 tonnes/km²/year). This corresponds to a general lowering of the surface of the land by about 40 inches (one meter) every 22000 years. At this rate these continents would be worn down to sea level in less than 20 million years, which in geological terms is a fairly short span of time.

In practice, the surface of the land would be most unlikely to suffer such a fate. Although isolated areas could be worn away, worldwide erosion on this scale and at a steady rate would be balanced or prevented by a number of factors, one of which is the continuing large-scale uplift of the land in other regions. Nevertheless long-term estimates do emphasize the cumulative effects of the apparently slow processes of erosion. Even man's own structures wear away. Already the portland stone of St. Paul's cathedral in London has lost half an inch (13 mm) overall in 250 years, aided by the additional force of atmospheric pollution.

Where do all the products of this erosion go? By far the largest accumulations of sediments occur in river deltas, and at many periods in the geological past great thicknesses of such deposits have been laid down in extensive subsiding troughs called geosynclines. A rate of deposition of 1/250 inch (0.1 millimeter per year is enough to lay down 12 miles (20 km) of strata in 200 million years.

The cycle of rock change

The agents of weathering
Gross break-up of the Earth's surface rocks is caused by earthquakes, the ceaseless cycle of diurnal and annual heating and cooling, and by the freezing of water trapped in fissures and crevices. The water of the seas, rivers and rain dissolves some rocks and in others leaches out particular minerals. Water is especially powerful as a weathering agent when it contains dissolved acidic chemicals. Today's main sources are plants and animals (1), but in the primeval world such chemicals were evolved mainly by volcanoes (2).

Erosion of the land
Only the material exposed at the surface of the Earth by volcanic action (2) or uplift (3) is subjected to erosion, but this material is constantly changing. Chemical erosion is an extension of the weathering process, converting the surface material into different and usually physically degraded substances. Physical erosion (4) is effected by running water and the wind (in both cases accelerated by the presence of an abrasive load) and by ice action and frost shattering.

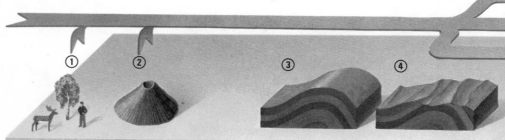

Extrusions
Most lavas are at a temperature of 900-1200°C. Acidic (granitic) lava is fairly viscous, but basic (basalt) lava flows relatively freely and when extruded from surface fissures or volcanoes can cover large areas (15). Lavas which have originated from partial melting of crustal rocks can also be erupted.

Basic magmas
Basic magma generated by partial melting in the mantle (14) may rise into and through the crust to be extruded from surface volcanoes. Basic magmas are the hottest, as well as the most freely flowing, and are often generated at very considerable depth. In their ascent they can intrude large areas of the crust and finally extrude through fissures in the surface.

Intrusions
Contact metamorphism is a form of baking and re-crystallization caused by the intrusion of hot magma into existing strata (13).

Granitic magmas
Partial melting deep in the crust generates new granitic magma—hot, rather viscous molten rock of an acidic nature which is able to migrate both upwards and laterally (12). This may then inject and mix with the surrounding rocks to form a migmatite complex.

Slow uplift
Strata can be slowly uplifted (11) until they once more appear at the surface; continued or violent uplift results in mountain-building. In either case, erosion begins afresh.

Deep metamorphism
If the strata are depressed far down, to depths up to about 25 miles (40 km), deep metamorphism at high pressures and high temperatures (10) results in complete re-crystallization. This gradually converts the original sediments into a complex of new rock types.

Erosion

Canyon erosion
Prolonged uplifting of the land, particularly in arid areas, often results in a river cutting a deep canyon in order to maintain a graded profile. The San Juan Valley, Utah, (above,) is a deeply entrenched meander still being cut. The Grand Canyon of the Colorado River (shown in section, left) has been cut a vertical distance of 10000 ft (3000 m) in a time now estimated at 21 million years.

Upper Permian

Lower Permian

Carboniferous

Devonian

Cambrian

Pre-Cambrian

Wind erosion
Laden with grains of sand and other air-transportable debris, the wind exerts a powerful sculpturing effect. Rate of erosion varies with rock hardness, giving rise to odd effects (Mushroom Rock, Death Valley, California, left). Desert sand forms 'barchan' dunes (right), which slowly travel points-first.

Sculpture by the sea
The ocean shapes the land by the pounding of the waves, scouring by the currents, chemical solution and deposition of debris. Around the Atlantic coast of the Portuguese Algarve are particularly fine wave-eroded rocks (at Piedade, left) while some of the principle mechanisms and coastal features are seen at right (key, far right).

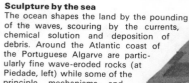

River development
The youthful river flows fast, eroding a narrow channel in an otherwise unchanged landscape. In maturity the channel is wider; flow is slower and some transported debris is deposited. The old river meanders across a broad flood plain (River Wye near Goodrich, left), some meanders becoming cut off as ox-bow lakes.

Glacial action
Briksdal Glacier, Norway (left), is a remnant of the Ice Ages, carving U-shaped valleys (2) in the pre-glacial rock (1). The bergschrund (3) forms close to the back wall, while other crevasses (4) form at gradient changes. Eroded rocks form a longitudinal moraine (5).

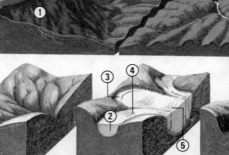

Transportation
As material is worn away from the surface rocks it is carried away by various processes. The most important transport system is flowing water (5), which can move sediments in suspension, in solution or carried along the beds of river channels. In open country, and especially over deserts, much solid debris is blown by the wind (6). Even slow-moving glaciers (7) perform a significant erosion and transport role by bearing heavy burdens of rock debris.

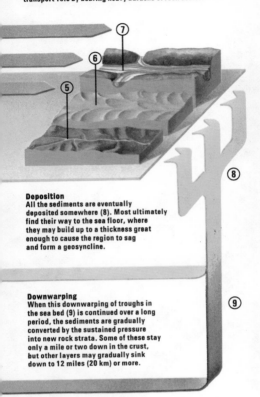

Deposition
All the sediments are eventually deposited somewhere (8). Most ultimately find their way to the sea floor, where they may build up to a thickness great enough to cause the region to sag and form a geosyncline.

Downwarping
When this downwarping of troughs in the sea bed (9) is continued over a long period, the sediments are gradually converted by the sustained pressure into new rock strata. Some of these stay only a mile or two down in the crust, but other layers may gradually sink down to 12 miles (20 km) or more.

250 million years ago
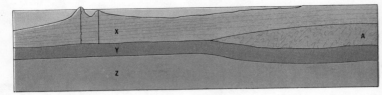

180 million years ago
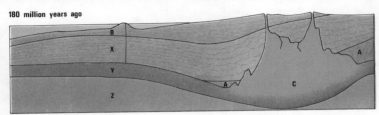

100 million years ago
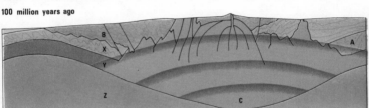

Present day

Late Paleozoic *left*
The formation of a geosyncline begins with the laying down of heavy sediments. In the creation of the Sierra Nevada range sediments X were deposited by the primeval ocean on top of Precambrian rock A, basalt crust Y and peridotite mantle Z.

Jurassic *left*
Downwarping of the crust causes the deposition of Mesozoic sediments B and carries the lower basalt crust and sediments into the zone of the mantle's influence. The bottom of the bulge is gradually converted into hot, fluid magma C.

Cretaceous *left*
In this period the geosynclinal process is in a mature stage. The inner rocks reach their maximum downward penetration into the mantle and are metamorphosed by high temperature and pressure. The deep metamorphism spreads (curved shading).

Present day *left*
Uplift and cooling opens the way to a new cycle of formation. The metamorphic rocks are exposed at the surface and subsequently eroded to yield today's complex landscape structure. Final withdrawal of the sea exposes marine sediments S.

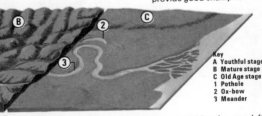

Wind-blown sand *left*
Sand deserts exhibit dunes of various forms. Unlike a barchan the parabolic blowout (1) travels with points trailing. In elongated form this becomes a parabolic hairpin (2), and a third form is the longitudinal ridge (3), known in the Sahara as a seif dune.

Emerging coastline *right*
Where the shoreline is rising, the continental shelf becomes exposed. River silt accumulates and forms an offshore bar, pierced by the river flow. Eventually infilling forms a tidal salt marsh through which the braided river reaches a new shore. Spain (far right) and Italy provide good examples.

Key
1 Dunes
2 Deposition
3 Spit
4 Arch
5 Stack
6 Raised beach
7 Caves

Key
A Initial stage
B Late youth
C Early maturity
1 Cut-off
2 Spit
3 4 Bars
5 Lagoon

Key
A Initial stage
B Bar development
C Emergence complete

Key
A Youthful stage
B Mature stage
C Old Age stage
1 Pothole
2 Ox-bow
3 Meander

Key
1 Esker
2 Recessional moraine
3 Drumlin
4 Lake
5 Terminal moraine
6 Outwash delta
7 Lake deposits
8 Kettle lake
9 Outwash plain
10 Kettle hole

Subsiding coastline *left*
Most coastal regions undergoing submergence are highly irregular. Drowned hills are eroded by the waves to form cliff headlands, or cut-offs ; spits and bars cross the submerged valleys, enclose them and form lagoons. Finally all these features wear back to a new shoreline.

Glaciated landforms *left*
Throughout a vast area of the temperate lands evidence of past glacial action is abundant. A geomorphologist, studying the landscape shown in the larger illustration, would deduce the former glacial situation depicted in the inset. Weight and sculpture by the ice carved out characteristic depressions, some later filled with water. Subglacial streams left alluvial deposits in the form of eskers and an outwash fan or delta, while the limit of the glacier is suggested by rocks deposited as a terminal moraine. Kettle holes result from the melting of ice within moraine debris.

Glaciated landscape *left*
The landscape shows evidence of former ice coverage. Broken rock debris forms valley-floor moraines (6), the peaks are sharp and knife-edged (7), and hanging valleys (8) mark the entry of the glacier's tributaries. Terminal moraines (9) are a characteristic feature.

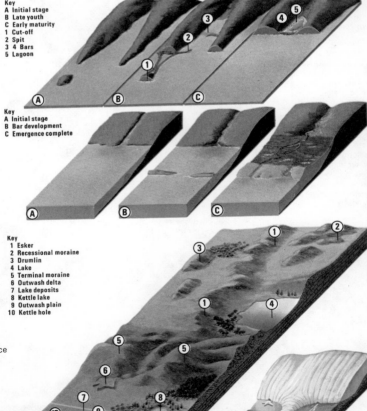

THE ACTIVE OCEANS

The surface of the oceans presents an infinite variety of contrasts ranging from glassy calm to terrifying storms with towering waves and wind-whipped wraiths of spray. But no part of the oceans is ever really still. Together the oceans comprise 300 million cubic miles (1250 million km³) of ever-active water. The whole mass ebbs and flows on a global scale with the tides. The surface is disturbed by winds into great patterns of waves which eventually break on the shores of the land. And the largest and most far-reaching movements of all are the ocean currents, some on or near the surface and others at great depths, which profoundly alter not only the oceans but also the weather.

Best known of all these currents is the Gulf Stream, which was discovered in late medieval times when early navigators found that their ships were consistently not in the place predicted by their calculations of course and estimated speed. Some 500 years ago it had become customary for Spanish captains voyaging to the New World to keep well south of the Gulf Stream on their outward journey and then use its swift four or five knot (8–9 km/hr) current to help them along on the return. The Gulf Stream brings mild weather to northwest Europe, and a corresponding role is played on the other side of the globe by the Kuroshio, a warm current which flows northeastward off Japan. Conversely, in the southeastern Pacific the Peru Current brings cold water from the sub-Antarctic region northward towards the equator. The surface flow is accompanied during most months of the year by an 'upwelling' of water rich in nutrients along the coast of Chile and Peru, and this, like many other cold currents elsewhere, supports great fisheries.

In coastal seas the water movements are often dominated by the currents that accompany the rise and fall of the tide. Because of the friction of the tides, the Moon is moving slowly further from the Earth.

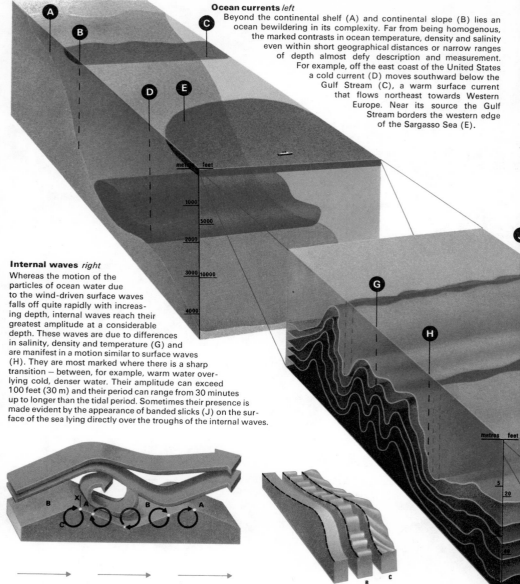

Ocean currents *left*
Beyond the continental shelf (A) and continental slope (B) lies an ocean bewildering in its complexity. Far from being homogenous, the marked contrasts in ocean temperature, density and salinity even within short geographical distances or narrow ranges of depth almost defy description and measurement. For example, off the east coast of the United States a cold current (D) moves southward below the Gulf Stream (C), a warm surface current that flows northeast towards Western Europe. Near its source the Gulf Stream borders the western edge of the Sargasso Sea (E).

Internal waves *right*
Whereas the motion of the particles of ocean water due to the wind-driven surface waves falls off quite rapidly with increasing depth, internal waves reach their greatest amplitude at a considerable depth. These waves are due to differences in salinity, density and temperature (G) and are manifest in a motion similar to surface waves (H). They are most marked where there is a sharp transition — between, for example, warm water overlying cold, denser water. Their amplitude can exceed 100 feet (30 m) and their period can range from 30 minutes up to longer than the tidal period. Sometimes their presence is made evident by the appearance of banded slicks (J) on the surface of the sea lying directly over the troughs of the internal waves.

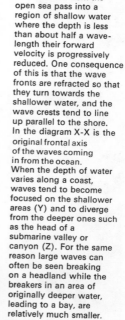

Wave generation *right*
Waves are generated on the surface by the wind. Once a slight undulation has been formed it will react on the air flow so that an eddying motion, with a reduced pressure, is produced on the lee side (A) of each crest. Combined with the wind pressure on the windward side (B), this causes the waves to grow in height. The wave travels forward in the direction of the wind, but the individual water particles (X) move in almost closed orbits (C).

Internal motion *right*
On the surface of deep water these orbits are almost circular. Below the surface the radii of the orbits decrease with depth and become very small at a depth equal to half a wavelength. In shallow water the orbits are ellipses, becoming flatter towards the bottom.

Shore and rip currents *below*
In addition to its circular movement, each water particle slowly moves in the direction of propagation. When waves approach a coast water tends to pile up at the shoreline. This leads to a return flow seaward (X) which is concentrated in narrow, fast-flowing rip currents (Y). Beyond the breaker zone these spread out into a head and gradually disperse (Z).

Waves and swell *above*
Ocean swell (A) is invariably present and travels hundreds of miles. On it the wind can superimpose small waves (B), which die out relatively rapidly. These smaller waves may be at any angle to the original swell (C).

Change of wave front *left, below*
When waves from the open sea pass into a region of shallow water where the depth is less than about half a wavelength their forward velocity is progressively reduced. One consequence of this is that the wave fronts are refracted so that they turn towards the shallower water, and the wave crests tend to line up parallel to the shore. In the diagram X-X is the original frontal axis of the waves coming in from the ocean. When the depth of water varies along a coast, waves tend to become focused on the shallower areas (Y) and to diverge from the deeper ones such as the head of a submarine valley or canyon (Z). For the same reason large waves can often be seen breaking on a headland while the breakers in an area of originally deeper water, leading to a bay, are relatively much smaller.

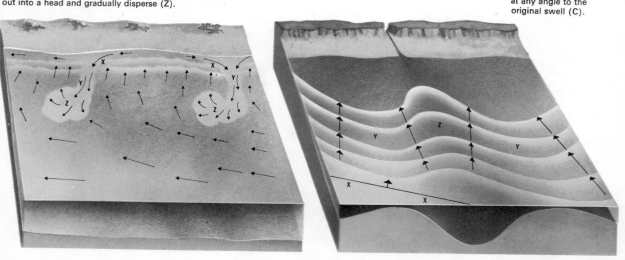

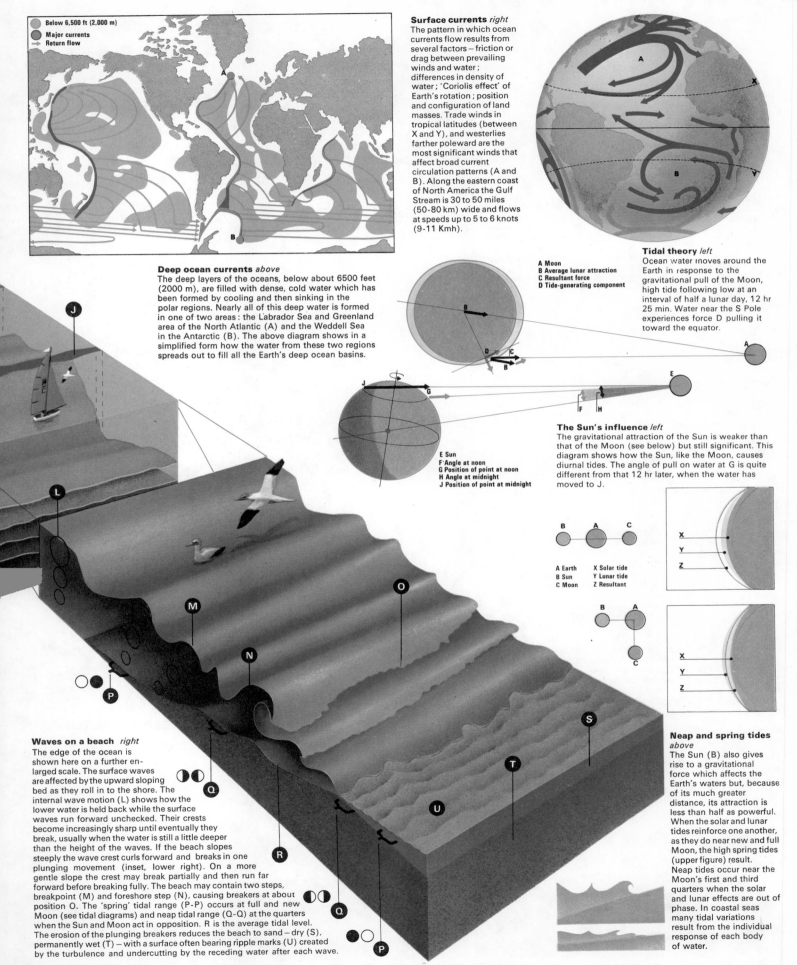

Below 6,500 ft (2,000 m)
Major currents
→ Return flow

Surface currents *right*
The pattern in which ocean currents flow results from several factors – friction or drag between prevailing winds and water; differences in density of water; 'Coriolis effect' of Earth's rotation; position and configuration of land masses. Trade winds in tropical latitudes (between X and Y), and westerlies farther poleward are the most significant winds that affect broad current circulation patterns (A and B). Along the eastern coast of North America the Gulf Stream is 30 to 50 miles (50-80 km) wide and flows at speeds up to 5 to 6 knots (9-11 Kmh).

Deep ocean currents *above*
The deep layers of the oceans, below about 6500 feet (2000 m), are filled with dense, cold water which has been formed by cooling and then sinking in the polar regions. Nearly all of this deep water is formed in one of two areas: the Labrador Sea and Greenland area of the North Atlantic (A) and the Weddell Sea in the Antarctic (B). The above diagram shows in a simplified form how the water from these two regions spreads out to fill all the Earth's deep ocean basins.

A Moon
B Average lunar attraction
C Resultant force
D Tide-generating component

Tidal theory *left*
Ocean water moves around the Earth in response to the gravitational pull of the Moon, high tide following low at an interval of half a lunar day, 12 hr 25 min. Water near the S Pole experiences force D pulling it toward the equator.

E Sun
F Angle at noon
G Position of point at noon
H Angle at midnight
J Position of point at midnight

The Sun's influence *left*
The gravitational attraction of the Sun is weaker than that of the Moon (see below) but still significant. This diagram shows how the Sun, like the Moon, causes diurnal tides. The angle of pull on water at G is quite different from that 12 hr later, when the water has moved to J.

A Earth   X Solar tide
B Sun   Y Lunar tide
C Moon   Z Resultant

Waves on a beach *right*
The edge of the ocean is shown here on a further enlarged scale. The surface waves are affected by the upward sloping bed as they roll in to the shore. The internal wave motion (L) shows how the lower water is held back while the surface waves run forward unchecked. Their crests become increasingly sharp until eventually they break, usually when the water is still a little deeper than the height of the waves. If the beach slopes steeply the wave crest curls forward and breaks in one plunging movement (inset, lower right). On a more gentle slope the crest may break partially and then run far forward before breaking fully. The beach may contain two steps, breakpoint (M) and foreshore step (N), causing breakers at about position O. The 'spring' tidal range (P-P) occurs at full and new Moon (see tidal diagrams) and neap tidal range (Q-Q) at the quarters when the Sun and Moon act in opposition. R is the average tidal level. The erosion of the plunging breakers reduces the beach to sand – dry (S), permanently wet (T) – with a surface often bearing ripple marks (U) created by the turbulence and undercutting by the receding water after each wave.

Neap and spring tides *above*
The Sun (B) also gives rise to a gravitational force which affects the Earth's waters but, because of its much greater distance, its attraction is less than half as powerful. When the solar and lunar tides reinforce one another, as they do near new and full Moon, the high spring tides (upper figure) result. Neap tides occur near the Moon's first and third quarters when the solar and lunar effects are out of phase. In coastal seas many tidal variations result from the individual response of each body of water.

THE EARTH UNDER THE SEA

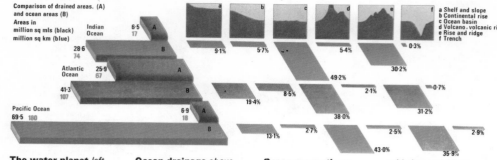

Comparison of drained areas. (A) and ocean areas (B)
Areas in million sq mls (black) million sq km (blue)

Indian Ocean 6·5 / 17 (A)
28·6 / 74 (B)

Atlantic Ocean 25·9 / 67 (A)
41·3 / 107 (B)

Pacific Ocean 69·5 / 180
6·9 / 18 (A)
(B)

a Shelf and slope
b Continental rise
c Ocean basin
d Volcano · volcanic ridge
e Rise and ridge
f Trench

9·1%   5·7%   5·4%   0·3%
    49·2%   30·2%
19·4%   8·5%   2·1%   0·7%
13·1%   2·7%   38·0%   31·2%   2·5%   2·9%
43·0%   35·9%

The water planet *left*
From directly over Tahiti the Earth appears to be covered by water. The Pacific averages 2.5 miles (4 km) deep, with great mountains and trenches.

Ocean drainage *above*
The ratio between the areas of the oceans and the land they drain varies greatly. Many large rivers feed the Atlantic but few discharge into the Pacific.

Ocean proportions *above*
The major oceans show a similarity in the proportions of their submarine topography. By far the greatest areas contain deep plains with rises and ridges. More prominent features, the mid-ocean volcanic ridges and trenches, occupy much smaller areas. About one tenth of each ocean is continental shelf.

At present the sea covers about 71 per cent of the Earth's surface. But if the continents could be sliced away and put into the deep oceans to make a perfectly uniform sphere the sea would have an average depth of about 8000 feet (2500 m) over the whole planet. In the distant past the level of the sea has fluctuated violently. The main cause has been the comings and goings of the ice ages. Glaciers and ice-caps lock up enormous volumes of water and the advance and recession of ice has alternately covered the continental shelves with shallow seas and revealed them as dry land. If the Earth's present polar ice-caps and glaciers were to melt, the mean sea level would rise by about 200 feet (60 m), which would submerge half the world's population. Average depth of the sea is more than 12000 feet (3600 m), five times the average height of the land above sea level.

The deep oceans

Below the level of the continental shelf lies the deep ocean floor with great topographical contrasts ranging from abyssal plains at a depth of about 13000 feet (4 km) to towering submarine mountain ranges of the mid-ocean ridges which reach far up toward the surface. Great advances have recently been made in exploring the ocean floors which were previously unknown. Most of the ocean area is abyssal plain which extends over about 78 million square miles (200 million km²). But a more remarkable feature of the deep ocean is the almost continuous mid-ocean mountain range which sweeps 40000 miles (64000 km) around the globe and occasionally – as at Iceland – is seen above sea level in the form of isolated volcanic islands. The basic symmetry of the oceans is the central ridge flanked by abyssal plain sloping up to the continental shelves. On the deep floor sediments accumulate at a rate of 30–35 feet (10 m) per million years; they also build up more slowly at the central ridges. No ocean sediments have been found older than 150 million years, which suggests that the material which now makes up the floors of the deep oceans was formed comparatively recently. Exploration and detailed mapping of the ocean bed is still in its infancy.

Submarine landscape

Principal features of the bed of the oceans can be grouped into a much smaller space than they would actually occupy. Although each ocean differs in detail, all tend to conform to the general layout of a central volcanic ridge (which can break the surface in places), broad abyssal plains with occasional deep trenches and shallow slopes and shelves bordering the continents.

Submarine relief *below*
The bottom of the sea is very far from being flat. If the ocean waters were removed a new landscape would become visible, with immense relief features.

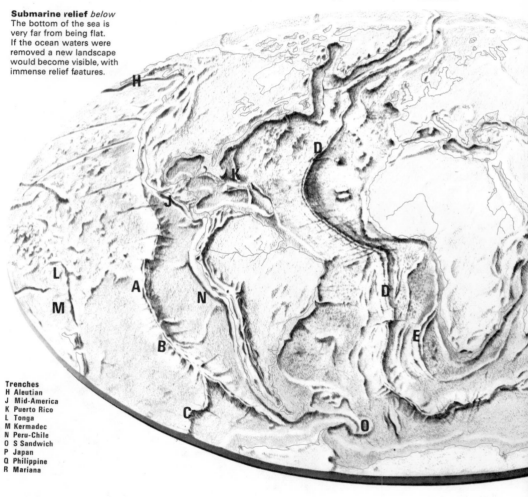

Trenches
H Aleutian
J Mid-America
K Puerto Rico
L Tonga
M Kermadec
N Peru-Chile
O S Sandwich
P Japan
Q Philippine
R Mariana

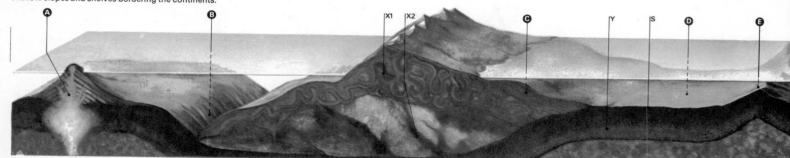

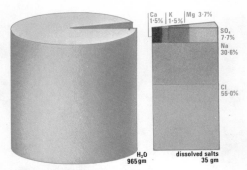

Composition of sea-water *above*
The water of the Earth's oceans is an exceedingly complex solution of many organic and inorganic salts, together with suspended solid matter. In a typical kilogram of sea-water there are 35 grams of chlorine, sodium, sulphates, magnesium, potassium and calcium.

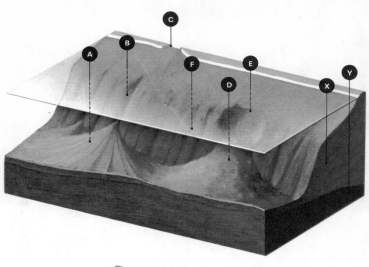

Continental shelf *left*
The submerged continental fringes lie at depths to about 450 feet (135 m) and have a total area of some 11 million square miles (28 million km²). The surface of the land is eroded and carried by rivers to form sedimentary deposits on the shelf. At its outer margin it slopes down to the abyssal plains of the deep ocean at about 2½ miles (4 km) below sea level.

A Scree fan
B Gully opposite river
C River delta
D Slump (turbidite) mass
E Scar left by (D)
F Continental slope
X Granite
Y Basalt

Rises and Ridges
A E Pacific
B SE Pacific
C Pacific-Antarctic
D Mid-Atlantic
E Walvis
F Indian Ocean
G SE Indian

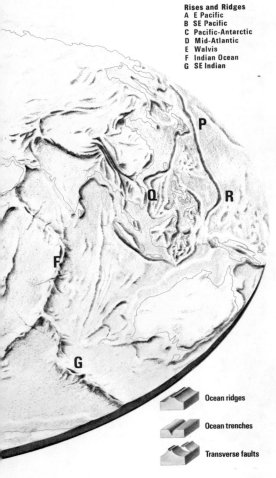

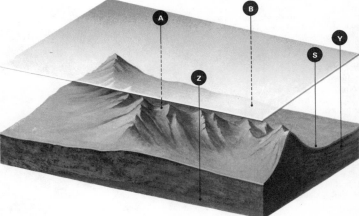

Mid-ocean ridge *left*
Well-marked ridges are found along the centers of the major oceans and form an extensive worldwide system. The central part of the ridge may have a double crest with an intervening deep trough forming a rift valley, or there may be several ridges. They are volcanic in nature and along them is generated new basaltic ocean crust. The volcanoes become progressively younger as the mid-ocean ridge is approached.

A Mid-ocean ridge
B Abyssal plain
S Ocean floor sediments
Y Basalt crust
Z Mantle

Ocean ridges

Ocean trenches

Transverse faults

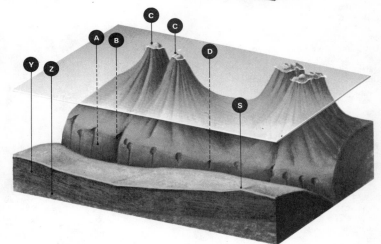

Oceanic trench *left*
These long and relatively narrow depressions are the deepest portions of the oceans, averaging over 30,000 feet (10 km) below sea level. Around the Pacific they lie close to the continental margins and in the western Pacific are often associated with chains of volcanic islands. Some trenches are slowly becoming narrower as the ocean floor plates on either side converge.

A Trench wall
B Canyon
C Island arc
D Trench
S Sediment
Y Basalt
Z Mantle

A Volcano in mid-ocean ridge
B Deep oceanic trench
C Continental shelf
D Abyssal plain
E Mid-ocean ridge
F Guyots
G Oceanic islands
X1 Upper granitic crust and sediments
X2 Lower granitic crust
Y Basaltic crust
Z Mantle

A sinking island *below*
A pre-requisite to the formation of a coral atoll is an island that is becoming submerged by the sea. Such islands are formed by the peaks of the volcanic mountains which are found on the flanks of the great mid-oceanic ridges.

Coral grows *below*
Millions of polyps, small marine animals, secrete a substance which forms the hard and often beautiful coral. The structure grows round the island in shallow water and extends above the sinking island to form an enclosed and shallow salt-water lagoon.

The mature atoll *below*
Continued submergence of the volcano results in the disappearance of the original island, but the upward growth of the coral continues unabated. The reef is then worn away by the sea and the coral debris fills in the central part of the lagoon.

A guyot *below*
Eventually the coral atoll itself begins to sink beneath the ocean surface. By this time the lagoon is likely to have become completely filled in by debris eroded from the reef, and the result is a submerged flat island, known as a guyot.

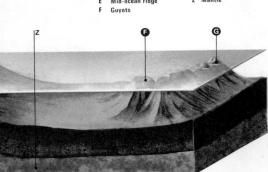

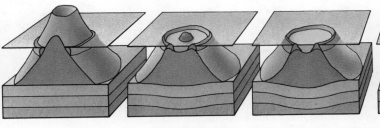

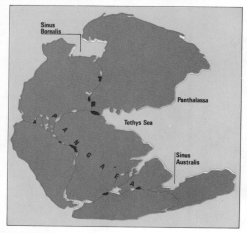

Pangaea *above*
About 200 million years ago there was only a single land mass on Earth, named Pangaea. The map shows how today's continents can be fitted together, with the aid of a computer, at the edge of the continental shelf at a depth of 1000 fathoms (6000 ft, 1830 m).

Although land and water first appeared on the Earth's surface several thousand million years before anyone could be there to watch, modern man has a very good idea of how it came about. The Earth's gravitational field caused the lighter, more volatile elements gradually to move outwards through the mantle and form a solid crust on the surface. By far the largest proportion of material newly added to the crust is basaltic volcanic rock derived from partial melting of the mantle beneath; in fact the oceanic crust which underlies the Earth's great water areas is made of almost nothing else. So the earliest crust to form was probably volcanic and of basaltic composition.

Air and water appear
The earliest records of the existence of an atmosphere of air and a hydrosphere of water are to be found in sediments laid down some 3300 million years ago from the residue of erosion of previously existing rocks. These sediments could not have been formed without atmospheric weathering, water transport and water deposition. The atmosphere was probably originally similar to the fumes which today issue from volcanoes and hot springs and which are about three-quarters water vapor. Once formed, the primitive atmosphere and oceans could erode the crust to produce vast layers of sediments of new chemical compositions. Gradually the oceans deepened and the land took on a more varied form. Convection in the mantle produced mountain ranges which in turn eroded to generate new sedimentary rocks. The ceaseless cycles of growth and decay had started, causing continually changing patterns of seas, mountains and plains. And in the past few years man has discovered how the continents and oceans have developed over the most recent 200 million years of geological time. The results of this research are to be seen in the maps on this page.

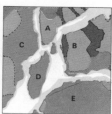

Another arrangement *left*
India (A) may have been separated by Australia (B) from East Antarctica (E) more than 200 million years ago on the evidence of today's geological deposition zones. Africa (C) and Madagascar (D) complete this convincing fit.

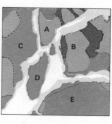

Migrant Australia *left*
By measuring the direction of magnetization of old Australian rocks it is possible to trace successive positions of that continent with respect to the Earth's magnetic pole. It appears to have moved across the world and back during the past 1000 million years.

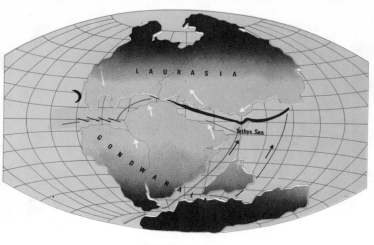

180 million years ago
At this time the original Pangaea land mass had just begun to break up. The continents first split along the lines of the North Atlantic and Indian Oceans. North America separated from Africa and so did India and Antarctica. The Tethys Sea, between Africa and Asia, closed somewhat, and the super continents of Laurasia to the north and Gondwanaland to the south became almost completely separated. In effect the Earth possessed three super landmasses, plus an India that had already begun to move strongly northward.

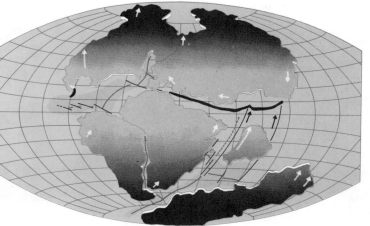

135 million years ago
After a further 45 million years of drifting, the world map had still not taken on a form that looks familiar today. But the two original splits, the North Atlantic and the Indian Ocean, have continued to open out. The North Atlantic is now about 600–650 miles (1000 km) wide. Rifting is extending towards the split which opened up the Labrador Sea and this will eventually separate Greenland from North America. India has firmly launched itself on its collision course with the southern coast of Asia, which is still 2000 miles (3200 km) away.

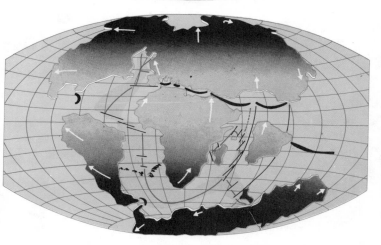

65 million years ago
Some 135 million years after the start of the drifting process the continents have begun to assume their present configuration. South America has at last separated from Africa and in Gondwanaland only Australia and Antarctica have yet to move apart. A continuation of the North Atlantic rifting will shortly bring about another big separation in Laurasia. Greenland will move apart from Europe and eventually North America will separate completely from the Eurasian landmass. The pink area (below) shows the extent of the crustal movements.

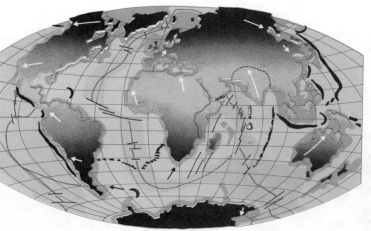

Today's positions
The Atlantic is now a wide ocean from Arctic to Antarctic, the Americas have joined and Australia has separated from Antarctica and moved far to the north. India has likewise moved northwards and its collision with Asia and continued movement has given rise to the extensive uplift of the Himalayas. All the continents which formerly made up the great land mass of Pangaea are now separated by wide oceans. Comparison of areas shows how much of India has been submerged by sliding underneath the crust of Asia (see facing page, far right).

Plate tectonics

This theory has revolutionized the way the Earth's crust – continents and oceans – is interpreted on a global scale. The crust is regarded as being made up of huge plates which converge or diverge along margins marked by earthquakes, volcanoes and other seismic activity. Major divergent margins are the mid-ocean ridges where molten lava forces its way upward and escapes. This causes vast regions of crust to move apart at a rate of an inch or two (some centimeters) per year. When sustained for up to 200 million years this means movements of thousands of miles or kilometers. The process can be seen in operation today in and around Iceland. Oceanic trenches are margins where the plates are moving together and the crust is consumed downward. The overall result is for the crustal plates to move as relatively rigid entities, carrying the continents along with them as if they were on a giant conveyor belt. Over further considerable periods of geologic time this will markedly change today's maps.

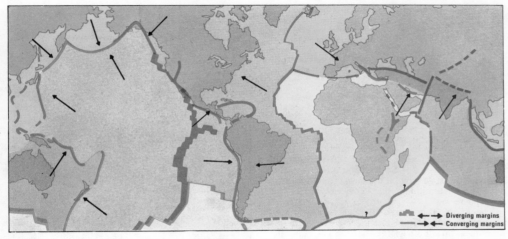

Diverging margins
Converging margins

Sea-floor spreading *left*
Arrows show how the lava flows on the ocean bed spread out on each side of a mid-ocean ridge. Evidence for such movement is provided by the fact the rock is alternately magnetized in opposing directions (coloured stripes).

Time scale (millions of years)
0 Pleistocene
2 Pliocene
7 Miocene
26 Oligocene
38 Eocene
54 Paleocene
65 Cretaceous
-------- Transverse faults

Plate movements
above and left
The Earth's crust is a series of large plates 'floating' on the fluid mantle. At their edges the plates are either growing or disappearing. Magnetic measurements in the S. Pacific (left) show rock ages on each side of the mid-ocean ridges.

Plate movements in cross-section *above*
The basic mechanism of plate movements is illustrated above in simplified form with the vertical scale greatly exaggerated. This figure is explained in detail in both of the captions below.

Crustal divergence
above and right
The Earth's crust (1) behaves as a series of rigid plates which move on top of the fluid mantle (2). At their mating edges some of these plates are moving apart (3). This was the mechanism that separated North America (A) from Europe (B). The plates moved to the north and also away from each other under the influence of convection currents in the mantle (C). Between the land areas appeared an oceanic gap with a mid-ocean ridge (D) and lateral ridges (E). The movements continued for some 200 million years, fresh volcanoes being generated by igneous material escaping through the plate joint (F) to add to the lateral ridges which today cross the Atlantic (G). The volcanoes closest to the median line in mid-Atlantic are still young and active — whereas those nearer to the continents are old and extinct.

Crustal convergence
above and right
Diverging plate margins occur only in the centers of the major oceans (see map above) but plates are converging on both sea and land. Where an oceanic plate (4, above) is under-riding a continental plate (5) a deep ocean trench is the result (6). Such trenches extend around much of the Pacific; those around the northwest Pacific include the deepest on Earth where the sea bed is almost seven miles below the ocean surface. The continental margin is squeezed upward to form mountains such as the Andes or Rockies (7). If continental masses converge, such as India (A, right) and Asia (B), the convection in the mantle (C) pulls the plates together so hard that the upper crust crumples (D). Sedimentary deposits between the plates (E) are crushed and squeezed out upward (F), while the mantle on each side is turned downward, one side being forced under the other (G). Continued movement causes gross deformation at the point of collision. The static or slow-moving crust is crushed and tilted, and giant young mountains (the Himalayas, H) are thrust upward along the collision just behind the edge of the crumpled plate.

A thin coating *left*
The protective atmospheric shell around the Earth is proportionately no thicker than the skin of an apple. Gravity compresses the air so that half its mass lies within 3.5 miles (5.5 km) of the surface and all the weather within an average depth of 12 miles (20 km).

Space exploration has enabled man to stand back and take a fresh look at his Earth. Even though we, like all Earth life, have evolved to suit the Earth environment, we can see today as never before how miraculous that environment is. And by far the most important single factor in determining that environment is the atmosphere.

The Earth orbits round the Sun in a near-total vacuum. So rarefied is the interplanetary medium that it contains little heat energy, but the gas molecules that are present are vibrating so violently that their individual temperature is over 2000°C. And the surface of the Sun, at some 6000°C, would melt almost everything on the surface of the Earth, while the tenuous chromosphere around the Sun is as hot as 1,000,000°C. From the chromosphere, and from millions of other stars and heavenly objects, come radio waves. Various places in the universe, most of them far beyond the solar system, send us a penetrating kind of radiation known as cosmic rays. The Earth also receives gamma rays, X-rays and ultraviolet radiation, and from the asteroid belt in the solar system (see pages 6A-7A) comes a stream of solid material. Most of these are small micrometeorites, no more than flying specks, but the Earth also receives meteors and meteorites.

A meteorite is a substantial mass that strikes the Earth; fortunately, none has yet hit in a populous area. Apart from these extremely rare objects, every other influence from the environment that would be dangerous to life is filtered out by the atmosphere. Meteors burn up through friction as they plunge into the upper parts of the atmosphere. To avoid burning up in the same way, spacecraft designed to return to the Earth from lunar or interplanetary flight require a special re-entry shield.

Much of the ultraviolet radiation is arrested many miles above the Earth and creates ionized layers known as the ionosphere which man uses to reflect radio waves. Much of the infra-red (heat) radiation is likewise absorbed, lower down in the atmosphere, and most of the cosmic radiation is broken up by collisions far above the ground into such particles as 'mu-mesons'. Only a few cosmic rays, harmless radio waves and visible light penetrate the blanket of air to reach the planetary surface and its teeming life.

Credit for our vital atmosphere rests with the Earth's gravitational attraction, which both prevents the molecules and atoms in the atmosphere from escaping into space and also pulls them down tightly against the Earth. As a result nearly all the atmosphere's mass is concentrated in a very thin layer; three-quarters of it lies below 29000 feet (8840 m), the height of Mount Everest. The highest-flying aircraft, 19 miles (30 km) up, are above 99 per cent of the atmosphere. The total weight of the atmosphere is of the order of 5000 million million tons. In the lower parts are some 17 million million tons of water vapor.

The water vapor plays a great part in determining the weather on Earth, the only way in which the atmosphere consciously affects daily human life. All the weather is confined to the lower parts of the atmosphere below the tropopause. In this region, called the troposphere, temperature falls away sharply with increasing altitude. The Sun heats up the Earth's surface, water is evaporated from the surface of the oceans and an immensely complicated pattern of global and local weather systems is set up. Every part of the air in the troposphere is in motion. Sometimes the motion is so slow as to be barely perceptible, while on other occasions, or at the same time in other places, the air roars over the surface with terrifying force at speeds of 200 miles (320 km) per hour or more. It erodes the land, lashes the surface with rain and clogs cold regions with snow. Yet it is man's shield against dangers, an ocean of air without which we could not exist.

Characteristics of the atmosphere *right*
Basically the Earth's atmosphere consists of a layer of mixed gases covering the surface of the globe which, as a result of the Earth's gravitational attraction, increases in density as the surface is approached. But there is very much more to it than this. Temperature, composition and physical properties vary greatly through the depth of the atmosphere. The Earth's surface is assumed to lie along the bottom of the illustration, and the various major regions of the atmosphere—which imperceptibly merge into each other—are indicated by the numbers on the vertical scale on the facing page.

Exosphere (1)
This rarefied region is taken to start at a height of some 400 miles (650 km) and to merge above into the interplanetary medium. Atomic oxygen exists up to 600 mi (1000 km); from there up to about 1500 mi (2400 km) helium and hydrogen are approximately equally abundant, with hydrogen becoming dominant above 1500 mi. The highest auroras are found in this region. Traces of the exosphere extend out to at least 5000 mi (8000 km).

Ionosphere (2)
This contains electrically conducting layers capable of reflecting radio waves and thus of enabling radio signals to be received over great distances across the Earth. The major reflecting layers, designated D, E, F1 and F2, are at the approximate heights shown. Meteors burn up brightly at heights of around 100 mi (160 km). Charged particles coming in along the lines of force of the Earth's magnetic field produce aurorae in the ionosphere at high latitudes, some of them of the corona type with a series of radial rays; and the ionosphere's structure alters from day to night and according to the influence of the solar wind and incoming streams of other particles and radiation.

Stratosphere (3)
This lies above the tropopause which varies in altitude from about 10 mi (16 km) over the equator to just below 7 mi (11 km) in temperate latitudes. The lower stratosphere has a constant temperature of -56°C up to 19 mi (30 km); higher still the 'mesosphere' becomes warmer again. One of the vital properties of the stratosphere is its minute ozone content which shields the Earth life from some harmful short-wave radiations which, before the Earth's atmosphere had developed, penetrated to the surface.

Troposphere (4)
Within this relatively very shallow layer is concentrated about 80 per cent of the total mass of the atmosphere, as well as all the weather and all the Earth's life. The upper boundary of the troposphere is the tropopause, which is about 36000 ft (11000 m) above the surface in temperate latitudes; over the tropics it is higher, and therefore colder, while it is at a lower altitude over the poles. Air temperature falls uniformly with increasing height until the tropopause is reached; thereafter it remains constant in the stratosphere. Composition of the troposphere is essentially constant, apart from the vital factor of clouds and humidity.

Structure and features | **Temperature** | **Pressure**

450mi 720km — 1 — 10^{-42}mb

400mi 640km — 10^{-37}mb

350mi 560km — 10^{-32}mb

300mi 480km — 10^{-27}mb

250mi 400km — 2227°C — 10^{-22}mb

— 2 —

200mi 320km — 10^{-17}mb

1487°C

150mi 240km — 10^{-12}mb

739°C

100mi 160km — 10^{-7}mb

-12°C
50mi 80km — -183°C — 10^{-2}mb
-63°C

— 3 —
2°C

-38°C
8mi 11km — -55°C / -63°C / -56°C — 15°C — 10^3mb
— 4 —

Chemical composition
- Nitrogen
- Oxygen
- Argon
- Carbon dioxide
- Water vapour
- Ozone

Temperature
The mean temperature at the Earth's surface is about 15°C. As height is gained the temperature falls swiftly, to —56°C at the tropopause. It remains at this value to 19 miles (30 km), becomes warmer again, and then falls to a very low value around 60 miles (100 km). It rises once again in space.

Pressure
At sea level the pressure is some 1000 millibars, or about 14.7 pounds per square inch. The total force acting on the surface of an adult human body is thus of the order of 20 tons. But only 10 miles (16 km) above the Earth the pressure, and the atmospheric density, have both fallen by some 90 per cent.

Composition
Chemical composition of the atmosphere varies considerably with altitude. In the troposphere the mixture of nitrogen, oxygen and other gases is supplemented by water vapor, which exerts a profound influence on the weather. Ozone in the stratosphere shields life from harmful ultraviolet rays.

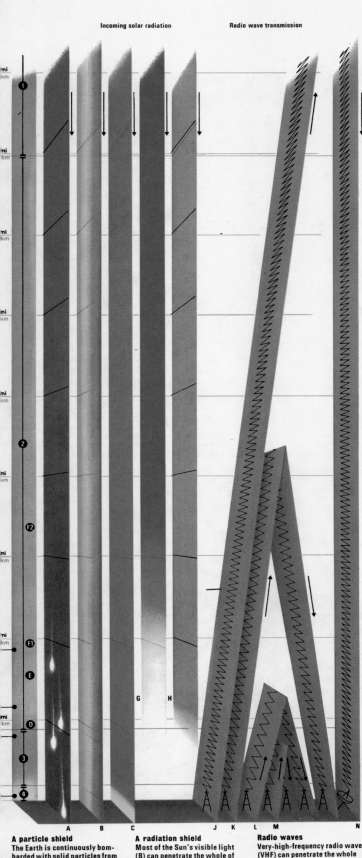

Incoming solar radiation

Radio wave transmission

A particle shield
The Earth is continuously bombarded with solid particles from elsewhere in the solar system and possibly from more distant parts of the universe. Only the largest meteors (A) reach the surface. Small meteorites generally burn up through friction caused by passage through the thin air more than 40 miles (65 km) up.

A radiation shield
Most of the Sun's visible light (B) can penetrate the whole of the atmosphere right down to the Earth's surface, except where cloud intervenes. But only some of the infra-red radiation gets through (C); the rest (G) is cut off, along with the harmful ultraviolet radiation (H), by atmospheric gases.

Radio waves
Very-high-frequency radio waves (VHF) can penetrate the whole depth of the atmosphere (J), but short-wave transmissions are reflected by the Appleton F2 layer (K). Medium (L) and long waves (M) are reflected at lower levels by the D, E or F1 layers. Yet radio waves from distant stellar sources can be received (N).

The circulation of the atmosphere *left*
The atmosphere maintains its equilibrium by transferring heat, moisture and momentum from low levels at low latitudes to high levels at high latitudes where the heat is radiated to space. This circulation appears to comprise three distinct 'cells' in each hemisphere. In the tropical (A) and polar (B) cells the circulations are thermally direct — warm air rises and cold air sinks — but the mid-latitude circulation, the Ferrel cell (C), is distorted by the polar front as shown in greater detail below.

Frontal systems *left*
Although the figure above shows a true general picture, the actual circulation is more complicated. A portion of the Earth on a larger scale shows how frontal systems develop between the polar and tropical air masses. The tropopause, the demarcation between the troposphere in which temperature falls with height, and the stratosphere above, is much higher in the tropics than in the polar cell. Between the cells the polar front causes constant successions of warm and cold fronts and changeable weather. Surface winds are shown, together with areas of low pressure and high pressure. The scale along the bottom, although exaggerated, indicates the greater height of the tropical tropopause compared with that in polar regions. Conventional symbols indicate warm and cold fronts.

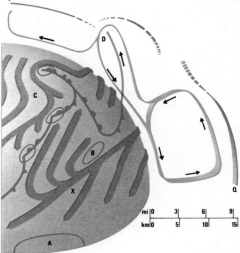

Warm front	A Area of low pressure
Cold front	B Area of high pressure
	C Area of low pressure
	D Polar front
	P Polar cell tropopause
	Q Tropical tropopause

Precipitation *left*
This map shows the mean annual rain, hail and snow over the Earth.

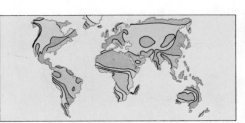

	Cm per year
0	
25	
50	
100	
200	

Evaporation *left*
Accurate estimates of evaporation can be made only over the oceans.

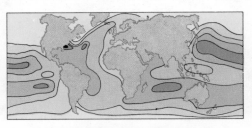

	Cm per year
0	
60	
100	
150	
200	
250	

Surface radiation *left*
Variations in heat output over the Earth's surface affect air and ocean circulations.

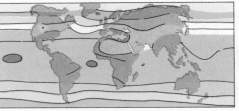

	K/cal per cm² per year
60	
40	
20	
0	
−20	
−40	
−60	

Until recently there were few scientists in the tropics or the polar regions, and the science of meteorology therefore evolved in the mid-latitudes. Likewise, the early concepts of meteorology were all based on observations of the mid-latitude atmosphere. Originally only two types of air mass were recognized: polar and tropical. Today a distinct equatorial air mass has been identified, as well as Arctic and Antarctic masses at latitudes even higher than the original polar ones. The concept of a 'front' between dissimilar air masses dates from as recently as 1919, and three years later the development of a cyclone – a large system of air rotating around an area of low pressure– was first described. Today satellite photographs have confirmed the validity of these early studies and enable the whole Earth's weather to be watched on daily computer processed photo-charts as it develops.

Why the weather varies

Anywhere in the Earth's mid-latitudes the climate is determined mainly by the frequency and intensity of the cyclones, with their frontal systems and contrasting air masses, which unceasingly alter the local temperature, wind velocity, air pressure and humidity. In turn, the frequency of the cyclonic visits is governed principally by the behavior of the long waves in the upper westerlies. When these waves change their shape and position the cyclonic depressions follow different paths. The major changes are seasonal, but significant variations also occur on a cycle of 5–6 weeks. It is still proving difficult to investigate the long wave variations. As a front passes, a fairly definite sequence of cloud, wind, humidity, temperature, precipitation and visibility can be seen. The most obvious change is the type of cloud, of which nine are shown opposite. Each cyclone contains numerous cloud types in its structure. Within these clouds several forms of precipitation can form; raindrops are the most common, but ice precipitation also forms, with snow in winter and hail in the summer when intense atmospheric instability produces towering cumulonimbus clouds topped by an 'anvil' of ice crystals.

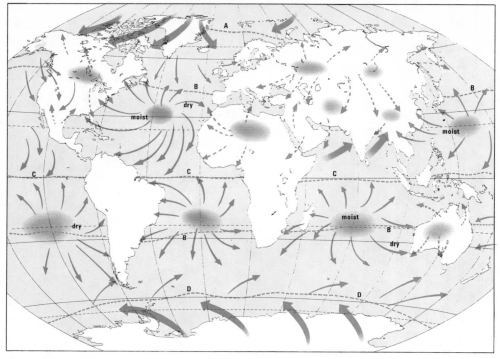

Air masses and convergences *above*
An air mass is an extensive portion of the atmosphere in which, at any given altitude, the moisture and temperature are almost uniform. Such a mass generally arises when the air rests for a time on a large area of land or water which has uniform surface conditions. There are some 20 source regions throughout the world. A second pre-requisite is large-scale subsidence and divergence over the source region. The boundary between air masses is a convergence or front. (A Arctic, B Polar, C Equatorial, D Antarctic.) The polar front is

particularly important in governing much of the weather in mid-latitudes. The pattern depicted provides a raw framework for the world's weather. It is considerably modified by the air's vertical motion, by surface friction, land topography, the Earth's rotation and other factors.

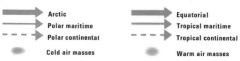

→ Arctic	→ Equatorial
--→ Polar maritime	→ Tropical maritime
--→ Polar continental	--→ Tropical continental
Cold air masses	Warm air masses

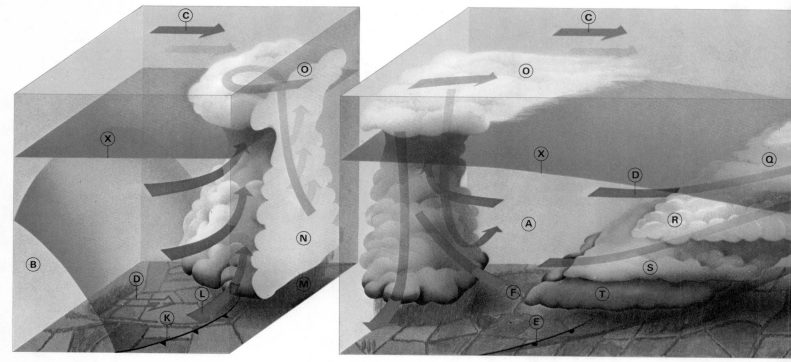

Anatomy of a depression

Seen in cross section, a mature mid-latitude cyclone forms a large system which always follows basically the same pattern. Essentially it comprises a wedge of warm air (A) riding over, and being undercut by, cold air masses (B). (Page 28A shows full development.) The entire cyclone is moving from left to right, and this is also the basic direction of the winds (C) and (D). To an observer on the ground the warm front (E) may take 12-24 hours to pass, followed by the warm sector (F) perhaps 180 miles (300 km) wide.

The cold front (K)

As this frontal zone, about one mile (1-2 km) wide, passes overhead the direction of the wind alters (L) and precipitation (M) pours from cumuliform clouds (N). If the air above the frontal surface is moving upwards then giant cumulonimbus (O) may grow, with heavy rain or hail. Cirrus clouds then form in air above the freezing level (X). Sometimes the front is weak with subsidence of air predominant on both sides of it. In this case there is little cloud development and near-zero surface precipitation.

The warm front (E)

The front is first heralded by cirrus clouds (P), followed by cirrostratus (Q), altocumulus (R), stratus (S) and finally nimbostratus (T). The descending layers are due partly to humidity distribution and partly to the warm air rising over the sloping frontal surface. Precipitation may be steady and last for hours. Alternatively some warm fronts have a predominantly subsident air motion, with the result that there is only a little thin cloud and negligible precipitation. Air temperature increases as the front passes.

Development of a depression *right*

Most mid-latitude depressions (cyclones) develop on the polar front (map above). An initial disturbance along this front causes a fall in pressure and a confluence at the surface, deforming the front into a wave (1, right). The confluence and thermal structure accelerate the cyclonic spin into a fully developed depression (2). The depression comprises a warm sector bounded by a sharp cold front (A) and warm front (B). The fast-moving cold front overtakes the warm front and eventually the warm sector is lifted completely clear of the ground resulting in an occlusion (3). The continued overlapping of the two wedges of cold air eventually fills up the depression and causes it to weaken and disperse (4). By the time this occurs the warm sector has been lifted high in the atmosphere. In this way, depressions fulfil an essential role in transferring heat from low to high levels and from low to high latitudes.

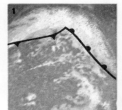
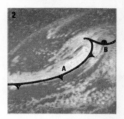
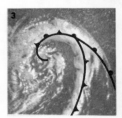
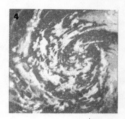

Plan view *left*

A developing cyclone will appear this way on the 'synoptic' weather chart. Lines of equal pressure (isobars) are nearly straight within the warm sector but curve sharply in the cold sector to enclose the low pressure focus of the system.

Examples of the three major cloud groups

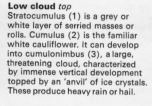

Low cloud *top*

Stratocumulus (1) is a grey or white layer of serried masses or rolls. Cumulus (2) is the familiar white cauliflower. It can develop into cumulonimbus (3), a large, threatening cloud, characterized by immense vertical development topped by an 'anvil' of ice crystals. These produce heavy rain or hail.

Medium cloud *left*

Nimbostratus (4) is a ragged grey layer producing drizzle or snow. Altocumulus (5) comprises rows of 'blobs' of ice and water forming a sheet at a height of 1.5-4.5 miles (2-7 km). Altostratus (6) occurs at similar heights but is a water/ice sheet either uniform, striated or fibrous in appearance.

High cloud *right*

Cirrus (7) is the highest cloud and appears as fine white ice filaments at 8–10 miles (13–16 km), often hair-like or silky. Cirro-cumulus (8) forms into thin white layers made up of very numerous icy globules or ripples. Cirrostratus (9) is a high-level veil of ice crystals often forming a halo round the Sun.

Four kinds of precipitation

Rain

Most rain results from the coalescence of microscopic droplets (1) which are condensed from vapor onto nuclei in the atmosphere. The repeated merging of small droplets eventually forms water droplets (2) which are too large to be kept up by the air currents. Rain drops may also form from melting of ice crystals in the atmosphere.

Glaze

In completely undisturbed air it is possible for water to remain liquid even at temperatures well below freezing point. So air above the freezing level (X) may contain large quantities of this 'supercooled water'. This can fall as rain and freeze on impact with objects, coating them with ice.

Dry snow

The origin of snow differs from that of rain in that the vapor droplets (1) settle on microscopic crystals of ice and freeze. The result is the growth of a white or translucent ice crystal having a basically hexagonal form (photomicrograph below). The crystals then agglomerate into flakes (2).

Hail

In cumulonimbus clouds raindrops (formed at 1,2) may encounter up-currents strong enough to lift them repeatedly back through a freezing level (X). On each pass (3) a fresh layer of ice is collected. The hailstone builds up like an onion until it is so heavy (4) that it falls to the ground.

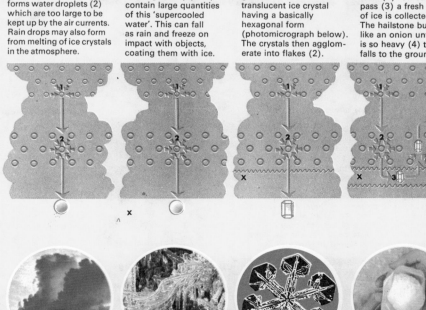

EXTREMES OF WEATHER

Tropical weather, between the Tropic of Cancer at 23½°N and the Tropic of Capricorn at 23½°S, differs fundamentally from that at higher latitudes. Overall there is a considerable surplus of heat, giving high mean temperatures; and the 'Coriolis force' due to the Earth's rotation, which deflects air currents to the right in the northern hemisphere and to the left in the southern, is almost non-existent. As a result, tropical weather hardly ever contains distinct air masses, fronts and cyclones. Instead the region is occupied mainly by the tradewinds, which are laden with moisture and potentially unstable. Thunderstorms are frequent, especially over land, and the pattern of land and sea leads to local anomalies, such as the monsoon of southeast Asia. This particular anomaly, too big to be called local, changes the prevailing wind over a vast area. It is superimposed on the apparently simple global circulation near the Equator.

Polar weather
At very high latitudes the atmosphere radiates heat to space. The Arctic is essentially an ocean surrounded by land, whereas the Antarctic is land surrounded by ocean. The land around the Arctic quickly takes up solar heat but the southern oceans transfer heat to deeper water to make the Antarctic the coldest region on Earth. Because the air is so intensely cold it can hold very little moisture, so the south polar region is a freezing desert with exceptionally clean air.

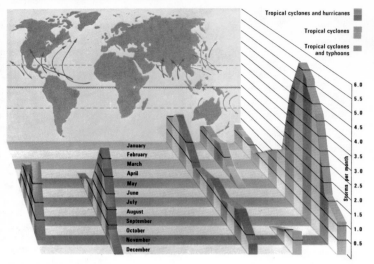

Tropical cyclones and hurricanes ■
Tropical cyclones ■
Tropical cyclones and typhoons ■

The afflicted areas *above*
Tropical cyclones build up over the warm oceans, and many of them—about half over the Caribbean and four-fifths over the western Pacific—develop into hurricanes. Precisely how a hurricane is triggered is still not fully known, but there is no doubt it is a thermodynamic engine on a giant scale which either misfires completely or runs with catastrophic effect.

Hurricanes *left*
These violent storms form over ocean warm enough (27°C) to maintain strong vertical circulation, except for the belt closest to the equator where lack of a Coriolis force prevents cyclonic spin from building up. Condensation of the moisture taken up from the ocean surface releases latent heat and thus provides energy to drive the storm. The daily energy can be equivalent to that released by several hundred H bombs. Despite their formidable power hurricanes are penetrated by specially equipped aircraft whose mission is both to provide early warning and to gather data enabling the storm's mechanism to be better understood.

Hurricane structure
A Spiral rainbands.
B High-altitude winds.
C Easterly tradewinds.

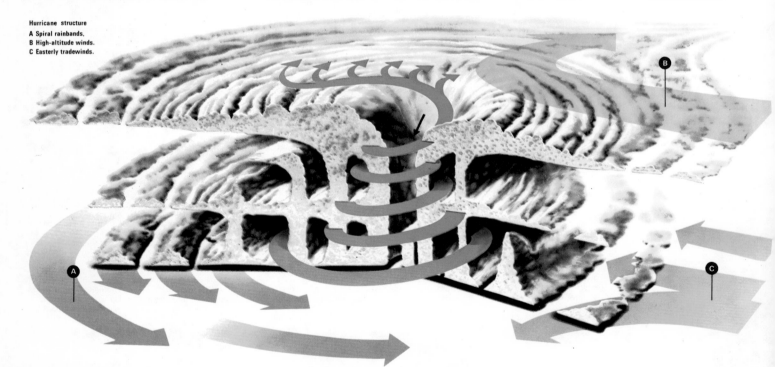

Structure of a hurricane *above*
A hurricane consists of a huge swirl of clouds rotating around a calm center known as the eye. This cyclonic circulation may be as much as 250 miles (400 km) in diameter, and it extends right through the troposphere which is about 9-12 miles (15-20 km) thick. The clouds, nearly all of the cumulonimbus type, are arranged in bands around the eye. The largest form the wall of the eye and it is here that precipitation is heaviest. The whole system is usually capped by streamers of cirrus. Wind speeds range from about 110 mph (180 kmh) at 20–25 miles (30–40 km) from the eye wall down to about 45 mph (72 kmh) at a distance of 90 miles (140 km). Warm, calm air in the eye is sucked downwards.

Hurricane development *below*

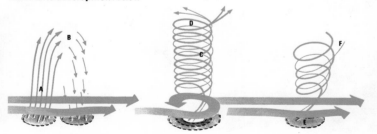

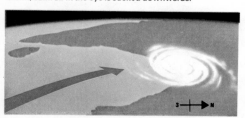

S ←→ N

Nature's giant energy *left and above*
A hurricane such as that which killed over half a million people in Bangladesh in November 1970 (left) dissipates thousands of millions of horsepower. The spiral structure is clearly visible from a satellite (above).

Birth of a storm.
Hurricanes usually have their origin in a low-pressure disturbance directing part of an easterly wind (A) to the north. The air rises to some 40,000 ft (12 km) where it releases heat and moisture (B) before descending.

The young hurricane
The Earth's rotation imparts a twist to the rising column which becomes a cylinder (C) spiralling round a relatively still core (D). Warm, moist air off the sea picks up speed and feeds energy at a very high rate to intensify the rising column.

Dying of starvation
The hurricane does not begin to die until it moves over colder water or over land (E). Then, cut off from its supply of energy, the speed of the spiralling winds falls away. The eye begins to fill with clouds, the hurricane expands (F) and dissipates.

The monsoon *right*

In principle the processes which give rise to the monsoon are the same as those causing a sea breeze but on a vastly larger scale in space and time. In southeast Asia each May and June warm, moist air streams in from the south causing heavy rain and occasional violent storms. In winter the circulation is reversed and winds come mainly from high pressure over Siberia. In detail the monsoon is considerably modified by the Himalayas and the positions of the waves in the westerlies in the atmosphere's upper levels, but its mechanism is not fully known.

Duststorm *right*

In arid regions strong wind circulations can become filled with dust and extend over considerable areas. The storm typically arrives in the form of an advancing wall of dust possibly five miles (8 km) long and 1000 ft (300 m) high. The haboobs of the Sudan, a recurrent series of storms, are most frequent from May to September and can approach from almost any direction. They usually occur, after a few days of rising temperature and falling pressure, where the soil is very dry. Dust-devils, small local whirlwinds forming pillars of sand, can dot the land.

Nacreous cloud *right*

At high latitudes, when the Sun is below the horizon, these clouds sometimes come into view as fine filmy areas containing regions of bright spectral color. They look rather like a form of cirrus, but are far higher. Nacreous cloud in the Antarctic—such as that in the photograph, taken in Grahamland—has been measured at heights from 8.5 to 19 miles (13.5-30 km), and Scandinavian observations lie in the 20-30 km range. Despite their great altitude, nacreous clouds are undoubtedly formed as a result of air being lifted by passage across high mountains.

The monsoon seasons *below*
In summer an intense low-pressure area over northwest India overcomes the equatorial low pressure region. In winter an intense high over central Asia blows cold, dry air in the reverse direction.

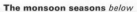

Summer

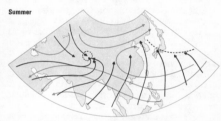

Winds near sea level → ⟶ Winds at about 20,000 ft (6000 m)

Winter

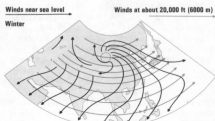

Flash flood *below*
In historic times floods have drowned millions. Even in a modern advanced country a major flood is a national disaster. The scene below is a flooded crossing on the road from Lake Grace to Dumbleyung, W Australia. It is a 'flash flood', caused by heavy rain and poor drainage.

After the hurricane *left*
Whereas a tornado can cause buildings to explode, as a result of the sudden violent difference in pressure between inside and outside, a hurricane just blows. But the wind can demolish sound houses, such as this residence in Biloxi, Mississippi.

Blown snow *above*
When the wind blows in polar regions it soon begins to lift dry powdery snow and ice granules from the surface. As the wind increases in strength this drifting snow forms a thicker layer, as at this British base in Antarctica. When the entrained material reaches eye level it is known as blown snow. Any further rise in wind velocity swiftly increases the concentration of particulate matter, causing the visibility rapidly to fall to zero. When this is the case the term blizzard is appropriate, as it also is when high winds are combined with a heavy snowfall.

All the past history of the Earth since the original formation of the crust is there to be discovered in the rocks existing today if only the appropriate techniques are used to find it. Sedimentary, igneous and metamorphic – the three basic types of rock – all have an enormous amount of information stored within them on such diverse aspects of the Earth's history as, for example, the variations of past climates in space and in time, the incidence of ice ages and the positions of former mountain ranges. The migrations of the ancient geo-magnetic poles at different periods of time can be discovered by studying some sedimentary and igneous rocks, while other types can yield their ages of formation or metamorphism – their changed character over long periods. The prevailing wind directions over certain regions, the direction of stream flow in river deltas that have long since vanished, or the ways in which the ice flowed in some past ice age are all there to be discovered. So are the past distributions of land and sea, areas of deposition, periods of uplift and the raising of great mountain chains (page 23A). Even lightning strikes millions of years old can be clearly seen.

The first task of the geologist is to make a map showing the positions and relative ages of the various rock types in a region. It is around this basic information incorporated into the geological map that all else is built, whether it is to be studies of the geological history and evolution of the region, or detailed investigations of the flora and fauna, or any of many other lines of research – such as the disentangling of various periods of deformation which have affected the region during which the rocks may have been folded or faulted (foot of this page) or eroded down to sea level. Two of the most important methods of dating, by which the age of rock is determined, are the study of fossils and the use of radiometric methods in which age is calculated by analyzing radioactive minerals having a known half-life (opposite page). Using a combination of 'correlation' techniques and either method of dating it is possible for a skilled geologist to compare the relative time sequences of geological events in any regions in the world.

A geological map *below*
A geological map records the outcrop pattern and the structural features of each region as they are today, corresponding with the final stage of the reconstruction—right.

How the story unfolds
right
The complex 3500 million year story of the rocks is very far from being superficially obvious. Even a skilled geologist can do no more than study the land as it is today, plot a geological map and then try to think backward over periods of millions of years in an endeavor to determine the sequences which produced the present terrain. On the right is depicted such a sequence, which might reasonably be arrived at after studying the map below, left. The history begins (A) with the landmass rising and the sea retreating, leaving behind 'off-lap' sediments. The landmass continues to rise and is folded by compressive forces, the fold tops then being eroded (B). Over a long period the landmass then subsides and tilts; the sea once more advances, laying down 'on-lap' sediments (C). Then a great upheaval causes the sea to retreat completely. The landmass is strongly uplifted and faulted, and the higher mass is at once attacked by erosion (D). Continued erosion gradually reduces the region to a more or less common level. Rivers, formed at stage C, carry eroded materials away and deposit them at lower levels (left side of E). Finally, the northeast part of the region is invaded by an extrusive mass of volcanic material. Of course, the processes of change would continue even now.

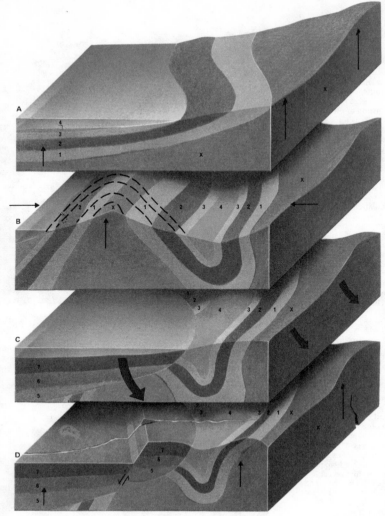

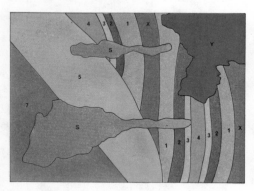

S	River sediments
Y	Volcanic extrusion
7	Later sedimentary sequence
6	
5	
4	Period of erosion
3	Early sedimentary sequence
2	
1	
	Period of erosion
X	Older basement rocks

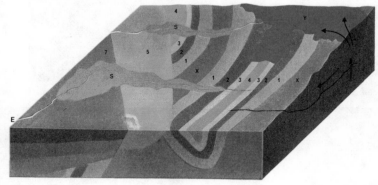

The language of geology

Plane of movement of a normal fault (1) displacing strata to right (downthrow side) relative to left (upthrow side).

Block of strata (2) dropped between two tensional faults forming a rift valley. Other strata are compressional.

Normal anticline (3) and syncline (4) with symmetrically dipping limbs on either side of the axial plane of the strata.

Positions of the axial planes (5, 6) passing through an asymmetrical anticline (5) and an asymmetrical syncline (6).

Compressional reversed fault (7). In this case the left side of the fault is over-riding basically horizontal strata on the right.

Monoclinal fold (8), with a relatively steep limb separating basically horizontal areas of strata at two levels.

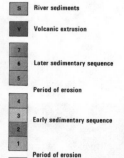
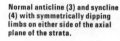
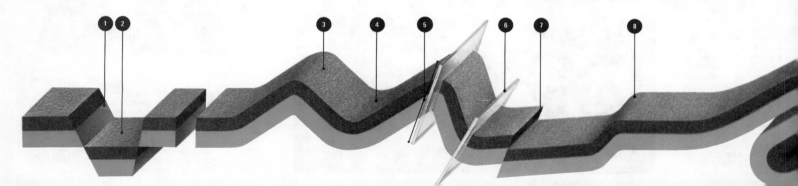

Geological dating

The relative dating of geological strata is found from the sequence in which the layers were deposited, the oldest being at the base of a local sequence and the youngest at the top. On this basis, together with correlations over wide areas based on the fossil evidence of the forms of life at different stages of the 'geological column', the main periods and sub-divisions can be worked out.

Prior to the Cambrian, the oldest epoch of the Paleozoic era (see scale at right), evidence of life is seldom found in the rocks. The extremely primitive earliest forms of life have generally not been preserved in the form of fossils, and so correlations by palaeontological methods cannot be applied to the Precambrian.

In recent years the progressive evolution of radiometric dating has enabled geologists to assign actual dates to the relative sequences of strata. Since the formation of the Earth's crust various isotopes have been present in it which are radioactive, spontaneously decaying over a precisely fixed period of time into a different element. For example a large number of geological dates have been based on the decay of potassium (K^{40}) to argon (A^{40}) and on that of rubidium (Rb^{87}) to strontium (Sr^{87}). The manner in which these valuable geological time-clocks decay over many millions of years is depicted below. No radioactive isotope is ever completely used up; millions of years later atoms are still present of both the original isotope and the end-product of its disintegration.

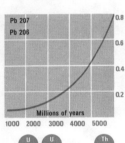

Half-life *left*
Radioactive materials decay according to a law. Each isotope has a characteristic half-life, the time required for the number of radioactive atoms to decay to half the original number. The half-life for each element is unalterable.

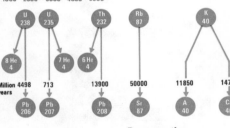

Degeneration
above and left
Some of the isotopes, shown above with their half-lives and end-products can be used for dating over the whole age of the Earth. For more recent dating, radio-carbon with a half-life of 5570 years is used (left).

1 Neutron
2 Nitrogen 14
3 Proton
4 Carbon 14
5 Nitrogen 14
6 β particle

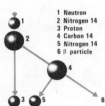

Overturned anticline (9) overlying an overturned syncline in a system distinguished by isoclinal (almost parallel) limbs.

Plane of thrusting (10) causes the overturned anticline (11) to ride over lower strata in form of a horizontally displaced 'nappe'.

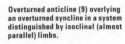

Million years	Major periods	Period scale	Million years
	Cenozoic		
	Mesozoic		65
500	Palaeozoic		
	Upper Proterozoic		100
1000	Lower Proterozoic		136
1500			190
			200
	Archaean		225
2000			280
			300
2500	Katarchaean		345
3000			395
			400
	Oldest known crust		430
3500			500
4000			570
4500	formation of the earth		600

Period

Quaternary
This most recent period of geological history leads up to the appearance of man and the present day. Changes of climate took place which brought on the great ice ages with glacial periods alternating with warmer sequences between them. And, of course, the period is still in progress.

Tertiary
A complex history of changes took place, each epoch of the Tertiary period from Paleocene to Pliocene showing a diverse sequence of volcanism and mountain-building in different regions. Shallow seas alternated with sub-tropical delta flats harboring the precursors of today's life.

Cretaceous
The Tethys Sea spread over large areas of the adjacent continents. Fossil evidence reveals a diverse flora and fauna. The South Atlantic reached a width of some 1900 miles (3000 km) and only Antarctica and Australia and the northern lands of the North Atlantic remained unseparated.

Jurassic
The North Atlantic had opened to a width of some 600 miles (1000 km). Sedimentary deposits formed marginal belts around the continents which had separated, and deeper-water sediments were deposited in the Tethys Sea. Extensive eruption of basalts accompanied the rifting of the South Atlantic.

Triassic
This was the period in which the continental drift began. The progressive opening of the North Atlantic was accompanied by rift-valley faulting and large outpourings of basalt along the eastern seaboard of what is today North America. Gondwanaland in the south began to break up.

Permian
Many areas were characterized by arid or semi-arid climates, with frequent salt lakes giving rise to evaporite deposits and red desert sandstones. Much volcanic activity took place on a local scale. This was the last period in which Pangaea remained a single continental mass. New flora were abundant.

Carboniferous
Extensive forest and deltaic swamp conditions led to the eventual formation of coal basins in North America and Europe. Phases of folding and mountain formation occurred in many places. In Gondwanaland widespread glaciation occurred, with glaciers radiating from a great central ice-cap.

Devonian
Large areas of arid continental and sandstone deposits formed, partly as the products of erosion of the mountains formed previously. Intervening basins of shallow sea or lagoonal deposits occurred, with abundant fossil fish. Distinct faunal provinces have been recognized from this period.

Silurian
In this period further widespread basins of thick sedimentary deposits were laid down. Many of these are characterized by the abundance of marine fossils, including corals. The Caledonian mountains were formed in Laurasia in which enormous volumes of granitic rocks were later emplaced.

Ordovician
Graptolites and trilobites continued to be important forms of marine life. Thick marine sediments continued to be laid down, and there were extensive and widespread outbursts of volcanic activity. In some regions deformation and uplift of the rocks created major mountain ranges.

Cambrian
Rocks of this period contain the earliest fossilized remnants of more complex forms of life such as graptolites, brachiopods, trilobites and gastropods. In many regions the Cambrian period was characterized by the deposition of thick sequences of sedimentary rocks, usually on an eroded basement.

Precambrian
By far the longest period of geological time is included in the Precambrian. This encompasses a complex history of sedimentation, mountain-building, volcanism, and granitic intrusions. Precambrian rocks form basements to many sedimentary deposits, and make up the nuclei of continents.

In 1833 Charles Lyell courageously proposed that the fragments of bones of animals and men that persistently cropped up in deep geological strata could mean only one thing: that the Earth had been created long before the date of 4004 BC accepted by Christianity. Since then practically the whole of our knowledge of man's early development has come from systematic digging. At first a lone archaeologist could do the whole job, but today digging for early man involves a team of specialized archaeologists, geologists, technologists and laboratory workers. They hope to identify everything significant, study it in relation to its resting place, the history of the region and nearby finds, and also subject chosen items to detailed laboratory tests — such as accurate age determination by the potassium/argon method (p. 31A). A major dig needs experts on rocks, on soils and on plant pollen.

Although there are remarkable instances of well-preserved human bodies being found (for example, in peat bogs) and of woolly mammoths whose flesh could be eaten after a million years in frozen Siberia, almost all archaeology rests on bones and on man's artifacts. Gradually, from small fragments of jaw, teeth, skull and other bones, it has been possible to piece together what appears to be a fairly complete history of human evolution. The artist can then cover a deduced skeleton with tissue, as has been done in these pages. But pigmentation of skin and degree of hairiness is still a matter for conjecture.

Among the significant factors studied in early man are his brain size, jaw structure, posture and locomotion. Today's great apes have a stooping, occasionally four-legged posture. So did ape-men from 20 million down to five million years ago; then, gradually, the hominid line learned to walk upright. Its members also learned to use tools, and to make them progressively better. Even later, true men began to leave behind evidence of their growing culture in their burials, their artifacts and their art. All these things can be studied in bone caves, such as the imaginary one illustrated on the right, and in excavation sites.

The cave in use
The cave is modeled after European examples of the Upper Paleolithic period of the order of 25000 years ago. It was at about this time that cave paintings appear to have become widespread. The river was then close to its present level, but the rock falls and piles of debris were still to come.

A bone cave *above and right*
From about 100,000 years ago caves provided many types of early men with a ready-made refuge. Probably most of these caves still exist. Although many are buried under later strata, and virtually all are greatly changed by subsequent developments, it is still possible with experience to read the message contained in them.

A burrow in the cave
Here a small animal has burrowed into the floor. It was deflected sideways by the hard flowstone until it could continue on down, throwing fossil bones up on to the floor above. Finally it died at the end of its burrow.

A buzzard's nest?
Just inside the lip of the cave mouth a bird of prey built its nest. Directly beneath it on the slope of the rock debris are scattered small rodent bones.

River level
In general, the lowest geological sediments are the oldest, but it is unwise to jump to this conclusion. In this hypothetical cave the earliest of all the deposits is a river terrace A above the cave on the hillside, indicating that the whole cave was originally submerged. At about this period insoluble limestone residue was settling on the cave floor at B. As the river cut its valley its level fell to C, leaving silt bed D. Continued deepening of the valley brought the river to its present level, leaving the cave dry and eroding the thick layer of silt at the mouth of the cave.

An obstructed mouth
Early man sheltered in the mouth of the cave and lit fires there for warmth and to cook food. The ashes of these fires gradually accumulated in three main layers, each denoting a long period of use. The 'contemporary' inset illustrates the third of these periods. Later the cave was abandoned by man and the mouth gradually became blocked by a pile of rock debris.

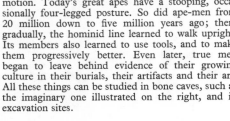

Mesolithic
About 10,000 years ago
About 20000 years ago the great ice sheets began slowly to recede, a process that is still continuing. As the climate grew warmer the Late Paleolithic people gave way to the Mesolithic (transitional) about the year 8000 BC. Milder conditions allowed man to exploit the rivers and seas, using fishing nets and even elaborate barricades and weirs made of woven saplings. The family had by now become a firm social unit, while people also explored the territory of their neighbors. For the first time there is evidence of large groups combining in habitation, hunting, art and making useful articles. Although farming of crops and animals had yet to come, the Mesolithic period saw a great enrichment of life and—probably— the development of a social conscience.

Neolithic
8000 years ago
The scene below depicts the greatest revolution ever wrought on Earth. The Neolithic ('new stone') people discovered some of the basic secrets of life—how animals can be reared in captivity and how plants can be grown from seed. The keeping of pets by children may have provided the key to animal husbandry by their parents. As a result men no longer had to risk their lives in finding and killing their prey; they kept them in a herd. And the organized growing of crops at last freed man from the role of passive and often desperate scavenger, and instead set him on his great path leading to mastery over his environment. Unlike all other Earth life he became able to shape the whole world around him and, to an increasing degree, become master of his life and future destiny. Many of the inhabitants of today's world still live in a basically Neolithic way.

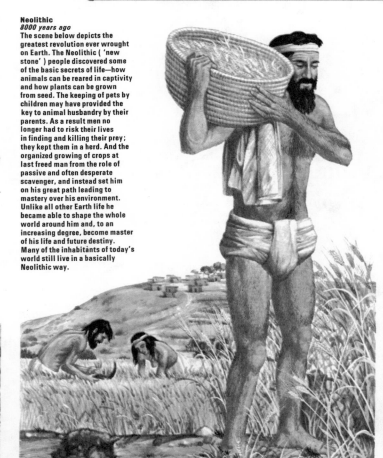

Cave art
Many well preserved cave paintings are masterpieces. Most show animals being hunted by early man, and their power, color and dynamic energy can be startling. But they are often in difficult, inaccessible places, and appear to have been part of the hunter's semi-religious efforts to insure his success and safety in finding and then killing a powerful and dangerous opponent.

The bear cult
Another manifestation of early man's hunting superstitions is to be found in carefully prepared arrangements of cave bear skulls, leg bones and other fragments. Men could hardly have chosen a more dangerous opponent, and they could find meat much more easily; yet the cave bear cult is evident in many forms, such as this stone compartment filled with skulls.

Human burial
Early men buried their own kind in various ways. Some societies buried skulls only, arrayed with possessions or ornaments; others buried men but left female corpses on refuse heaps. This skeleton shows evidence of careful burial in a sleeping posture similar to that of the Grimaldi remains in the Grotte des Enfants, Monaco. Later the grave was overlain by rock debris, here removed.

Petrification
Even the interior of a structurally stable cave changes over a long period, and in this case a sudden gross alteration has resulted from a large fall of rock from the roof. Subsequent to this, slow seepage through the limestone roof of water containing dissolved minerals, especially calcium carbonate, caused gradual growth of pendulous stalactites and upright stalagmites.

Animal remains
The cave is littered to a depth of well over a foot (0.3 m) with the debris of the food and other refuse of carnivores. The great cone above the fall of rock is littered with the remains of animals which fell in through the hole above; and on top of the cone is a pile of bat dung.

A rock fall
A massive collapse of the cave roof left a pile of rock on the floor of the cave and a gaping open shaft above. New layers of flowstone accumulated, earth and rock debris built up above the growing cone reached the roof. Sediments then filled the shaft.

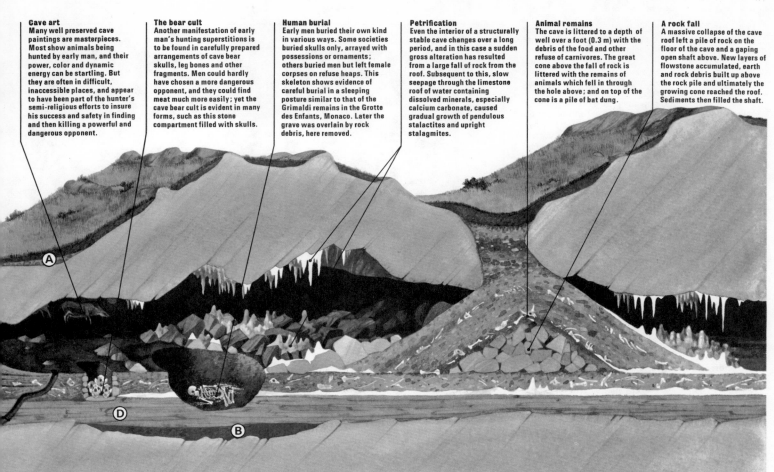

	LOWER PALEOLITHIC		MIDDLE PALEOLITHIC	UPPER PALEOLITHIC	MESOLITHIC
	Over 2 million yrs / AUSTRALOPITHECUS	500,000 yrs / HOMO ERECTUS	100,000 yrs / H. SAPIENS NEANDERTHALENSIS	40000 yrs / H. SAPIENS SAPIENS (MODERN MAN)	10000 yrs
Hunting and fishing methods	Food gathering (roots, berries, grubs, eggs). Hunting small game. Killing with stones and stabbing sticks.		Food gathering. Hunting large game. Use of fire hardened spears and stone clubs. Group hunting using ambush and stampede.	Food gathering, fowling and fishing. More specialized hunting of herd animals using traps and falls.	Food gathering, fowling and fishing with traps. Collection of shell fish. Beginnings of agriculture and domestication of animals.
Material culture	Oldowan pebble tools. / Oldowan pebble tools 500,000 yrs ago	Chopping tools and hand axes. Wooden spears. Use of fire (Pekin man). / Hand axe Tortoise core tool	Development of varied stone tool kits (scrapers, burins points, blades). / Pointed flake tool Point tool Cutting tool	Throwing spears with separate heads. Harpoons and fish-spears. Implements of bone, horn and ivory. / Bone fish spear with barb insets Pronged fish spear / Antler spear point Spear point on shaft / Microlith arrowhead Flint point	Use of bow and arrows. Transport by canoe, skis, and sledges. Development of basketry and pottery. / Fishhook and net making needle / Fish gorge / Dug-out canoe and paddle
Dwellings	Wind breaks, hunting hides and temporary shelters.	Use of caves, usually as temporary dwelling. Better shelters constructed.	Permanent cave dwellings and more sophisticated shelters.		Evidence of village communities, particularly in coastal areas.
Intellectual and religious activities		Possible existence of cannibalism. / Skull: evidence of cannibalism. / Death met violently, hole in skull base to extract brain.	Ritual burial (La Ferrassie). Possible cannibalism (Solo man). Growth of religious beliefs. / Neanderthal burial, figure clasping boar's jawbone.	Personal adornment and ritual mutilation. Development of cave painting and sculpture. / Carved antler (art) / Engraving of wounded aurochs (magic)	Carved ivory figurine (magic) / Necklace of carnivore canines (personal adornment)

One of the wonders of the Earth must be the subtle interplay between light and structure that transforms common minerals into precious jewels. In most cases man's hand can be detected in their creation, but even in the natural state many minerals have a range of color, shape, texture and form that makes them the treasures of the Earth.

By popular definition, anything that is mined is called a mineral and on this basis coal and oil are the most important minerals (pages 38A-39A). However, geologists reserve the term for naturally occurring materials which have an unvarying chemical composition and crystalline structure. The basic structural elements are arranged in a rigid pattern within three-dimensional crystal matrices.

Each crystal grows from a nucleus by adding atoms layer by layer. A freely growing crystal assumes one of seven basic forms, depending on the relative angles of its faces and the distances between opposite parallel pairs. But in practice the shape of naturally occurring crystals is generally influenced by the space in which it is constrained to grow. Thus in nature crystals develop characteristic habits or over-all shapes. The faces may be all of the same size or unequal. They may occur in narrow layers or grow like a bunch of grapes.

Minerals can be identified by their structure, habit, hardness, density, and the ease with which they can be cleaved along particular planes. Hardness, for example, is normally measured against a scale of increasing hardness from talc to diamond, devised in 1822 by the Austrian mineralogist, F. Mohs. Color is frequently the result of minute proportions of impurities. These often result in minerals of such startling beauty that they are coveted by man as gemstones. The brilliance of transparent gems is due to the way light is reflected inside the stone, and man has learned how to cut gems to enhance their optical properties. The stone is cut or ground to a precise external form with face angles arranged to insure the maximum brilliance based on the refractive index of the material. Rocks (below) are composed of different combinations of a limited number of minerals.

Basic igneous rock
Dolerite, a basic igneous rock, is composed of laths of plagioclase (grey and black), pyroxene (yellow and orange) and oxides of iron and titanium (blackish regions).

Sedimentary rock *above*
Limestone is composed of finely crystalline calcite. It shows the fossilized remains of foraminifera.

Acid igneous rock *below*
Granite is a hard igneous rock made up of quartz, potassium feldspar and red-brown crystals of biotite.

Azurite
Carbonate of copper, possibly the first metal used by man.

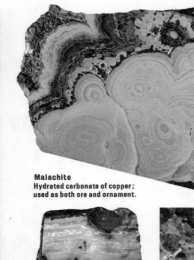

Malachite
Hydrated carbonate of copper; used as both ore and ornament.

Opal
Amorphous silicon dioxide with a variable content of water.

Hemimorphite
A zinc silicate, botryoidal crystal found with other zinc deposits.

Cerussite
Very clearly defined crystals of lead carbonate.

Pyromorphite
A bed of fine hexagonal columns of lead chlorophosphate.

Crystal size
Although crystal shapes are governed by internal structure, individual sizes are controlled only by conditions of growth. For example, plates of mica— seen as minute biotite flakes in granite sections (lower left)— have reached 33ft (10m) by 14ft (4.3m) wide as in one 90-ton example discovered in Canada.

Quartz
Columnar crystals of silicon dioxide.

Sphene
Silicates are abundant; sphene is calcium titanium silicate.

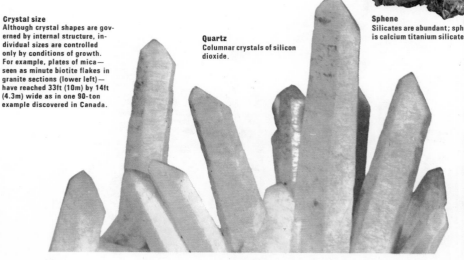

Beryl
Beryllium aluminium silicate is
known in crystals of 25 tons.

Torbernite
Hydrous copper uranium
phosphate; a uranium source.

Pyrite on calcite
Crystals of iron disulphide,
on calcium carbonate.

Calcite
Often occurs as stalactites and
stalagmites.

Cassiterite
Tin was one of man's earliest
metals; this is the dioxide ore.

Wavelite
Crystals of hydrous basic
aluminium phosphate.

Citrine
The yellowish variety of quartz
(silicon dioxide).

Diamonds in kimberlite
Native diamonds (crystalline
carbon) in their original rock.

Ruby in host rock
The deep red variety of
corundum (aluminium oxide).

Polished diamond
For use as a gemstone the
diamond is skilfully cut.

Polished ruby
Large rubies are among the most
precious of all gemstones.

Sulphur
Crystalline sulphur (brimstone)
occurs in nature.

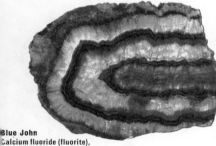

Blue John
Calcium fluoride (fluorite),
occurs in various colorful forms.

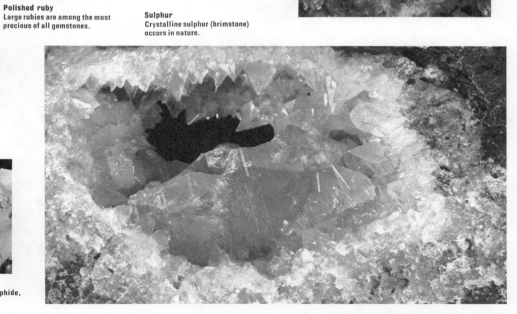

Galena
Cubic crystals of lead sulphide,
a major ore of lead.

MINERALS UNDER THE LAND

Of about 2000 minerals in the Earth's crust only 100 or so are of economic importance. These are distributed very irregularly, so that no country today can boast all the minerals it needs. As a result minerals are a source of great national wealth, exploitation and even of rivalry. And the strife is likely to intensify as man's demands grow, because the total of the Earth's minerals is limited.

Against this background of uneven distribution, economic warfare and sharply increasing demand, man's use of minerals constantly changes. Coal, in 1920 the most important mineral in the world on a tonnage basis, is today unable to compete in several of its former markets because of the high cost of transporting it, and its use is increasingly changing from that of a fuel to that of a raw material for plastics and chemicals. Nitrates for fertilizers and explosives sustained the economy of Chile until 1914, when Germany found a way to 'fix' nitrogen from the atmosphere. Aluminum, one of the most abundant minerals, was costly and little used until a large-scale refining process was discovered which made use of cheap hydroelectricity.

Taking the broad view, the Earth's minerals are seen as a stern test of man's ability to make proper use of the resources available to him. Already some nations have amassed enormous stockpiles of what are today considered to be strategically important minerals. Nickel is one such metal, and the bulk of the world's supply comes from Canada. Another is manganese, and in this case the dominant supplier is the Soviet Union; but manganese is one of the many minerals which might be dredged from the sea bed.

Uneven distribution of minerals is paralleled by uneven consumption. Paradoxically, the industrialized countries which owed their original development to the presence of mineral resources, particularly iron and coal, now rely for their continued prosperity on developing nations. If the latter were to develop a similar demand for materials a mineral famine would ensue which would have repercussions throughout the world.

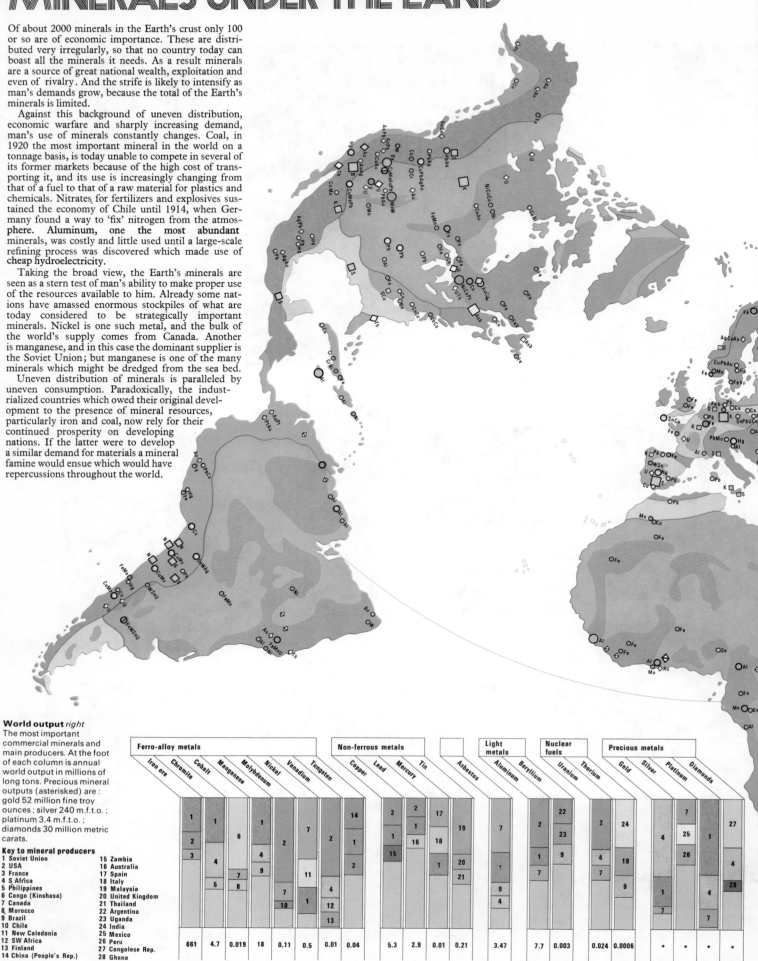

World output *right*
The most important commercial minerals and main producers. At the foot of each column is annual world output in millions of long tons. Precious mineral outputs (asterisked) are: gold 52 million fine troy ounces; silver 240 m.f.t.o.; platinum 3.4 m.f.t.o.; diamonds 30 million metric carats.

Key to mineral producers

1 Soviet Union	15 Zambia
2 USA	16 Australia
3 France	17 Spain
4 S Africa	18 Italy
5 Philippines	19 Malaysia
6 Congo (Kinshasa)	20 United Kingdom
7 Canada	21 Thailand
8 Morocco	22 Argentina
9 Brazil	23 Uganda
10 Chile	24 India
11 New Caledonia	25 Mexico
12 SW Africa	26 Peru
13 Finland	27 Congolese Rep.
14 China (People's Rep.)	28 Ghana

Ferro-alloy metals								Non-ferrous metals					Light metals	Nuclear fuels		Precious metals			
Iron ore	Chromite	Cobalt	Manganese	Molybdenum	Nickel	Vanadium	Tungsten	Copper	Lead	Mercury	Tin	Asbestos	Aluminum	Beryllium	Uranium	Thorium	Gold	Silver	Platinum	Diamonds
	1	1		1		7	14	2	2	2	17		7	2	22	2	7	7	7	27
	2		6		2			1	1	16	18	19		23		24	4	25	1	
	3	4		4			2	15			20		1	1	9	4	19	26		4
		5	7	9		11		2			21		9	7		7				28
			8		7		4						4			9			7	
				10	1		12													
							13													
661	4.7	0.019	18	0.11	0.5	0.01	0.04	5.3	2.9	0.01	0.21	3.47	7.7	0.003	0.024	0.0006	*	*	*	*

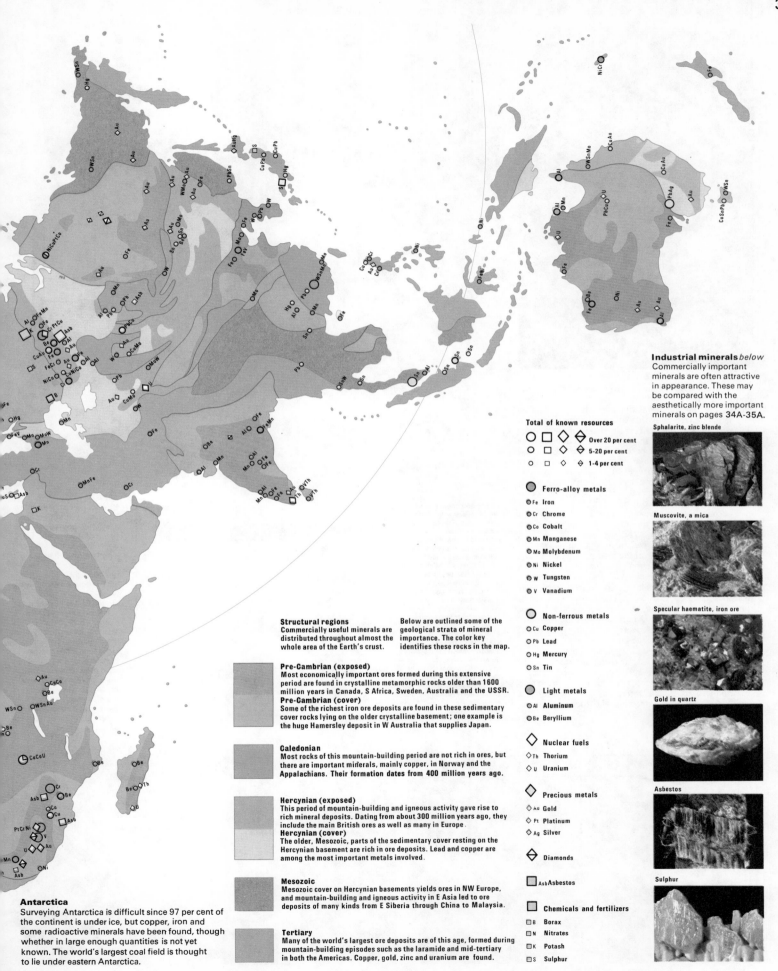

Industrial minerals *below*
Commercially important minerals are often attractive in appearance. These may be compared with the aesthetically more important minerals on pages 34A–35A.

Sphalarite, zinc blende

Muscovite, a mica

Specular haematite, iron ore

Gold in quartz

Asbestos

Sulphur

Total of known resources

○	□	◇	◈ Over 20 per cent
○	▫	◇	◈ 5–20 per cent
○	▫	◇	◈ 1–4 per cent

Ferro-alloy metals
- Fe Iron
- Cr Chrome
- Co Cobalt
- Mn Manganese
- Mo Molybdenum
- Ni Nickel
- W Tungsten
- V Vanadium

Non-ferrous metals
- Cu Copper
- Pb Lead
- Hg Mercury
- Sn Tin

Light metals
- Al Aluminum
- Be Beryllium

Nuclear fuels
- Th Thorium
- U Uranium

Precious metals
- Au Gold
- Pt Platinum
- Ag Silver

Diamonds

Asb Asbestos

Chemicals and fertilizers
- B Borax
- N Nitrates
- K Potash
- S Sulphur

Structural regions
Commercially useful minerals are distributed throughout almost the whole area of the Earth's crust.

Below are outlined some of the geological strata of mineral importance. The color key identifies these rocks in the map.

Pre-Cambrian (exposed)
Most economically important ores formed during this extensive period are found in crystalline metamorphic rocks older than 1600 million years in Canada, S Africa, Sweden, Australia and the USSR.

Pre-Cambrian (cover)
Some of the richest iron ore deposits are found in these sedimentary cover rocks lying on the older crystalline basement; one example is the huge Hamersley deposit in W Australia that supplies Japan.

Caledonian
Most rocks of this mountain-building period are not rich in ores, but there are important minerals, mainly copper, in Norway and the Appalachians. Their formation dates from 400 million years ago.

Hercynian (exposed)
This period of mountain-building and igneous activity gave rise to rich mineral deposits. Dating from about 300 million years ago, they include the main British ores as well as many in Europe.

Hercynian (cover)
The older, Mesozoic, parts of the sedimentary cover resting on the Hercynian basement are rich in ore deposits. Lead and copper are among the most important metals involved.

Mesozoic
Mesozoic cover on Hercynian basements yields ores in NW Europe, and mountain-building and igneous activity in E Asia led to ore deposits of many kinds from E Siberia through China to Malaysia.

Tertiary
Many of the world's largest ore deposits are of this age, formed during mountain-building episodes such as the laramide and mid-tertiary in both the Americas. Copper, gold, zinc and uranium are found.

Antarctica
Surveying Antarctica is difficult since 97 per cent of the continent is under ice, but copper, iron and some radioactive minerals have been found, though whether in large enough quantities is not yet known. The world's largest coal field is thought to lie under eastern Antarctica.

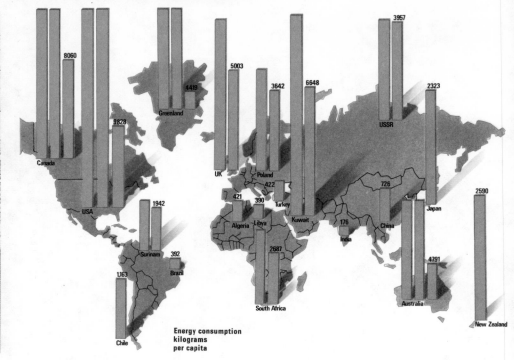

Energy consumption
kilograms
per capita

The concept of energy arose only very recently in the period of man's life on Earth, but already it dominates the whole quality of this life. Early man had no mechanical energy but that of his muscles. By about 2500 years ago he had learned to harness draft animals, such as the ox and horse, and to devise crude water wheels to harness part of the energy of the flow of water in a river. Soon afterwards he added sails to make the fickle wind propel his ships, and by 1000 years ago had started to dot his landscape with windmills. By this time he was adept at burning combustible materials, and during the past 500 years his energy has been increasingly based upon fire, first using wood, and subsequently coal, gas made from coal, petroleum, and natural gas.

All these energy sources, including animal muscle and the wind, are based on the energy radiated by the Sun. Although modern man has begun to use this energy directly in a few trivial installations in hot countries, almost all his energy is derived from solar heat locked up in fossil fuels. The known reserves of these fuels are tending to increase, as a result of prospecting, even faster than man is burning them up. But if no more were discovered most of man's world would come to a halt inside 20 years.

But there should be no energy gap. The promise of nuclear energy is such that, by using fast reactors that breed more fuel than they consume, energy should become one of the very few really plentiful and cheap commodities in man's world of the future. The challenges reside in extracting the fuels and using them effectively.

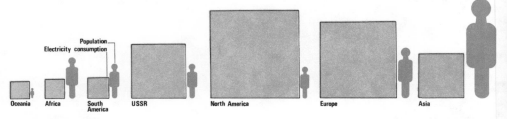

Power and people *above*
World consumption of energy is very uneven. One way of measuring it is to reduce all forms of energy to an equivalent weight of coal burned. The columns on the world map are proportional to the 'coal equivalent' of selected national consumptions expressed in kilograms per head. Electricity consumption is even more disproportionate, as witness the square areas and figure heights immediately above.

Fuels and energy *right*
The caloric value of a fuel is the quantity of heat generated by burning a unit mass. Figures are in British Thermal Units per pound. The surrounding curve shows the increase in the rate at which man is consuming energy; one joule (j) per second is equal to one watt.

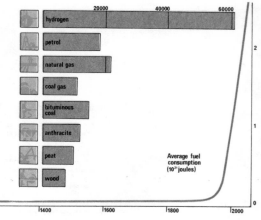

Average fuel consumption ($10^{??}$ joules)

Sources of power *below*
For many centuries the only alternative sources of power to muscles were wood fires, waterwheels and windmills – and the latter had too slight an effect to be shown on the figure below. The left portion shows the way in which, since 1850, the United States has enjoyed successive new sources of energy. In 1920 the US economy was not untypical in being based on coal, but since then more energetic, cleaner and more efficiently used fuels have dominated the picture. In the future, nuclear power, shown in the right-hand figure, promises to make good shortages of fossil fuels.

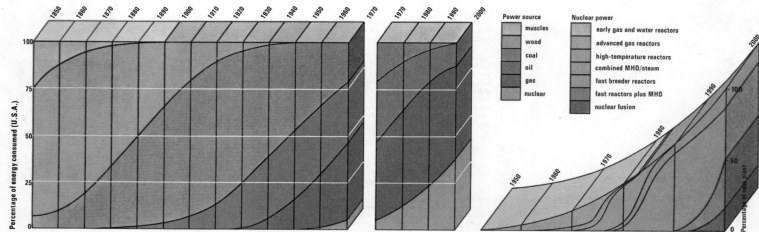

Percentage of energy consumed (U.S.A.)

Power source	Nuclear power
muscles	early gas and water reactors
wood	advanced gas reactors
coal	high-temperature reactors
oil	combined MHD/steam
gas	fast breeder reactors
nuclear	fast reactors plus MHD
	nuclear fusion

Coal into electricity
To reduce costs modern coal-fired generating stations are sited on coalfields ; Lea Hall colliery feeds Rugeley power station (background).

Flare in the desert
Once oil has been struck, harmful gases are burned off in the atmosphere. Similar 'flares' are a prominent feature of petroleum refineries.

Drilling for gas
To reach natural gas trapped in submarine strata a drill rig is used to bore a hole at a location determined by the prospectors

Nuclear power station
Nearly all today's nuclear energy is used to generate electricity. One of the largest stations is Wylfa, Wales, rated at 1180 million watts.

Coal

For three centuries the most important of the fossil fuels, coal is the result of some 300 million years of subterranean decay of vegetation. Many thousands of generations of the Carboniferous trees have become compressed and hardened, first into peat, then into lignite, then into bituminous coal and finally into anthracite. Until this century coal was used inefficiently as a source of heat. Today it is becoming equally important as a raw material producing plastics, heavy chemicals, insecticides, perfumes, antiseptics, road surfaces and many other products. Great advances have been made in automating the mining of coal, but it remains a laborious task and is therefore becoming increasingly expensive. However, coal mining remains a worldwide industry that passes on to modern man the products of the solar energy captured by a younger Earth.

Petroleum

Like coal, oil is a mixture of fossil remains, but yields few clues as to its origin. Crude oil, from the locations shown on the map at right, is carried by tanker ships to refineries in the user countries. Here it is heated in pipe stills until the various constituent 'fractions' are boiled off. The result is a wide range of products from gasoline through kerosene and gas oil to heavy fuel oils, lubricants and vaseline, with a wide range of other by-products used in many thousands of chemicals and plastics materials. Petroleum fuels are replacing coal in heating and transport applications, partly owing to their easier handling and partly to reduce air pollution by sulphurous compounds. LPG, liquefied petroleum gas, is even cleaner burning and may become more important than gasoline and kerosene in road vehicles and aircraft over the next 25 years.

Gas

In 1807 a London street was lit by town gas, a mixture of hydrogen (about 50%), methane, carbon monoxide and dioxide and other gases, formed by cooking coal at high temperature in a retort. By 1950 this manufactured gas was an important fuel, but in many advanced countries its place is now being taken by natural gas, a primary fuel consisting mainly of methane piped straight from deposits sometimes conveniently sited from the user's point of view (right). Intensive prospecting is discovering natural gas faster than it is being used, and during the past 20 years natural gas has become man's largest single source of energy. In refrigerated form, as a compact liquid, it promises to become an attractive fuel for transport vehicles. A major benefit is that the exhaust from such a vehicle would contain less pollutants than from those using gasoline.

Nuclear energy

In 1956 Britain opened the world's first electricity generating station using the heat of nuclear fission. It was fuelled with rods of natural uranium, a heavy silvery metal containing a small proportion of atoms capable of spontaneous fission when struck by a free neutron. Fission releases further neutrons capable of sustaining a continuous chain reaction. Such a reaction generates heat which is used to provide steam for turbines. The prime advantage of nuclear power is that the fuel is used extremely slowly. Now the fast reactor, which uses raw 'fast' neutrons instead of ones artificially slowed down, has been developed. Not only can the fast reactor generate great energy from a small bulk but it creates fresh fuel faster than the original (plutonium) fuel is consumed. Fast reactors, using uranium from granite, could provide limitless cheap energy.

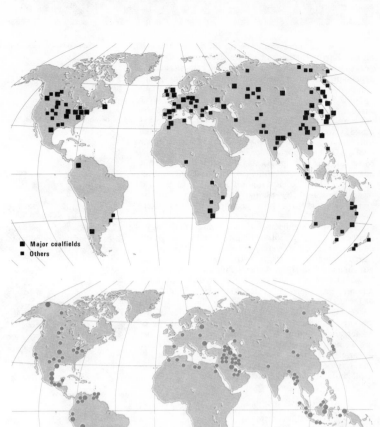

■ Major coalfields
■ Others

● Massive producers
· Smaller oilfields

● Gas-producing areas

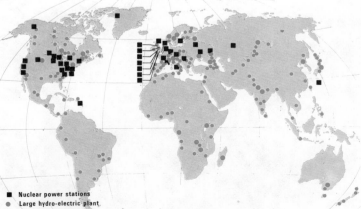

■ Nuclear power stations
● Large hydro-electric plant
· Smaller hydro schemes

Without water there would be no life as we know it on the Earth. Life began in the oceans and the life of the land, both plant and animal, still remains utterly dependent on water for its survival. The atmosphere plays a vital role in the terrestrial water system. Spurred by the energy of the Sun, the moist layer surrounding the globe forms a vast heat engine, operating at a rate of billions of horsepower. All the exposed water surface is constantly being converted into vapor. Eventually the air holding the vapor cools, and the vapor condenses as rain, hail or snow. Most of this precipitation falls into the sea, but nearly a quarter of it falls on the land. Altogether about two-thirds of it evaporates back into the air, or is transpired by plants; the rest runs off in rivers, or filters through the ground to the water table beneath.

Satisfying the collective thirst of man and his industry grows daily more difficult. Almost always the demand is for fresh water; but the proportion of the Earth's water in rivers and streams is less than one part in a million. If the Antarctic ice cap were to melt, it would feed all the rivers for 800 years. Although schemes have been suggested for towing giant fresh-water icebergs from Antarctica to the Californian coast, man is unlikely to make extensive use of the ice cap. Far more promising is the large supply of subterranean water. At the same time great strides are being made in desalination of sea water, using a variety of methods. Management of the Earth's water resources is seen ever more clearly as a technical challenge of the greatest magnitude.

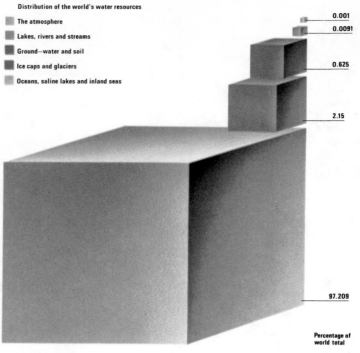

Distribution of the world's water resources

- The atmosphere
- Lakes, rivers and streams
- Ground—water and soil
- Ice caps and glaciers
- Oceans, saline lakes and inland seas

	Percentage of world total
	0.001
	0.0091
	0.625
	2.15
	97.209

The world's water *left*
The total volume of the Earth's water is 317 million cubic miles (1330 million km³). Practically all of it is in the oceans, in a form rich in dissolved salts. Solar heating is constantly evaporating this mass, converting it ultimately into precipitation of fresh water which falls back to the surface. Run-off from the surface in rivers and streams is one of the forms of terrestrial water most visible to man, but it accounts for a negligible fraction of the total. Some 80 times as much water lies in salt lakes and inland seas, 90 times as much in fresh-water lakes, more than 6000 times as much in ground water beneath the land surface, and almost a quarter-million times as much in ice caps and glaciers. So far man has made little attempt to use these sources of fresh water. Instead he interrupts the hydrologic cycle in the easy places: the rivers and lakes, where, because of the small volumes and flows available, he causes significant pollution.

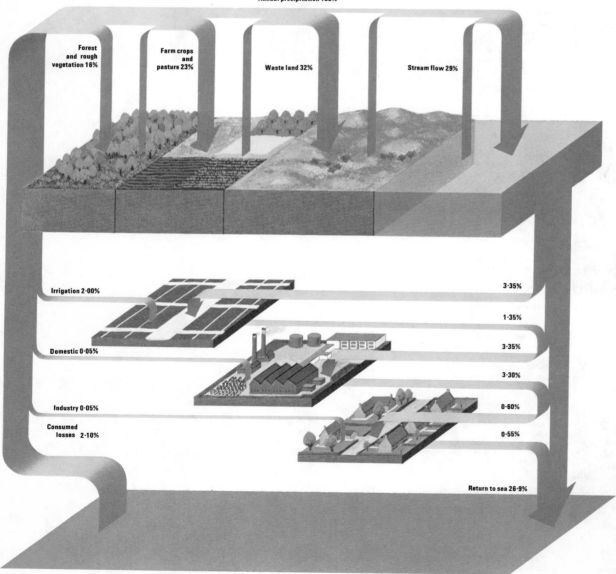

Annual precipitation 100%

Forest and rough vegetation 16%

Farm crops and pasture 23%

Waste land 32%

Stream flow 29%

Irrigation 2·00%   3·35%

1·35%

Domestic 0·05%   3·35%

3·30%

Industry 0·05%   0·60%

Consumed losses 2·10%   0·55%

Return to sea 26·9%

A valued resource *above*
Shiupur head, the head-waters of the Gang canal in Rajasthan province, India. This and other canal systems are gradually bringing to this arid province an assured supply of irrigation water from the Himalayas.

The hydrologic cycle *left*
This diagram is drawn for United States, but the basic features of the cycle are common to most of the Earth's land. Just over three-quarters of the rain snow and hail falls on the oceans. The usual measure for water in huge quantities is the acre-foot (one acre of water, one foot deep). Each year about 300 thousand million acre-feet of water falls on the oceans and 80 thousand million on the land. In the diagram all the figures are percentages. In the US, which is not unusual in its proportion of farmland, less than one-quarter of the water falling on the land falls directly on crops or pasture. A greater amount falls into rivers and streams, from which man takes varying small fractions for his own purposes. It can be seen that, even in the US, the total quantity of water withdrawn for use is only 7.3 per cent of the fraction of water falling on the land. Yet, to attain even this performance, Americans spend more than $10000 million each year on improving their water supplies.

Domestic use of water

In some countries the total consumption of water is less than one gallon per head, but in the United States more than 70 US gallons are consumed by each person daily, on average, in domestic use alone. The way this consumption is split up varies greatly, but these percentages, for 'an average home in Akron, Ohio' are typical for modern urban areas having piped water to flush toilets. Total domestic water consumption in the industrially advanced countries is usually between five and 30 per cent of the national total.

Flushing toilet 41%

Washing and bathing 37%

Kitchen use 6%

Drinking 5%

Laundry 4%

Household cleaning 3%

Garden 3%

Cleaning car 1%

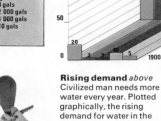
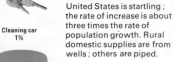

	Process	Requirement
1	Family car	100,000 gals
2	Filling radiator	2 gals
3	One gallon of gas	70 gals
4	One tire	42 000 gals
5	One ton of steel	44 000 gals
6	One ton of glass	130 gals

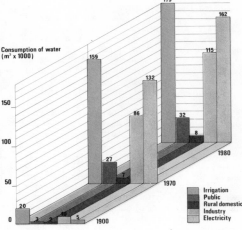

Consumption of water (m³ x 1000)

Irrigation
Public
Rural domestic
Industry
Electricity

Rising demand *above*

Civilized man needs more water every year. Plotted graphically, the rising demand for water in the United States is startling; the rate of increase is about three times the rate of population growth. Rural domestic supplies are from wells; others are piped.

Irrigation *below*

Irrigation of land by man is at least 7000 years old, yet still in its infancy. The grey areas on the world map are virtually without irrigation. The last column of data shows the percentage of each continent irrigated. Only Japan and the UAR exceed 50 per cent.

Most liquid wastes are generated by mixed human concentrations—including habitations, businesses and industry. Before reclamation, any wastes having excessive or toxic mineral content must be segregated from the main flow.

Oilfields on the land invariably generate large and varied liquid wastes, particularly including concentrated brines, which must be excluded from conventional reclamation processes.

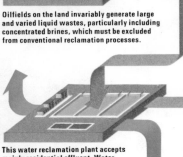

This water reclamation plant accepts mainly residential effluent. Water reclaimed is returned for re-use, while sludge and grease are returned to the sewer and piped to the main sewage treatment plant. A proportion of the output is supplied to spreading grounds at the coast (below) to replenish the ground water table.

Liquid wastes from residential and business areas normally comprise sewage suitable for reclamation without pre-treatment or segregation.

This water reclamation plant supplies water to the city (above) and to agriculture and industry (below, right). Sludge and grease are returned to the sewer (route, far right).

Reclaimed waters may be used to maintain underground supplies by spreading them on percolation beds (above), where the water filters down to the storage basin.

Below, the main sewage treatment plant can operate by a variety of methods, including long-term open storage, aeration, mechanical filtration and softening.

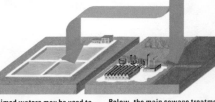

Reclaiming used water

In almost every country the quality of the water pumped into domestic supplies is subject to precise controls, and the proportion of some substances may not exceed one or two parts per million. National water systems make maximum use of water reclaimed close to the point of consumption by plant which returns the heavy sludges and greases to the sewer for treatment at a large sewage works. This facilitates effluent quality control and also provides an emergency outlet for a temporarily overloaded or faulty reclamation plant. In the example here the main treatment plant discharges wastes into an ocean outfall (left), while the fresh water spreading grounds just inshore replenish the water table and thus prevent infiltration by the ocean water.

Continent	Area : million acres (1 acre = 4047m²)			Ratio of B to A (x 100)
	Total	Cultivated (A)	Irrigated (B)	
Africa	898	37	11.2	30
Asia	5062	1289	296.9	23
Australia	1900	38	3	8
Europe	288	122	5.8	5
N America	2809	485	49	10
S America	4620	187	13	7
USSR	5540	568	23	4
Grand total	21117	2726	401.9	15

Desalination

Man's growing demand for fresh water cannot readily be met without an enormous increase in his capacity to desalinate salt water. A choice between several ways of doing this is invariably made on economic grounds. Nearly all the large installations in use are multi-stage flash evaporators in which some form of heat — if possible, heat otherwise wasted - is used to convert sea water to steam which is condensed by the incoming salt water. But in some circumstances more economic results can be obtained by freezing, reverse osmosis or other methods.

GROWTH OF DESALTING CAPACITY 1961 TO 1968

Year Ending	Municipal water use M gal per day	Industrial/other uses M gal per day	Total
1961	17.6	42.2	59.8
1962	20.9	45.5	66.4
1963	28.4	50.4	78.8
1964	32.5	53.5	86.0
1965	39.3	58.9	98.2
1966	52.6	101.6	154.2
1967	102.2	115.3	217.5
1968	121.4	125.8	247.2
Historical annual growth %	32	17	23
Projection to 1975	835	415	1250
Projected annual growth %	32	19	26

SIZE RANGES OF THE WORLD'S DESALTING PLANTS

Size range M gal per day	Number of Plants	Total capacity M gal per day
0.025—0.1	351	17.8
0.1—0.3	218	35.3
0.3—0.5	34	13.0
0.5—1.0	31	21.3
1.0—5.0	46	95.4
5.0—7.5	3	17.5
over 7.5	3	46.9
TOTAL	686	247.2

A submerged land almost equal to the area of the Moon is being urgently explored for its store of minerals. The continental shelf around the Earth's land has the proportions of a seventh continent; around Britain or Japan its area is several times larger than that of the land itself. The shelf is rich in minerals, some of which are accumulating faster than man can at present use them.

By far the most important resources of the shallow seas are the deposits of oil and gas locked in the strata below the bed. About 200 drilling rigs are constantly looking for new deposits, and already nearly 20 per cent of the world's supplies, worth annually $4800 million, are taken from under the sea. Geologists estimate that oil and gas resources under the oceans are at least as great as those under the land. Next to oil and gas the most important marine minerals are lowly sand and gravel. It is becoming increasingly difficult and costly to extract these from the land, and marine deposits are fast becoming of great commercial importance. Often their extraction is combined with land reclamation. The Dutch, for example, have devised several systems that help to create new land and, as at Europoort, deep-water channels.

Last in importance, but very high in speculative interest, come the heavy minerals. Some, such as gravels rich in ilmenite, rutile and zircon, have been concentrated by the sorting action of the waves. Others, including tin, gold and diamonds, have been derived from igneous deposits. But in most cases these minerals can still be obtained more cheaply on land, except in one or two freak instances where concentrated deposits can be easily reached.

Exploiting the shallow sea

One of the most important recent discoveries of oil and natural gas has occurred in the North Sea, on the very doorstep of industrial Western Europe. The North Sea gas is found mainly in layers of a porous sandstone deposited under desert conditions. Since both natural gas and oil are thought to have originated from the compressed remains of animals and plants that swarmed in the warm seas of the Carboniferous period, the gas could not have formed in the rocks where it is now found.

Immediately below the sandstone lie thick coal measures, and the gas appears to have risen from these into the porous sandstone until halted by a thick layer of salt and limestone. Where the limestone is broken and porous, the gas has risen into it and become trapped under salt domes. In the Gulf of Mexico these domes have themselves become a source of minerals. While drilling down to a promising dome an oil company came across the third largest sulphur deposit in the United States.

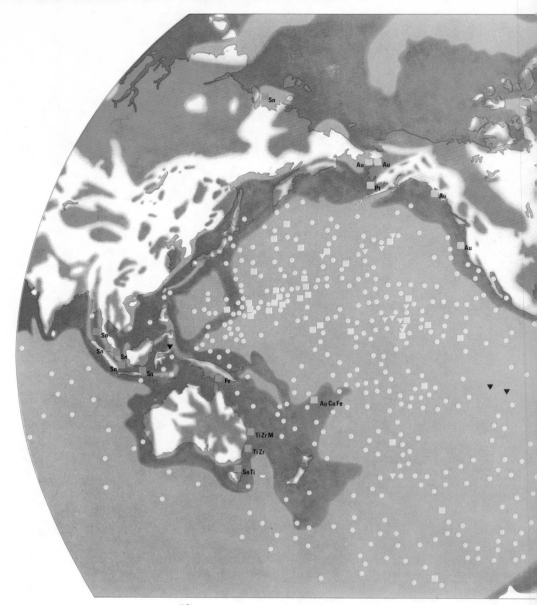

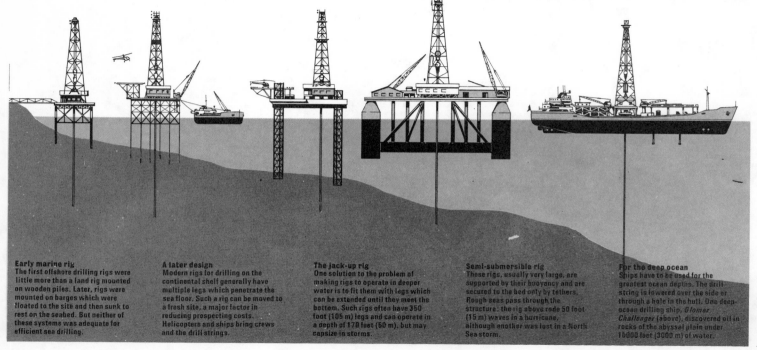

Early marine rig
The first offshore drilling rigs were little more than a land rig mounted on wooden piles. Later, rigs were mounted on barges which were floated to the site and then sunk to rest on the seabed. But neither of these systems was adequate for efficient sea drilling.

A later design
Modern rigs for drilling on the continental shelf generally have multiple legs which penetrate the sea floor. Such a rig can be moved to a fresh site, a major factor in reducing prospecting costs. Helicopters and ships bring crews and the drill strings.

The jack-up rig
One solution to the problem of making rigs to operate in deeper water is to fit them with legs which can be extended until they meet the bottom. Such rigs often have 350 foot (105 m) legs and can operate in a depth of 170 feet (50 m), but may capsize in storms.

Semi-submersible rig
These rigs, usually very large, are supported by their buoyancy and are secured to the bed only by tethers. Rough seas pass through the structure: the rig above rode 50 foot (15 m) waves in a hurricane, although another was lost in a North Sea storm.

For the deep ocean
Ships have to be used for the greatest ocean depths. The drill-string is lowered over the side or through a hole in the hull. One deep-ocean drilling ship, *Glomar Challenger* (above), discovered oil in rocks of the abyssal plain under 16000 feet (3000 m) of water.

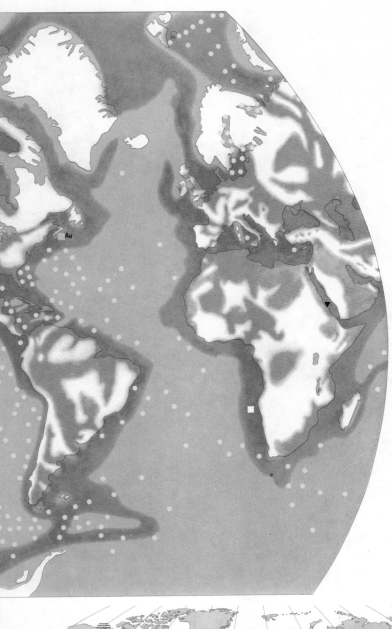

Undersea resources left

Deep ocean basins

Sedimentary basins locally favourable for petroleum

Au: gold

Sn: tin

Fe: iron

Ti: titanium

D: diamonds

Mn sampled

Mn photo 25+ per cent.

Mn photo 25— per cent.

Metal-bearing muds

The large map gives a broad general picture of the distribution of petroleum resources, shown as favorable sedimentary basins, and of major subsea mineral deposits, but does not attempt to indicate commercial value or even which regions are worth exploiting. These are multi-billion dollar questions which are taxing mining companies in many countries. The manganese oxide deposits are shown only where they have been sampled or photographed (with symbols to indicate whether the nodules cover more or less than one-quarter of the sea floor). The metal-bearing muds are a recent exciting discovery. Deep down in the Red Sea, off Indonesia and elsewhere, prospectors have discovered concentrated brines rich in valuable industrial metals.

Mining the oceans below

For 20 years industry has been tantalized by the prospect of literally sucking or sweeping valuable minerals off the ocean floor. But the most widespread loose nodules (see photograph below) have a composition ill-matched to world demand (foot of page), and even the mining system sketched below, in which ships operate what is in effect a giant vacuum cleaner, has yet to be used on a commercial scale. The technical, economic and political problems associated with such ventures are immense: but the potential rewards are great enough to sustain interest.

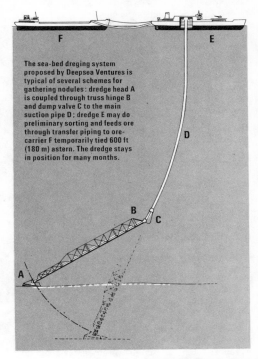

The sea-bed dreging system proposed by Deepsea Ventures is typical of several schemes for gathering nodules: dredge head A is coupled through truss hinge B and dump valve C to the main suction pipe D; dredge E may do preliminary sorting and feeds ore through transfer piping to ore-carrier F temporarily tied 600 ft (180 m) astern. The dredge stays in position for many months.

Manganese nodules

One of the most tempting concepts is to scoop minerals off the bed of the ocean. One of the few products which could thus be harvested is manganese, which is found in the form of potato-sized nodules scattered on the ocean floor.
Unfortunately not only are there technical difficulties standing in the way of such an operation but production would be out of step with world needs. The undersea production of the world's needs of manganese, equivalent to more than 18.6 million tons of ore, would lead to a 453 per cent glut of cobalt. Similarly, if all the world demand for copper were met from the same source, the glut of cobalt would be no less than 11335 per cent (right).

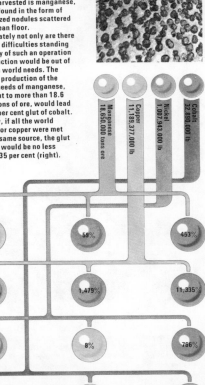

Manganese 18,650,000 tons ore	Copper 11,189,377,000 lb	Nickel 1,007,943,000 lb	Cobalt 32,890,000 lb
4%	59%		453%
2,502%	1,479%		11,335%
169%	8%		786%
22%	0.9%		13%

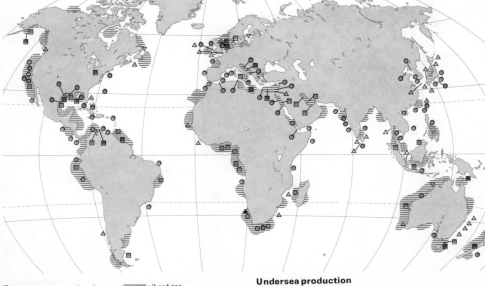

Undersea production

Man's commercial use of the ocean minerals is so far confined almost entirely to the continental shelves around the land.

oil

gas

tin

iron

coal

salt

heavy minerals

sulphur

diamonds

magnesium

fresh water

other minerals

oil and gas exploration

Fish and shellfish were probably the first marine resources to be exploited by man. Many of his early settlements in coastal and estuarine areas bear witness to this with their ancient mounds of oyster and mussel shells. Even now, coastal fisheries remain a vital source of high quality protein for numerous primitive communities. And yet, in spite of this long history of coastal fishing, the commercial fisheries have been dominated by a mere handful of nations until recent times. Three-quarters of the world fish catch is still accounted for by only 14 countries.

The world fish catch is the only source of food that has managed to increase dramatically since the end of World War 2. In the decade from 1958-68 alone, it rose from below 34 million tons to 64 million tons. Although the catch fell by two per cent in 1969, it is expected to continue to improve and may even top the 120 million ton mark by the mid-1980s.

The steady growth of the commercial fisheries since the war has relied on improvements in technology and boats, and the spread of these modern techniques from traditional northern fisheries to newer ones being developed in the southern oceans. Peru, for example, now has the world's largest single species fishery, catching some 10 million tons of anchoveta a year: in 1958 the catch was only 960,000 tons. However, the time is fast approaching when few fish stocks will remain unexploited.

Already many established fisheries are beginning to suffer from the effects of over-fishing with too many boats pursuing too few fish, leading to the capture of younger, smaller fish and a decline in the fish stocks and the fisheries that they support. Only the briefest respite may be needed for the fish to recover: a single female fish can lay thousands of eggs in a single season. Over-exploitation of the whales and turtles is a much more serious matter. Already several species of whale are on the verge of extinction and, with one young born to a female every two years, the prospects for their recovery are poor.

The living resources of the oceans must be conserved and managed if they are to continue to provide mankind with food. It is now clear that the world fish catch has a finite limit, possibly about 200 million tons. With adequate international agreement and controls, this limit might one day be approached. The productivity of the oceans could be increased further only by harvesting animals lower than fish in the marine food chain or by artificially fertilizing and farming the seas. Some of the first steps in this direction are now in progress. Perhaps in the future a new pattern of exploitation will emerge, with fleets harvesting the oceanic fish while other fish, shellfish and crustaceans such as lobster and prawn are farmed in the shallow coastal waters.

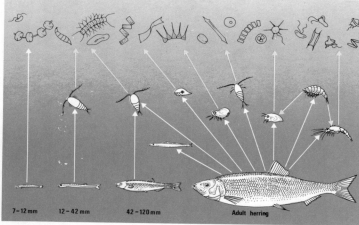

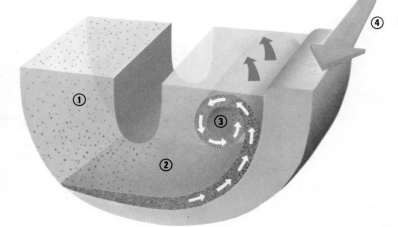

Marine food web *above*
The path leading to food fish such as the herring involves a succession of feeding and energy levels. The plants drifting in the plankton first convert the Sun's energy into a usable form through the process of photosynthesis (top band). The plants are then eaten by small planktonic animals (middle band). These in turn are eaten by the fish during its growth (bottom band). However, as the arrows indicate, the path from plant to fish is far from simple. At each point in the web, energy is exchanged and lost so that the adult fish receives less than a thousandth of the original energy captured in photosynthesis. This loss of energy has prompted suggestions for short-circuiting the process by harvesting members of the plankton itself — either the plants or the small crustaceans and other animals that feed on them.

Upwelling *above*
Most of the world's great fisheries occur in regions of upwelling where nutrient-rich water rises to the surface and supports prolific marine life. Deep ocean waters accumulate the remains of dead and decaying organisms (1) that rain down from the surface. When this nutrient-rich water (2) rises to the surface (3) it contains all the minerals and salts necessary for plant growth in approximately the ratio best suited to stimulate maximum growth. The actual mechanism which causes the water to rise to the surface can vary, but a common source is the interaction between surface winds and ocean currents running along the edge of continents. The wind (4) causes the surface water to move away from the coast, enabling the deep water to swirl up to the surface where it renews the supplies of plant nutrients.

7–12 mm   12–42 mm   42–120 mm   Adult herring

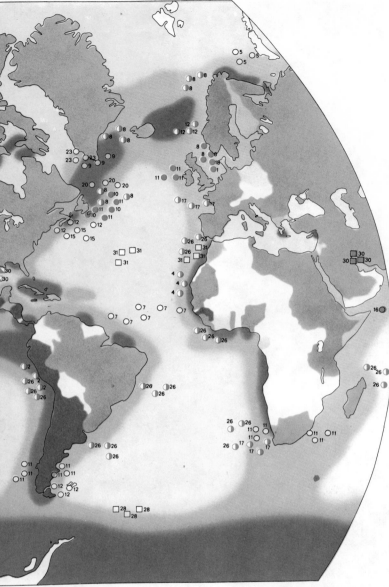

World fisheries *left*
With more nations claiming a share of the oceans' living resources few productive regions remain unexplored by fishing fleets. Already many fisheries show signs of over-exploitation and some coastal states are demanding exclusive rights to very large areas of sea, e.g. Iceland's demand for a 50 mile limit.

Biological productivity

- Very favorable conditions for the growth of marine life
- Moderately favorable conditions for the growth of marine life

Exploitation of fish stocks

- ● Over-exploited by 1949
- ◐ Over-exploited by 1968
- ○ Under-exploited

Exploitation of crustaceans

- ◨ Over-exploited by 1968
- ☐ Under-exploited

Key to numbers

1	Alaska pollack	17	Pilchard
2	Anchoveta	18	Plaice
3	Anchovy	19	Pamfret
4	Demersal fish	20	Red fish
5	Capelin	21	Rock fish
6	Carangidae	22	Salmon
7	Clupeidae	23	Sand eel
8	Cod	24	Sardine
9	Flat fish	25	Saury
10	Haddock	26	Tuna
11	Hake	27	King crab
12	Herring	28	Krill
13	Jack mackerel	29	Red crab
14	Mackerel	30	Shrimp
15	Menhaden	31	Squid
16	Pelagic		

Fishing limits

- Nations claiming a 3 mile exclusive zone
- Nations claiming a 6 mile exclusive zone
- Nations claiming a 12 mile exclusive zone
- Nations claiming more than 12 miles

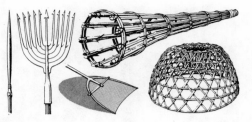

Fishing gear
Primitive fisheries use a wide range of techniques (above) including spears, nets and basket traps.

Mainstays of the modern commercial fisheries (below) are the gill net (top), the seine net and the otter trawl (bottom).

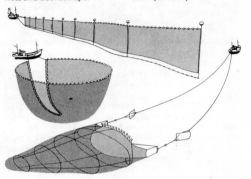

Anchoveta — 5 in, 13 cm, 2-3 oz, 85 g

Herring — 12 in, 30 cm, 8 oz, 227 g

Commercial fish
Although the oceans contain many thousands of different fish species, very few of these support large commercial fisheries. The anchoveta supplies the largest single species fishery in the world with an annual catch of about 10 million tons. This is slightly greater than the total catch of the other species illustrated here.

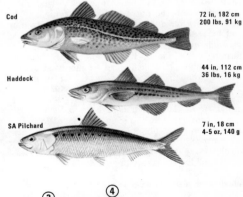

Cod — 72 in, 182 cm, 200 lbs, 91 kg

Haddock — 44 in, 112 cm, 36 lbs, 16 kg

SA Pilchard — 7 in, 18 cm, 4-5 oz, 140 g

The first marine farms, *right*
An early use of marine stockades was to keep alive fish caught at sea until they were needed for eating (A). An advance on this is to catch young fish and then fatten them in fertile coastal waters (B). But marine farming really begins with the production of 'seed fish' which can be reared until they are large enough to survive at sea (C). Such a scheme was proposed in the early 1900s as a means of increasing the productivity of the North Sea fisheries. The proposal was rejected, although marine fish hatcheries existed at the time. These hatcheries, however, were unable to feed their young fish once the yolk sacs had become exhausted. Success became possible with the discovery that brine shrimps, hatched in large numbers, could be used as fish food and that antibiotics would prevent marine bacteria from coating the eggs and killing or weakening the fish embryos inside. The point has now been reached at which fish farming is possible, although fish reared in this way are still too expensive to compete with those caught at sea. In one scheme, eggs collected from adult fish kept in ponds are hatched and the young fed on diatoms and brine shrimps until large enough to be put into marine enclosures (D).

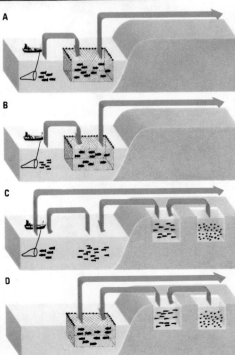

Enriching the sea *right, below*
Some marine farms in the future will exploit the store of nutrients that lie in the cold, deep ocean water. The value of this marine 'fertilizer' is clearly seen in areas where deep water rises to the surface. One project to create an artificial upwelling was started in the Virgin Islands in 1970. When completed it could include both a marine farm and provide fresh water supplies. In this system the cold nutrient-rich water (1) would be raised to the surface by a pump (2) driven by the warm, humid, prevailing winds (3). The cold water would then pass through a condenser (4) where it would be used to cool the wind and release its store of fresh water (5). Finally, the water, now warmed to the temperature of the surface waters, would be used to promote the growth of marine plants and animals such as shellfish, prawn and valuable food fish within net enclosures in the lagoon (6). Deep ocean water may also be used to combat thermal pollution, particularly in tropical areas where marine organisms live close to their upper temperature limit. The cold water would cool down the warm effluent discharged from power stations as well as provide valuable nutrients for marine aquiculture.

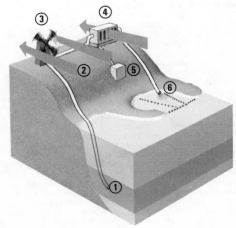

Combine harvester discharging wheat into trailer

Agriculture has always been a cornerstone of human civilization. Until man was able to give up the life of a nomadic hunter he could not be called civilized, and it was the settled life based on the land which enabled progress toward modern society to begin. Today agriculture is the occupation of more people than all other industries, but the pattern of their work varies greatly. In poor or developing lands as many as 90 per cent of the population live directly off the land, whereas in the most industrialized countries the proportion can be as low as three per cent.

The underlying purpose of farming is to convert the energy of sunlight into a form in which it can be assimilated by humans. Initially this can be done only by photosynthesis in green plants, and here the efficiency of the conversion process – expressed in terms of assimilable food energy obtained from a given amount of sunlight – varies from about two per cent down to less than one part in 1000. Further stages involve the consumption of plants by livestock to provide meat and other food for man, or the direct consumption of fruit, vegetables and cereals by man himself. Each additional step in this food chain involves large losses in energy, lowering the overall 'efficiency' of the process.

For many years research has led to improved methods of producing crops, by developing new plant strains with a higher edible yield or greater resistance to disease, by increasing both the area of land under cultivation and the nutritional value of the soil, by devising swifter and surer techniques of cultivation and by reducing the labor effort needed. Improved methods are especially needed in regions of poor farming. The 'Green Revolution' of SE Asia has already shown how yields can be increased dramatically, although at a greater cost in terms of agricultural chemicals and water supplies. Another promising way of increasing food supplies is to extract protein from plants such as soybean and even grass, and to convert them into forms that have the texture and taste of meat. For the more distant future there are prospects of growing single-cell protein and other revolutionary foods which in theory could at least double the Earth's ability to produce food.

World crop production and trade *right above*
In the large map, symbols and shading indicate the pattern of distribution of a selection of the most important crops used for human food. The distribution shown is that of growing area. This is often far removed from the plant's original center, and today the world crop pattern is being subjected to dramatic changes. For example, enormous increases have taken place in Italy's yield of maize (corn) and the United States' production of rice. Pie diagrams are used to show world crop trade, the pie area giving output and the color segments the products (key, far right).

Some important crops *right*
Eight of the world's chief human food crops are described individually at right. The figure below the name is the aggregate world production expressed in metric tons (1m. ton is 0.984 British ton and 1.12 US tons). The pie diagrams in the form of segmented drums show the percentage of the world total raised by the three largest producing countries (in each case China is the People's Republic). The sketches illustrate the mature plant and its fruit, a form often unfamiliar to consumers. Similar panels on the next two pages deal with livestock, fish and oils.

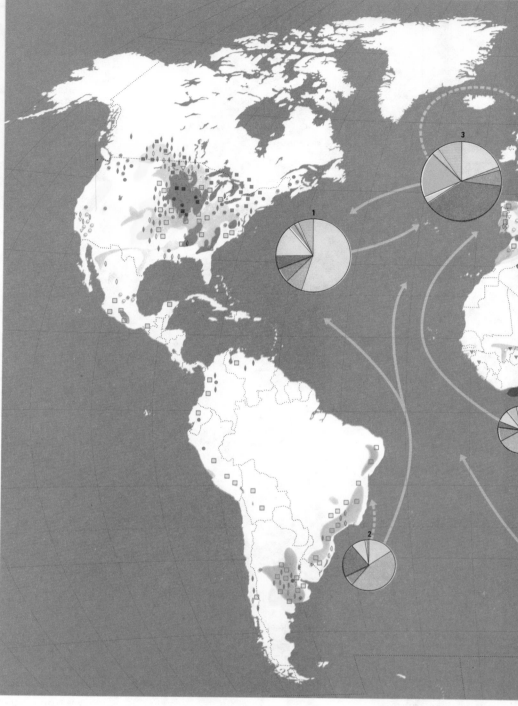

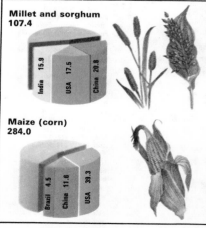

Millet and sorghum
107.4

India 15.9 | USA 17.5 | China 20.8

Several species of plant of the millet family form staple food crops throughout the Earth's warmer countries. The main genuses are *Panicum*, *Pennisetum*, and *Sorghum* or African millet. Chief growing regions are tropical and warm temperate Asia and Africa.

Maize (corn)
284.0

Brazil 4.5 | China 11.6 | USA 39.3

Maize was originally brought from America by Columbus. Although it needs a growing period of 140 days in a soil rich in nitrogen, it can be made into bread and is the subsistence diet of much of Asia and Africa and is important in North America and Britain.

Potatoes
352.0

China (M) 10.4 | Poland 14.4 | USSR 29.0

Grapes
53.7

USSR 8.4 | France 16.4 | Italy 19.2

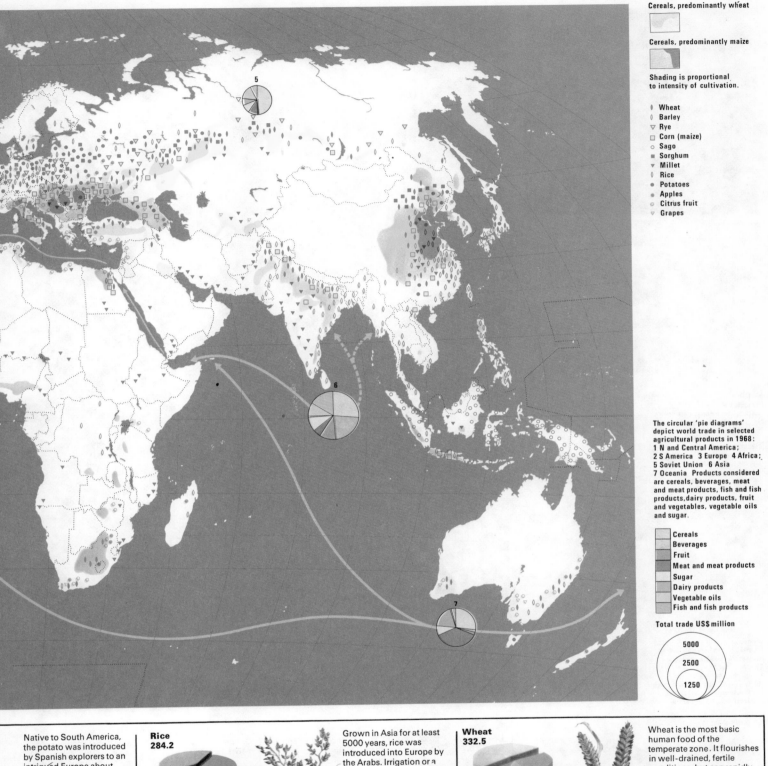

Cereals, predominantly wheat

Cereals, predominantly maize

Shading is proportional
to intensity of cultivation.

⟊ Wheat
⟊ Barley
▽ Rye
☐ Corn (maize)
○ Sago
▪ Sorghum
▽ Millet
◊ Rice
● Potatoes
● Apples
○ Citrus fruit
▽ Grapes

The circular 'pie diagrams'
depict world trade in selected
agricultural products in 1968:
1 N and Central America;
2 S America 3 Europe 4 Africa;
5 Soviet Union 6 Asia
7 Oceania Products considered
are cereals, beverages, meat
and meat products, fish and fish
products, dairy products, fruit
and vegetables, vegetable oils
and sugar.

Cereals
Beverages
Fruit
Meat and meat products
Sugar
Dairy products
Vegetable oils
Fish and fish products

Total trade US$ million

5000
2500
1250

Native to South America,
the potato was introduced
by Spanish explorers to an
intrigued Europe about
1572. Although it needs a
long, cool growing season,
and a high nutrient level, it
yields more food per area of
land than cereals. It is a
source of alcohol.

The vine thrives in warm,
temperate areas, although
the quality of its rootstock
is critical to its nutrient
demand and its resistance
to disease and drought.
About 80 per cent of the
world crop is made into
wine, but large quantities
are dried for raisins.

Rice
284.2

Pakistan 7.1 | India 21.0 | China 32.0

Rye
33.4

W Germany 9.5 | Poland 25.5 | USSR 42.2

Grown in Asia for at least
5000 years, rice was
introduced into Europe by
the Arabs. Irrigation or a
very heavy rainfall is
essential for growing rice,
with the fields being flooded
for most of the season. The
main source of vitamins, the
husk, is removed in milling.

Gradually giving way to
other cereals, rye is
important where soils are
sandy and acid and the
winters long and harsh.
From Britain deep into
Siberia it remains a staple
foodstuff used for animal
feeds, for various forms of
bread and for whisky.

Wheat
332.5

China 8.1 | USA 12.9 | USSR 28.1

Barley
145.1

USA 6.3 | China 9.9 | USSR 19.9

Wheat is the most basic
human food of the
temperate zone. It flourishes
in well-drained, fertile
conditions, but can rapidly
exhaust the soil. New breeds
have been genetically
tailored to improve yield
and resistance to disease

Barley has a very short
growing season and so can
be produced further north
and at a higher altitude than
any other cereal. It needs
good drainage and non-
acid soil. More than half the
world crop is eaten by
livestock, and 12 per cent
goes into making beer.

Unloading frozen lamb carcasses.

Beverages
Coffee, cocoa and tea are grown in the tropics for export to economically advanced countries where their chief role is to add flavor rather than to provide nutrition. Tea is the cheapest at present.

● Coffee
● Cocoa
● Tea

Spices
Invariably these are pungent, aromatic vegetable products. They have been important European imports since pre-Roman times, and a major source today is Indonesia. Spices are extracted from buds, bark and pods.

■ Pimento
▲ Ginger
◆ Nutmeg
● Mace
■ Pepper
◆ Cloves
● Cinnamon
■ Cassia
▲ Vanilla

Alcohol and tobacco
Originally native to South America, tobacco was brought to Europe by the Spanish 400 years ago. Today, it is grown all over the world in various climates and soils. The US is the biggest producer.

■ Beer
● Wine
▲ Spirits
Tobacco

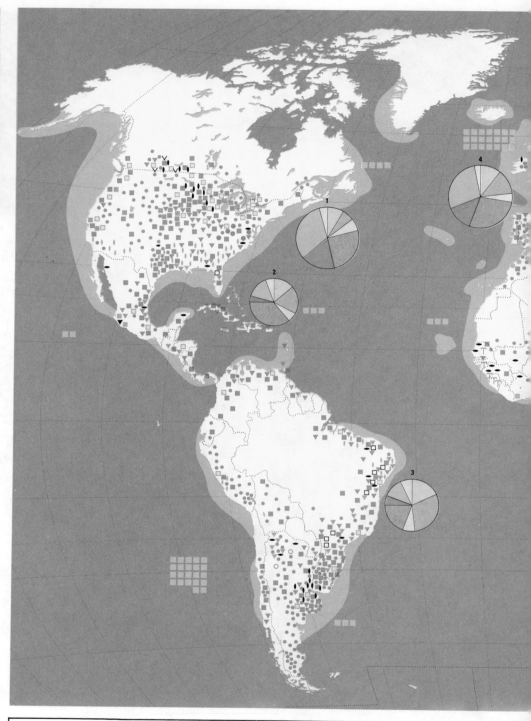

Beef cattle
Beef 29.7

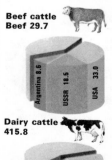

Argentina 8.6 | USSR 18.5 | USA 33.0

The two principal types of domestic cattle, the Eurpopean and the tropical Zebu or humped type, are found all over the world in every type of climate. There is an urgent need in the developing countries for better breeding, disease control and management.

Dairy cattle
415.8

France 8.1 | USA 13.8 | USSR 20.3

Specialized dairy farming takes place mainly near densely populated urban areas with a high standard of living, though there is an increasing trend towards combined milk/meat herds. Various forms of processing, such as canning and freezing, extend product life.

Sheep
Mutton 4.5

India 8.2 | Australia 15.0 | USSR 22.3

Sheep are kept mainly for meat and wool, although in southern Europe they may be milked and in the tropics the hides are the most important product. Sheep do not lend themselves readily to 'factory farming' and are raised on marginal land only.

Pigs
Pork 24.5

China 11.0 | USSR 16.7 | USA 24.1

Because they are often kept indoors, the distribution of pigs depends more on food supply than on the climate. They are often found on mixed farms where they are fed on by-products such as skim milk. Their breeding cycle is complete in about six months.

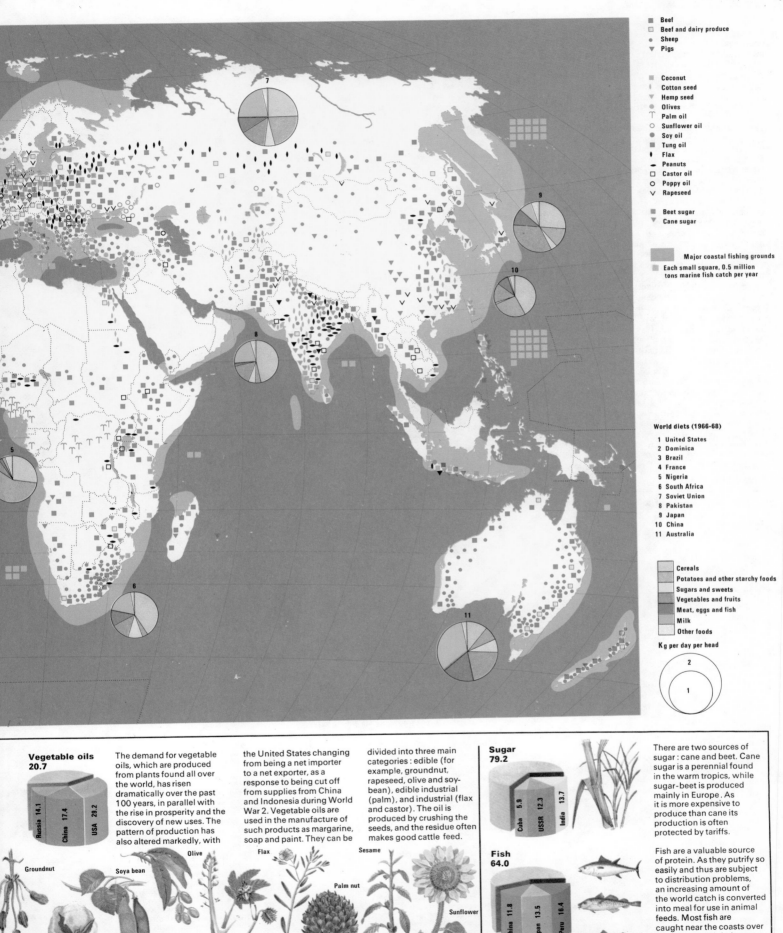

Beef
Beef and dairy produce
Sheep
Pigs

Coconut
Cotton seed
Hemp seed
Olives
Palm oil
Sunflower oil
Soy oil
Tung oil
Flax
Peanuts
Castor oil
Poppy oil
Rapeseed

Beet sugar
Cane sugar

Major coastal fishing grounds

**Each small square, 0.5 million
tons marine fish catch per year**

World diets (1966-68)

1 United States
2 Dominica
3 Brazil
4 France
5 Nigeria
6 South Africa
7 Soviet Union
8 Pakistan
9 Japan
10 China
11 Australia

Cereals
Potatoes and other starchy foods
Sugars and sweets
Vegetables and fruits
Meat, eggs and fish
Milk
Other foods

Kg per day per head

2

1

**Vegetable oils
20.7**

Russia 14.1 China 17.4 USA 29.2

Groundnut   Soya bean   Olive   Flax   Sesame

Cotton   Castor   Not to scale   Palm nut   Sunflower

The demand for vegetable oils, which are produced from plants found all over the world, has risen dramatically over the past 100 years, in parallel with the rise in prosperity and the discovery of new uses. The pattern of production has also altered markedly, with the United States changing from being a net importer to a net exporter, as a response to being cut off from supplies from China and Indonesia during World War 2. Vegetable oils are used in the manufacture of such products as margarine, soap and paint. They can be divided into three main categories: edible (for example, groundnut, rapeseed, olive and soybean), edible industrial (palm), and industrial (flax and castor). The oil is produced by crushing the seeds, and the residue often makes good cattle feed.

**Sugar
79.2**

Cuba 5.9 USSR 12.3 India 13.7

There are two sources of sugar: cane and beet. Cane sugar is a perennial found in the warm tropics, while sugar-beet is produced mainly in Europe. As it is more expensive to produce than cane its production is often protected by tariffs.

**Fish
64.0**

China 11.8 Japan 13.5 Peru 16.4

Fish are a valuable source of protein. As they putrify so easily and thus are subject to distribution problems, an increasing amount of the world catch is converted into meal for use in animal feeds. Most fish are caught near the coasts over the continental shelves.

To survive, animals must be adapted to their environment. They must be able to resist cold if they live in polar regions, drought if they live in deserts. They must find food, escape from predators and reproduce. Their offspring must mature and reproduce in turn. Adaptations of anatomy, physiology and behavior have evolved, so that today animals are found in all the Earth's diverse environments.

Ecologists divide the Earth into natural zones or 'biomes', each with its own highly adapted and integrated animal and plant communities. Inside each broad climatic zone animals have become adapted to various local environments or habitats. In tropical forests, for example, there are several layers of vegetation from the ground up to the tallest trees, and different animals with contrasting ways of life live in different layers. One species eats leaves and another eats berries, and so they avoid competition. Indeed the animals and plants of a community are interdependent. Herbivores eat plants, and carnivores eat herbivores. Food chains and the whole balance of a natural community can be altered by destroying one part of it. Thus, insecticides kill insects but also poison other animals in the area and the predators which prey on them.

Today's animals and plants are those whose ancestors survived immense changes. Continents drifted apart and moved together, seas rose and fell, mountains erupted and were levelled by erosion, glaciers advanced and retreated. Life evolved. Some animals became extinct; others adapted to the changes and spread to new areas. Sometimes they met impassable oceans, mountains and deserts. Groups of animals then became isolated and continued to evolve independently. Marsupials, mammals with pouches, were isolated in Australia before placental mammals, whose young are nourished for a long time in the mother's uterus, evolved in Europe and Asia. Placental mammals then supplanted marsupials everywhere but in Australia. Scientists divide the world into six zoogeographical realms each containing animals not found elsewhere. Some animals mix in transitional zones such as the Sahara Desert and the Himalayas.

Environmental factors

Climate is determined by the Sun's radiation on the Earth's atmosphere, oceans and continents. It varies with the time of day and season. Winds generated by the solar heating carry moisture inland, and heat away from the tropics. Ocean currents affect the prevailing temperature over large regions. Solar radiation, winds and ocean currents, together with latitude, altitude and the form of the land, combine to produce each local climate.

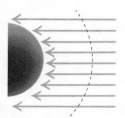

Solar heating *left*
The tropics are hotter than the poles because the Sun's rays pass almost vertically through a shallow depth of atmosphere and so are less attenuated. The Sun's vertical rays shift seasonally between the Tropics of Cancer and Capricorn, altering the length of daylight.

Wind and weather *left*
Hot air at the equator rises and moves north and south to higher latitudes. It subsides, producing trade winds, deflected by the rotation of the Earth, back again to the tropics. Westerly winds blow from the sub-tropics highs poleward toward the sub-polar lows.

Oceans *left*
Surface currents created by prevailing winds and variations in the density of the water are deflected by landmasses and the Coriolis effect' of rotation. Onshore winds across ocean currents are a major climatic control.

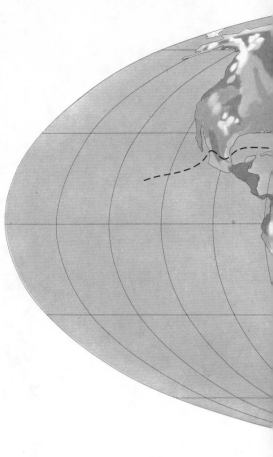

The zoogeographical classification of environments

Roe deer
Flycatcher
Warbler
Dunnock
Wild ass
Hedgehog
Edible dormouse
Wild Sheep

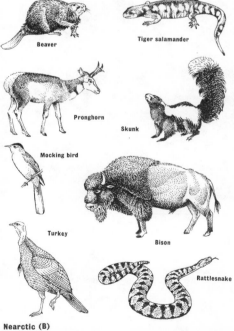

Beaver
Pronghorn
Skunk
Mocking bird
Turkey
Bison
Rattlesnake

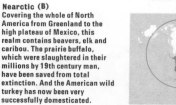

Tiger salamander

Orangutan
Tree shrew
Gibbon
Fairy bluebird
Tiger
Peacock
Indian elephant

Palearctic (A)

This zoogeographical realm, the extent of which is shown on the map at right, is often grouped with the Nearctic to form the so-called Holarctic region. Roe deer, hedgehogs, dormice and the Asian wild ass are all unique here. Ancestors of modern horses crossed into it from North America during an ice age when the continents were bridged with ice.

Nearctic (B)
Covering the whole of North America from Greenland to the high plateau of Mexico, this realm contains beavers, elk and caribou. The prairie buffalo, which were slaughtered in their millions by 19th century man, have been saved from total extinction. And the American wild turkey has now been very successfully domesticated.

Oriental (C)
Comprising the southern part of Asia, Indonesia and the Philippines, this realm is largely isolated from the Palearctic realm to the north by the great folded barrier of the Himalayas, thrown up when the Indian subcontinent collided with Asia. Indigenous animals include tree shrews, tarsiers, gibbons, orangutans and the Indian elephant.

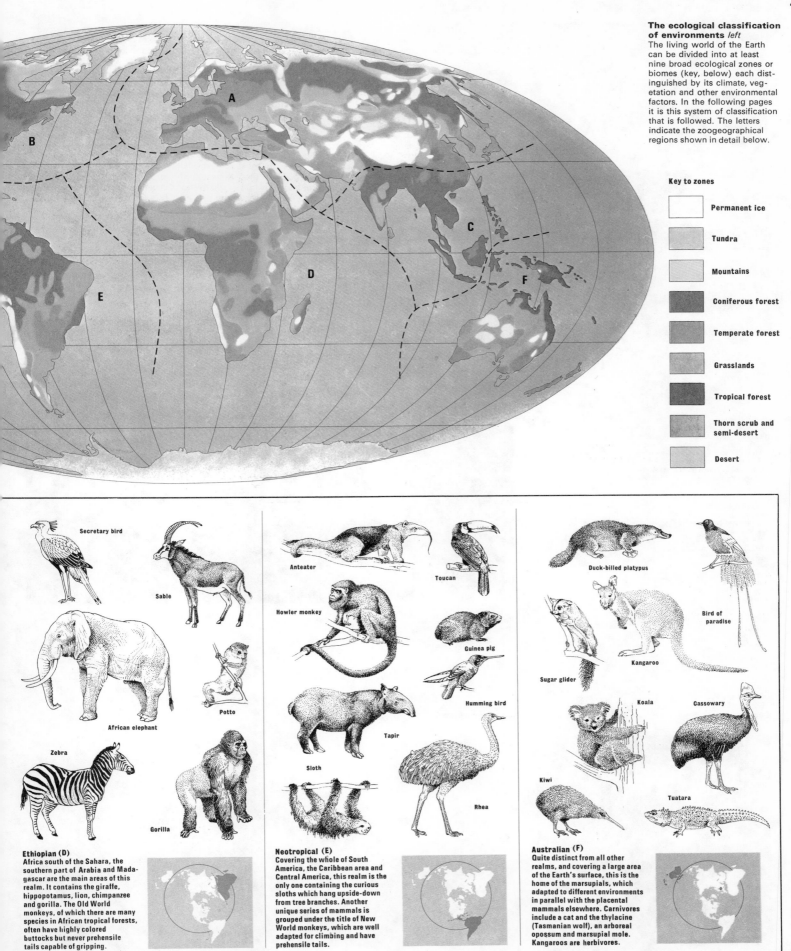

The ecological classification of environments *left*
The living world of the Earth can be divided into at least nine broad ecological zones or biomes (key, below) each distinguished by its climate, vegetation and other environmental factors. In the following pages it is this system of classification that is followed. The letters indicate the zoogeographical regions shown in detail below.

Key to zones

Permanent ice

Tundra

Mountains

Coniferous forest

Temperate forest

Grasslands

Tropical forest

Thorn scrub and semi-desert

Desert

Secretary bird

Sable

African elephant

Potto

Zebra

Gorilla

Anteater

Toucan

Howler monkey

Guinea pig

Humming bird

Tapir

Sloth

Rhea

Duck-billed platypus

Bird of paradise

Sugar glider

Kangaroo

Koala

Cassowary

Kiwi

Tuatara

Ethiopian (D)
Africa south of the Sahara, the southern part of Arabia and Madagascar are the main areas of this realm. It contains the giraffe, hippopotamus, lion, chimpanzee and gorilla. The Old World monkeys, of which there are many species in African tropical forests, often have highly colored buttocks but never prehensile tails capable of gripping.

Neotropical (E)
Covering the whole of South America, the Caribbean area and Central America, this realm is the only one containing the curious sloths which hang upside-down from tree branches. Another unique series of mammals is grouped under the title of New World monkeys, which are well adapted for climbing and have prehensile tails.

Australian (F)
Quite distinct from all other realms, and covering a large area of the Earth's surface, this is the home of the marsupials, which adapted to different environments in parallel with the placental mammals elsewhere. Carnivores include a cat and the thylacine (Tasmanian wolf), an arboreal opossum and marsupial mole. Kangaroos are herbivores.

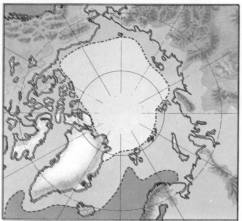

--.-- Pack ice limit   ---- Drifting ice limit

The Arctic ice cap is the opposite of Antarctica in much more than mere location. It is principally an area of permanently frozen sea ice, although it also includes part of Greenland. It has an indigenous human population, despite the average annual temperature of −24°F on the Greenland ice cap, who have managed to adapt themselves to a ferocious environment by copying the animals around them. Just as the seals and polar bears shelter under the snow, bearing their cubs in dens, the Eskimos developed the igloo built from blocks of wind-packed snow. These ice homes are windproof and the temperature inside can rise to 59°F.

Fur and feathers are good heat insulators because each hair or feather is surrounded by air, which conducts heat poorly and thus lessens the amount of body heat escaping. Polar animals have very thick fur. Eskimos wear two layers of skins, one fur side in and the other fur side out. But fur is less efficient if it is wet, so seals and walruses have a thick layer of fatty blubber under the skin. Fat, like air, is a poor heat conductor. Circulation can be restricted so that some animals maintain two body temperatures: one normally warm-blooded inside the body and one as cold as the environment in the feet, flippers and nostrils, which must be free of fur or blubber to function. Extremities from which heat is easily lost, such as ears, are small in polar bears and absent in seals. Heat lost through radiation is proportional to the body's surface. Relative to its volume, a large animal has less surface area than a small one. So a large animal will lose heat more slowly. Polar bears, for instance, are bigger than bears in more temperate regions.

Few eskimos are still hunters of seals, walruses and whales. There has been mass slaughter of seals for their skins, and the population has rapidly declined. Life in the Arctic is changing. Uranium, titanium and other minerals have been discovered. In Alaska oil is bringing prosperity and industrialization. Much of the energy devoted to opening up these great 'lands of tomorrow' has been triggered by military needs. Now the main spur is becoming an economic one.

Polar bears
Bigger animals have less surface area for each unit of body weight than small animals, and thus lose heat less rapidly. Polar bears are larger than all other bears. The adult male (top right) can be 11 feet (3.4 m) long, compared with the 9-10 ft (2.7-3 m) of the brown grizzly (center right) and 4-4.5ft (1.3m) of the sun bear (bottom right). Most polar bears winter in a den roughly eight feet (2.4 m) long, but two-room dens have been found.

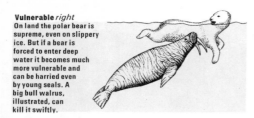

Vulnerable *right*
On land the polar bear is supreme, even on slippery ice. But if a bear is forced to enter deep water it becomes much more vulnerable and can be harried even by young seals. A big bull walrus, illustrated, can kill it swiftly.

Walrus bulls *below*
Weighing up to a ton, the 12 foot (3.7 m) bull walrus uses its tusks for digging out shellfish, breaking air-holes in the ice and fighting. One-third of its weight is blubber, in a 2½ inch (63.5 mm) thick layer under the skin (right).

Dermis
Follicle
Gland
Fat projections

Blubber with blood vessels

Muscle

Pack ice *above*
Open pack ice, stretching as far as the eye can see, reflects the pink rays of the low Sun. Such ice is seldom more than one year old and usually gets crushed or melted in a shorter time. Unlike the dangerous bergs, it is no hazard to navigation.

Seal and tern *below*
The shores of the Irish Sea are among the wide areas of rocky coast on both sides of the North Atlantic inhabited by the grey seal (female illustrated : the male is larger) and sandwich tern (once common at Sandwich in Kent).

Arctic tern *below*
Distinguished from other terns by its vivid beak and feet, the Arctic tern migrates down the coasts of Europe and Africa to the Antarctic before returning to the Arctic to nest. The round trip (left) can be a remarkable 24000 miles (39000 km).

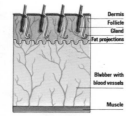

Sandwich tern

Female grey seal

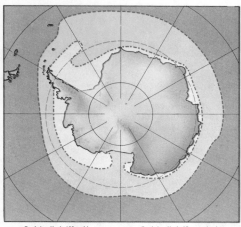

In complete contrast to the North Polar region, the Antarctic is a frozen continent encircled by ocean. Mountains surround low-lying land covered with ice so thick that it forms a high plateau. It is the coldest region on Earth. Throughout almost all of Antarctica no monthly average temperature exceeds 0°C, and the average annual temperature at the South Pole is −60°C. Blizzards blow when a shallow layer of colder air over the ice-sheet flows downslope, and the snow is packed into a hard pavement.

Around the continental edges, icebergs up to 1000 feet (300 m) thick break off the ice caps or valley glaciers and fall into the sea. The ice, formed of compacted and recrystallized snow, is only slightly less dense than sea-water, so icebergs float low in the ocean with five-sixths to eight-ninths of their bulk below the surface. The Antarctic icebergs are tabular, with flat tops and cliff-like sides; Arctic bergs from the Greenland ice cap are peaked and rarely break off in the sizes common in Antarctica, where the floating ice islands can be as much as ten miles (16 km) long.

Until 450 million years ago the Earth had no ice caps. In the Antarctic, ice formed in the center of the continent and moved out towards the sea. Cooling at the North Pole probably occurred later.

In summer, when the ice breaks up and the amount of daylight increases, there is a rapid growth of tiny floating plants called phytoplankton. These plants provide 'grazing' for the zooplankton, small animals of which the shrimp-like krill are the most numerous, which in turn are eaten by the larger animals, among them seals and whalebone whales. One of these whales, the blue whale, is the largest animal ever to inhabit the Earth. A variety of birds live in the Antarctic, including penguins and the skuas which prey on them, snow petrels and albatrosses. These warm-blooded animals all have to keep their body temperature well above that of the environment. Many birds avoid the polar winter by migrating to temperate lands. But emperor penguins stay, and in an Antarctic blizzard colonies of them huddle tightly together to reduce the exposed surface area of their bodies.

18in, 45cm

Adélie penguins *above*
They make devoted parents and may, as shown here, produce two chicks at different times in one season.

Emperor penguin *right*
Easily the largest penguin, the emperor (41 in, 104 cm) breeds on Antarctic sea ice and coasts (see below).

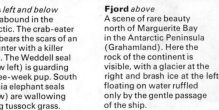

Seals *left and below*
Seals abound in the Antarctic. The crab-eater (left) bears the scars of an encounter with a killer whale. The Weddell seal (below left) is guarding its three-week pup. South Georgia elephant seals (below) are wallowing among tussock grass.

Fjord *above*
A scene of rare beauty north of Marguerite Bay in the Antarctic Peninsula (Grahamland). Here the rock of the continent is visible, with a glacier at the right and brash ice at the left floating on water ruffled only by the gentle passage of the ship.

Incubating *above*
The male emperor hatches the eggs, which rest on the feet beneath a warm brood flap of fatty skin.

Macaroni *left*
There are several species of crested penguins. Tallest is the macaroni, here seated on its nest. (18 in, 45 cm)

Great skua *right*
Skuas are scavengers. They steal food and eggs, kill young chicks and prey on weak adults.

Lichen *below*
The red lichen on this rock could be 1000 years old. Its slow metabolism survives the cold.

The cold lands *above*
In the northern hemisphere there are vast areas of land at latitudes higher than 60°. The warmer parts of these regions are colonized by immense numbers of conifers (facing page) which extend right across the Earth's widest land mass. Where the climate is too severe for trees, the forest gives way to tundra.

Permanent residents of the tundra

Life is hard in the Arctic tundra, but a great variety of animal life is adapted to it. Grass and other plant food grows for no more than two out of each 12 months, but many animals live off it all the year round and even eat the roots while the surface is covered with snow. Carnivores depend to a great degree on the population of lemmings (below) which reaches a peak about every third year. In spring the land becomes ablaze with flowers, and birds abound.

Lemmings
These small rodents are about five inches (125 mm) long. They have short tails, and ears hidden by thick fur. Every three or four years a population explosion triggers a mass migration in which thousands of lemmings die.

Seasonal plumage
Many of the Arctic birds and animals change their appearance to blend into the contrasting summer and winter backgrounds. For example, the rock ptarmigan is mottled brown in July (left) but white in winter until May (below). Both hunted animals, such as

Surrounding the Arctic Ocean are the Arctic tundra and, further south, the coniferous forest. There is no land at such high latitude (60°-70°) in the southern hemisphere. Seasonal changes are extreme. The Sun may shine continuously in summer and not at all in mid-winter. Winter cold and summer heat are greatest in the continental interiors, where it is also drier than around the coasts. Interaction between polar and tropical air masses causes storms.

In the treeless tundra the average temperature of the warmest month is below 10°C. The land is forested where the average for at least one month is above that temperature. In some places the tundra and forest are divided by a distinct tree-line; in other regions the true coniferous forest is preceded by grasses, sedges and lichens. The soils are affected by 'permafrost' and are almost permanently frozen. In summer the surface becomes waterlogged and often flooded, but the seasonal thaw reaches a depth of only 4-24 inches (100-600 mm). Soil water under the plants melts, and a thick mud forms which may flow

the Arctic hare, and their predators change their color. The Arctic fox, which preys on the rock ptarmigan, is white or very pale in winter (above) but changes into a summer coat which is usually brown but in the so-called "blue-foxes" is deep blue-grey (right).

downslope making bulging terraces. Because of recent glaciation there are many lakes and swamps, called muskeg in Canada.

Lemmings feed on the vegetation of the tundra. In winter they dig for roots in an underground network of tunnels where it is about 10°C warmer than on the surface. If their population increases so much that there is competition for space, masses of lemmings move into the forest and cross streams, lakes and rivers as they go. Many drown.

Herds of American caribou and closely related European reindeer migrate up to several hundred miles from their summer pasture on the tundra to find winter food on the forest fringes. Nomadic Lapps follow the reindeer and use them for transport, food and clothing. They milk them and make cheese. In contrast, the caribou have never been domesticated: the Indians of northern Canada were hunters. Their skill as trappers was exploited by the European fur trade. And in the Siberian tundra every resource is being vigorously exploited; a new land is opening up.

Winter and summer
above and left
In winter the cold lands are dull and seemingly barren, although at the edges of the tundra stunted conifers are dotted among the lakes. But in summer the plant life flourishes. Reindeer graze among flowers from Norway to the Pacific.

Arctic color *below*
Tundra is not always dull. In the Alaskan September plant life is in full bloom.

Early blooms *above*
The Pasque flower is in evidence throughout Alaska as early as May.

Except for the Siberian larch, which sheds its needles in winter, the trees of the coniferous forest are evergreen. Spruce, fir, pine and hemlock (associated near water with mountain ash, poplar, balsam, willow and birch) are widespread through Eurasia and North America. The similarity between the distribution of plants and animals is the result of frequent freezing of the Bering Strait which allowed migration between the continents.

The forest animals depend on the trees for food. Beavers eat bark, and squirrels and birds eat buds and seeds. In summer, when there is more food, multitudes of birds migrate to the forest to nest.

The cold forests are of enormous extent. Lumbering is a major industry, and the numerous rivers are used to transport the logs to the sawmills. Great volumes of softwoods are consumed every year, mainly in the building industry and for papermaking. Minerals are now being mined in the cold lands. Iron ore is mined in Labrador and Quebec, and Alaska's gold, copper, iron, oil and gas are being exploited.

The beaver's handiwork
Throughout northern America, and in northern Europe and Asia, the beaver gnaws through trees to secure the soft inner bark from the upper branches. It stores these in a still pool formed by damming a river, and nearby constructs a remarkable lodge with as many as eight underwater entrances.

Tree types *above*
Temperate broad-leaved trees could not survive the northern winter. Most cold forest trees are conifers, with needle-like leaves. From the left : scots pine ; larch, which sheds its leaves ; Norway spruce ; Douglas fir.

Burrowers *right and below*
The woodchuck (right) is one of the cold forest dwellers that hibernates. Its winter metabolism falls almost to a standstill ; then it awakens in March and is busy until fall. The European polecat (below) sometimes kills marmots and uses their burrows.

Grizzlies *above*
Although a carnivore, the giant brown bear often digs for roots, as here.

Ground squirrel *below*
The striped ground squirrel does not climb trees but eats roots, leaves and insects.

Contrasting diets
above and right
Despite its formidable appearance the moose lives on small plants, berries and tree shoots. Only the male has antlers. But the lynx (right) is a carnivore, whose population follows that of its principal prey, the hare.

South of the coniferous forest is extensive deciduous woodland of oak, beech and chestnut which flourishes wherever there is an annual rainfall of 30-60 inches (750-1500mm) distributed throughout the year. Woodland once covered large areas of the northern hemisphere, but most has now been cleared for agriculture. There are different mid-latitude climates on the east and west sides of continents: east coast climates are continental, with hot summers and cold winters, while winds blowing off the ocean bring rain to the more equable west coasts.

In winter the deciduous trees shed their broad leaves which would be vulnerable to frost. The leaves slowly rot to a rich humus, and in boggy places peat forms. Nutrients circulate by water draining through the soil and then being drawn up by evaporation and transpiration through the leaves.

Tree types

In North America and Asia the oak, beech, hickory and maple dominate; in Europe the oak, ash, lime and chestnut, with beech in cool moist areas. On damp ground near rivers willow, alder, ash and elm are found. Conifers grow faster so that they often supplant deciduous trees in managed forests. They form the natural forest on the west coast of North America, where some of the largest trees are found.

Near the tropics are the broadleaf evergreen forests. In Japan and the southeast of the United States there are evergreen oaks, laurel and magnolia, with palms, bays and ferns in the swamps of the Mississippi delta. The warm wet forest of New Zealand's South Island contains conifers, podocarp and evergreen beeches, with tree ferns, palms and bamboos. In a Mediterranean type of climate the summers are hot and dry. Cork oaks have hard, leathery leaves covered with a thick cuticle to minimize water loss. The Mediterranean forest is now only a narrow coastal belt. Tree felling and frequent summer fires have left scrub known as the maquis. The chaparral of California and Mexico is similar.

Redwoods *above*
Along the west coast of the United States is a foggy coastal belt where the redwood forests flourish. The giant redwoods and sequoias may be several thousand years old and up to 400 feet (120 m) high. They are among the Earth's oldest living things.

Beechwoods *left*
Typical of the cool northern deciduous forest, Burnham Beeches, near London, generates millions of beech leaves each year. Littering the ground, they decompose into a rich humus which overlies the soil and supports plant life, worms and a variety of insects.

Little owl *above*
Predator of woodland animals, its forward-facing eyes give good binocular vision for judging distance in dim light.

Luna moth *above*
Found in American deciduous forest, the moth prefers a diet of rhododendrons. India has a tropical variety.

Animal variety
above and left
Woodland inhabitants of the New England states are the box turtle and wood frog (above). The Yugoslavian four-lined snake (left) has the slender body and angled scales common to snakes which need to obtain purchase on bark.

Forest birds
The crossbill (left) can pry open tough pine cones; the pheasant (below,) of which there are 49 species, is concealed on the ground by its camouflage.

The ecology of an oak

Oaks of various sub-species are among the most important trees in the northern deciduous forests, and they play a major role in local wildlife. Oaks have a history dating back over 50 million years, and 7000 years ago covered vast tracts of temperate land. Throughout recorded history man has prized the oak for its hard, durable wood, which has been favored above all others for making houses, ships, furniture and other artifacts. The oak population has thus dwindled, and in modern managed forests the faster-growing conifers are preferred. But each remaining oak is a microcosm of nature. The autumn leaf-fall returns valuable nutrients to the soil, providing a source of humus. In the spring up to a quarter of a million new leaves grow, providing an area for photosynthesis as great as 10000 sq ft (930 m²). Small streamers of flowers are pollinated by wind-borne pollen, leading in midsummer to the crop of acorns which are stored by grey squirrels, badgers and many other animals for the coming winter. As many as 200 species of insect can feed on one tree. Largest is the leaf-eating stag beetle, and the most prominent the gall wasp whose marble gall houses the larva. The damage insects inflict often results in the tree producing a second crop of midsummer leaves. The serotine bat and tawny owl are the main nocturnal predators of the oak forest. The former takes winged insects in flight, while small rodents form the staple diet of the owl.

Marble gall showing larva of gall wasp

Serotine bat

Tawny owl

Grey squirrel

Stag beetle

Badger

The mature oak *right*

The extensive buttressed roots of an old oak can provide the portal through which a fox (1) tunnels to its lair. Low on the trunk a beefsteak fungus (2) may grow, providing fruiting bodies upon which feed many kinds of animals and insects. The trunk often decays locally (3), providing a home for both bats and owls. The fallow deer (female, 4) and jay (5) collect acorns, while in the branches a clump of mistletoe (6) grows, nurtured by the tree on which it is a parasite.

Record in the rings *above*

In deciduous trees each year's growth adds a ring of new tissue to the trunk, as shown by this section segment from an oak with an age of 24 years. Within the first five years is the dark heartwood (1). Between years 7-10 growth was slowed (2), possibly by drought or the crowding of other trees. Growth was also slow in years 19-22, and in the 21st year part of the tree was burned, leaving a scar (4) which gradually heals with further growth. Present growth takes place in the cambium (3) just inside the bark (5).

Paper wasp
The queen starts the football-like nest, which is made of chewed wood and has a paper-like consistency. Her subjects enlarge it.

Mole
Moles live in burrows excavated underground by their strong front claw-feet. Emerging into the open, their eyes see poorly.

Dormouse
Most of the forest rodents store food for the winter, but the dormouse hibernates, at a reduced body temperature.

Dormouse nest
Although the dormouse lives deep in the undergrowth, it is very agile, and builds a spherical nest above ground level.

Sparrowhawk
Like many birds of prey the sparrowhawk makes a substantial nest of twigs and forest debris high in a tree, where its young are safe.

Blue tit
A favorite choice of home for the blue tit is a hole in a tree. Inside the cavity it constructs a nest of moss and soft debris.

Common oak
Widespread and important to commerce and forest life, the oak grows slowly and is yielding to other species.

Silver birch
Mature at 50, the silver-barked birch is found in all temperate forest and extends far into the tundra.

Beech
Big and densely packed, the beech is very beneficial. Essentially a forest tree, it prefers drained chalky soil.

Ash
Although it exhausts soil, the ash produces tough wood. Its multi-leaflet leaves are one foot (0.25 m) long.

Sweet chestnut
Originally from Asia Minor, the sweet chestnut fruit is a preferred food of many forest animals.

Sycamore
One of the maple family, the sycamore prefers exposed positions where its seeds can travel on the wind.

Alder
The inconspicuous alder prefers marshy ground and river banks. Although not a conifer, it bears cone fruit.

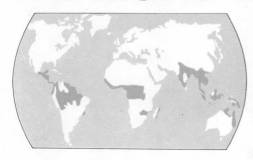

The hot, humid conditions in equatorial rainforests which encourage a profusion of life, change very little over the year, daily variations being greater than seasonal ones. The average temperature is about 27°C, while the rainfall, which is as high as 80-160 inches (2000-4000 mm) a year, falls regularly in heavy thunderstorms.

Tropical forests are the highest, densest and most varied on Earth, in spite of having infertile soil. This is because nutrients are contained in the plants which grow, flower and fruit throughout the year. As leaves and fruits fall to the ground and decay, the minerals are rapidly taken up again by the roots of the growing shrubs and trees. The crowns of the tall, broad-leaved trees form a canopy of foliage. Underneath, it is shady and the tree trunks are smooth and unbranched, while lianas and creepers thrust upwards to the light.

Forest animals find a variety of habitats in the different layers. Monkeys, apes, sloths, lizards and frogs are adapted to climbing or swinging through trees. Multitudes of birds feed on nectar, insects or fruit. Many animals browse on the forest floor, and a vast number of animal and plant species co-exist.

Lianas *below*
Long rope-like stems loop from tree to tree, ever climbing toward the light that pierces the canopy.

Deep rainforest *right*
The hot, humid atmosphere of tropical rainforest encourages most luxuriant plant growth.

Flowers *right and below*
Tropical blooms are famed for their size and beauty. The very small seasonal variation in climate means plants can germinate, grow and flower without interruption throughout the year. Right, blossoms of Royal Poinciana; below, Strelitzia, native to Africa.

Contrasting predators
right and below
Tropical forests are the home of the largest spiders and largest snakes. But, whereas the monkey spider of Trinidad (right) kills its prey by a venomous bite, the 30 foot (10 m) royal python (below) crushes and suffocates its victim.

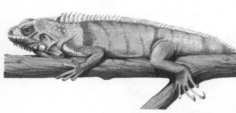

Butterflies
right and below
There are more butterflies and moths in the rainforest than in all the rest of the Earth; typical species are the Ulysses butterfly (right), *Precis almana* (below right) and Rajah Brooke's bird-wing *Trogonoptera brookiana* (below).

Hovering jewel *right*
Hummingbirds, such as Pucheran's emerald variety illustrated here, are found only in the Americas. Their wings, which beat about 100 times a second and allow them to hover while drinking nectar, are covered with iridescent feathers of brilliant hues.

Forest reptiles
above and right
As large as a man, the iguana (above) has feet with long digits provided with hard scales and curved claws adapted to tree-climbing. Another climber is the African grey tree frog (right) whose nest of foam overhangs the water.

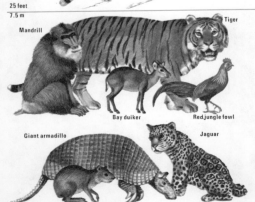

Life in the forest

The emergents

Some trees break through the canopy formed by the main tree population. Many of these emergent trees reach to 150 ft (46 m), although all tree heights are reduced with increasing altitude or distance from the equator. Life at this topmost level is almost wholly insects and birds. The swifts, which fly above the forest at up to 200 mph (320 kmh), catch insects on the wing. The harpy eagle preys on animals in the upper branches.

The canopy

This is one of the major life zones of the tropical forest, and it exerts a powerful effect on all the lower levels. Most of the forest trees grow to 100-120 ft (30-37 m) and form an almost continuous layer of leafy vegetation at this height, cutting off direct sunlight from below and markedly altering the climate 'inside' the forest to a shady coolness. Most of the trees of tropical forests have straight stems which do not branch until quite close to the canopy; emergent tree (1) passes straight through without branching. Many tropical trees are cauliflorous—they produce flowers which grow directly out of the trunks and branches and frequently dot the canopy with color (2). Inside the forest is a tangle of creepers and climbers which tend to bind the branches of the canopy into a tight mass. The fauna of the canopy is adapted to specialized feeding from particular flowers, fruit or other food. Winged insects and animals range readily through the whole stratum. Many of the birds (for example, the great hornbill and toucan) have long bills with which they can reach food through the mat of vegetation. The non-flying animals are invariably adapted to running along branches, swinging from one branch to another and even leaping 50 ft (15 m) or more.

The middle layer

There may be no sharp division between this layer and the canopy, but in general the middle is made up of smaller trees whose crowns do not form a continuous mat. In this layer are found nest epiphytes (3), non-parasitic plants growing in sunlight on trees where they seed in cracks in the bark. Some store water while others absorb it through hanging roots (4). Cauliflorous growths (5) hang from some trees, while many trunks are covered in vines and lianas (6). The trees are sturdy enough to bear heavy animals. Whereas many inhabitants of the canopy seldom if ever come down to ground level, a considerable proportion of the middle-level animals spend part of their life on the forest floor.

The lower levels

The bottom strata of the humid tropical forest can be divided into a shrub layer below 15 ft (4.5 m), a herb layer below 3 ft (1 m) and a fungus layer on the surface. The fallen tree (7) may have died from strangulation by parasitic vegetation. At the right air roots (8) pick up moisture, while a trunk (9) is almost hidden by two types of epiphyte. Fungi (10) cover the ground near a massive buttressed tree root (11), while in the rear is a stilt root (12) of a kind common in swamp forest. The ground here is covered in sparse vegetation (13) typical of the shady floor. The features illustrated are typical of hot rain forest throughout the tropics, but the elephant (14) is Indian.

Flat or rolling grasslands lie between the forests and deserts in the dry interiors of all the continents, in the transitional zones where dry and moist climates merge into each other. There are two major types of grassland, the temperate which is hot in summer and cold in winter and the tropical which has a fairly uniform high temperature all the year round. The Russian steppe, North American prairie, South American pampas, South African veld and Australian downland are examples of temperate grassland, while more than one third of Africa is covered by tropical savanna.

The height of the grass is dependent upon the annual rainfall. There are few trees on these wide plains to break the wind or provide shelter. In spring or summer there is a short rainy season when the grasses and shrubs flourish and there is rich grazing; then the long dry season comes and growth halts as a severe drought develops. The grasslands may result from frequent fires during this period, which kill the trees and shrubs leaving grass-roots unharmed.

Animal life
Throughout most of the tropical grasslands the climate is semi-arid, the soil poor, yet their meager grazing supports a rich and varied assortment of animals. In most grassland regions the fauna has been used by man with care for the future, but in the biggest savanna of all, that of Africa, man has done little but misuse and destroy the grassland animals. To a considerable degree this has been the result of emphasis by both Africans and white ranchers, on domestic cattle. Such beasts graze only on certain species of grass, and have been bred principally for the temperate regions of Europe. In contrast, the natural fauna makes full use of the whole spectrum of vegetation, grazing selectively at different levels and in different places. As a result there is no deterioration of the environment despite the large numbers of animals supported by each area of land. Moreover, the wild animals need not be fed or sheltered, nor inoculated against the sleeping sickness carried by the tsetse fly which ravages cattle. Now that game can be seen to have a distinct commercial value the grassland animals, particularly easily domesticated species such as the eland, are at last being more generally preserved so that controlled game-cropping can provide an additional source of high quality protein.

The dust bowls
Man has often interfered in the grassland environment sometimes with disastrous consequences. The American grassland soil is rich and farmers have turned the wetter tall-grass prairie into the corn belt and the short-grass prairie into the wheat belt. Further west is the cattle country. But in years of drought crops fail and the valuable topsoil, lacking the protective cover of grass, blows away in great dust clouds, leaving behind large areas of barren land.

Venomous snakes *left* Grasslands in every continent harbor dangerous snakes. The Egyptian cobra (far left) is the largest cobra in Africa. The prairie rattlesnake (near left) is the most common venomous snake in the United States and causes many deaths each year.

African savanna *above* The Serengeti plains of Tanzania are among the most beautiful areas of big game country in the world. Here animals of a great range of species graze on fine grassland amongst the kopjes — rocky outcrops which are characteristic of central Africa.

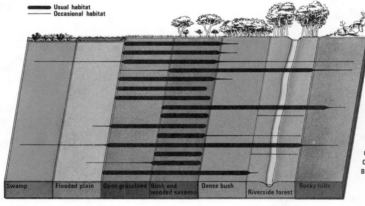

Ecological co-existence *above* The African savanna supports a very large and varied animal population. Most of the animals are herbivores which have each adapted to a particular habitat and a particular section of the available food. These sections are divided geographically, as shown here, and also into different feeding levels above the ground.

Buffalo *above*
African buffalo at Manyara, Tanzania. Buffalo live in herds of up to 100 or more males and females of all ages, with a firm hierarchy among the males. They use their horns and horn-bosses in pushing contests that help to decide their ranks.

Impala *below*
African grassland has 72 species of antelope, weighing from a few pounds to 1800 lb (800 kg).

Tick bird *left*
The yellow-billed oxpecker rides on the backs of rhinos and other large animals and eats ticks and flies living in or on the hide. Sometimes the birds swoop off their perch to take large insects which have been disturbed by the animal.

Leopard *right*
Stealthy and athletic, the leopard is found through most of Africa and southern Asia. It often rests in trees, and this fine specimen has pulled its prey, a reedbuck, onto a high branch.

Giraffes *left*
Tallest of all land animals, the giraffe eats acacia leaves and other greenery high above the ground (see large illustration below). Here a group gallops past zebras across a bare patch of ground.

7ft, 213cm

Griffon vulture *left*
Vultures soar at high altitudes on their large wings while searching to the horizon for carrion.

Jackrabbit *above*
Big ears are not only for keen hearing : they help radiate heat and control body temperature.

Ostrich *below*
The tall ostrich can see for miles across the African plains and run swiftly from danger.

8ft, 240cm

Feeding habits
The great grasslands of Africa, and to a lesser degree those of other continents, teem with wild life of remarkable variety. In this wide open environment concealment is difficult and the majority of animals survive by having good long-distance vision and by being fleet of foot. Some of the smaller plant eaters escape their predators by burrowing. The key to the co-existence of the herbivores is that they tend to feed at different levels. The elephant can reach up to 15 feet (4·5 m) above the ground to tear at broad-leafed trees, while the giraffe can feed on its favored acacias at even higher levels. The rhino, buffalo, gerenuk and eland eat not only low shrubs and trees but also grass. Only the gnus, zebras and some rhinos compete for the same areas, but these areas are so large that there is little fear of over-grazing. The baboon delves for roots and whatever it can find, while the carnivores include the carrion-eating hyenas and vultures and the predatory lion, cheetah and leopard. Left to themselves, the wild animals of the savanna do little harm to their habitat, but the growing herds of domesticated cattle and goats pose a threat. Whereas the native fauna leaves living shoots which can sprout into a fresh plant, the cattle and goats eat the whole of the grass and tree shoots so that the vegetation is soon eradicated. Over-grazing and poor range management are encouraged by the fact that some African tribes still regard cattle as symbols of wealth. The value of the indigenous savanna animals has been forcefully demonstrated in parts of South Africa and Rhodesia where ranges run down by domestic cattle have been restored by grazing 10 to 12 varieties of antelope in their place.

Impala   Giraffe   Cape eland   Kirk's dik-dik   African elephant   Gerenuk   Cape buffalo   Black rhinoceros

THE DESERTS

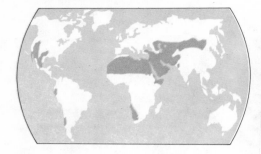

The desert is a harsh, arid and inhospitable environment of great variety where the average rainfall for a year is less than five inches (125 mm) and in some years there is none at all. The cloudless sky allows the Earth's surface to heat up to 30–40°C by day and cool near to freezing at night. Relative humidity is low. On the basis of temperature arid lands are divided into low-latitude hot deserts and mid-latitude deserts. The latter, in central Asia and the Great Basin of the United States, are bitterly cold in winter. In the coastal deserts of Peru and Chile the cold offshore current flowing northward from the Antarctic Ocean cools the moist air producing a swirling sea fog.

Landscapes are rocky, and weathered to strange shapes by the winds and sudden rains (p. 16A). Sand dunes shifted and shaped by the wind are common in Saudi Arabia and the Sahara. The dunes are almost sterile, but most deserts have some sparse plant cover. Stems and leaves are hard, to prevent loss of water and protect the plant from sand erosion. Succulent cacti and euphorbias store water in fleshy stems or leaves, and have widespread shallow roots to absorb the dew. Sahara oases were probably cultivated 7000 years ago, producing grain, olives, wine, figs and dates. The Egyptians channelled the waters of the flooding Nile to irrigate the land, and today the Imperial Valley of the Californian desert and the Arizona desert near Phoenix are highly productive agricultural land.

Water in the desert
Most of the world's deserts are neither billowing sand dunes (such as that on the opposite page) nor totally devoid of water. But in all deserts water, especially fresh water, is a precious commodity. In the great stony deserts brief rains allow stunted vegetation to provide a basis for animal life. The neighborhood of Monument Valley, Utah (above) is surprisingly full of life which has adapted to arid conditions. Some life is also found in the Sahara, where sudden torrential rains cause flash flood erosion (south of Ouargla, left) leaving smooth ridges and deep gullies Sometimes the water table is at the surface. The water may be brackish and undrinkable, as in Cyrenaica west of the Siwa Oasis (below), but the true oasis contains fresh water at which a camel can drink copiously (right). Even the meager dew is stored by plants — nothing is wasted.

Desert plants *right*
Deserts test the ability of plants to adapt to a near absence of water. Plants survive by throwing out large catchment areas for dew at night, minimizing water loss by evaporation during the day, growing deep roots to find water far below the surface, storing what water they find, and in extreme cases by lying dormant during dry years and springing to life as soon as it rains.

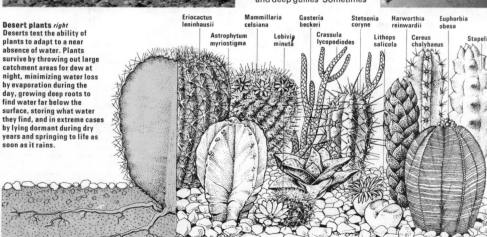

Eriocactus leninhausii
Astrophytum myriostigma
Mammillaria celsiana
Lobivia minuta
Gasteria beckeri
Crassula lycopodiodes
Stetsonia coryne
Lithops salicola
Harworthia reinwardii
Cereus chalybaeus
Euphorbia obesa
Stapelia

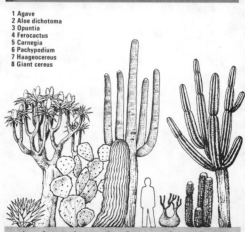

1 Agave
2 Aloe dichotoma
3 Opuntia
4 Ferocactus
5 Carnegia
6 Pachypodium
7 Haageocereus
8 Giant cereus

Desert animals

Many animals are so well adapted to retain water that they survive on the moisture in their food. Some, such as the armadillo lizard, scorpions, insects and spiders, have hard, impenetrable skins to reduce water loss. The urine of camels and gazelles is very concentrated to minimize excretion of water. Arabian camels can lose 30 per cent of their body weight (which would be lethal for a man) without distress, and then regain it by drinking up to 27 gallons (120 liters) at a time. This does not dilute their blood dangerously. A camel does not sweat until its body temperature reaches 40°C, and it loses heat easily during the cold night because it stores its fat in the hump and not as a layer under the skin. Its fur insulates against the heat, as do the loose clothes of the people. Snakes hide in crevices, and sand-swimming lizards burrow to avoid extreme temperatures. Jerboas and kangaroo rats hop along, and some lizards run on their hind legs to keep their bellies off the ground. As soon as it rains, swarms of dormant life surge into activity.

Desert Burrowers

White-footed mouse — Burrow taken over by horned lizard — Horned lizard — American badger — Pocket mouse — Kit fox — Kangaroo rat in nest — Food store — Green-collared lizard — Kangaroo rat

Ant lions *right and below*
Some types of ant lion catch their prey — mainly ants — by digging a smooth conical pit and waiting at the bottom; others bury themselves in the sand with only eyes and jaws protruding. The larval stage (right) precedes the winged adult (below).

Sand desert *above*
Only one-seventh of the Sahara looks like this Hollywood-style vista of giant dunes in Algeria.

Dung beetles *left*
These female scarabs are rolling a pellet of animal dung into a ball containing an egg.

Painted lady *above*
N African desert thistles provide nectar for their migration through Europe as far as Iceland.

Gila monster *right*
This venomous N American lizard tracks its prey with the aid of a sensor in its mouth (right, lower).

20in, 51cm

Nasal cavity — External nostril — Sensory part of Jacobsons organ — Duct — Internal nostril

8in, 21cm

Scorpion and snake
When scorpions mate, the male deposits a patch of sperm on the ground and then contrives to maneuver a female over it in what looks like a square dance (above, left). The dangerous rattlesnake (above) senses the heat radiated by its prey using organs on its face.

Plants and predator
The leopard tortoise (left) enjoys a meal of cactus, a plant which stores water and minimizes evaporation (Ferocactus of Arizona, right). Other desert blooms include Echinopsis rhodatricia and Chamacerus silvestri (far right, upper and lower).

The mountain environment varies enormously with height and the direction of the prevailing wind. Temperature falls about 2°C (3.4°F) for each 1000 feet (300 m) increase in altitude. Barometric pressure also falls until lack of oxygen makes any human exertion cause shortness of breath. Before people adjust to the conditions they often suffer from mountain sickness —headache, weakness and nausea.

Sun temperature may be 28°C (83°F) hotter than in the shade or at night, and the slope of a mountain facing the equator is warmer than the other sides. Mountains force rain-bearing winds to rise, so that they cool and have to release moisture. Clouds form, and rain falls on the windward slope; on the opposite slope the descending winds are drying.

High-altitude life
Altitude has the same effect on vegetation as latitude. At about 5000 feet (1500 m) tropical rainforest changes to montane forest resembling a temperate rainforest. At twice this height the broad-leaved trees disappear but there are conifers and shrubs such as laurel. Above the treeline, where the average monthly temperature never exceeds 10°C, is alpine tundra or heath. The snowline at the equator is at about 15000 feet (4500 m). In Peru irrigated sugar and cacao cover the lower slopes, and above the timberline corn grows at 11000 feet, wheat at 12000, barley at 13000 and potatoes up to 14000 feet. The Incas had terraced the Andes and had an efficient agricultural system by 1000 AD.

The mountain life zone which is unique is that above the treeline. The animal communities are isolated, since mountains act as a barrier to migration. Most plants and insects on mountain tops can withstand freezing. Some animals burrow or shelter under rocks where temperature variations are smaller. Ibexes, yaks, deer and sheep all have thick coats but move down the mountain-side in winter. Mountain animals have enlarged hearts and lungs and extra oxygen-carrying red blood corpuscles to make the most of the thin air. The vicuna, for example, has nearly three times the number of red corpuscles per cubic millimeter of blood as man.

Near Murren *above right*
The environment on a high mountain is essentially polar, even in a tropical country: Above the timberline ice and snow replace animals and plants, and the conditions are further modified by intense solar radiation and low atmospheric pressure.

Lichens *above and right*
Lichens comprise a fungus and an alga in close association. The alga govern the color (page 53A for red lichen). The metabolism of lichens is exceedingly slow; barely alive, they can subsist on mountain rock in harsh conditions for hundreds of years.

Tortoise *above*
The margined tortoise is native to mountainous regions in Greece and the Balkans.

Plants *left*
Purple gentian and (upper) auricula are typical of mountain dwarf perennials; some can resist freezing.

Altitude and latitude *right*
At extreme latitudes – for example, in the Antarctic – the climate is so severe at sea level that no very pronounced change takes place even as one climbs a mountain, although the mountain's presence can strongly modify the local weather. In contrast, mountains near the equator rise from hot, steamy forests into freezing, arid peaks, with almost every kind of Earth environment in between. To most kinds of terrestrial life large mountains are barriers. As altitude increases, plants and animals become adapted to the environment and then peter out entirely.

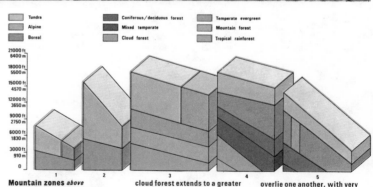

Tundra	Coniferous / deciduous forest	Temperate evergreen
Alpine	Mixed temperate	Mountain forest
Boreal	Cloud forest	Tropical rainforest

Mountain zones *above*
At high latitudes a mountain offers fewer contrasts; much of New Zealand (1) has cool, humid cloud forest, topped by alpine heath and tundra. In SE Australia, SE Africa and S Brazil (2) the cloud forest extends to a greater altitude, with only tundra above. The high tropical Andes (3) afford contrasts surpassed only by the mountainous regions of the eastern Himalayas and SE Asia (4), where six distinct regions overlie one another, with very local regions of tropical mountain forest. Mountains of Europe (5) lie in regions where there are already great contrasts in climate at sea level. Boreal is a north-facing mountain region.

Butterflies
Mountains are often rich in insects. The six-spot burnet (mating, left) is common. Some Apollo butterflies (below) are found above 17000 feet (5200 m) in the Himalayas. Erebia (right) is carrying an orange mite, a parasite which can survive freezing. Mountain insects rely for much of their food on pollen, seeds and even insects swept up in the frequent updraft of winds from the warm lowlands.

4in, 8cm

African birds of prey
Small mountain rodents make a tasty meal for the jackal buzzard (left), a bird with exceedingly acute vision. The black eagle (with three-week chick, right) lives on rats and lizards but can tackle animals as large as the 7 lb (3.2 kg) rock hyrax. It nests in July.

Rodents
Whereas the alpine marmot (below) hibernates in winter, the pika of Tibet (in group, below right) stores its supplies. The chinchilla and cavy both come from South America. Above 10000 ft (3000 m) rodents outnumber all other animals.

Salamander *right*
This Pyrenean salamander is climbing out of a cool mountain stream, but the true alpine salamander has had to become adapted to an arid habitat. Much darker than the lowland varieties, it does not lay its eggs in water but bears its young alive. It remains amphibious.

American cougar *left*
Also known as the puma or mountain lion, the cougar hunts by day above the timberline. When it makes a large kill it is able to store the carcass for weeks at sub-zero temperature. Most of these beasts range over a fixed area, although some wander down to lower levels.

Yak *right*
Domesticated in its native Tibet, the shaggy yak is still found in local wild herds in central Asia. It is a hardy animal, adapted to eating snow in the absence of water, and moss and lichens when no better vegetation is available. It is found up to 20000 ft (6000 m).

Grazers
Sure-footed, the mountain goat (left) inhabits the northern Rockies. The chamoix (above) is scattered through mountain regions of southern Europe, while ibexes (right) are a very widespread family. Specialized sheep also graze at high altitudes.

Freshwater environments range from puddles to lakes which cover thousands of square miles, from small streams to rivers that stretch hundreds of miles from mountain source to the ocean. Together, they provide a diversity of habitats that supports a wide range of plant and animal life.

In rivers the type and variety of life is controlled by the depth and speed of water. Fast mountain streams have few plants and the fish are either fast swimmers or shelter among stones. The slower, wider lowland rivers are rich in vegetation and many of the fish have mouths adapted to sucking food from the rich silt of the river bed. In the brackish waters of the estuary few freshwater animals can survive because of the increasing salinity. But migratory fish, such as eels and Atlantic salmon, adapt to fresh and salt water at different stages of their life cycles.

In standing water the surface is often much warmer than the depths. This produces layers which are so distinct that separate habitats are created. The deeper waters may be completely devoid of oxygen because they do not mix with the well-aerated surface layers. Lakes go through three stages of development: oligotrophic with barren sides and clear water; eutrophic when the lake has begun to silt up and is rich in life; and, finally, dystrophic with decayed organic matter developing into swamp or peat bog. This natural process of eutrophication normally takes thousands of years, but man can, by his indiscriminate pollution and over-enrichment of some lakes condense this process dangerously into a few decades.

Near its source a river is cold, clear and well oxygenated, and flows swiftly.

In the middle reaches the river runs deep, but is still clear and fast-flowing.

A mature river is broad and sluggish; it may be clouded and polluted.

Fish of the river *below*
In the swift-flowing upper reaches only the powerful swimming fish can survive, although small fish nestle near the bottom. The water is well oxygenated, and remains so into the less tumultuous middle reaches. The sluggish lowland river contains deep-bodied fish.

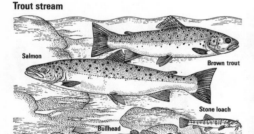

Trout stream

Salmon
Brown trout
Stone loach
Bullhead

Minnow reach

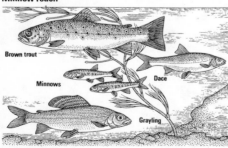

Brown trout
Minnows
Dace
Grayling

Lowland river

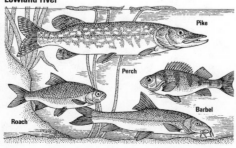

Pike
Perch
Roach
Barbel

Salmon leaping *above*
Mature salmon return from the ocean to the rivers in which they hatched. Swimming against the current, and leaping up rapids and waterfalls, they finally gain the upper reaches where they spawn. After 1-3 years, the next generation migrates to the sea.

Kingfisher *above*
These colorful birds are by far the most numerous of the many species that take fish while on the wing. Plunging across the surface in a shallow dive, they seize in their long beaks prey they had spotted while on the branch of a tree. Average size 7 in (18 cm).

Teeming with life *left*
Most lakes begin life in the oligotrophic stage, barren of life and with clear, bright waters. After a time the water is colonized, and gradually a community rich in plant and animal species occupies the freshwater habitat. Such a lake is eutrophic.

A swamp *left*
The Indian name of Lake Okeefenokee, Georgia, means 'land of trembling earth'. Measuring some 30 miles by 60 (50 by 100 km), it is a region of perfect mirror-like reflections and teeming wild life.

Swamp butterfly *above*
There are many sub-species of swallowtail ; this is the eastern tiger swallowtail from the marshes of Georgia. Average size 4 in (10 cm).

Tree frog *above*
Devouring flies and gnats by the million, green tree frogs breed in the warm swamp waters. Average size is 2½ in (6 cm).

Lubber grasshopper *left*
Bigger even than the majority of desert locusts, it makes a tasty meal for birds and young alligators.

Alligator *above*
Generally not aggressive, they keep open the channels in American swamps. Average size is 10 ft (3 m).

Terrapin *above*
The Suwannee river terrapin is sometimes found in the Gulf of Mexico. Average size is 7 in (18 cm).

Swamp turtle *above*
The soft-shelled turtles have a leathery skin without an outer covering of horny plates. Size 14 in (36 cm).

The pond environment *left*
1 Common frog (male, × 0.5)
2 Starwort (× 0.5)
3 Water crowfoot (× 0.25)
4 Aplecta hypnorum (× 2)
5 Wandering snail (× 0.75)
6 Keeled ramshorn snail (× 0.5)
7 Curled pondweed (× 0.25)
8 Bithynia (× 1)
9 Ramshorn snail (× 0.3)
10 Water lily root (× 0.25)
11 Great pond snail (× 0.8)

Pond life *below*
The essential characteristic of pond life is adaptation to a freshwater environment without a flowing current. As in almost every other habitat on Earth the life is divided into distinct zones —atmosphere, surface film, middle depths and bed—although many species cross from one zone to another. The newt, for example,

is active everywhere from the bed of a pond to dry land. Throughout the ecology of freshwater life all food is manufactured by green plants. First-order animals, such as zooplankton and many fish and insects, feed directly on the plants; everything else feeds on predators lower in the food chain or web. The water itself is very far from being a pure compound of

hydrogen and oxygen. It contains dissolved oxygen and nitrogen salts and much organic material. The life of the pond establishes ecological cycles which constantly balance inputs and outputs between water, air, and life. For example, the supply of nitrates washed in from the land is augmented by the decomposition of dead organisms in the water itself

Near the surface
12 Pond skater (× 0.5)
13 Whirligig beetle (× 0.25)
14 Water boatman (× 1)
15 Non-biting midge (× 5)
16 Mosquito pupa (× 5)
17 Dragonfly (male, × 0.65)
18 China-marks moth (× 0.75)
19 Mayfly (female, × 0.2)

Middle depths
20 Water flea (Daphnia, × 2.5)
21 Smooth newt (male, × 0.5)
22 Cyclops (typical of species, × 8)
23 Flagellate (× 650)
24 Great diving beetle (male, × 1)
25 Hydra (× 4)
26 Stickleback (male, × 0.5)
27 Common frog tadpole (× 1.5)
28 Flagellate (Euglena, × 180)
29 Water mite (× 5)

The bottom
30 Caddis-fly larva in case
31 Chaetonotus (× 150)
32 Horny-orb shell (× 1)
33 Tubifex worms (× 0.2)
34 Midge larva (× 3.5)
35 Pond sponge (× 0.2)
36 Leech (Helobdella sp., × 4)
37 Water hog-louse (× 2.5)
38 Flatworm (× 2)

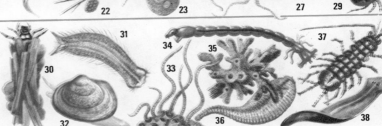

The oceans are a continuous mass of 5000 million million tons of water; but variations in light, pressure, salinity, temperature, currents, waves, and tides interact to create numerous regions each with its own typical forms of life.

Plants are the basis of ocean food chains, just as they are on land. Since all plants need sunlight they are found only in the upper layer of the sea. Myriads of tiny marine plants called phytoplankton are eaten by the small floating zooplankton and by tiny fish, which in turn support a succession of predators. Deep-water animals are adapted to great pressure and to darkness. Most are predators but some of them are scavengers which depend on a rain of food debris from above.

Some ocean islands are coral, built by millions of polyps resembling sea anemones which produce a hard stony skeleton (p. 21A). But most are thrust up by volcanic eruptions. They are completely isolated and were never joined to a continent. Such islands are usually wet and windswept.

Island plant and animal communities evolved from the few original forms which crossed the ocean and colonized. Island colonization is difficult, and is seldom accomplished by land mammals apart from bats, nor even by amphibians. Land and freshwater animals may have evolved from sea-dwelling ancestors. Once a species has colonized an island it interbreeds, because of its isolation, and adapts to its new conditions and competitors. Often new endemic species evolve.

The first colonizers are usually sea birds. They bring nutrients, so seeds and the spores of mosses, lichens and ferns carried by the wind can take root. The wind also brings insects, spiders and bats, and occasionally land birds in storms, but such birds rarely establish themselves. Reptiles and some land animals may cross the sea on driftwood rafts. Many island reptiles, perhaps because of the lack of mammals, have become unusually large. Examples include such creatures as the Komodo dragon and the giant tortoises of the Galapagos.

The ocean layers

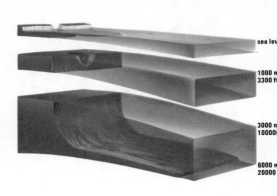

sea level
1000 m 3300 ft
3000 m 10000 ft
6000 m 20000 ft

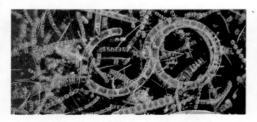

Phytoplankton *above*
All marine life depends ultimately on microscopic plant plankton, which is mostly single-celled. (x 20)

Tiger cowrie *right*
Cowries are tropical marine snails. This spotted example is feeding, with its mantle extended below.

Zooplankton *above*
These microscopic animals feed on the phytoplankton and on each other. In turn they support fish. (x 8)

Leopard coral *right*
The derivation of the name of this hard coral is obvious. Each 'spot' is an individual in the colony.

Air and surface life
The seabirds (right) are typical of a range of species, some of them exceptionally large birds, which navigate unerringly over thousands of miles of ocean. Most have wide wingspans and use favourable airflow over the waves to soar apparently without effort. Sunlight penetrates the warm upper layers of the ocean to provide energy for photosynthesis, permitting the prolific growth of the phytoplankton (plant life). This is the starting point for the whole complex web of marine life which leads ultimately to large predatory fish such as the tuna and marlin, and to human foods.

Soft coral *above*
Photographed in Mauritius, a bluish coral has almost finished reproducing by splitting into two.

Sea urchin *below*
This 'slate pencil' variety from Mozambique coral reefs contrasts with spiny types. Size 10 in (25 cm).

Sea slug *above*
Many of these marine relatives of land slugs are colorful. This one from the Indian Ocean is 4 in (10 cm).

Feather star *below*
Another of the starfish and sea urchin group from Mozambique, this has four inch (10 cm) arms.

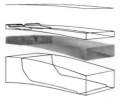

Near the surface *above and right*
Seabirds generally keep below 1000 ft (300 m) but can be found much higher. The upper layer of ocean is taken to extend down to 3300 ft (1000 m). Water temperature is about 10 °C and sunlight may reach to 650 ft (200 m).

Middle dwellers
In this range of depths, most of which (down to 6000 ft) is known as the bathyal or bathypelagic zone, the water cools to 4 °C, the temperature at which the density of water reaches its peak. Little or no light penetrates, and the life is made up of free-swimming fish, crustaceans and cephalopods (squids, for example) possessing body fluids at the same hydrostatic pressure as the environment and having approximately the same degree of salinity. At night some middle dwellers migrate to the surface to feed on other animals which in turn congregate to 'graze' on the plankton.

Middle depths *above and right*
The horizontal 'slice' of ocean water in which live the middle-depth species illustrated opposite is taken to extend from 3300 down to 10000 ft (1000-3000 m). Here the temperature falls from 10 °C down to below 4 °C at the lower level.

The abyss *above and right*
The bottom layer of the ocean is here taken to extend down to about 20000 ft (6000 m). Temperature is always below 4 °C, hydrostatic pressure is enormous and the environment is perpetually devoid of sunlight.

Bottom dwellers
Below 3000 meters the life comprises a range of animals, most of them very small, adapted to living in near-freezing water at extremely high pressures. The only light in this region comes from the curious luminescent organs common to many deep-sea creatures. Although the deep waters contain abundant salts and nutrient minerals, these are useless without the energy of sunlight. Every abyssal organism is therefore either a scavenger, depending for its supply of food on a rain' of debris from above, or a predator. Yet the abyssal zone supports a surprising variety of life.

Great Shearwater
span 8½ in 0.2 m

Wandering albatross
span 11 ft 3.35 m

Red-billed tropic bird
span 1 ft 0.3 m

Magnificent frigate bird
span 8 ft 2.45 m

Portuguese man o' war
11 in 0.28 m
(tentacles 100 ft 30 m)

sea level

Flying fish
9 in 0.23 m

Marlin
10 ft 3 m

Ocean sunfish
10 ft 3 m

Anchovies
6 in 0.15 m

Basking shark
40 ft 12 m

Dolphin fish
4 ft 1.2 m

Squid
1 ft 0.3 m

Bluefin tuna
7 ft 2 m

Ocean bonito
2 ft 0.6 m

Mackerel shark
12 ft 3.6 m

Lantern fish
3 in 0.075 m

Diretmus argentus
2 in 0.05 m

Photostomias guerni
7 in 0.18 m

1000 m
3300 ft

Giant squid
55 ft 17 m

Hatchet fish
1 in 0.025 m

Oarfish
20 ft 6 m

Ghost shark
4 ft 1.2 m

Chiasmodus niger
3 in 0.075 m

Gulper eel
4 ft 6 in 1.4 m

3000 m
10000 ft

Angler fish
3 in 0.075 m

Viper fish
1 ft 0.3 m

Deep sea swimming cucumber
4 in 0.1 m

Prawn
4 in 0.1 m

Angler fish
2 in 0.05 m

Pelican eel
10 in 0.25 m

Deep sea jellyfish
3 in 0.075 m

Rat tail
18 in 0.45 m

Tripod fish
10 in 0.25 m

Abyssal octopus
4 in 0.1 m

Brotulid
6 in 0.15 m

Abyssal sea cucumber
¾ in 0.02 m

Sea snail
9 in 0.23 m

Brittle star 3 in 0.075 m

The story of man's use of the land is one of increasing diversity and complexity. Preagricultural man developed perhaps six land uses; hunting, trapping, fishing, gathering wild fruits, fashioning tools and sheltering in caves. Modern man has developed several thousand forms, and frequently concentrates hundreds within a single square mile. For most of them he has created distinctive environments; one can tell at a glance whether the land is being used to grow carrots, make cement, repair ships, treat sewage, sell antiques, mine coal or educate children.

Although every place is unique in the ways its land uses intermingle, we can nevertheless recognize five major land-use patterns. Each has sprung into prominence at some major crossroads in human history. The first of the five is wildscape, which man uses so lightly and so rarely that nature is still in chief control. Some of it is still almost wholly natural, as in the remote parts of the Antarctic icecap. Other areas have been quite profoundly changed, as on the Pennine moorlands where generations of sheep have nibbled away tree seedlings and prevented the regeneration of forest, or where polluted air is now preventing the growth of sphagnum moss. But these areas are still wildscape. Man uses their resources but he leaves nature to replenish them.

The rural landscape evolves

Farmscape dates from man's first great technical advance, the Neolithic agricultural revolution of about 8000 years ago. For the first time he began to alter the landscape and live with the results instead of moving on; he ploughed and harvested, enclosed fields and diverted water for irrigation. During subsequent millennia this more controlled form of land-use spread over enormous areas of every continent, with a cumulative stream of diversifications as man applied his ingenuity to it in different environments. The rural landscape was now distinctively divided into the wild and the cultivated.

Townscape also existed from an early date, but had to await man's second great technical advance before it could develop at all extensively. Not until the twin agrarian and industrial revolutions of the 18th century did agriculture develop sufficiently to support a vastly greater population than its own labor force, or industry develop sufficiently to be able to employ a vast non-agricultural population. Once this possibility was established as a world trend, townscape began to develop rapidly.

Conflicts in land use

There are now three 'scapes' of increasing artificiality and complexity, respectively dominated by nature, the individual farmer and the public authority. So different are these three 'scapes' that problems tend to arise where they confront and interact with each other. Unfortunately such fringes of conflict have been intensified as side effects of two otherwise beneficial transport revolutions.

The first, or long-distance, transport revolution began with the steamship and the train in the 19th century. It opened up competition in foodstuffs on a global scale: the benefit was cheaper food from more favored areas, and the cost was the decline of less-favored areas. Some farmscape reverted to wildscape, resolving the problem. Elsewhere, the land remained good enough to reclaim in times of booming prices but too poor to be profitable in times of recession. The result in such areas is recurrent farm poverty.

The long-distance transport revolution also had a similar effect upon less competitive mining areas which tended to become derelict as a result, forming rurban (rural-urban) fringe. The main growth of rurban fringe, however, was stimulated by the second, or personal, transport revolution, in which the car gave city workers the opportunity to live in the country and commute daily to a neighboring city. The result was an unprecedented intermingling of urban areas and farmland, and an unprecedented degree of conflict between the two. Farmland became fragmented and subjected to many kinds of urban pressures so that much of it became uneconomic to farm. The urban area, on the other hand, experienced many difficulties in service facilities, because its sprawling layout multiplied distances and costs. Thus both marginal fringe and rurban fringe have become areas of patchy, conflicting landuses.

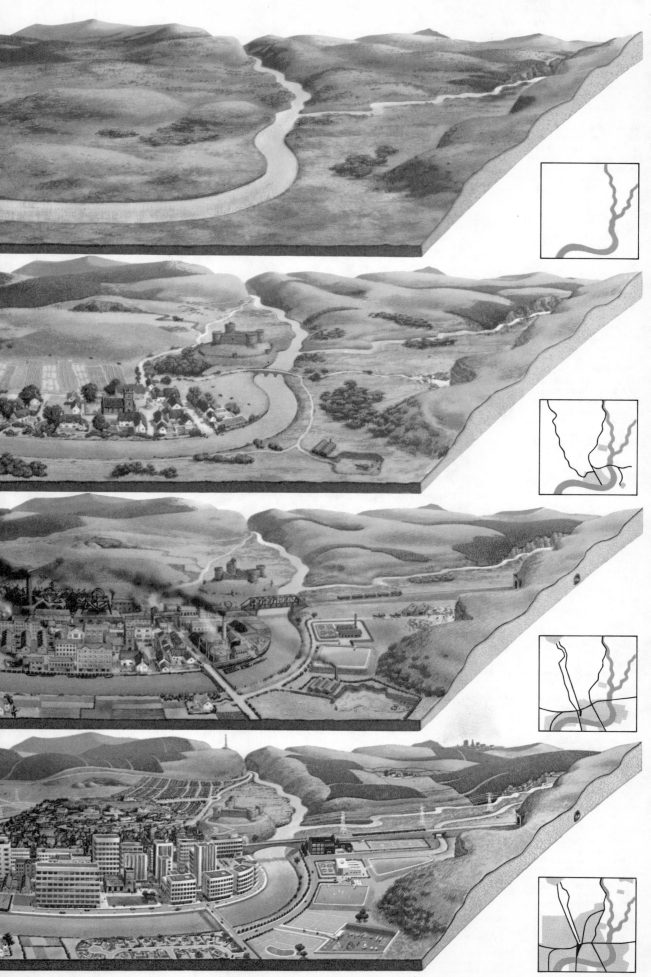

Prehistoric landscape

The natural prehistoric landscape consisted of a series of wildscape ecosystems wherein all forms of life interacted in a stable balance of nature. The land falls from distant hills to a coastal plain where the river widens into a broad estuary. Woodlands partially cover the plains, thinning into scrub on the hills. Stone age man used this wildscape in diffuse and restricted ways. He roamed the forest and heath hunting game but, apart from a cave shelter or toolmaking floor, rarely set aside land for a particular use. He exerted no perceptible influence upon the landscape apart from the fact that grazing animals gradually retarded the regeneration of the forest and led to a more open vegetation. But the presence of flat land, water, coal, stone and good access were ideal for later man.

Medieval

After he had developed agriculture man was able to use the land in more ways. It is possible by this time to detect at least a dozen types of stable land use. This was basically an age of slowly developing farmscape, when wildscape was reclaimed for food production and most settlement was designed to serve agricultural communities. Villagers are cultivating open strip fields in rotation for winter corn, spring corn and fallowing, surrounded by common grazing lands. The improved standard of shelter is reflected in clearance of forest to obtain timber, and the land is quarried for clay (near left), stone (left) and iron ore (back-ground). With such burdens man has improved his transport methods. And the river is now becoming polluted.

19th Century

The industrial revolution was a marked change in man's use of land. Coal was deep-mined as a source of unprecedented power which led to the concentration of crafts in large factories. Gasworks, flour mills and textile mills were basic industries, in turn leading to an industrial townscape. Different types of land use can be measured by the score. Building stone and brick-making continue to flourish, but imports have replaced the old ironworkings. Agriculture plays its part by more efficient production from larger fields to support the growing population. Greatly improved communications are evident. But there is marked pollution of both the river and the atmosphere, and filter beds and clean-water reservoirs are necessary.

Modern

Land uses are now so differentiated as to be countless. Many hundreds of new uses are service functions, ranging from financial institutions to children's playgrounds (the former brick pit) and hairdressers. Dwellings abound in great variety, many of them made of new materials by new methods Electricity has wrought a revolution that extends to virtually every human construction, and the urgent demand for better transport has led to a complete transformation of the scene on this ground alone. A more subtle effect of better transport is that uneconomic local farming has given way to imported food, and much of the land is being reforested. Perhaps most important of all is the fact that man has become concerned about his environment.

Pollution is harmful waste. All living creatures produce waste, often with marked effects on the environment. Pine leaves blanket out the flowers which would otherwise grow on the forest floor; the droppings of seabirds can cover nesting islands meters deep in guano. Plants as well as road vehicles give off carbon dioxide; volcanoes as well as power stations emit sulphur dioxide.

What turns man's waste into pollution? First, we produce too much waste: only man lives in such vast communities that his excreta de-oxygenates whole rivers. Secondly, the unwanted by-products of man's industrial metabolism change so rapidly that the environment has little hope of accommodating it. African grassland has evolved over millions of years to accept piles of elephant dung, with many species of animals specially adapted to living inside dungheaps and helping to decompose them. But the ecosystem is often unable to cope with our latest pollutants: few bacteria are able to digest plastics. Thirdly, man's waste is often extremely persistent: DDT may remain unchanged for decades, passing from one animal to another, poisoning and weakening them all.

Pollution may harm man directly: smoke causes bronchitis, and fouled drinking water can spread typhoid. Pollution may harm us indirectly, reducing the capacity of the land, rivers and seas to supply us with food. But perhaps the most insidious effects are the least obvious. Small doses of separate pollutants, each harmless by itself, may together weaken wild populations of animals so that they cannot recover from natural disasters. Acute pollution kills tens of thousands of animals; chronic pollution gradually reduces the quality of the entire human environment.

Pollution is wasteful. Too often modern technology painstakingly extracts a metal from the crust, uses it once and then discards it. For example, once unwanted chromium or mercury is released into the seas it will be diluted many millions of times and is unlikely ever to be recoverable except at prohibitive expense. If man is not to face raw material famines in the foreseeable future, he must learn to recycle everything from air and water to the rarer elements.

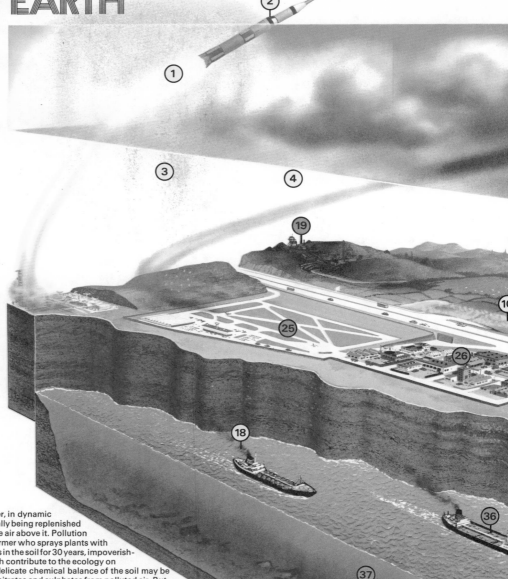

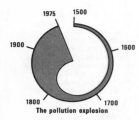

1975 1500
1900   1600
1800   1700

The pollution explosion

Pollution of the land

The soil is a living organic layer, in dynamic equilibrium with, and continually being replenished by, the rocks beneath it and the air above it. Pollution affects it in many ways. The farmer who sprays plants with insecticides may leave residues in the soil for 30 years, impoverishing the micro-organisms which contribute to the ecology on which his crops depend. The delicate chemical balance of the soil may be disrupted by rain loaded with nitrates and sulphates from polluted air. But the land is also a de-pollutant. Some substances can be buried in the knowledge that before they can re-appear they will have been oxidized to harmless compounds.

● Pollution of the air

1 Rocket exhaust contains a variety of combustion products.

2 Space launchings leave jettisoned propellants and other debris orbiting above the atmosphere.

3 Nuclear weapon testing can leave fall-out on a global scale.

4 Increased air traffic creates noise pollution over wide areas.

5 Jet efflux contains kerosene combustion products, unburned fuel and particles of soot.

6 Nuclear weapons can cause radioactive contamination; together with chemical and biological devices they could eradicate all life on Earth.

7 Jet aircraft cause intense local noise, and supersonic aircraft create a shock-wave boom.

8 Large-scale aerial transport of pollutants distributes particles and gaseous matter.

9 Carbon dioxide build-up and 'greenhouse effect' traps solar heat within the atmosphere.

10 Pesticide spraying can cause widespread contamination, and organochlorine residues (such as DDT) can build up in animals and disrupt natural food chains.

11 Nuclear power station is potential source of escaping radioactive or liquid coolant.

12 Thermal (coal or oil fired) power station causes thermal and chemical pollution from exhaust stacks.

13 Power station cooling towers transfer waste heat to the air.

14 Sulphur dioxide from high roof-level chimneys falls into 'canyon streets' causing irritation to eyes and lungs.

15 Refinery waste gases burned in the air cause heavy pollution unless the flame is extremely hot.

16 Road vehicle exhausts and crankcase gases contain lead, unburned hydrocarbons, carbon monoxide and oxides of nitrogen, and can cause widespread pollution; action of sunlight on nitrogen oxides creates smog.

17 Most domestic fuels are very inefficiently burned, causing smoke and chemical pollution.

18 Steam boilers or diesel smoke can cause persistent trails of gaseous and particulate matter.

● Pollution of the land

19 Coal mining leaves unsightly and potentially dangerous tips.

20 Electricity transmission pylons are a classic of visual pollution.

21 Powerful air-conditioning cools buildings in summer by heating the immediate surroundings.

22 Visual pollution of highways is accentuated by billboards.

23 Unreclaimed wastes are often dumped and not recycled.

24 Quarrying leaves unsightly scars.

25 Growth of air traffic is reflected in increasing size and number of airports which occupy otherwise valuable land.

26 Even modern industrial estates invariably cause chemical and thermal pollution, and pose waste-disposal problems.

27 Large motorways, especially intersections, occupy large areas of land.

28 Caravan and chalet sites may cause severe local chemical, as well as visual, pollution.

29 Modern litter includes high proportion of non-biodegradable plastics materials.

○ Pollution of the water

30 Nuclear power station discharges waste heat into river and can cause radioactive contamination.

31 Industrial wastes are often poured into rivers without treatment.

32 Cooling water from thermal power stations can cause very large-scale heating of rivers, changing or destroying the natural fauna and flora.

33 Refinery and other chemical plants generate waste heat and liquid refuse which may be discharged directly into the river.

34 Oil storage installation can cause intermittent pollution.

35 When it reaches the sea the river is heavily polluted by nitrates and phosphates from fertilizers and treated sewage, as well as by heavy toxic metals.

36 Tanker too close inshore risks severe beach pollution from accidental release of cargo.

37 Radioactive and corrosive wastes often dumped without enough knowledge of local conditions to insure that the containers will not leak before contents have decomposed; nothing should be dumped on continental shelf and adequate dilution is essential.

38 The main influx of pollutants into the sea is via rivers; typical categories include agricultural and industrial chemicals, waste heat, treated and untreated sewage and solid matter.

39 Excess nutrients from untreated sewage, agricultural chemicals and nuclear wastes can lead to 'blooms' of toxic marine plankton or, through their oxidation and decay, to severely reduced oxygen levels in the water.

40 Sewage sludge dumped at sea contains persistent chemicals such as PCB (polychlorinated biophenyl) compounds, toxic heavy metals and nutrients.

41 Large oil slicks are released by tanker accidents or deliberate washing at sea, and by oil-rig blow-outs.

42 Sediments stirred by mineral exploitation, dumped from ships or carried by rivers may form thick layers on the ocean floor which suffocate the organisms living there.

43 Clouds of particulate matter, both organic and inorganic wastes, reduce the penetration of sunlight and sharply curtail marine productivity.

44 Oil rigs suffer explosive blow-outs, a serious problem off the California coast.

45 In some waters wrecks, many of them uncharted, pose hazards to shipping which may lead to further pollution.

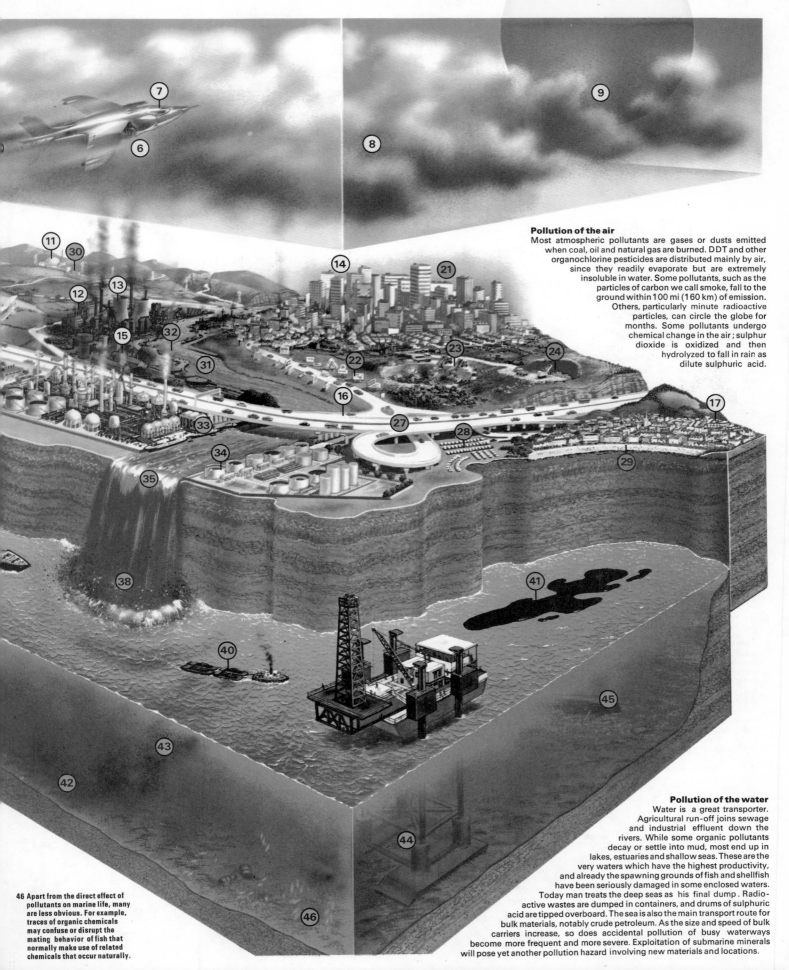

Pollution of the air

Most atmospheric pollutants are gases or dusts emitted when coal, oil and natural gas are burned. DDT and other organochlorine pesticides are distributed mainly by air, since they readily evaporate but are extremely insoluble in water. Some pollutants, such as the particles of carbon we call smoke, fall to the ground within 100 mi (160 km) of emission. Others, particularly minute radioactive particles, can circle the globe for months. Some pollutants undergo chemical change in the air; sulphur dioxide is oxidized and then hydrolyzed to fall in rain as dilute sulphuric acid.

Pollution of the water

Water is a great transporter. Agricultural run-off joins sewage and industrial effluent down the rivers. While some organic pollutants decay or settle into mud, most end up in lakes, estuaries and shallow seas. These are the very waters which have the highest productivity, and already the spawning grounds of fish and shellfish have been seriously damaged in some enclosed waters. Today man treats the deep seas as his final dump. Radio-active wastes are dumped in containers, and drums of sulphuric acid are tipped overboard. The sea is also the main transport route for bulk materials, notably crude petroleum. As the size and speed of bulk carriers increase, so does accidental pollution of busy waterways become more frequent and more severe. Exploitation of submarine minerals will pose yet another pollution hazard involving new materials and locations.

46 Apart from the direct effect of pollutants on marine life, many are less obvious. For example, traces of organic chemicals may confuse or disrupt the mating behavior of fish that normally make use of related chemicals that occur naturally.

PATHWAYS OF POLLUTION

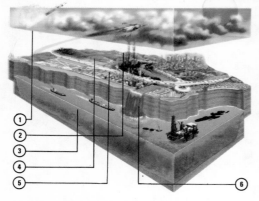

Pollution and health

Eyes

Ozone from various industrial processes is extremely toxic and irritates the eyes

Sulphur dioxide is generated by burning all sulphurous fuels: coal, oil and gas

Smoke is mainly particulate carbon plus mixed carbohydrate molecules, some of them carcinogenic

Dust, varied particulate and fibrous matter, is caused by ash, mineral extraction and abrasion

Photochemical smog is a suspension of irritant and carcinogenic molecules of nitro-oxide origin

Ears

30 decibels: watch ticking

60 db: normal conversation

90 db: close heavy truck

102 db: modern big jetliner

110 db: car horn, football crowd

120 db: older jet at 500 ft (180 m)

130 db: loud pop group, air raid siren

150 db: laboratory rats paralysed

180 db: presumed lethal to humans

Nose

Carbon monoxide, formed when anything is incompletely burned, inactivates blood hemoglobin in humans

Nitrogen oxides, caused by almost all fuel burning, combine with other elements to form harmful compounds

Smoke particles inhaled by humans form a black oily coating on the lungs; cigarettes are the main source

Sulphur dioxide is a choking irritant in high concentrations. Its action on the lungs is complex

Mineral particles are released by clothing and other fabrics and have an irritant effect on the lungs

Lead compounds, often from gasoline vapor, are inhaled and then washed from the lungs to the throat and stomach

Skin

Dieldrin is used to make woollen cloth mothproof and is thus brought into prolonged contact with the skin

Detergents and enzyme compounds generally pass into or through the skin, causing dermatitis

Insecticides can usually enter the body through the skin, in extreme cases having harmful effects

Organophosphorus insecticides, such as Dieldrin, invariably penetrate the skin and require protective clothing

Mouth (water)

Pesticides can become concentrated to dangerous or lethal levels (see opposite page)

Heavy metals, such as cadmium, zinc and nickel, are difficult to eliminate from water and foodstuffs

Chlorine, fluorine, selenium and copper compounds in drinking water can have complex adverse effects

Pathogenic bacteria are released mainly from raw sewage, causing typhoid, diarrhea and other ills

Mouth (food)

Pesticides enter the body mainly on food, and are particularly prevalent on the skins of fruit and vegetables

Dyes of many kinds are added to restore what the public considers to be a desirable color to food

Mercury, in organic compounds, is one of the few really dangerous elements to humans (see diagram below)

Modern processed foodstuffs contain numerous forms of flavoring and preservatives in small quantities

Pollution often travels along strange pathways, and these must be unravelled if the menace is to be controlled and its effects predicted. It is unwise ever to assume the obvious. DDT was found in the soil of apple orchards in Kent months after spraying, and it was also detected in local rivers. The obvious conclusion was that it was leaching down through the soil into the groundwater. But analysis of the springs and wells showed no DDT at all. In fact the insecticide was leaving the surface by evaporation and falling again as rain.

Pollution can be distributed over vast distances. The insecticide BHC is carried by the prevailing westerly winds from the Soviet Union across China and N America and to Europe. Water likewise carries contaminants down rivers to oceans. But the most important pathway is the food chain. A pollutant is released into the air, soil or sea. It is absorbed by plants. These are eaten by a herbivore, which in its turn is eaten by a carnivore which is itself eaten by a predator. The chain may have many links or only a few, but at every stage the pollutant is more concentrated. If a hawk eats 100 birds which each ate 100 insects it may die from pollution 10000 times the strength met by the insect.

① Radiation *right*
No pollutant has been so continuously monitored as nuclear radiation. But it is not a problem created solely by modern man. In the modern world nearly all the radioactivity issues from the rocks, and, as far as humans are concerned, from the body.

Rocks	50 %
Cosmic	25 %
Body	$23\frac{1}{4}$ %
Tests	$1\frac{1}{2}$ %
Waste	$\frac{1}{4}$ %

② Radiation and life *right*
Living cells concentrate radiation. In an above-ground nuclear-weapon test all heavy radioactive particles drop within hours in a narrow region down-wind of the explosion. Their residence time in the atmosphere varies from four weeks in the troposphere to ten years in the mesosphere. One such product, strontium 90, is taken up from the soil by plants. Eaten by cattle and released in their milk, it ends up in human bone where it is only slowly liquidated. As it decays it can destroy the marrow which produces red blood cells, in extreme cases causing death through pentaemia. Radiation pollution can also arise from power reactors or nuclear waste. Plankton can concentrate radioactivity a thousandfold. Fish eat plankton, and on migration can disperse the radiation far from its source. In the 1950s this mechanism caused radiation sickness in Japanese fishermen hundreds of miles from US test sites in the Pacific.

Concentration of atomic waste (phosphorus 32) in animal food chains

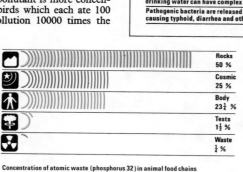

Water 1
Aquatic invertebrates 35
Ducks 7500
Duck eggs 200,000
Egg yolks 2,000,000

③ Deadly mercury *right*
Compounds of mercury have for 1000 years been known to be highly toxic. An industrial plant often discharges such compounds, but it was thought these rested at the sea bed. Man has now learned that bacteria can convert inorganic mercury compounds to deadly methyl mercury, which can then be successively concentrated in marine food chains. Shellfish are particularly good concentrators of methyl mercury. When eaten by humans they cause severe disabling of the central nervous system, and in extreme cases cause death (below).

brains

liver

kidneys

Minimata tragedy *right*
In 1953 people living in this Japanese city became ill. Ultimately over 120 were afflicted, and 43 (black) died. The cause was methyl mercury concentrated in sea-foods. Some acetaldehyde plants still emit methyl mercury.

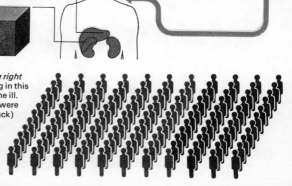

④ The DDT menace *right*
Introduced during World War 2, DDT appeared to be ideal. It would kill lice on soldiers weeks after the treatment of their clothes. Houses sprayed against malaria remained lethal to mosquitoes long after the health teams had departed. But the persistence brought its own problems. DDT and other organochlorine pesticides, such as BHC, Dieldrin, Endosulfan and Heptachlor, are only slightly broken down by animal metabolism. An insect receiving a non-lethal dose of DDT retains it in its body and passes it on up the food chain. Animals at the head of the chain often build up large residues in their fatty tissues. Under stress these residues can be released and fatally damage the liver, kidney and brain. DDT can evaporate from soil, travelling round the globe, before being adsorbed on to dust and falling as rain. The organochlorines soon penetrate every corner of an ecosystem.

DIELDRIN

Seed that has been 'dressed' is eaten by a wood pigeon. The bird finds the seeds palatable, and may eat dozens to hundreds in a day.

The pigeon is devoured by a badger (or a cat, fox, hawk or other predator). The badger may build up poison from eating many pigeons.

In this case the pesticide-soaked grain is attractive to a yellowhammer, typical of many small birds which pick seeds off the land.

The yellowhammer has fallen prey to a sparrowhawk. In a few weeks dieldrin may build up causing death or inability to breed.

DDT

Sap-sucking insects, such as aphids, feed on sprayed wheat and build up a DDT concentration not sufficiently high to kill them.

A predator ladybird climbs wheat grain devouring aphids in large numbers. It soon builds up a very large residue of DDT in its body.

On a nettle at the edge of the field the ladybird is in turn eaten by a whitethroat, spotted flycatcher or other insect-eating bird.

Finally the bird, suffering from severe DDT toxicity, is devoured by a hawk. In many countries birds of prey have almost vanished.

⑥ Misuse of a river by overloading *above and left*
In moderation, man can safely pour his effluents into the rivers. A farmhouse beside a river (above) causes a little local pollution which is soon oxidized; the fish population does not suffer. A village causes no lasting pollution but merely a depression of the dissolved oxygen in the water for a mile or two downstream. But a large city pours out so much effluent that the river is completely de-oxygenated. All the fish and plants are killed and the river becomes foul in an irreversible way (left). Whereas a river may be capable of processing pollutants from 50000 people, pollutants from 100000 may destroy the ecological cycle.

⑤ The PCB problem
PCBs (polychlorinated biphenyls) are persistent and can be scattered in smoke from burning or washed down a drain adsorbed on dust particles. Virtually all these molecules end up in the sea in the form of non-biodegradable particles which can be intensely concentrated as they move within the marine food chain. Their lethal effect was first driven home when the population of Irish sea birds, especially guillemots, 'crashed' in 1969. Almost all the corpses were found to have liver and kidney lesions characteristic of PCB poisoning. Fat, healthy birds can carry a large PCB load safely, but the Irish birds were starving and had drawn on their fatty reserves, where the PCB was stored. Passing into the circulation, the chemical accumulated in the birds' organs in lethal amounts.

PCB uses *left*
Polychlorinated biphenyls have numerous uses in modern industry. They serve as plasticizers in paints, as fillers in plastics and in electrical capacitors.

Guillemots *right*
These sea birds live on fish and thus form the end link in a marine food chain.

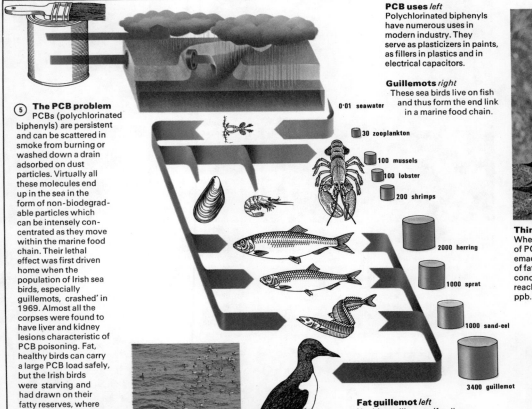

0·01 seawater
30 zooplankton
100 mussels
100 lobster
200 shrimps
2000 herring
1000 sprat
1000 sand-eel
3400 guillemot

Thin guillemot *below*
When a guillemot with 3400 ppb of PCB in its body becomes emaciated it draws on its reserves of fat. The chemical becomes concentrated in its organs, reaching a lethal level of 60000 ppb.

Fat guillemot *left*
Healthy guillemots (feeding at sea, far left) can have 3400 parts per billion (ppb) of PCBs in the body but only 400 in the liver.

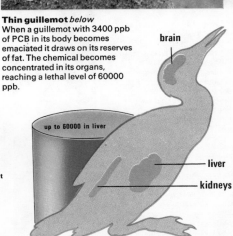

brain

up to 60000 in liver

liver

kidneys

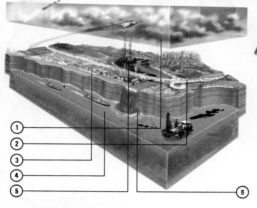

Pollution is a global problem. It affects the land, the sea and the atmosphere in an inter-related way that is incredibly complex and often very subtle. At least in the industrially developed countries man has learned that he must do better than merely bury his unwanted materials in the ground, pour them into the rivers or burn them to pollute the air. But learning the best ways of disposing of them – or, preferably, of storing them until they can be used again – is a difficult, long-term process; and time is not on man's side.

Once pollutants are dispersed, controlling them becomes extremely costly or even impossible. The answer is to prevent their release, wherever possible, into the arterial pathways of water and air. The growing awareness of this is reflected in the legislation of many countries. It is seen in the Clean Air Act of the UK, the German convention banning harmful detergents, the tight California restrictions on car exhaust gases, and so on. But this is only the start of the movement to clean-up the environment and conserve its resources.

Much of the action against pollution has been piecemeal in nature, often in response to particular disasters. Now comes the promise, in no small part due to the public mood, for more widespread action against pollutants that are already known to be harmful to the environment and man. For example, public health authorities in most countries are alive to the hazard of mercury contamination in fish and other foods. At the international level, the convention on oil pollution is being strengthened and the permissible levels of radioactive discharges reviewed. At the same time, industry is slowly becoming persuaded that waste should be regarded as a valued resource which is often capable of being recycled over and over again instead of discarded.

Percentage composition of domestic waste in U S A

Paper 45
Miscellaneous 19
Vegetable and animal matter 12
Cinders, ash, coal dust 10
Metallic waste 8
Glass 6

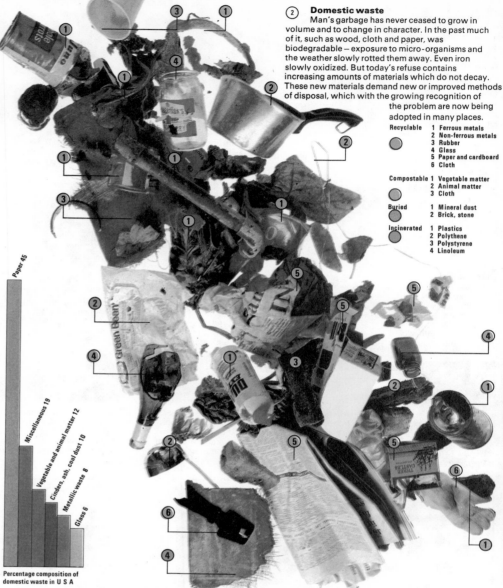

(2) Domestic waste
Man's garbage has never ceased to grow in volume and to change in character. In the past much of it, such as wood, cloth and paper, was biodegradable – exposure to micro-organisms and the weather slowly rotted them away. Even iron slowly oxidized. But today's refuse contains increasing amounts of materials which do not decay. These new materials demand new or improved methods of disposal, which with the growing recognition of the problem are now being adopted in many places.

Recyclable 1 Ferrous metals
2 Non-ferrous metals
3 Rubber
4 Glass
5 Paper and cardboard
6 Cloth

Compostable 1 Vegetable matter
2 Animal matter
3 Cloth

Buried 1 Mineral dust
2 Brick, stone

Incinerated 1 Plastics
2 Polythene
3 Polystyrene
4 Linoleum

(1) Air pollution in cities
Smoke is one of the commonest, most dangerous and most visible of all air pollutants. It is the direct cause of bronchitis and other respiratory diseases. But many nations are cleaning their urban atmosphere by introducing smokeless zones. Since 1956 winter sunshine in British city centers has increased by over 50 per cent. Smoke from railways (violet segment, right) has dwindled as steam traction has been superseded. Industrial smoke has likewise been reduced, although iron oxide dust from steelworks (above) remains a problem as do domestic coal fires.

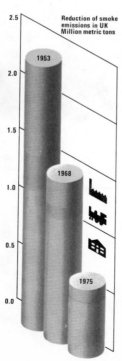

Reduction of smoke emissions in UK Million metric tons

1953 — 2.0+
1968 — 1.0
1975 — 0.3

The menace of the car *below*
Dramatic reductions in air pollution will result as soon as simple alterations are universally adopted. One of the worst sources, the crankcase breather (1), is not opened to the air but piped through a vacuum-sensing valve (2) back to the intake. Fuel-tank vapor (3) is filtered and similarly dealt with. The exhaust is made oxygen-rich with extra fresh air (4) to burn up all but a few combustion products; the residue is oxidized to harmless compounds by passage through a high temperature furnace (5) in the presence of a chemical catalyst which promotes the desired reactions.

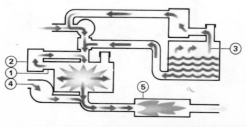

(3) Saving the eagle *right*
In the early 1960s ecologists became sure that organo-chlorine insecticides (DDT and Dieldrin, for example) were the cause of the sudden drop in breeding success of many predatory birds. But the charge could not be proved, and in most countries the use of these pesticides continued. One bird affected was the golden eagle. Scottish highland sheep were dipped in Dieldrin to kill ticks. The chemical became dissolved in the mutton fat, and this eagle lives largely on sheep carrion. In one area the proportion of eagle eyries producing young fell from 72 to 29 per cent, following the introduction of Dieldrin sheep dips in 1960. Scotland's 300 pairs of eagles seemed doomed. But in 1966 Britain banned Dieldrin sheep-dips. By the early 1970s more than enough young survived to maintain the eagle population.

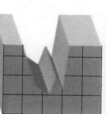

Golden eagle: percentage breeding successes
1960 1963 1966 1969

④ Oil pollution

Every year millions of tons of oil enter the oceans either directly through spills, accidents or deliberate discharge or indirectly via air and water from the land. Hardly any part of the ocean remains free from contamination. Some oil pollution is the disturbing result of industrial society's dependence on an oil-based technology. Equally, there is no doubt that much oil pollution is unnecessary and can be controlled or prevented. One of the earliest attempts to do this occurred in 1926 when the United States tried to obtain international agreement to limit the discharge of oil. This and later attempts by the United Kingdom failed and it was not until 1958 that the International Convention for the Prevention of Pollution of the Sea by Oil came into force — four years after it was agreed. Even then, the Convention did not ban completely the release of oil into the sea. This must be the ultimate goal. However, even if this is achieved, the problem will persist — oil pollution from sources on land is more than double that occurring directly at sea. One of the chief offenders are gasoline and diesel engines. The crankcases of such engines contribute at least 2.8 million metric tons of oil to the sea every year. A serious waste of a vital resource, steps are at last being taken in some countries to curb it.

The Torrey Canyon disaster

In 1967 the sea had its first major case of oil pollution when the Torrey Canyon ran aground off the Cornish coast (above left). Within a few days the first oil began to sweep onto the beaches. To disperse it, large quantities of detergent were sprayed both from boats (above) and on the shore, turning the sea creamy white with a froth of oily emulsion (center left). Unfortunately the use of these detergents probably caused more damage to marine life than did the oil — except for the early kill of seabirds (bottom left). The oil also drifted across to France coating the shore with congealed oil (right).

Oil movements *left*
Increased transport is reflected in the percentage growth of the world tanker fleet (below).

Thousand million tons

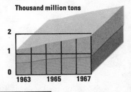

Oil tankers' new load-on-top system *below*
Before the introduction of this system, ballast water and tank washings, along with a hundred or so tons of oil which had originally stuck to the internal steelwork, were discharged into the sea before taking on a new cargo. In the load-on-top system, one cargo compartment (A) is used as a 'slop tank'. Water in a ballast tank (B) is run off until only oil and oily water remains (C). The residue together with washings from the tanks are collected in the slop tank (D). Here the mixture is finally separated before running clean water off (E). The load goes on top of the remaining oil.

Major oil routes

Oil entering the oceans — Million metric tons

- Industrial machine waste — 1.3
- Motor vehicle waste — 1.8
- Refineries — 0.3
- Accidental spillage — 0.2
- Offshore drilling — 0.1
- Tanker operations — 0.53
- Other ships — 0.5

Sources of oil pollution *left*
Although the spectacular incidents such as tanker collisions and drilling rig accidents receive most publicity, they release little oil compared with motor vehicles and industrial machines.

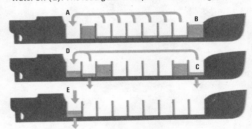

Main pollutants : percentages

Phosphate	20	43	37
Nitrate	9	17	73

☐ Lakeshore sewage
▨ Sewage from tributaries
▨ Natural inflow from rivers

⑤ Thermal pollution *above and below*

Man throws away a great deal of unwanted heat into rivers. This is done on the largest scale by electricity generating stations whose condensers cycle cooling water in vast quantities. In Britain the hot effluent is spread as a thin film on an otherwise cool river, causing visible steam (above, River Trent) but minimal disturbance to river life. The problem is accentuated by the spread of very large nuclear stations (in the US, below), which for safety reasons have so far generally been sited miles from urban areas on rivers which previously were quite unpolluted. In Britain all such stations are on the sea shore or wide estuaries.

Nuclear power stations

○ Operating
○ Under construction

⑥ Lake pollution

Lakes pass through a sequence of physical and chemical states from youth to maturity (p66A). Man's sewage and industrial effluents accelerate the intake of nutrient salts — such as the phosphates and nitrates shown in the bar chart above the map — which feed the natural population of algae. Combined with sunny weather the result can be an algal 'bloom'. Billions of algae use up the water's dissolved oxygen, killing fish and other life. The aerobic (oxygen-breathing) bacteria needed to degrade sewage and other organic matter are replaced by anaerobic forms which decompose the refuse not to carbon dioxide and water but to foul gases and black slimes. Eventually the bloom is replaced by an algal 'crash' and the countless bodies, often visible as a colored tide, evolve toxic decomposition products which, concentrated in food chains, can prove lethal to sea birds and even humans. The answer is better water treatment plants, possibly combined with new forms of fertilizers, detergents and other products of modern civilization which contain smaller quantities of nutrient salts.

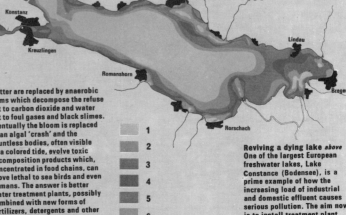

Numbers indicate increasing pollution: 1 2 3 4 5 6 7

Reviving a dying lake *above*
One of the largest European freshwater lakes, Lake Constance (Bodensee), is a prime example of how the increasing load of industrial and domestic effluent causes serious pollution. The aim now is to install treatment plant at source rather than use the lake as a liquid refuse dump.

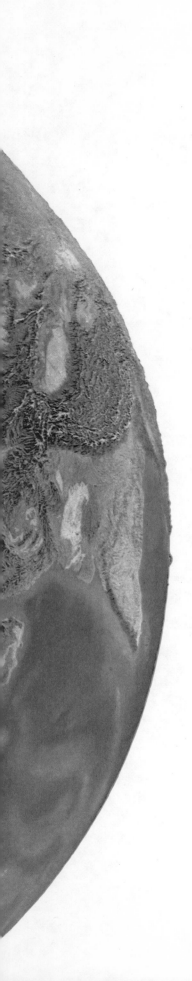

EUROPE

This global view centers on the western extension of Asia, the region the world knows as the continent of Europe. Often the two are linked together under the name Eurasia. This peninsula, or arm, of the great Asian landmass, itself is comprised of numerous peninsulas—those of Scandinavia, Iberia, Italy, and the Balkans—and many offshore islands, the most important group being the British Isles.

The thrust of this arm of Asia into the Atlantic Ocean, the North and Mediterranean seas provides a clear-cut western terminus. But the limits of Europe are not so clearly defined on its eastern flank where no natural barriers exist. For the sake of a "boundary" geographers have come to recognize the low Ural Mountains and the Ural River, the Caspian Sea, the Caucasus Mountains, and the Black Sea as the eastern and southeastern border.

From Europe's eastern limits, where the north to south dimension is approximately 2,500 miles, the irregularly shaped continent tapers toward the southwest and the surrounding bodies of water. Through Europe's history its miles of coastline encouraged contact with the other continents, and the seas became avenues of exchange for culture, politics, and technology with other regions of the world.

Internally Europe embraces a varied landscape comparable to no other region of its size in the world: In a total area of only 3,850,000 square miles are found extremes from zero winters and dry steppes in the east to year-round humid, mild climates in the west; extremes in elevation from the heights of the Alps to the below-sea-level Belgian and Netherlands coasts; and a variation in the distribution of inhabitants from the densely populated, industrialized northwest to the sparsely peopled areas in the agricultural south and east. Thirty-three independent nations, each with its own national, religious, cultural, and political heritage, add to this diverse landscape.

Because much of Europe is neither too hot or cold, or too high or low, a great extent of its land has been developed, aided by an impressive river-canal system, dominated by the Rhine and Danube. Its natural and cultural wealth has made possible an economic-social-political system which has long influenced the economic, political, and social structure of the rest of the world.

Today, because of its density of population, strategic location, politics, history, economic strength, and cultural tradition, Europe still may rightfully and strongly claim to be one of the hubs of the world.

Urban
Cropland
Cropland & Woodland
Cropland & Grazing Land
Grassland, Grazing Land
Forest, Woodland
Swamp, Marshland
Tundra
Shrub, Sparse Grass, Wasteland (pattern)
Barren Land
Oasis

Reykjavik

Narvik

Murma

Trondheim

Ume

Gulf of Bothnia

Bergen

Oslo

Helsinki

LENINGRAD

Tallinn

Stockholm

Göteborg

Rīga

Copenhagen

Baltic Sea

Glasgow

North Sea

Belfast

MANCHESTER

Dublin

Kaliningrad

Minsk

LONDON

Amsterdam

Hamburg

Elbe

BERLIN

Warsaw

Pripyat

Antwerp

Essen

Oder

Leipzig

Brest

Frankfurt

Kraków

L'vov

PARIS

Seine

Strasbourg

Prague

CARPATHIANS

Loire

Rhine

Danube

Munich

VIENNA

Dnest

La Coruña

Bay of Biscay

Lyon

Zürich

BUDAPEST

Bordeaux

Garonne

A L P S

MILAN

Tisza

Bilbao

Rhône

Venice

Zagreb

Sava

Douro

PYRENEES

Genoa

Belgrade

Lisbon

MADRID

Ebro

Marseille

Bucharest

Danube

BARCELONA

CORSICA

Adriatic Sea

Sofia

Sevilla

ROME

Tirane

SARDINIA

Naples

Tanger

ISLAS BALEARES

Tyrrhenian Sea

Aegean Sea

Oran

Algiers

Palermo

Athens

Casablanca

Tunis

SICILY

ATLAS MOUNTAINS

M e d i t e r r a n e a n   S e a

MALTA

CRETE

ATLANTIC OCEAN

Longitude West of Greenwich   0°   Longitude East of Greenwich

Scale 1: 16 000 000; one inch to 250 miles. Conic Projection

0 50 100   200   300   400   500 Miles
0   100   200   400   600   800 Kilometers

White Sea

Nar'yan-Mar

Pechora

Ob'

Novosibirsk

Ob'

Irtysh

Archangelsk

50°

Omsk

U R A L S

SVERDLOVSK

Perm'

Karaganda

Kirov

Vologda

Kazan'

Kama

Ufa

Balkhash

Volga

Gorki

Magnitogorsk

MOSCOW

Kuybyshev

Orsk

Kzyl-Orda

Syr-Dar'ya

Tula

Volga

PESKI
KYZYLKUM

Saratov

Ural

Aral'skoye
More
(Aral Sea)

40°

DEPRESSION

Amu Dar'ya

Khar'kov

VOLGOGRAD

CASPIAN

Kiev

Don

Volga

Astrakhan'

PESKI KARAKUMY

Dnepropetrovsk

Donetsk

MANYCH

DEPRESSION

Dnepr

Ashkhabad

Odessa

Krasnodar

C a s p i a n

Black   Sea

C A U C A S U S   M T S.

BAKU

S e a

TBILISI

Yerevan

İSTANBUL

ELBURZ   MTS.

DASHT-E-KAVIR

Ankara

TEHRAN

30°

TOROS

AĞRI

Kerman

Tigris

ZAGROS

Nicosia

CYPRUS

Euphrates

Baghdad

MOUNTAINS

Beirut

Ābādān

A-550000-95 1-2°
COPYRIGHT BY
RAND McNALLY & COMPANY
MADE IN U.S.A.

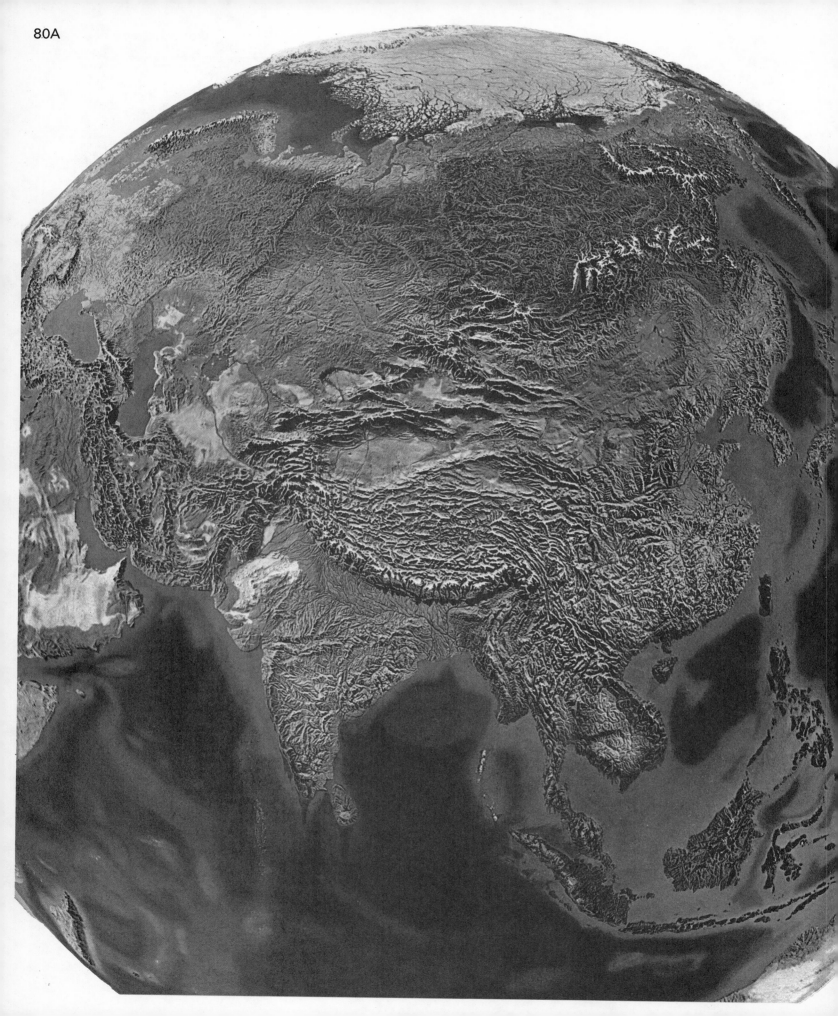

ASIA

Asia, the massive giant of continents, spreads its 17,000,000 square miles from polar wastes to regions of tropical abundance, and from Oriental to Occidental hearthlands. Much of Asia's vastness, however, is occupied by deserts, steppes, and by frozen and near-frozen wastes. Rugged upland areas stretch from Turkey and Iran, through the two-mile-high Tibetan Plateau, to the Bering Strait, leaving only one-third of Asia suitable for human habitation. These barriers also separate the two dominant, sharply contrasting parts of Asia—the realm made up of Southwest, South, and Southeast Asia from that of "European" Asia.

Rimming the south and east coasts of the continent are the most densely populated regions of the world, each dominated by a life-giving river system—the Tigris-Euphrates, the Indus and Ganges, the Brahmaputra, the Irrawaddy and Salween, the Menam and Mekong, the Yangtze and Hwang Ho, as well as innumerable small river valleys, plains, and islands. Separated from one another by deserts, massifs, and seas these regions account for over one-half of the world's population.

The civilizations associated with this population (where rural densities frequently may exceed 1,000 people per square mile) were developed largely upon the strength of intensive agricultural systems. Today these systems occupy more than 60 per cent of the populace, who manage only to win a bare subsistence. Changeover from subsistence agricultural economic systems to industrialized economies has been successful only in Japan and parts of the U.S.S.R.

North of the great Gobi Desert and the mountain barriers of the interior is the second Asia which, on almost every hand, differs from the southern portion of the continent. In the far north severe climatic elements send temperatures to −90°F., and permanently frozen ground impedes growth of vegetation. Only the scattered settlements next to the Trans-Siberian Railway give the area an indication of development. The activities of most of the populace are clearly directed toward Europe rather than Asia.

These two realms of the Asian continent do share two common characteristics. One is vast, yet generally inaccessible, natural resources—extensive forests, minerals, and hydroelectric potential—and the second is the drive to industrialize in order to "catch up" to the general material well-being of the Western World.

In the future, as the common characteristics, resources and drive, are developed, Asia's two realms may witness a change. A material way of life may result consistent with their heritage and historic contributions to the world.

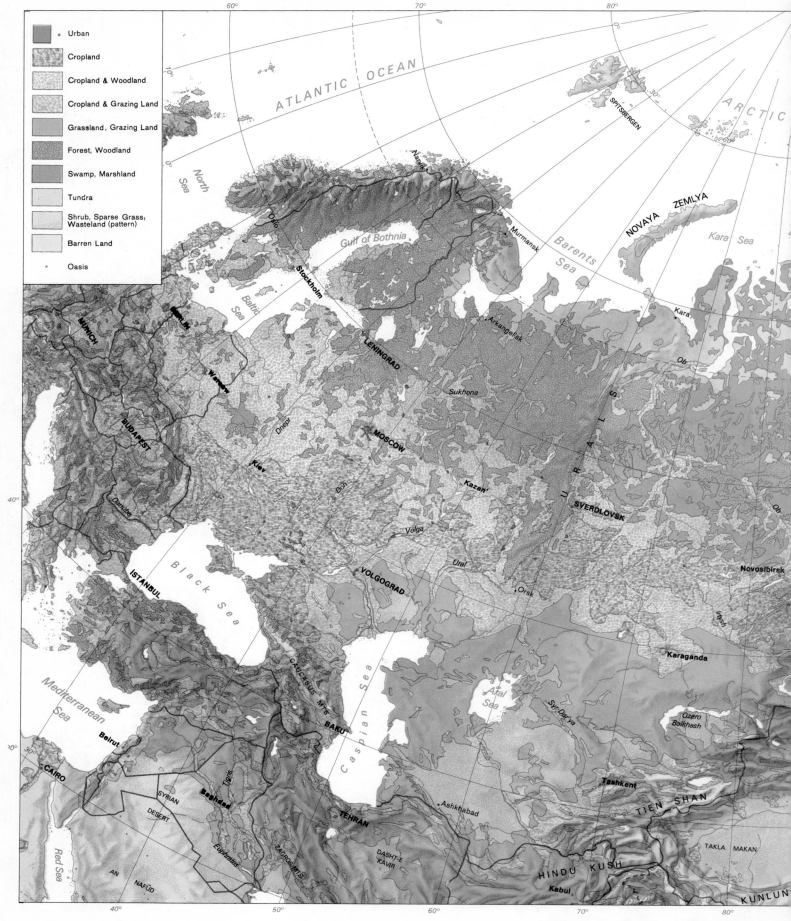

Urban
Cropland
Cropland & Woodland
Cropland & Grazing Land
Grassland, Grazing Land
Forest, Woodland
Swamp, Marshland
Tundra
Shrub, Sparse Grass,
Wasteland (pattern)
Barren Land
• Oasis

ATLANTIC OCEAN

ARCTIC

SPITSBERGEN

NOVAYA ZEMLYA

Kara Sea

Barents Sea

Murmansk

Narvik

North Sea

Gulf of Bothnia

Kara

Ob

Oslo

Stockholm

Baltic Sea

Arkangelsk

Sukhona

BERLIN

LENINGRAD

U R A L S

MÜNICH

Warsaw

MOSCOW

Ob

BUDAPEST

Dnepr

Kiev

Don

Kazan'

SVERDLOVSK

Danube

Volga

Novosibirsk

Ural

Irtysh

Black Sea

VOLGOGRAD

Orsk

ISTANBUL

CAUCASUS Mts

Karaganda

Mediterranean Sea

BAKU

Aral Sea

Ozero Balkhash

Beirut

Caspian Sea

CAIRO

Baghdad

Tigris

SYRIAN DESERT

Ashkhabad

Tashkent

TIEN SHAN

TEHRAN

DASHT-E KAVIR

Euphrates

ZAGROS Mts

Red Sea

AN NAFŪD

Kabul

HINDU KUSH

TAKLA MAKAN

KUNLUN

Scale 1:24,000,000; one inch to 380 miles. Lambert Azimuthal Equal-Area Projection

Mediterranean Sea

Red Sea

CAIRO

Beirut

CAUCASUS MTS.

BAKU

Caspian Sea

Aral Sea

Karaganda

Syr-Dar'ya

Ozero Balkhash

Tashkent

Ashkhabad

TEHRAN

DASHT-E KAVIR

Kermân

SYRIAN DESERT

Baghdad

Tigris

Euphrates

ZAGROS MTS.

AN NAFŪD

Mecca

Riyadh

Persian Gulf

TIEN SHAN

TAKLA MAKAN

HINDU KUSH

Kabul

KUNL

Rawalpindi

Indus

PLA

DELHI

AR RUB' AL KHĀLĪ

Muscat

KARACHI

DANAKIL

Aden

Gulf of Aden

Berbera

Arabian Sea

BOMBAY

Nāgpur

WESTERN GHATS

EASTERN GHATS

MADRAS

Calicut

CEYLON

Colombo

INDIAN OCEAN

Scale 1:24,000,000; one inch to 380 miles. Lambert Azimuthal Equal-Area Projection

Legend:

- Urban
- Cropland
- Cropland & Woodland
- Cropland & Grazing Land
- Grassland, Grazing Land
- Forest, Woodland
- Swamp, Marshland
- Tundra
- Shrub, Sparse Grass, Wasteland (pattern)
- Barren Land
- • Oasis

A-568600-96 -1-1-2P
COPYRIGHT BY
RAND MCNALLY & COMPANY
MADE IN U.S.A.

ALTAI
MTS.

GOBI (DESERT)

GREATER KHINGAN MTS

Har'hpin

Vladivostok

Sea
of
Japan

HONSHŪ

TOKYO

Ulaan Baatar

MUKDEN

SEOUL

KYŪSHŪ

Tihua

PEKING

Yellow
Sea

PACIFIC

OCEAN

Hwang Ho

Chengchou

SHANGHAI

East
China
Sea

OUNTAINS

WUHAN

TIBET

CHUNGKING

T'aipei

Tropic of Cancer

Mekong

FORMOSA

HIMALAYAS

K'unming

CANTON

Brahmaputra

Philippine

Sea

Ganges

CALCUTTA

Hanoi

HAINAN TAO

Mandalay

MANILA

Salween

Cebu

Mekong

South

China

MINDANAO

Bay   of

Rangoon

Sea

Bengal

BANGKOK

SAIGON

Andaman

Gulf

Celebes

Kota Kinabalu

Sea

Manado

of

Sea

Siam

Medan

Kuching

SINGAPORE

BORNEO

CELEBES

SUMATRA

Udjung Pandang

Equator

Java   Sea

DJAKARTA

JAVA

0   100 200   400   600   800 Miles

0 150 300   600   900   1200 Kilometers

90°   100°   110°   120°

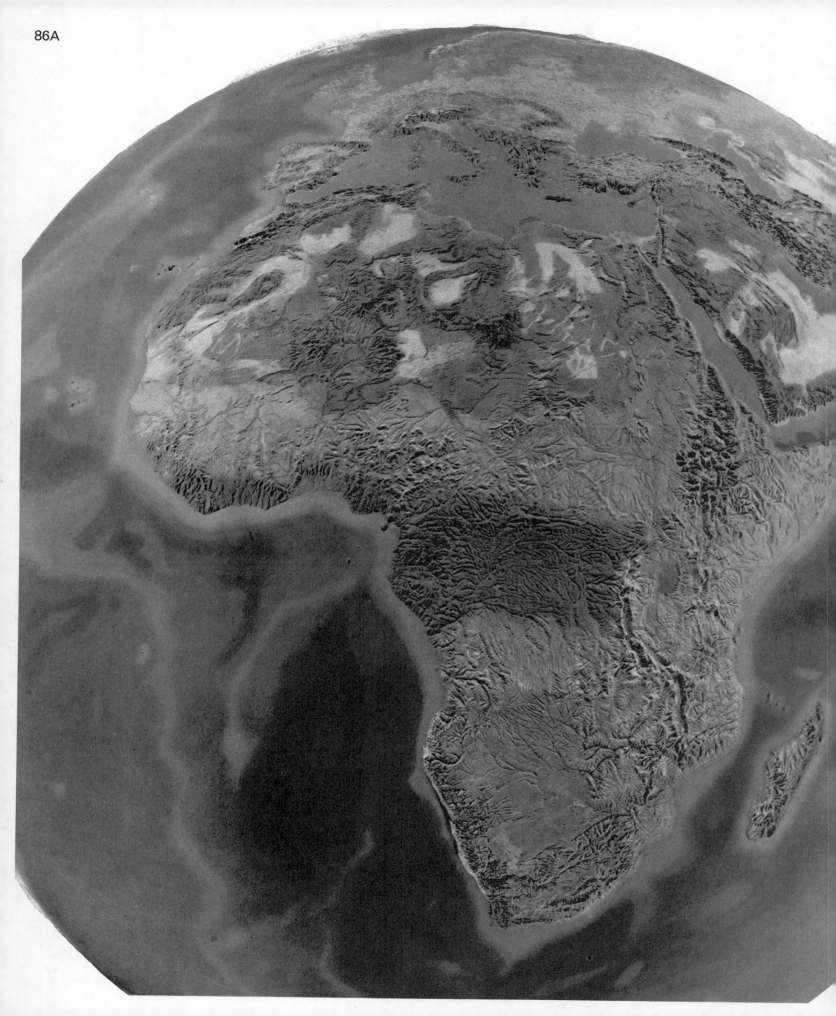

For centuries most of Africa's 11,500,000 square miles was unknown to outsiders. Access by one available avenue, the Nile, was impeded by the cataracts above Aswan. Since much of the interior is upland or plateau, usually dropping off rather sharply near the coasts, most of Africa's great rivers have rapids or falls close to the seaboard and so have not provided convenient routes to the interior. Moreover, the coastline is very regular, with few of the natural harbors of the other continents.

Once penetrated, much of the interior proved inhospitable to man. In the north, the world's largest desert, the immense expanse of the Sahara, blocks Africa's north rim from the central and southern portions. Near the other end of Africa, the Kalahari Desert helps separate the pleasant southernmost portion from the rest of the continent. In the center, the vast Congo Basin, humid, thinly settled, and unattractive, runs from the Atlantic seaboard east to the foot of the rugged highlands of East Africa, marked by the Rift Valley, which can be identified by the string of elongated lakes.

Africa's most important internal boundary is the Sahara. North of it the Mediterranean coastal countries are Moslem in tradition and have had close connections with Europe and the Near East. South of the Sahara are the many rich and varied cultures of Negroid tribal Africa. Unlike in many ways though they are, Mediterranean and Black Africa have until recently shared a common history of domination by non-African colonial powers. As late as 1945 there were only four independent nations in the entire continent. Now, spurred by the forces of nationalism, one new nation after another has emerged.

Past developments in communications, transport, education, and agricultural and industrial techniques, though limited, have formed a legacy from the old colonial powers on which the new African nations can build. Resources of iron ore, gold, oil, copper, timber, and a host of other vital raw materials are available. And there are many areas where climate and soil conditions are conducive to commercial agriculture, particularly for peanuts and cacao.

LONDON

BERLIN

PARIS

ALPS

Athens

CRETE

Mediterranean Sea

Alexandria

CAIRO

Red Sea

ARABIAN DESERT

Nile

Lake Nasser

NUBIAN DESERT

Nile

ROME

SICILY

MALTA

Banghazi

LIBYAN DESERT

CORSICA

SARDINIA

Tripoli

Tunis

ISLAS BALEAR

M

Algiers

MADRID

PYRENEES

ATLAS

MOUNTAINS

Casablanca

GRAND ERG OCCIDENTAL

GRAND ERG ORIENTAL

AHAGGAR

A

H

A

G

G

A

R

TIBESTI

ENNEDI

Al-Fashir

D

U

Lake Chad

Ndjamena

Kano

Tamanrasset

S

ADRAR
DES IFORAS

S

S

Niger

Yaoundé

CANARY ISLANDS

Aaiun

EL DJOUF

Tombouctou

Niger

Lagos

Gulf of Guinea

ATLANTIC OCEAN

Tropic of Cancer

Bamako

Lake Volta

Abidjan

ATLANTIC OCEAN

Dakar

CAPE VERDE
ISLANDS

Freetown

Scale 1:24,000,000; one inch to 380 miles. Lambert Azimuthal Equal-Area Projection

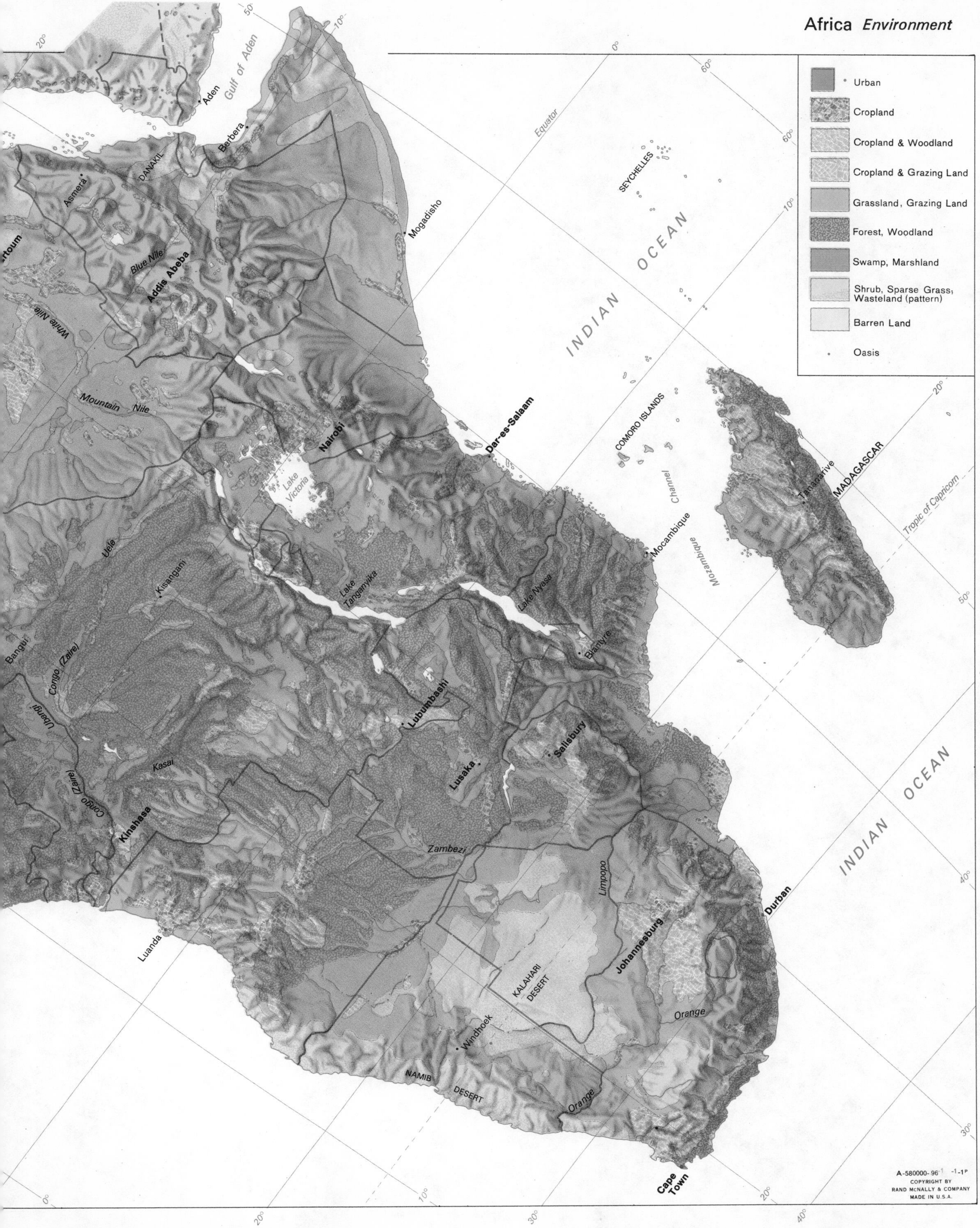

Gulf of Aden

Aden

DANAKIL

Berbera

Asmera

Blue Nile

Addis Abeba

White Nile

Mountain Nile

Uele

Kisangani

Ubangi

Bangui

Congo (Zaire)

Kasai

Congo (Zaire)

Kinshasa

Luanda

NAMIB DESERT

Lake Victoria

Nairobi

Lake Tanganyika

Lake Nyasa

Dar-es-Salaam

Mogadisho

INDIAN OCEAN

SEYCHELLES

Equator

COMORO ISLANDS

Mozambique Channel

Moçambique

MADAGASCAR

Tananarive

Tropic of Capricorn

Blantyre

Lubumbashi

Salisbury

Lusaka

Zambezi

Limpopo

Johannesburg

Orange

Durban

INDIAN OCEAN

KALAHARI DESERT

Windhoek

Orange

Cape Town

	• Urban
	Cropland
	Cropland & Woodland
	Cropland & Grazing Land
	Grassland, Grazing Land
	Forest, Woodland
	Swamp, Marshland
	Shrub, Sparse Grass, Wasteland (pattern)
	Barren Land
	• Oasis

0   100   200   400   600   800 Miles

0   150   300   600   900   1200 Kilometers

AUSTRALIA AND OCEANIA

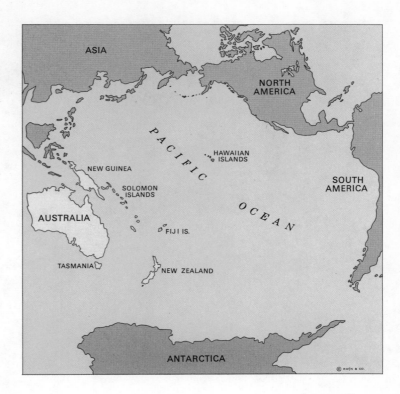

This region of the world is composed of the island continent of Australia, the substantial islands of New Zealand and New Guinea, clusters of smaller islands, and the many pinpoint atolls scattered throughout the expanse of the central and southern Pacific. Extreme isolation and their island nature are common characteristics held by these realms, but other similarities are few.

Australia's size compares with that of the forty-eight conterminous United States. Dry air masses sweep across the western interior from the west, creating the largest desert outside of the Sahara. Along the eastern coast higher temperatures and humidity have combined to produce climates conducive to a varied agricultural system, and therefore, the population is concentrated along this favorable coastal strip. The mountains of the east tend to isolate the population in a number of distinct clusters. Sydney, Melbourne, Brisbane, and Adelaide are the four principal centers, acting as chief exporters of the wool and wheat, and the importers, manufacturers, and distributors for the continent.

New Zealand, like Australia, is an enclave of a European settlement in the Pacific. Upon the vegetation of this climatically mild area the descendants of European settlers have established a thriving economy based upon the exportation of butter, beef, and mutton. The mountainous spine running the length of New Zealand provides some magnificent scenery and the gamut of climatic types.

New Guinea is closely related to both Indonesia and Melanesia, and so links Southeast Asia with Oceania. Although much larger, it typifies the larger islands of the Southwestern Pacific. Like New Guinea, these islands have a mountainous core and narrow, alluvial coastal plains. Upon the plains, under tropical heat and humidity, a variety of tropical agricultural products are raised and some of the islands, such as Fiji, have well developed commercial economies.

Unlike New Guinea and the larger islands are the speck-like atolls scattered throughout the central and southern Pacific. These South Sea Islands are famed for isolation, mild climate, and scenic beauty. But their size, limited resources, and small population, keep their economies at a subsistence level.

SUMATRA
BORNEO
CELEBES
SERAM
Djajap
Palembang
Bandjarmasin
Java   Sea
Udjung Pandang
DJAKARTA
Surabaja
Arafura   Sea
JAVA
SUMBA
TIMOR
Timor
Sea
Darwin
CAPE
YORK
Gulf   of
PENINSL
Carpentaria

I N D I A N   O C E A N

KIMBERLEY
PLATEAU
Broome
Fitzroy
Daly
Victoria

Mount Isa

GREAT SANDY DESERT

Alice Springs

GIBSON DESERT
SIMPSON
DESERT
GREAT
ARTESIAN
BASIN

Tropic   of   Capricorn
Carnarvon

GREAT VICTORIA DESERT
Lake
Eyre

Kalgoorlie
NULLARBOR PLAIN
Lake
Gairdner
FLINDERS RANGES
Broken
Hill
Murray

DARLING RA.
Great Australian Bight

Perth
Adelaide

I N D I A N   O C E A N

Legend

■	• Urban
(pattern)	Cropland
(pattern)	Cropland & Woodland
(pattern)	Cropland & Grazing Land
■	Grassland, Grazing Land
■	Forest, Woodland
■	Swamp, Marshland
(pattern)	Shrub, Sparse Grass, Wasteland (pattern)
■	Barren Land

Scale 1:24,000,000; one inch to 380 miles. Lambert Azimuthal Equal-Area Projection

NEW
GUINEA

NEW BRITAIN

t Moresby

SOLOMON ISLANDS

Coral   Sea

Cairns

Townsville

NEW
HEBRIDES

NEW
CALEDONIA

ÎLES
LOYAUTÉ

Nouméa

Rockhampton

GREAT
DIVIDING
RANGE

Brisbane

SYDNEY

Canberra

GREAT DIVIDING RANGE

MELBOURNE

Tasman   Sea

TASMANIA

Hobart

Equator

GILBERT
ISLANDS

P A C I F I C   O C E A N

SAMOA ISLANDS

Pago Pago

FIJI
ISLANDS

Suva

TONGA ISLANDS

Auckland
NORTH ISLAND

SOUTHERN ALPS

Wellington

Christchurch

SOUTH ISLAND

STEWART
ISLAND

Dunedin

P A C I F I C   O C E A N

150°   160°   170°   180°   170°   160°

0°

10°

20°

30°

40°

0   100   200   400   600   800 Miles
0   150   300   600   900   1200 Kilometers

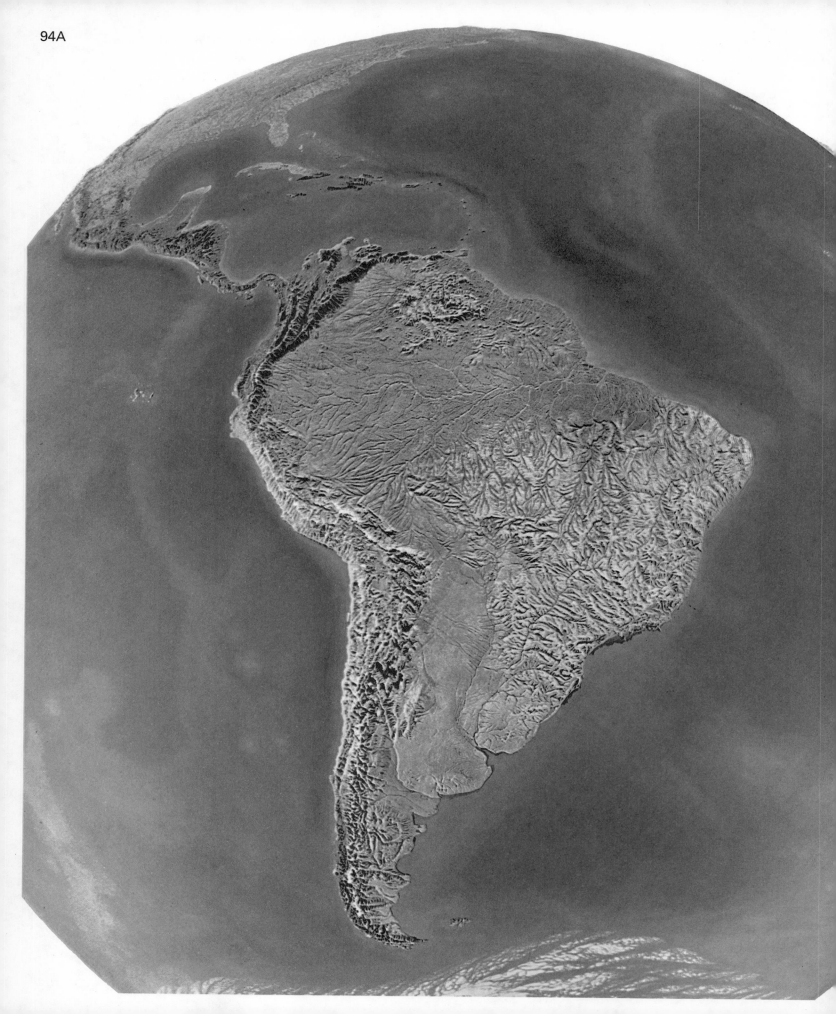

SOUTH AMERICA

Triangularly shaped South America is surrounded by water except at the narrow Isthmus of Panama. No great peninsulas extend into its seas or oceans, and its outlines are more regular than those of most other continents.

The Andes Mountains rise like a wall along the western shores, and this formidable chain runs the entire length of the continent, rising to altitudes of over 20,000 feet. It is the longest continuous mountain chain in the world.

The bulk of the continent slopes eastward from the eastern face of the Andes. From north to south, landforms include plains drained by the Orinoco and the eroded plateau areas of the Guiana and Brazilian highlands, the tropical lowlands of the Amazon Basin, savanna called the Gran Chaco, which is drained by the Paraná-Paraguay-Plata river systems, the pampas, and the plains of Patagonia.

The shape of the continent, its position astride the Equator, the water surrounding it, and the mountainous terrain have resulted in a variety of climates. The area east of the Andes from Venezuela to Northern Argentina, is dominated by moisture-laden air masses of the Atlantic. This two-thirds of the continent has a tropical or subtropical environment. Most of the remaining portion is under the influence of the relatively dry, cool Pacific air masses, which create the driest region in the world —the Atacama Desert of Chile. These cool Pacific air masses, too, on crossing the Andes in the narrow southern portion of the continent, create the Patagonian Desert of Argentina. In the higher altitudes of the mountain chain climates familiar to mid and upper latitudes are found.

Much of the interior of South America is still inaccessible, owing to extensive regions of mountains or jungle. Most of the settlement has been around the periphery of the continent. Spanish and Portuguese settlers, and later Germans and Italians, have developed highly specialized commercial economies in certain of the peripheral areas. Around Buenos Aires, São Paulo, Santiago, Bogotá economies based on agricultural products have been developed— wheat, beef, coffee, citrus fruit to name a few. Exported minerals—oil from Venezuela, tin from Bolivia, and copper from Chile— are economic mainstays of other countries.

ATLANTIC

OCEAN

Tropic of Cancer

Equator

Havana

CUBA

BAHAMAS

HISPANIOLA

Kingston

JAMAICA

San Juan

PUERTO
RICO

Caribbean Sea

Panama

Barranquilla

Maracaibo

CARACAS

Port of Spain
TRINIDAD

Georgetown

BOGOTÁ

Quito

Orinoco

Negro

Amazon

Manaus

Belém

Iquitos

Rio Branco

SELVAS

LLANOS

ANDES

LIMA

La Paz

Fortaleza

Recife

São Francisco

Salvador

Brasília

Cuiabá

MATO

GROSSO

Scale 1:24,000,000; one inch to 380 miles. Lambert Azimuthal Equal-Area Projection

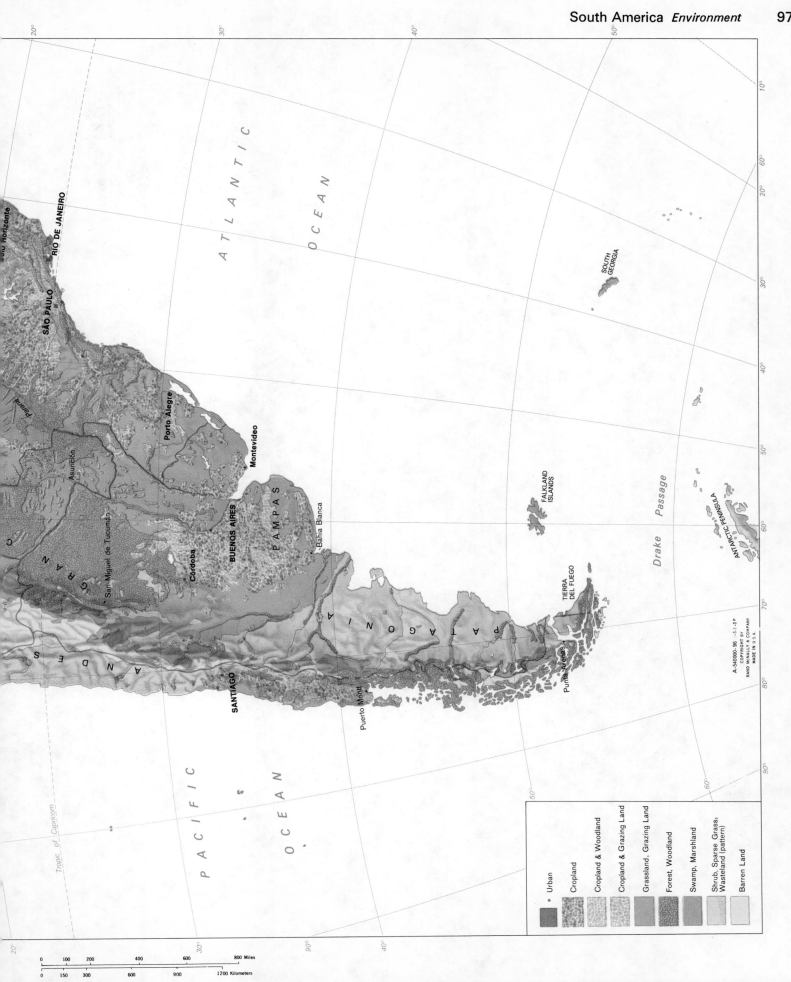

ATLANTIC

OCEAN

SÃO PAULO

RIO DE JANEIRO

Belo Horizonte

Porto Alegre

Montevideo

Asunción

P A M P A S

BUENOS AIRES

Bahía Blanca

San Miguel de Tucumán

Córdoba

G R A N

A N D E S

P A T A G O N I A

SANTIAGO

Puerto Montt

Punta Arenas

TIERRA DEL FUEGO

PACIFIC

OCEAN

Tropic of Capricorn

SOUTH GEORGIA

FALKLAND ISLANDS

Drake Passage

ANTARCTIC PENINSULA

A-540000-96 -1-1-1P
COPYRIGHT BY
RAND McNALLY & COMPANY
MADE IN U.S.A.

- Urban
- Cropland
- Cropland & Woodland
- Cropland & Grazing Land
- Grassland, Grazing Land
- Forest, Woodland
- Swamp, Marshland
- Shrub, Sparse Grass, Wasteland (pattern)
- Barren Land

0   100   200   400   600   800 Miles
0   150   300   600   900   1200 Kilometers

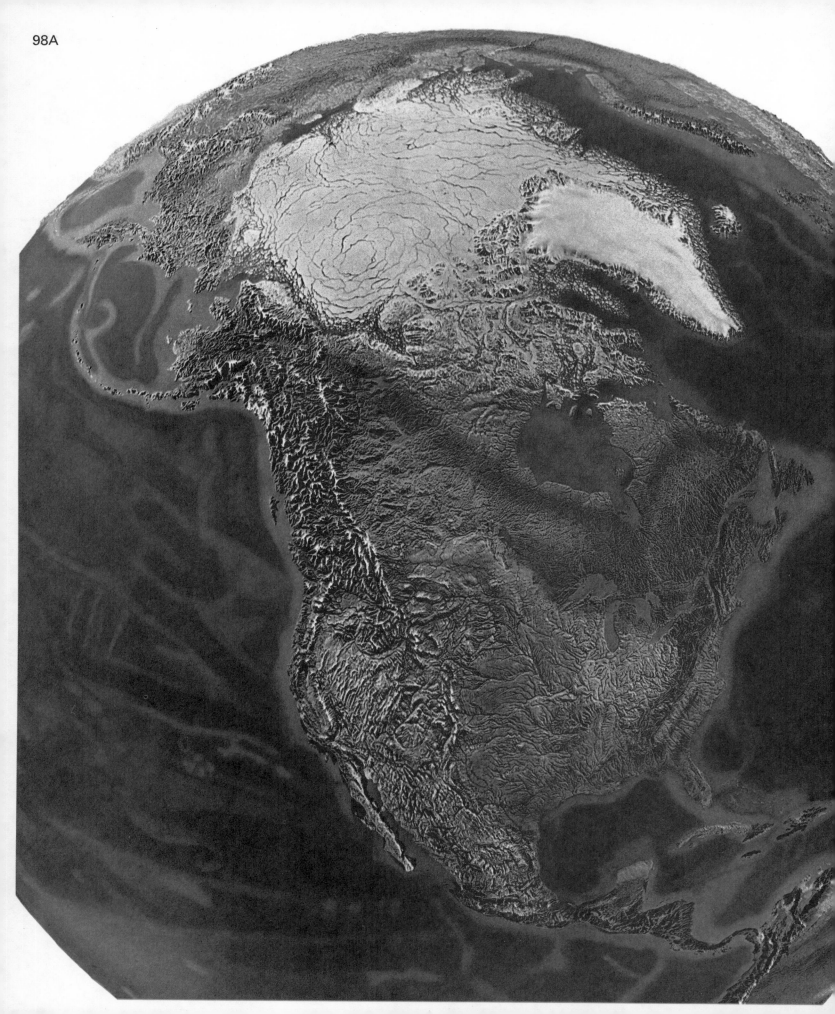

NORTH AMERICA

Physically the North American continent extends from the ice-covered Arctic Ocean in the north to the tropical Isthmus of Panama in the south. North America, like Africa and South America, tapers from north to south. Canada, the United States, and Mexico occupy over 85 per cent of its total area of nearly 9,500,000 square miles. Central America, the West Indies, and Greenland make up the remainder.

Within this vast area, differences, rather than similarities, abound. All major types of climate can be found in North America ranging from the cold, perpetual ice cap of Greenland to the hot, moist tropical rain forests of Central America. Landforms vary from the towering chain of the Rocky Mountains, through the high plateau of Mexico, the relatively low Appalachian Highland, the featureless expanses of the Arctic tundra, the regularity of the Great Plains, and the fertile fields of the interior lowlands and coastal plains. Soils, vegetation, temperature, precipitation—all reflect the differences that can be expected over such an area.

Similarly, the development of agriculture and industry has varied considerably over the North American continent. Modern methods and the extensive use of machinery characterize agriculture in the flat to gently rolling areas of Midwestern United States and the Prairie Provinces of Canada. Stockgrazing is prevalent in the more arid areas of the continent. Agriculture in Middle America is characterized by the extensive use of hand labor. Here subtropical crops are important, for instance, bananas in Central America and sugar cane in the West Indies.

Early settlement, access to raw materials, a well developed transportation network, and a density of population providing both labor and markets have led to a heavy concentration of industrial development in the northeast quarter of the United States and the southeastern rim of Canada. Other industrial development has taken place in scattered locations in southern and western United States and in the largest cities of Middle America.

GREENLAND

Arctic Circle

Godthab

Labrador Sea

Baffin Bay

BAFFIN ISLAND

ELLESMERE ISLAND

DEVON ISLAND

UNGAVA PENINSULA

A R C T I C   O C E A N

North Pole

MELVILLE ISLAND

VICTORIA ISLAND

BANKS ISLAND

Cambridge Bay

Hudson Bay

Churchill

Beaufort Sea

Great Slave Lake

Winnipeg

Regina

Edmonton

Peace

BROOKS RANGE

Calgary

Fairbanks

R O C K Y   M O U N T A I N S

Bering Strait

Yukon

ALASKA RANGE

Nome

Anchorage

Juneau

Gulf of Alaska

Prince Rupert

British Columbia

Vancouver

Seattle

Portland

B e r i n g

S e a

P A C I F I C   O C E A N

A L E U T I A N   I S L A N D S

Scale 1:24,000,000; one inch to 380 miles. Lambert Azimuthal Equal-Area Projection

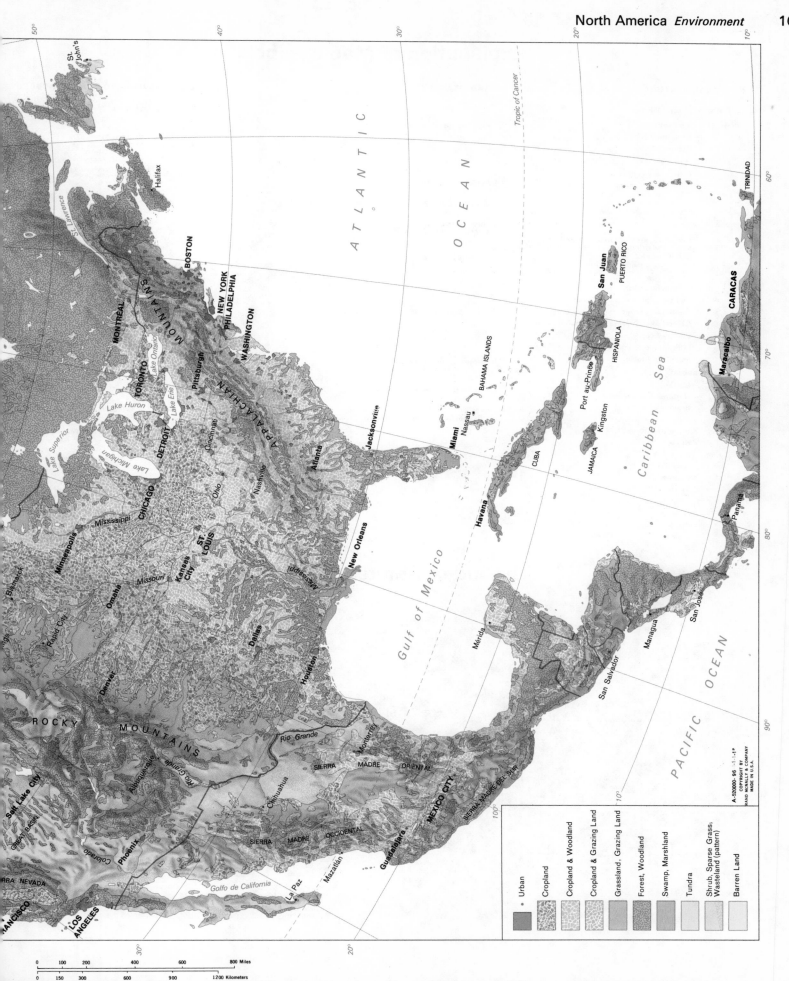

Legend:
- Urban
- Cropland
- Cropland & Woodland
- Cropland & Grazing Land
- Grassland, Grazing Land
- Forest, Woodland
- Swamp, Marshland
- Tundra
- Shrub, Sparse Grass, Wasteland (pattern)
- Barren Land

A-500000-96 -1-.1.-1P
COPYRIGHT BY
RAND McNALLY & COMPANY
MADE IN U.S.A.

0   100   200   400   600   800 Miles

0   150   300   450   600   750   900   1200 Kilometers

Explanation of Map Symbols

CULTURAL FEATURES

Political Boundaries

══════ International
────── Secondary (State, province, etc.)
────── County

Populated Places

Cities, towns, and villages

·•••●● Symbol size represents population of the place

Chicago
Gary
Racine
Glenview
Edgewood
Type size represents relative importance of the place

▨ Corporate area of large U.S. and Canadian cities and urban area of other foreign cities

▨ Major Urban Area
Area of continuous commercial, industrial, and residential development in and around a major city

○ Community within a city
⊛ Capital of major political unit
☆ Capital of secondary political unit
◉ Capital of U.S. state or Canadian province
⊙ County Seat
▲ Military Installation
⊙ Scientific Station

Miscellaneous

▨ National Park
▫ National Monument
▨ Provincial Park
▨ Indian Reservation
△ Point of Interest
∴ Ruins
■ ⌂ Buildings
▱ Race Track
------- Railroad
-+-+-+- Tunnel
────── Underground or Subway
⚱ Dam
Bridge
Dike

LAND FEATURES

Passes =
Point of Elevation above sea level + 8,520 FT.

WATER FEATURES

Coastlines and Shorelines →
Indefinite or Unsurveyed Coastlines and Shorelines →
Lakes and Reservoirs →
Canals →
Rivers and Streams →
Falls and Rapids →
Intermittent or Unsurveyed Rivers and Streams →
Directional Flow Arrow →
Rocks, Shoals and Reefs →

TYPE STYLES USED TO NAME FEATURES

A S I A — Continent
DENMARK / CANADA — Country, State, or Province
B É A R N — Region, Province, or Historical Region
C R O C K E T T — County
PANTELLERIA (ITALY) — Country of which unit is a dependency in parentheses
ANGOLA (PORT. WEST AFRICA) — Former or alternate name
Rome (Roma) — Local or alternate city name
Naval Air Station — Military Installation
MESA VERDE / SAN XAVIER — National Park or Monument, Provincial Park, Indian Res.,
UINTA DESERT — Major Terrain Features
MT. MORIAH — Individual Mountain
STROMBOLI / NUNIVAK — Island or Coastal Feature
Ocean / Lake / River / Canal — Hydrographic Features

Note: Size of type varies according to importance and available space. Letters for names of major features are spread across the extent of the feature.

The Index Reference System

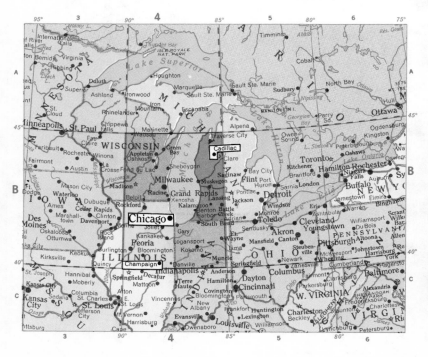

Place	Location	Pop.	Index Key	Page
Cacequi, Braz., 9,976			D2	30
Cacouna, Que., Can., 1,001			B8	42
Caddo, Okla., 886			C5	79
Cadillac, Mich., 9,990			B4	58
Cadiz, Ky., 1,987			D2	62
Cádiz, Sp., 134,342			D2	8
Cadyville, N.Y., 800			f11	75
Chambly, Que., Can., 11,469			D4	42
Chambly, co., Que., Can., 190,464			D4	42
Chambord, Que., Can., 1,106			A5	42
Champaign, Ill., 56,837			B4	58
Champaign, co., Ill., 163,281			C5	58
Champigny-sur-Marne, Fr., 70,419			g11	5
Champion, Ohio, 5,000			A5	78
Champlain, N.Y., 1,426			f11	75
Cheyenne, Wyo., 40,914			E8	89
Chiang Mai, Thai., 83,729			B1	19
Chiapas, state, Mex., 1,381,500			D6	34
Chiari, It., 9,000			B2	9
Chiautla de Tapia, Mex., 5,847			n14	34
Chiba, Jap., 482,133			I10, n19	18
Chiba, pref., Jap., 3,366,624			*I10	18
Chicago, Ill., 3,369,357 (*7,582,700)			B4	58
Chichester, Eng., 20,830			E6	4
Chichibu, Jap., 60,867			m18	18
Chickasaw, co., Iowa, 14,969			A5	60
Chiclana, Sp., 21,524			D2	8
Chiclayo, Peru, 148,932			C2	31

The indexing system used in this atlas is based upon the conventional pattern of parallels and meridians used to indicate latitude and longitude. The index samples beside the map indicate that the cities of *Chicago, Cadillac,* and *Champaign* are all located in B4. Each index key letter, *in this case "B,"* is placed between corresponding degree numbers of latitude in the vertical borders of the map. Each index key number, *in this case "4"* is placed between corresponding degree numbers of longitude in the horizontal borders of the map. Crossing of the parallels above and below the index letter with the meridians on each side of the index number forms a confining "box" in which the given place is certain to be located. It is important to note that location of the place may be anywhere in this confining "box."

Insets on many foreign maps are indexed independently of the main maps by separate index key letters and figures. All places indexed to these insets are identified by the lower case reference letter in the index key. A diamond-shaped symbol in the margin of the map is used to separate the insets from the main map and also to separate key letters and numbers where the spacing of the parallels and meridians is great.

Place-names are indexed to the location of the city symbol. Political divisions and physical features are indexed to the location of their names on the map.

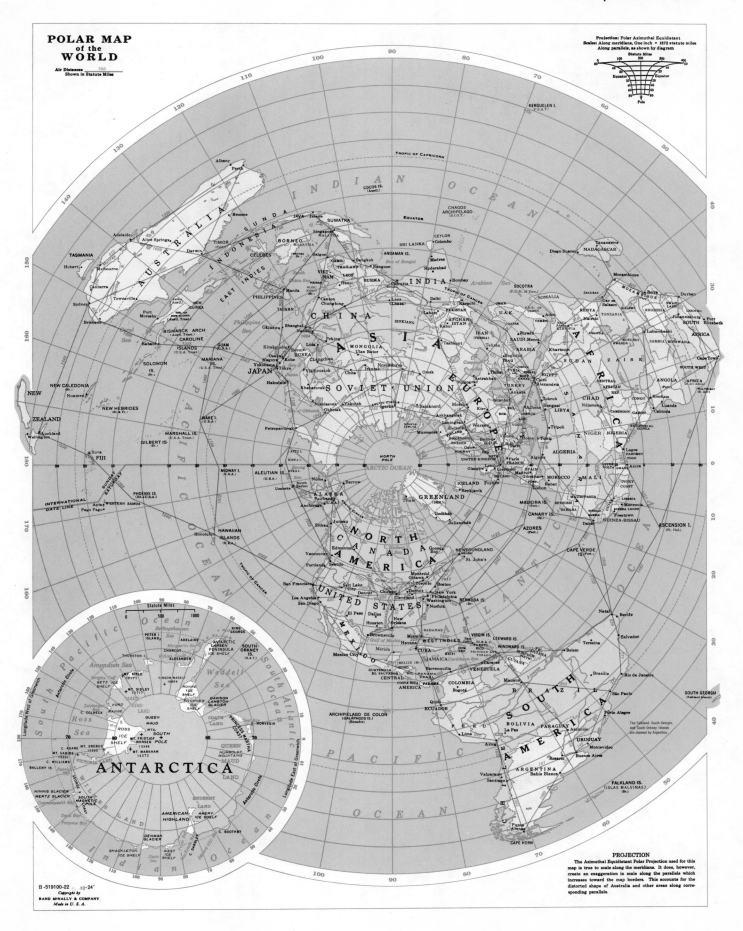

POLAR MAP of the WORLD

Air Distances
Shown in Statute Miles

Projection: Polar Azimuthal Equidistant
Scales: Along meridians, One inch = 1872 statute miles
Along parallels, as shown by diagram

PROJECTION

The Azimuthal Equidistant Polar Projection used for this map is true to scale along the meridians. It does, however, create an exaggeration in scale along the parallels which increases toward the map borders. This accounts for the distorted shape of Australia and other areas along corresponding parallels.

B-519100-22   10-24"
Copyright by
RAND McNALLY & COMPANY
Made in U.S.A.

The Falkland, South Georgia, and South Orkney Islands are claimed by Argentina.

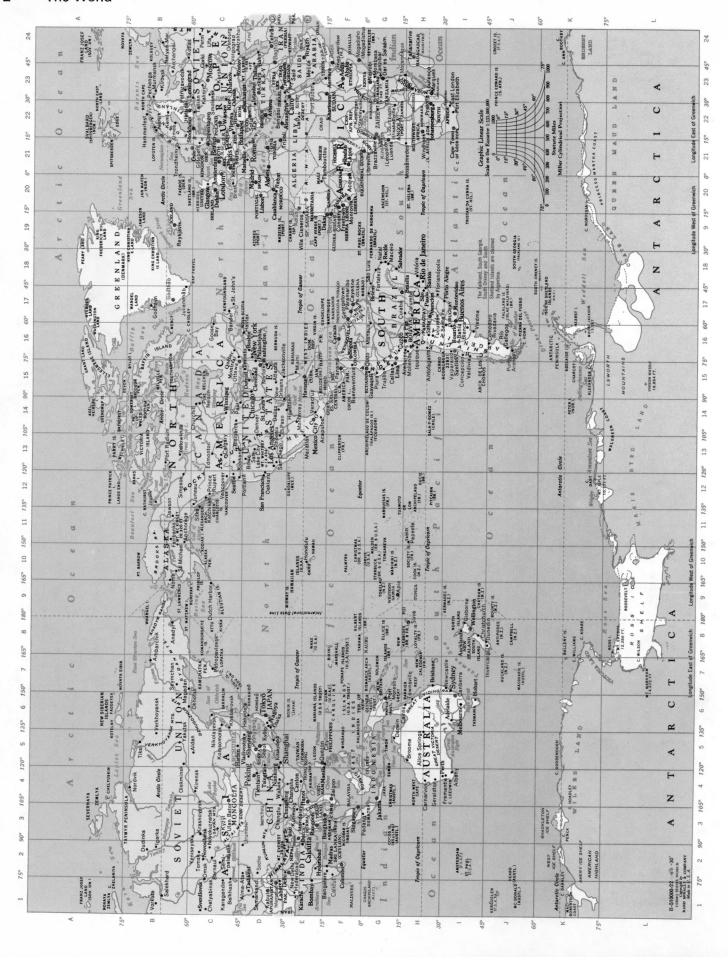

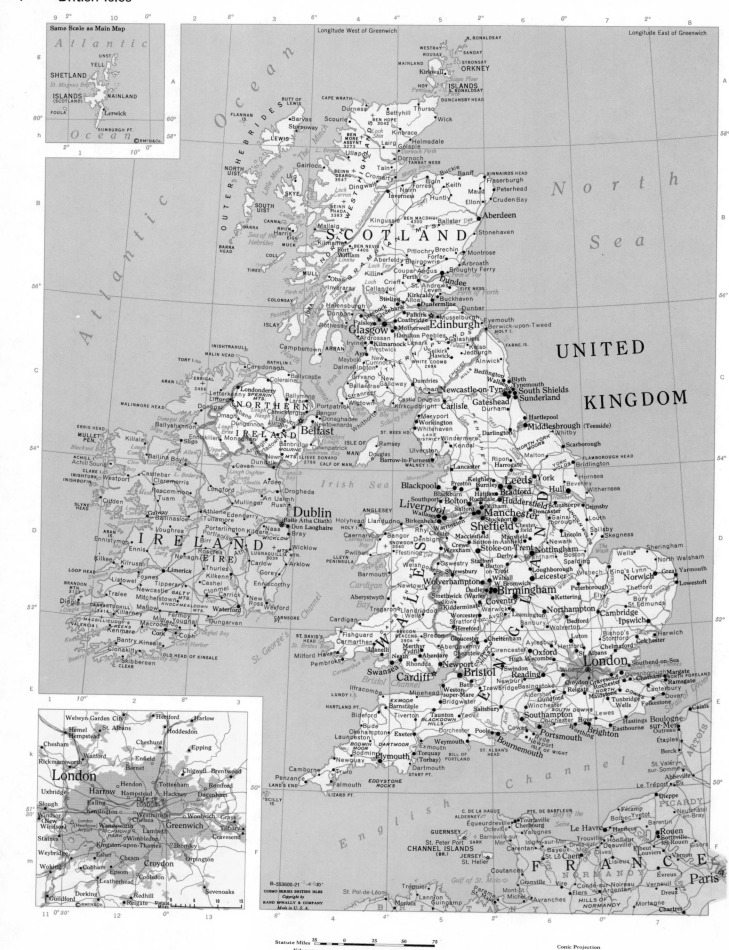

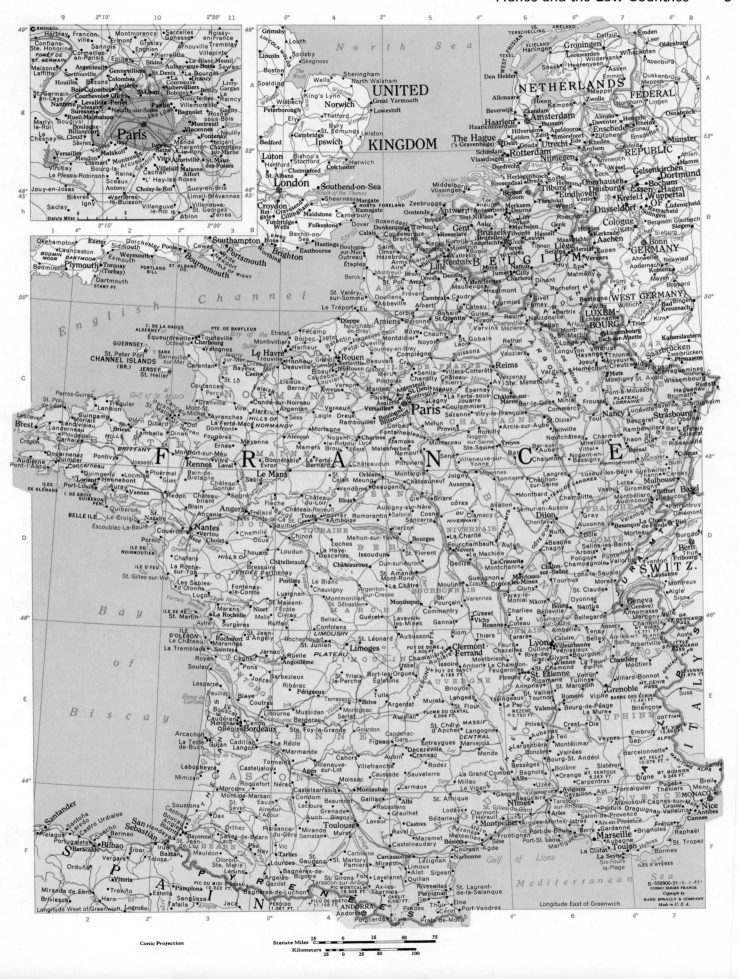

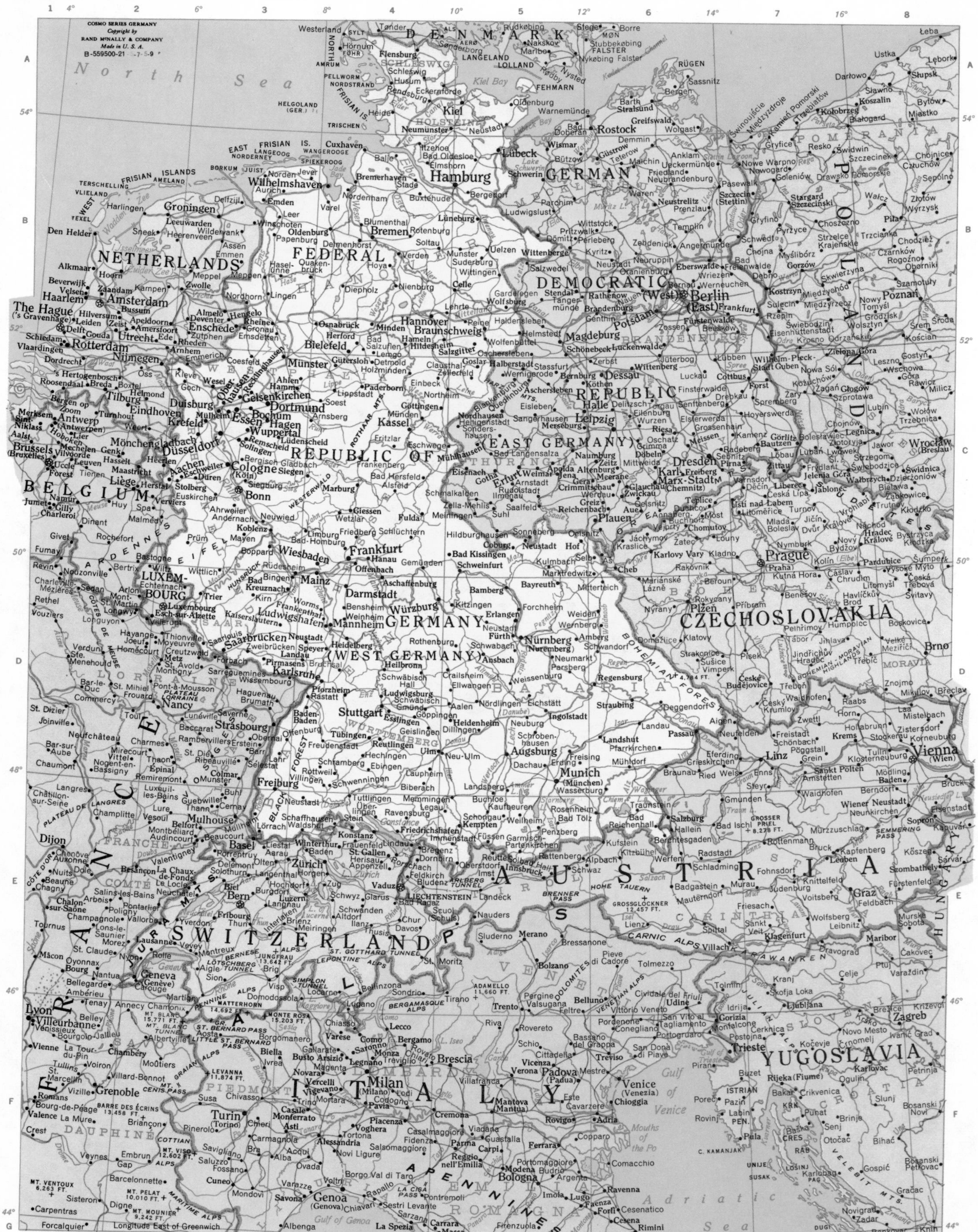

COSMO SERIES GERMANY
Copyright by
RAND McNALLY & COMPANY
Made in U.S.A.
B-559500-21 -7 5-9

North Sea

DENMARK

NETHERLANDS

FEDERAL REPUBLIC OF GERMANY (WEST GERMANY)

GERMAN DEMOCRATIC REPUBLIC (EAST GERMANY)

POLAND

BELGIUM

LUXEMBOURG

FRANCE

SWITZERLAND

LIECHTENSTEIN

AUSTRIA

CZECHOSLOVAKIA

ITALY

YUGOSLAVIA

HUNGARY

Adriatic Sea

Statute Miles   25   0   25   50   75
Kilometers   25   0   25   50   100

Conic Projection

Longitude East of Greenwich

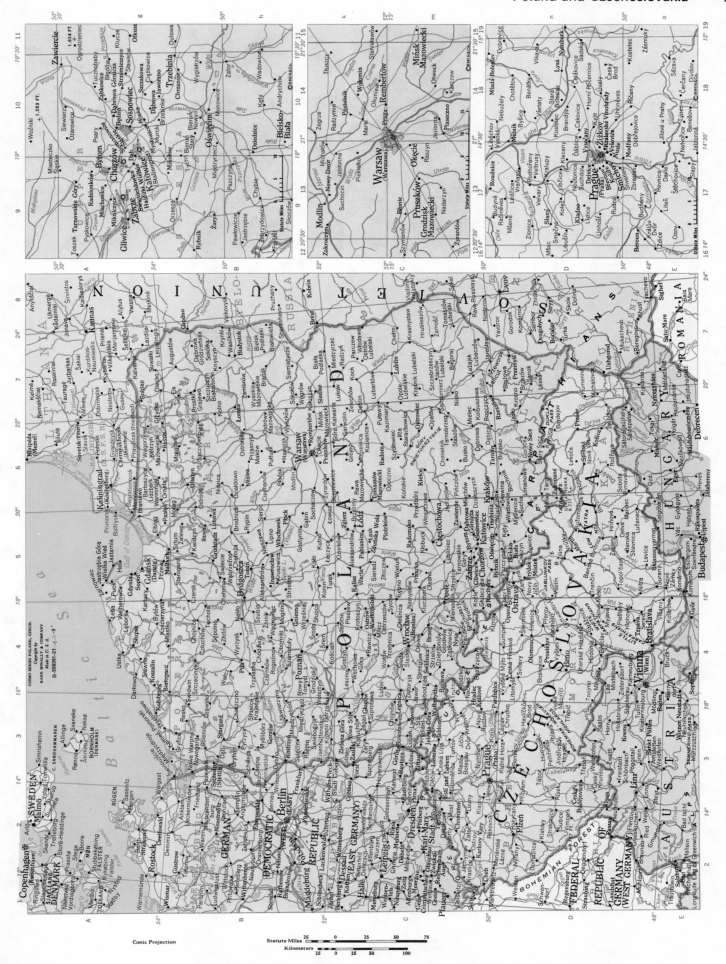

Conic Projection

Statute Miles 25 0 25 50 75

Kilometers 25 0 25 50 100

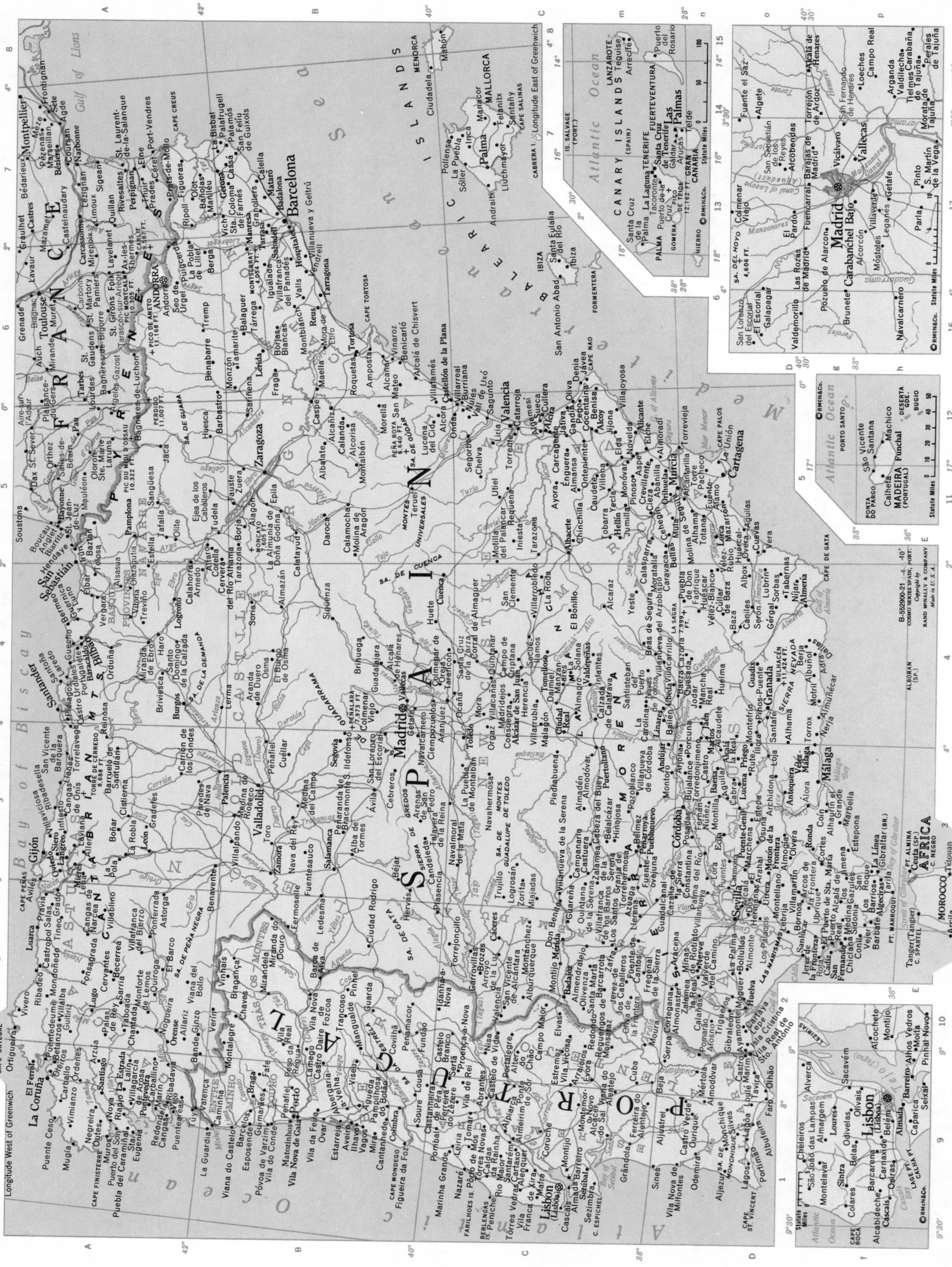

Longitude West of Greenwich

Longitude East of Greenwich

CANARY ISLANDS (SPAIN)

MADEIRA (PORTUGAL)

Madrid

Statute Miles   25   0   25   50   75

Kilometers   25   0   25   50   109

Conic Projection

COSMO SERIES SPAIN, PORT.
Copyright by
RAND McNALLY & COMPANY
Made in U.S.A.

Conic Projection

Statute Miles

Kilometers

Longitude East of Greenwich

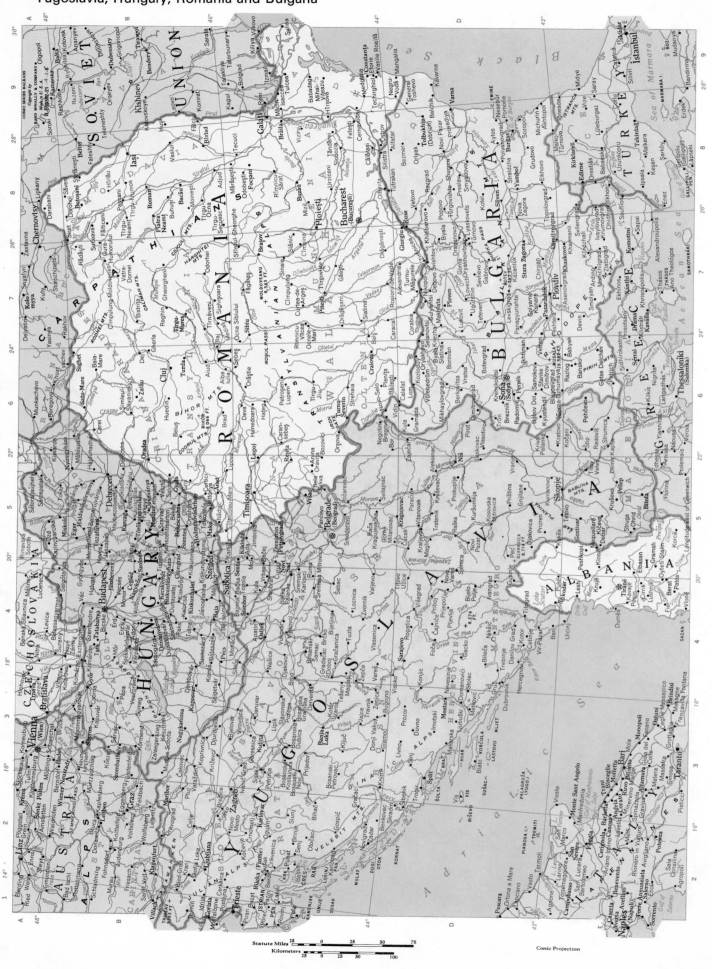

Statute Miles
Kilometers

Conic Projection

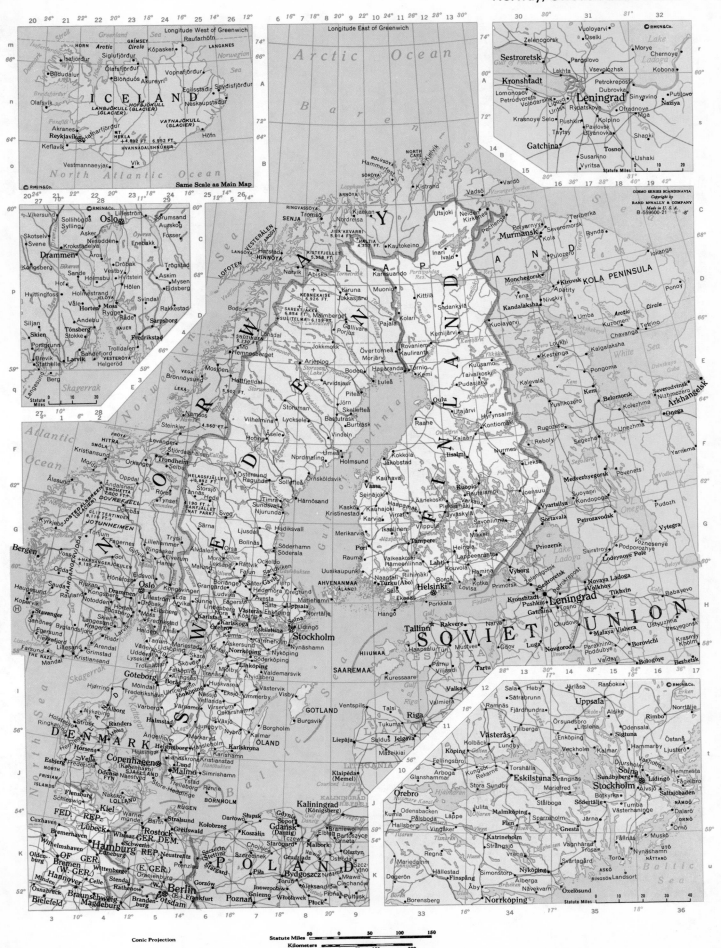

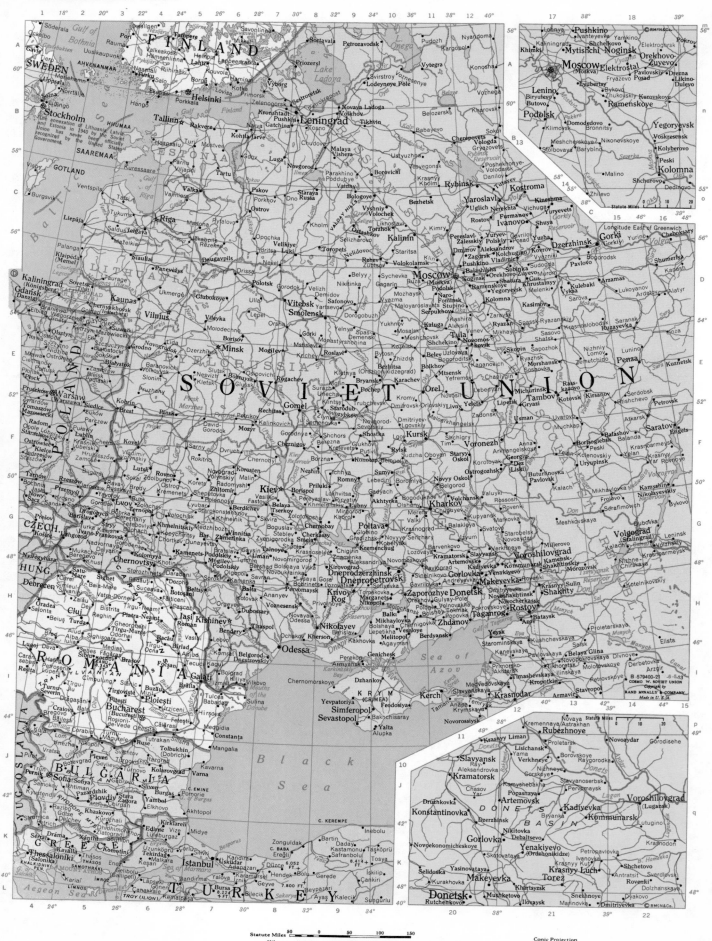

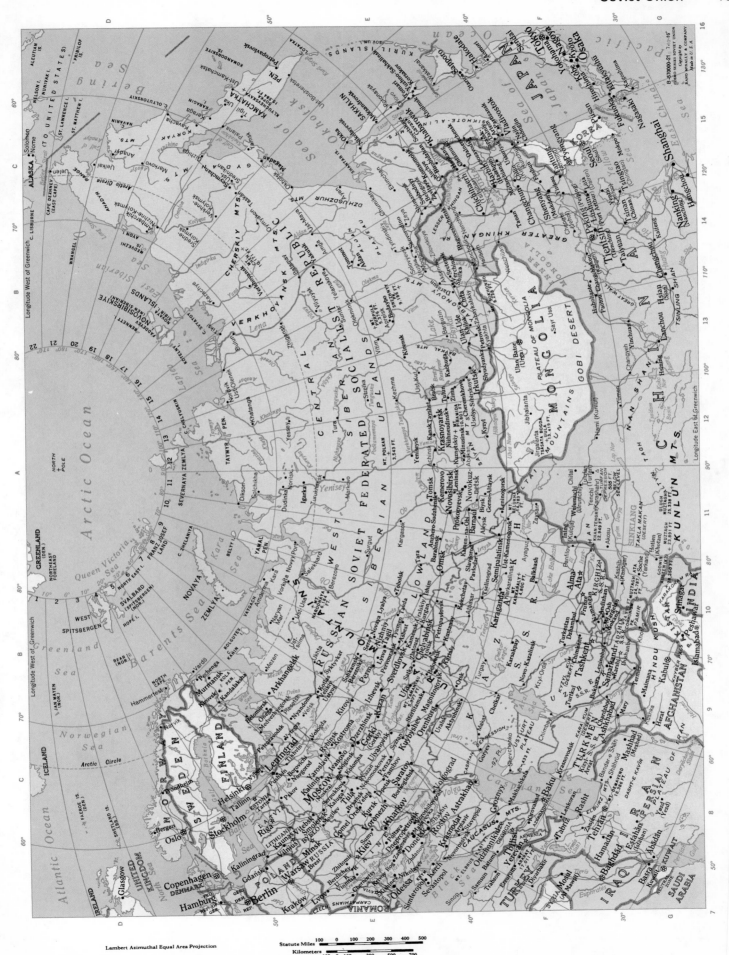

Lambert Azimuthal Equal Area Projection

Statute Miles   100 0 100 200 300 400 500

Kilometers   100 0 100 300 500 700

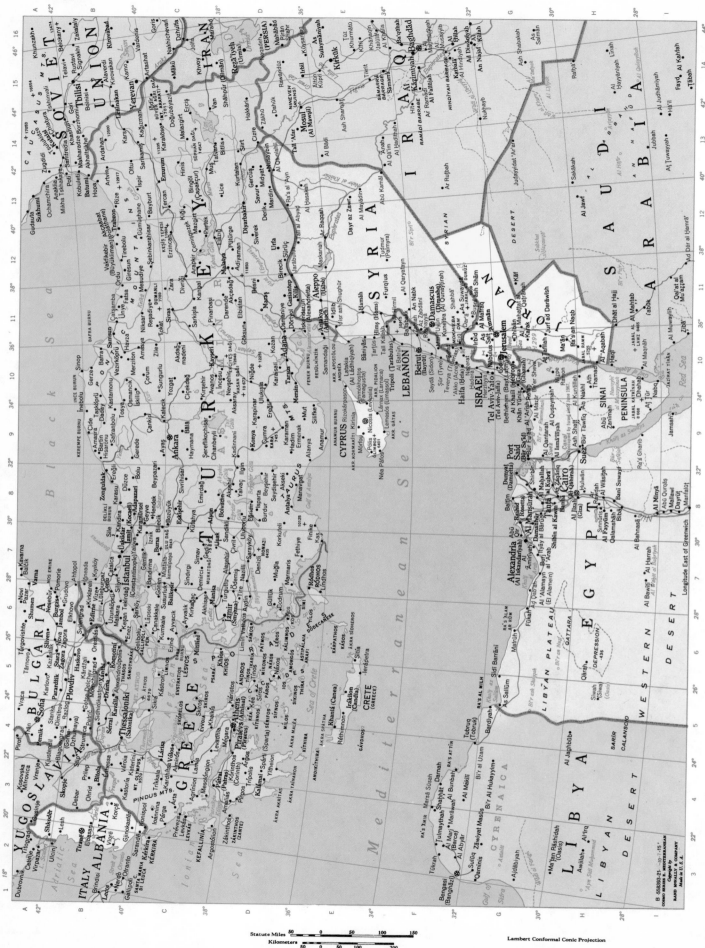

Statute Miles 50   0   50   100   150
Kilometers 50   0   50   100   200

Lambert Conformal Conic Projection

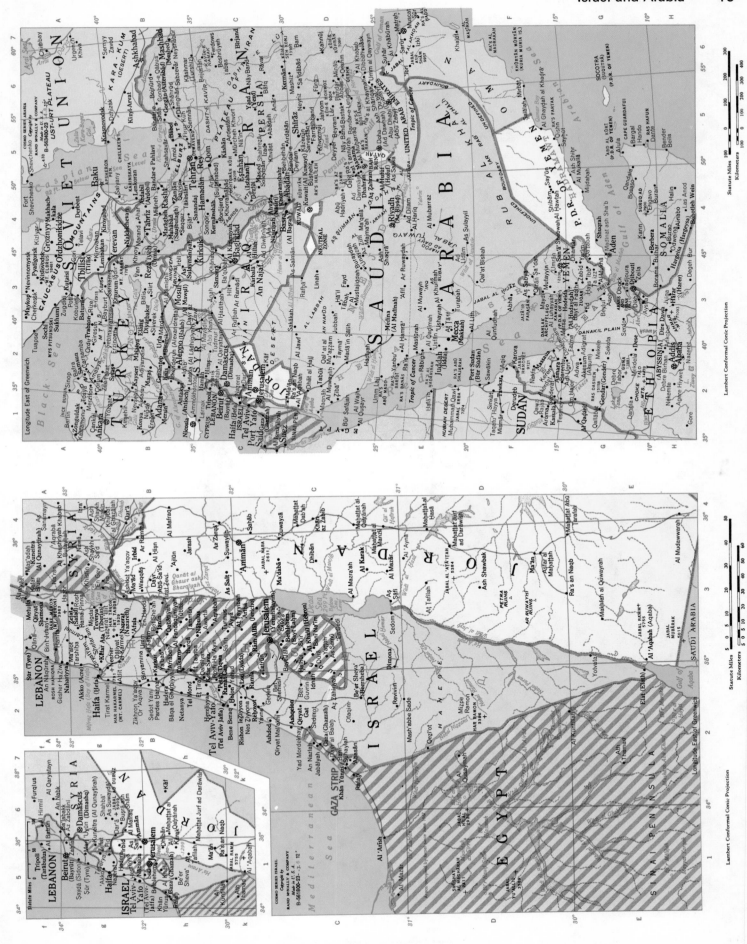

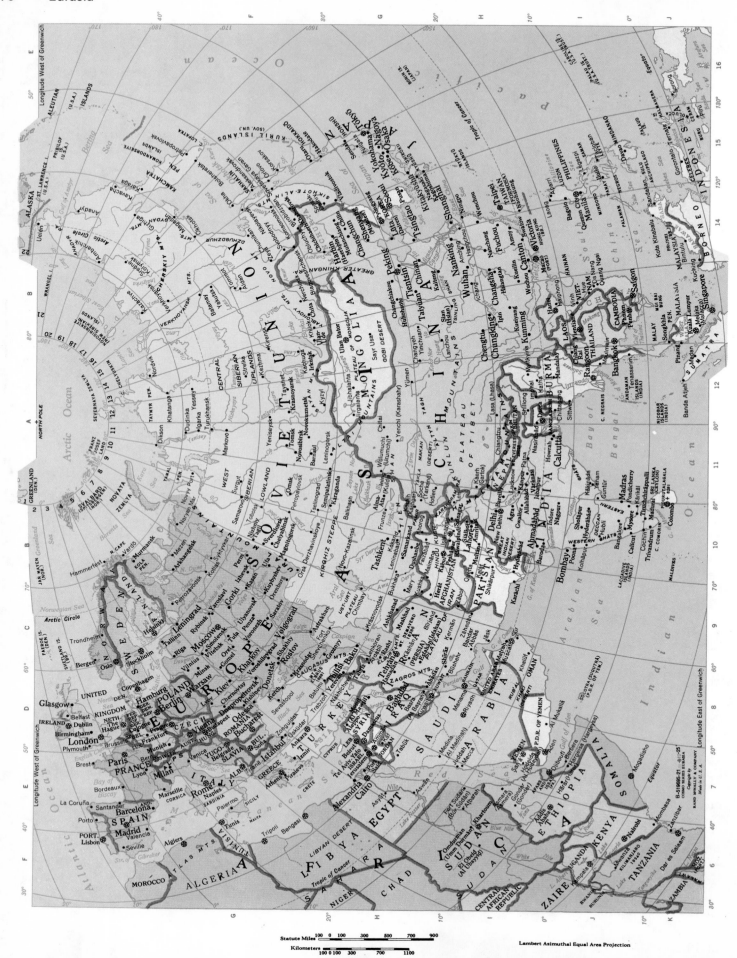

Statute Miles 100 0 100   300   500   700   900

Kilometers 100 0 100   300   700   1100

Lambert Azimuthal Equal Area Projection

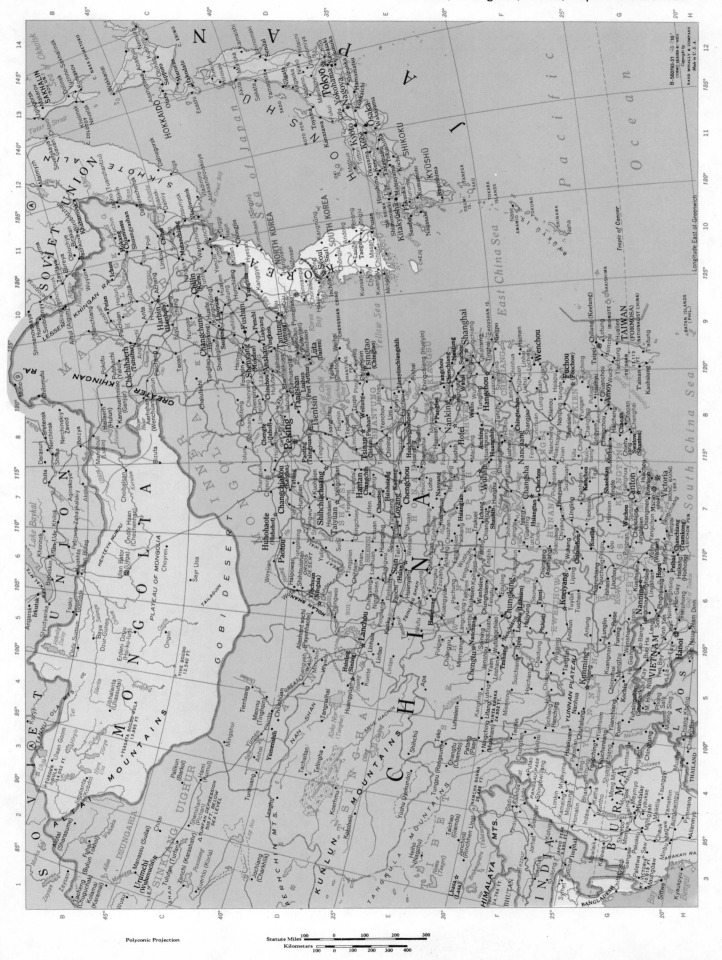

Polyconic Projection

Statute Miles

Kilometers

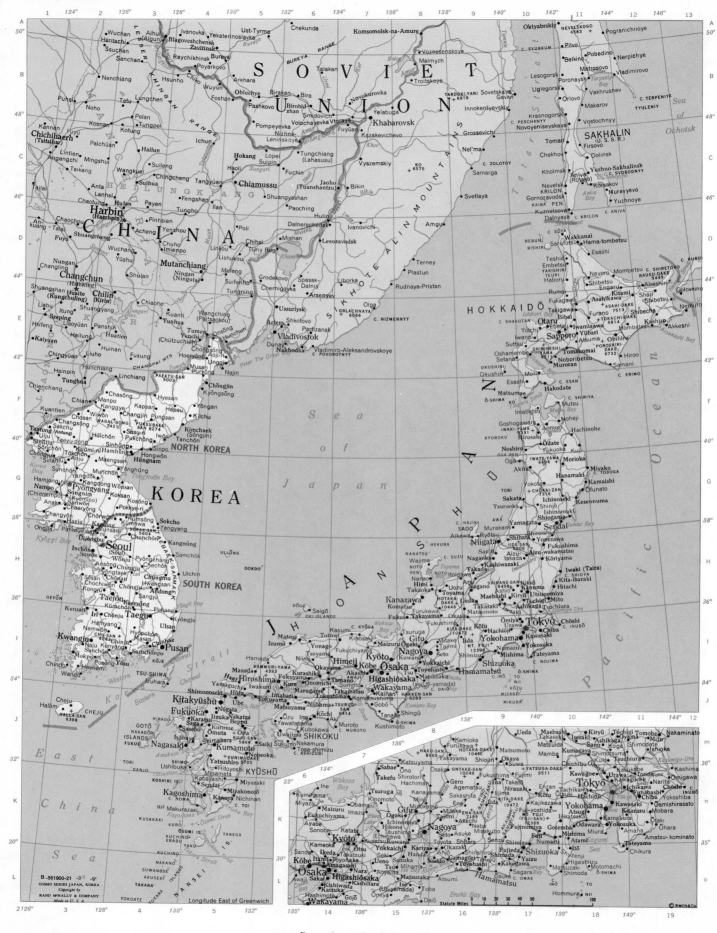

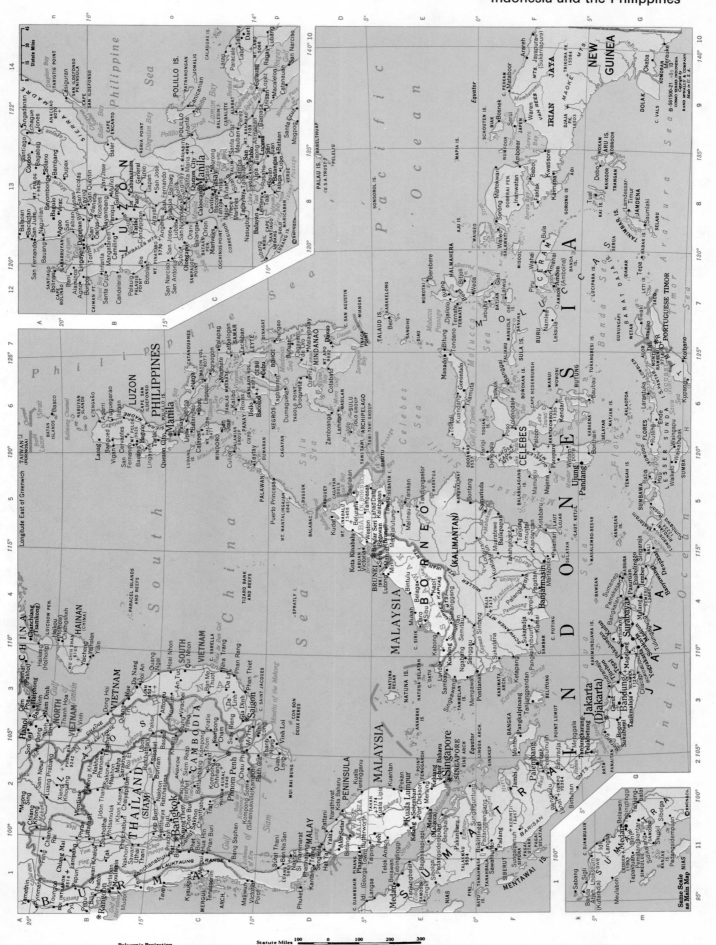

Polyconic Projection

Statute Miles 100   0   100   200   300

Kilometers 100   0   100   200   300   400

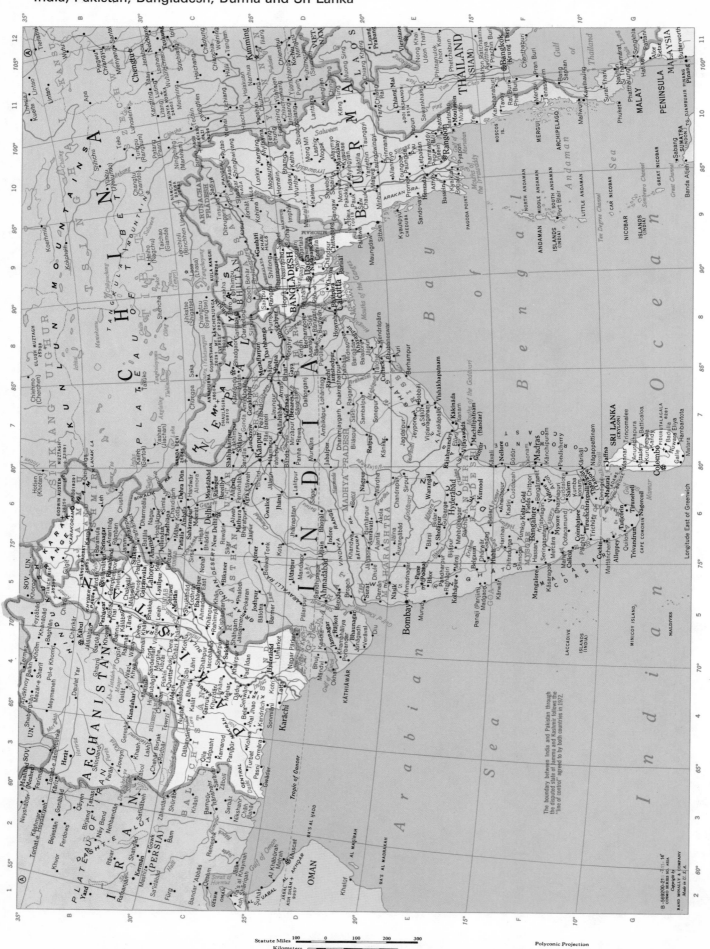

The boundary between India and Pakistan through
the disputed state of Jammu and Kashmir follows the
"line of control" agreed to by both countries in 1972.

Statute Miles 100   0   100   200   300

Kilometers

Polyconic Projection

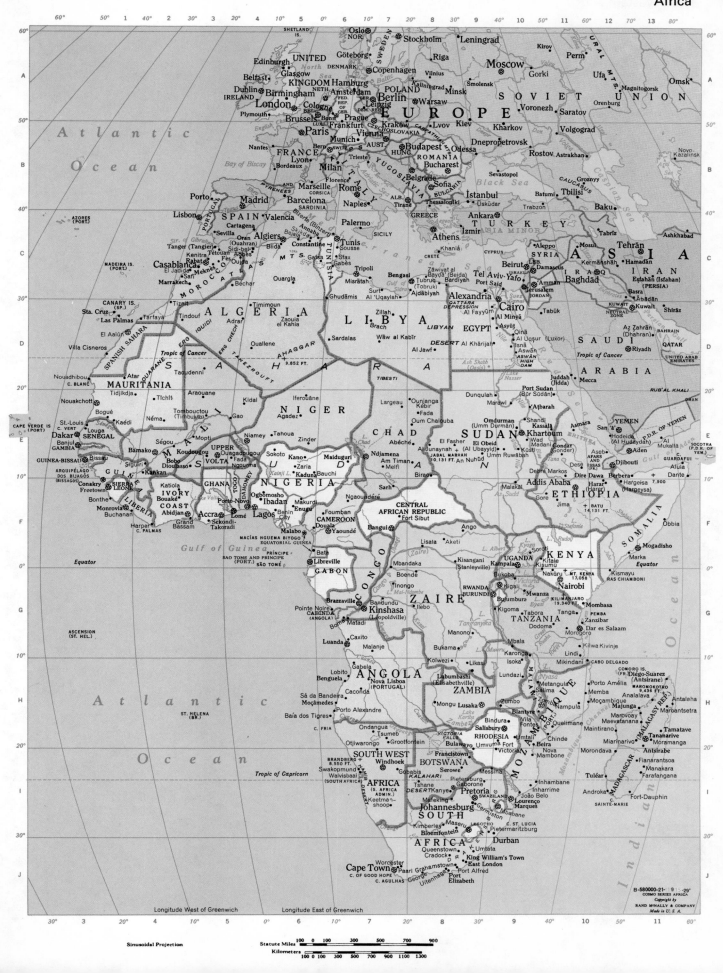

Sinusoidal Projection

Statute Miles
100 0 100   300   500   700   900

Kilometers
100 0 100 300 500 700 900 1100 1300

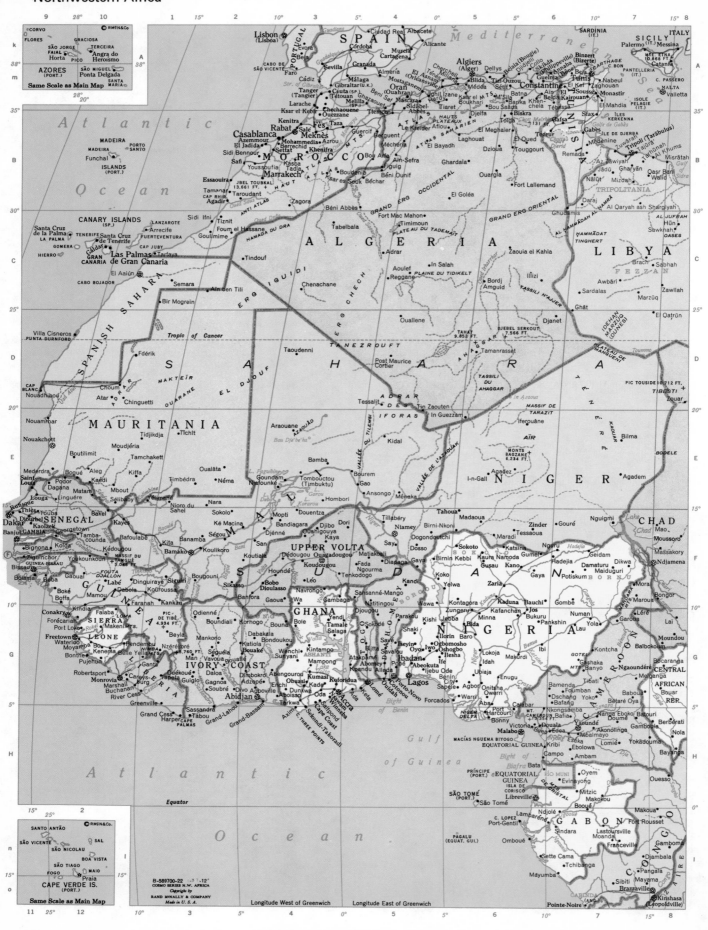

Statute Miles 100 0 100 200 300
Kilometers 100 0 100 200 300 400

Longitude West of Greenwich   Longitude East of Greenwich

Sinusoidal Projection

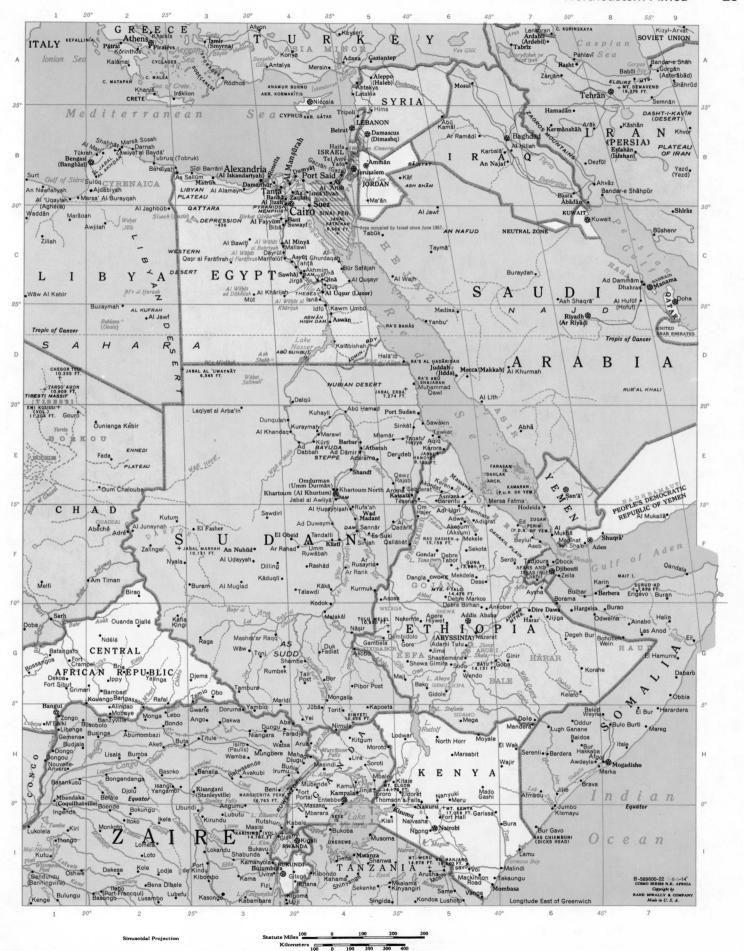

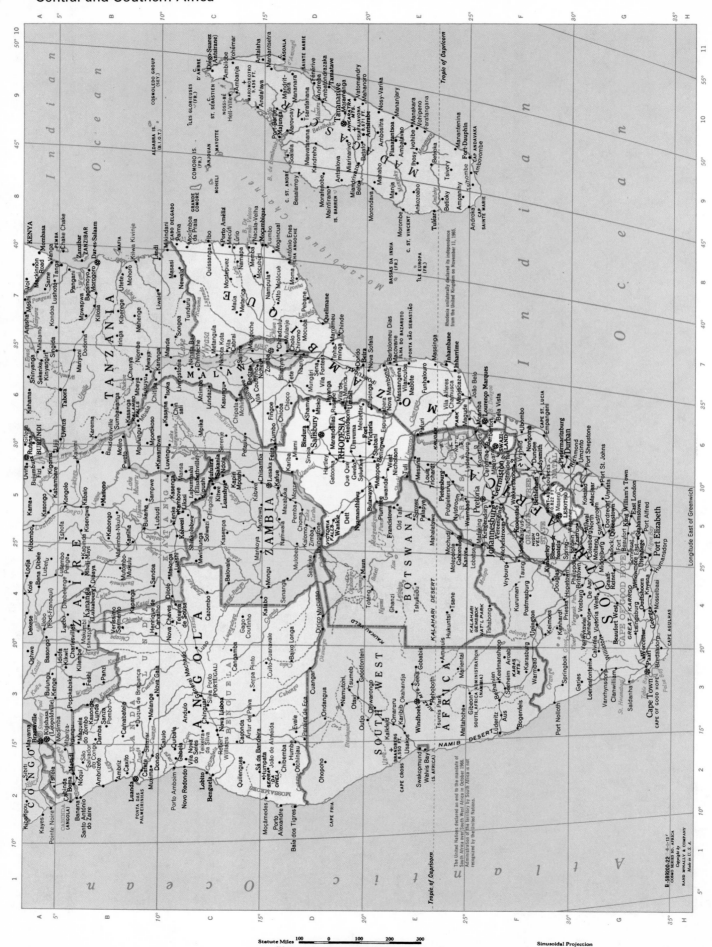

Statute Miles

Kilometers

Sinusoidal Projection

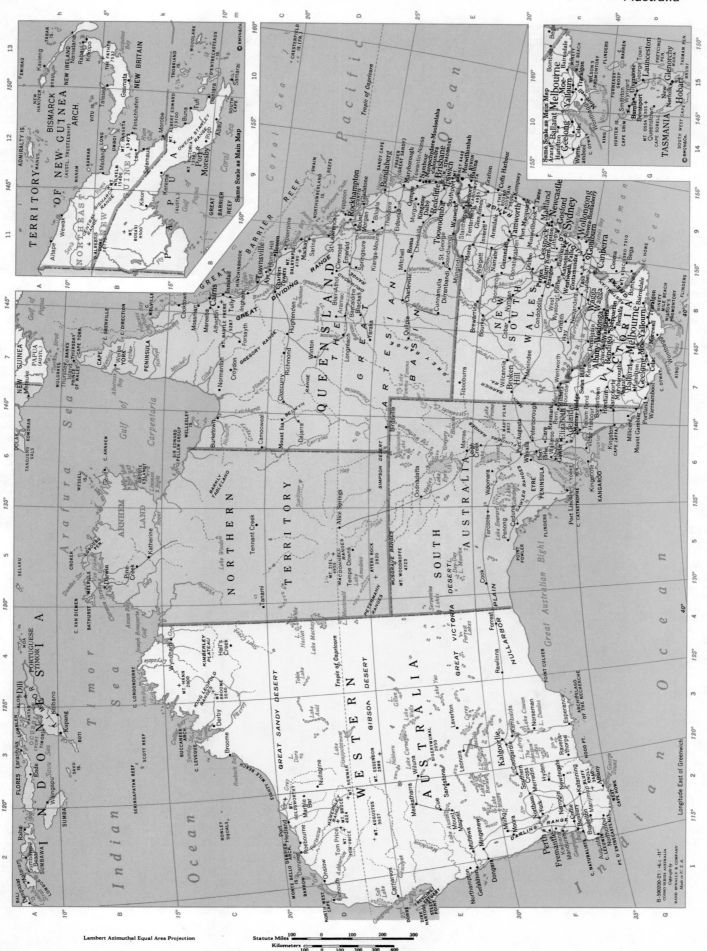

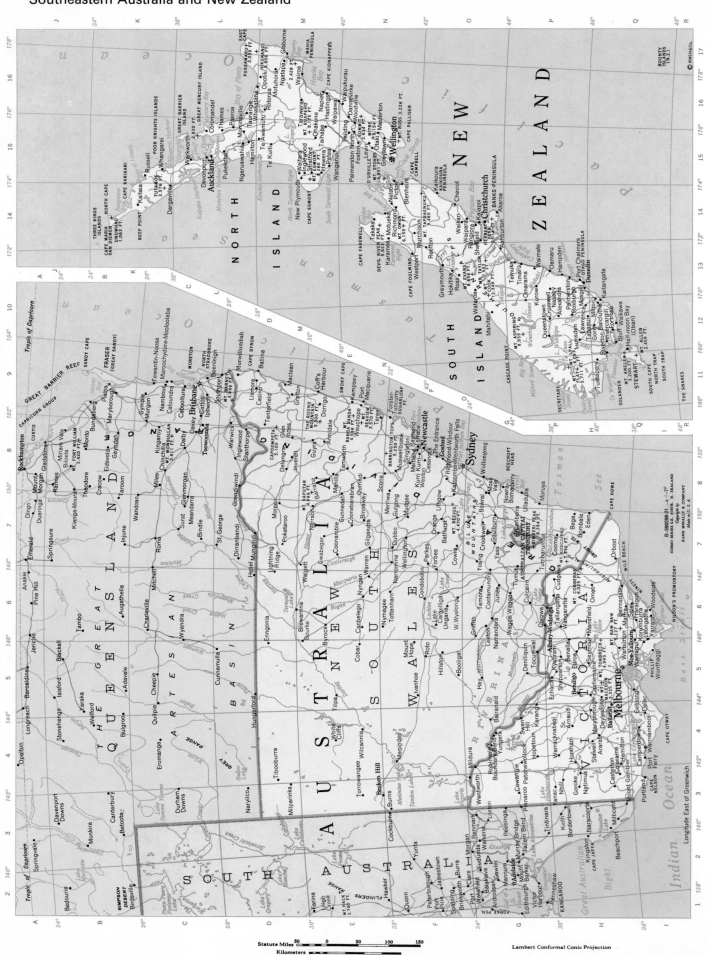

Statute Miles 50 0 50 100 150

Kilometers 50 0 50 100 200

Lambert Conformal Conic Projection

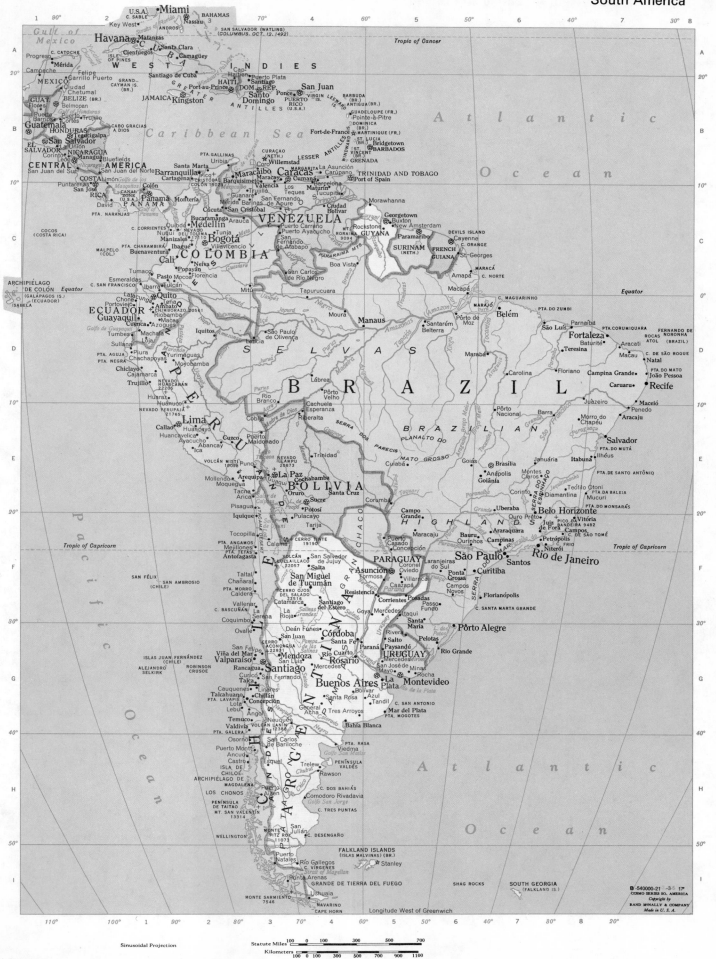

Sinusoidal Projection

Statute Miles
100 0 100   300   500   700

Kilometers
100 0 100 300 500 700 900 1100

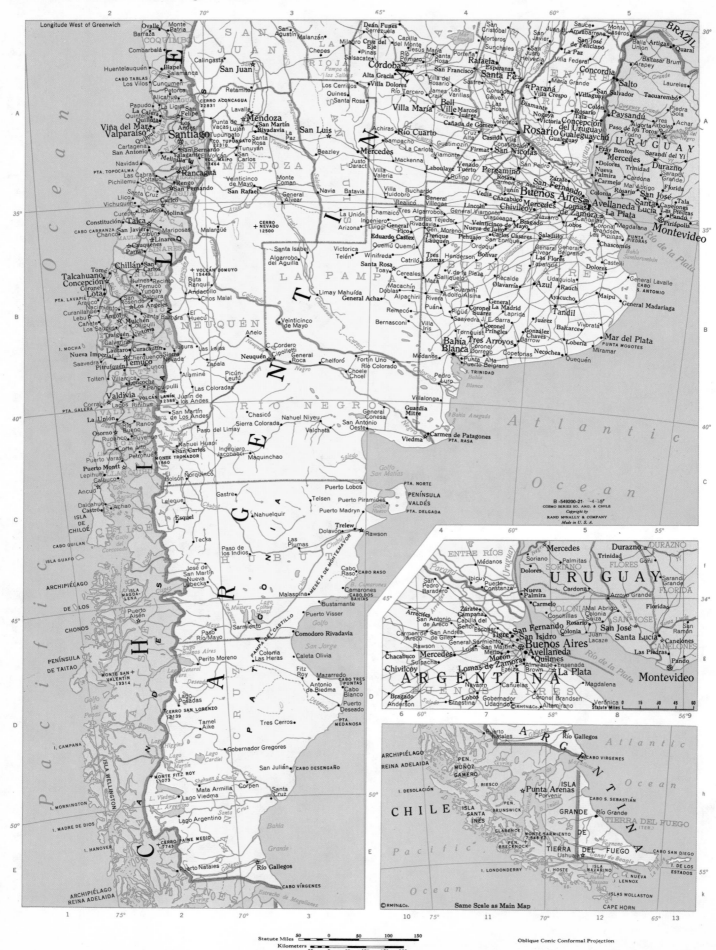

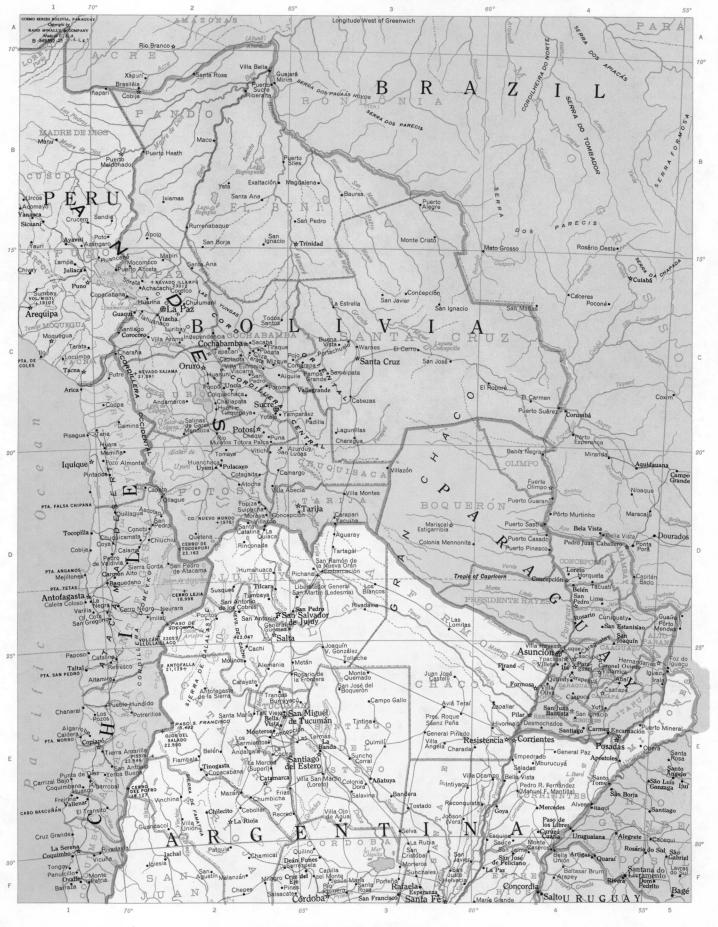

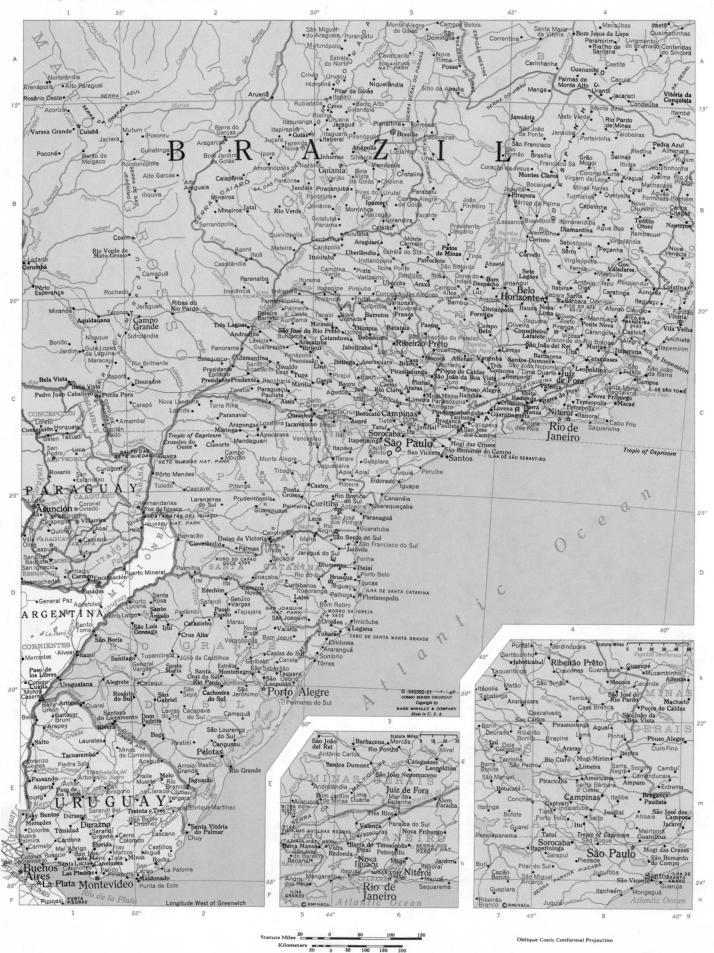

Statute Miles

Kilometers

Oblique Conic Conformal Projection

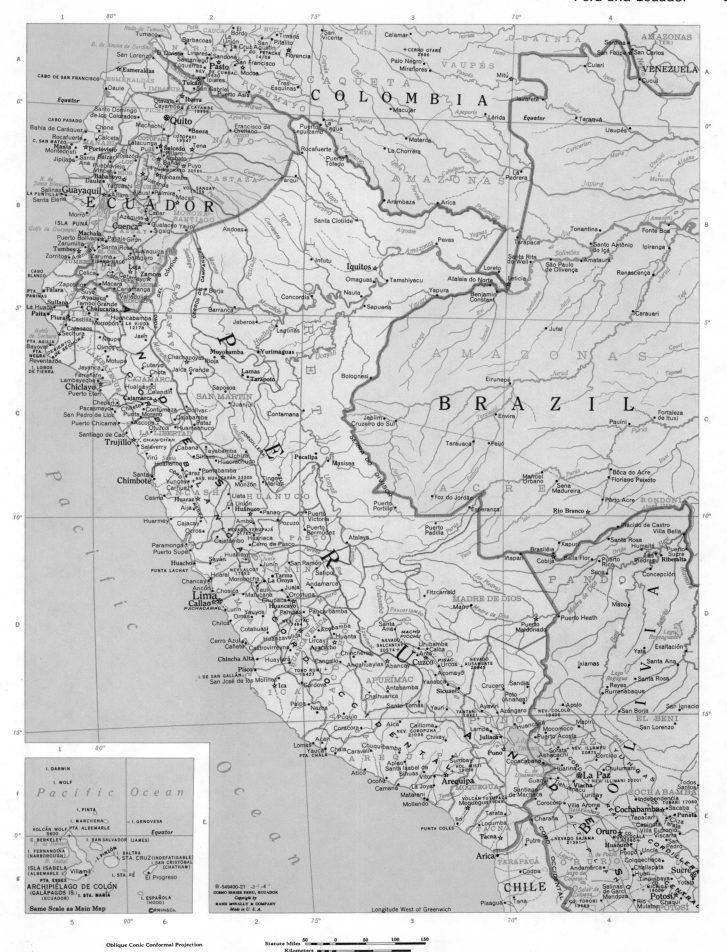

B-549400-21 -3-4 -4
COSMO SERIES PERU, ECUADOR
Copyright by
RAND McNALLY & COMPANY
Made in U.S.A.

Longitude West of Greenwich

Oblique Conic Conformal Projection

Statute Miles
50   0   50   100   150

Kilometers
50 0 50 100 150 200

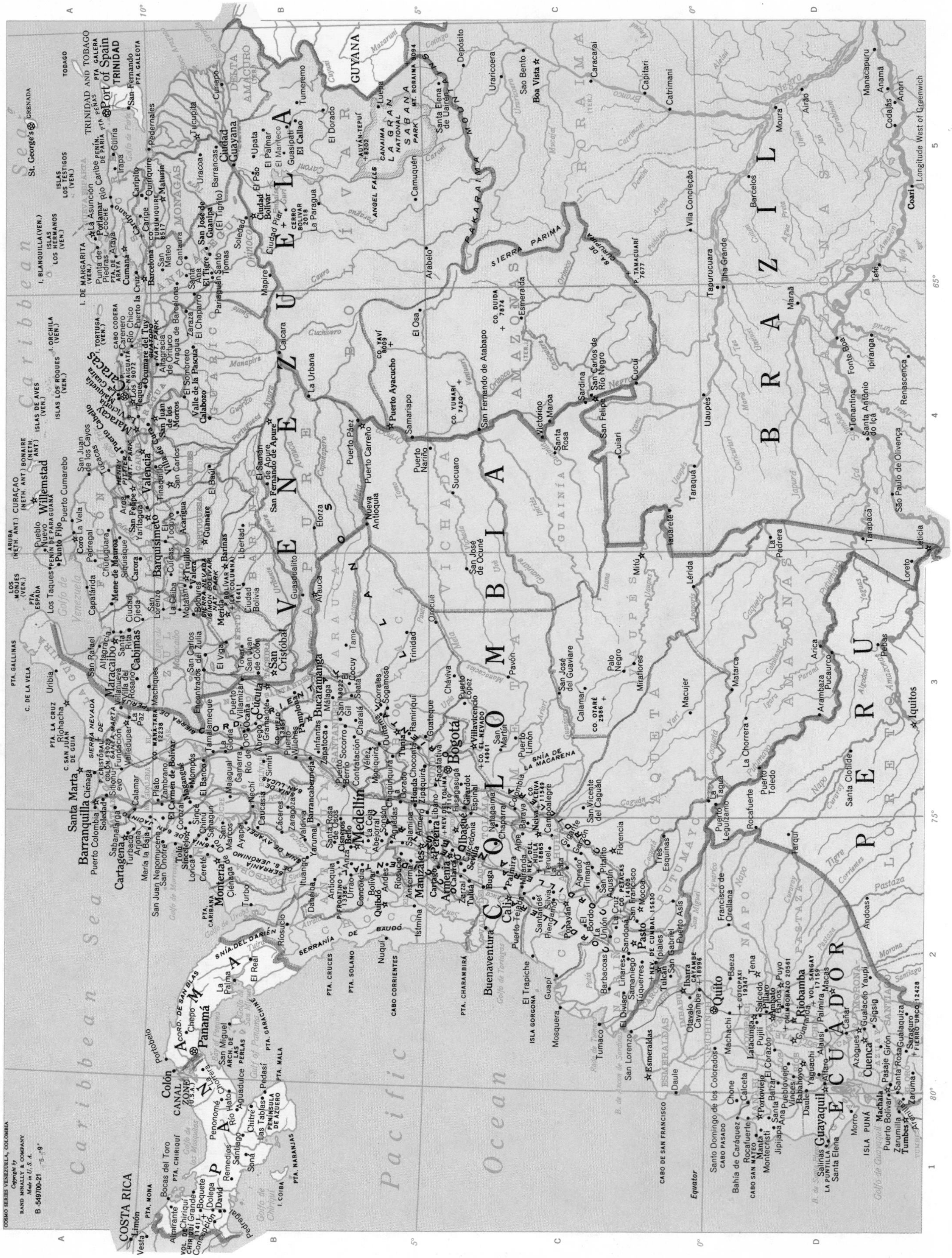

Colombia and Venezuela

Caribbean Sea

Pacific Ocean

VENEZUELA

COLOMBIA

BRAZIL

PERU

ECUADOR

GUYANA

PANAMÁ

COSTA RICA

TRINIDAD AND TOBAGO

Port of Spain

Caracas

Bogotá

Medellín

Cali

Maracaibo

Barranquilla

Cartagena

Valencia

Barquisimeto

Ciudad Guayana

Ciudad Bolívar

Cúcuta

Bucaramanga

Santa Marta

Manizales

Pereira

Armenia

Buenaventura

Pasto

Quito

Guayaquil

Cuenca

Riobamba

Iquitos

Leticia

Ciudad Ojeda

Cabimas

Mérida

San Cristóbal

Maturín

Cumaná

Barcelona

Puerto Ayacucho

San Fernando de Atabapo

Puerto Carreño

Villavicencio

Florencia

Mocoa

ANGEL FALLS

GRAN SABANA NATIONAL PARK

CANAIMA NATIONAL PARK

SIERRA PARIMA

DELTA AMACURO

CANAL ZONE

Colón

Panamá

St. George's

GRENADA

Oblique Conic Conformal Projection

Statute Miles 50 0 50 100 150

Kilometers 50 0 50 100 150 200

COSMO SERIES VENEZUELA, COLOMBIA
Copyright by
RAND McNALLY & COMPANY
Made in U.S.A.
B-549706-21

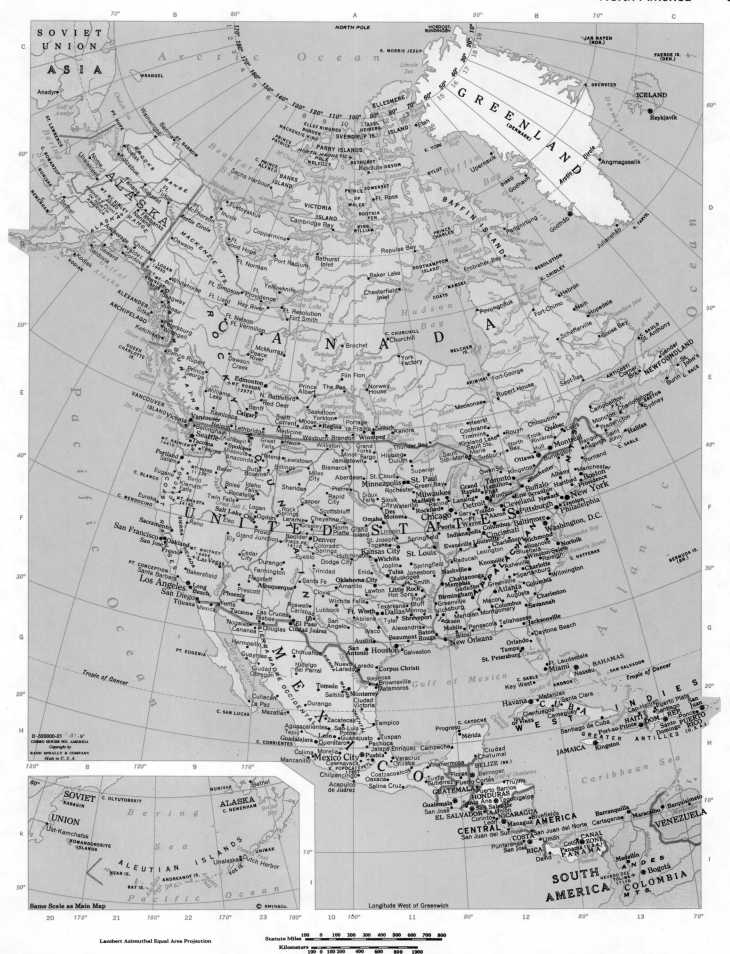

Lambert Azimuthal Equal Area Projection

Statute Miles
100 0 100 200 300 400 500 600 700 800

Kilometers
100 0 100 200 400 600 800 1000

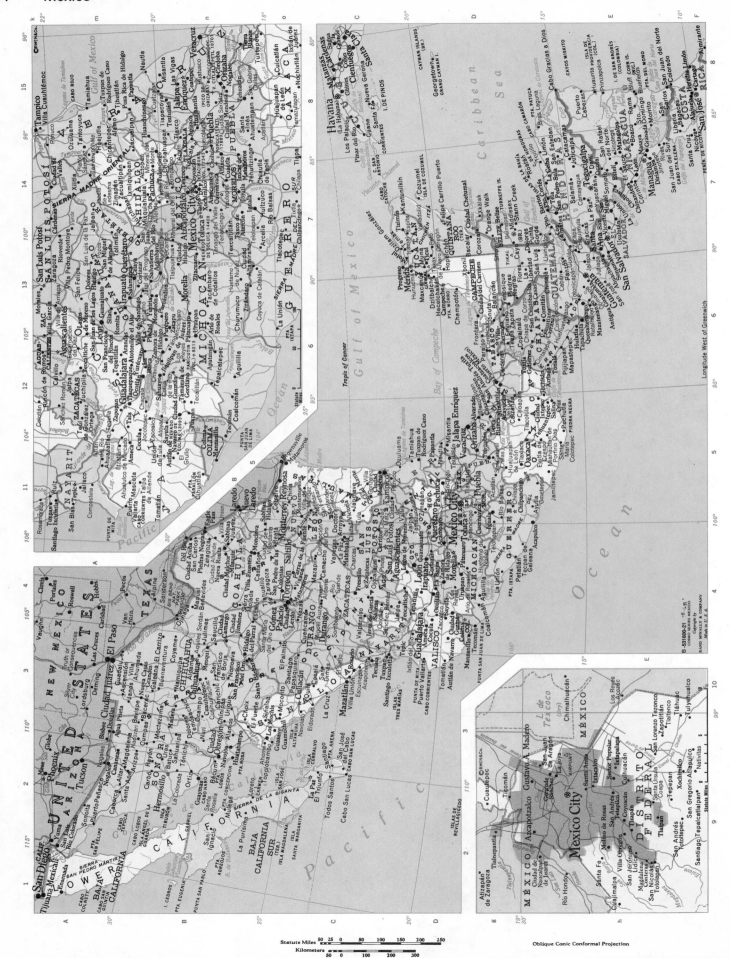

Statute Miles 50 25 0   50   100   150   200   250
Kilometers 50 0   100   200   300

Oblique Conic Conformal Projection

Statute Miles 25 0 25 75 125
Kilometers 25 0 25 75 125 175

Statute Miles
Kilometers

Lambert Conformal Conic Projection

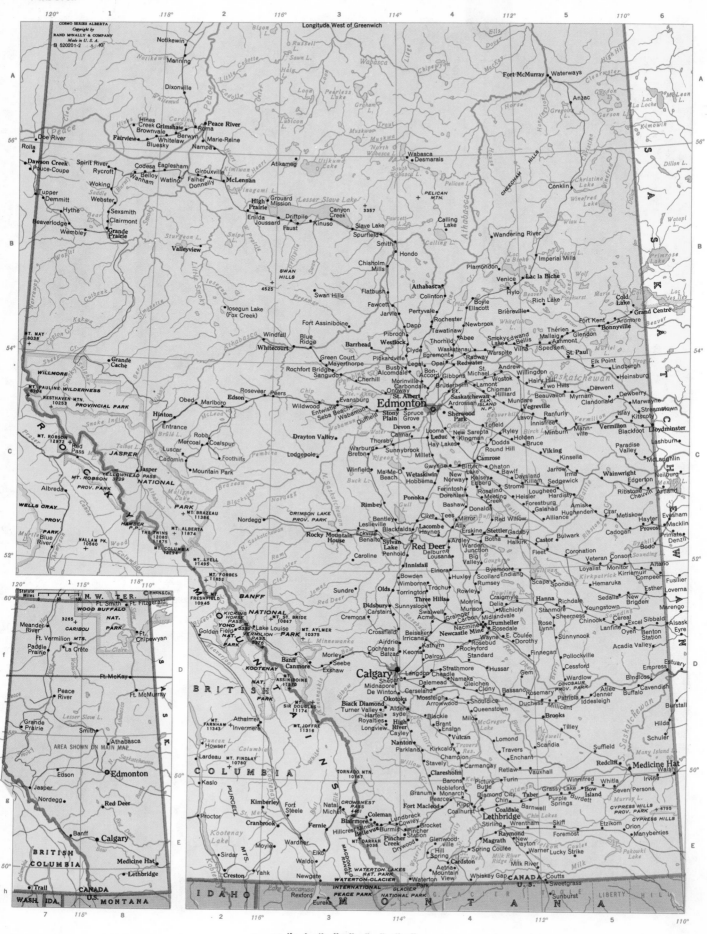

Statute Miles
Kilometers

Oblique Cylindrical Projection

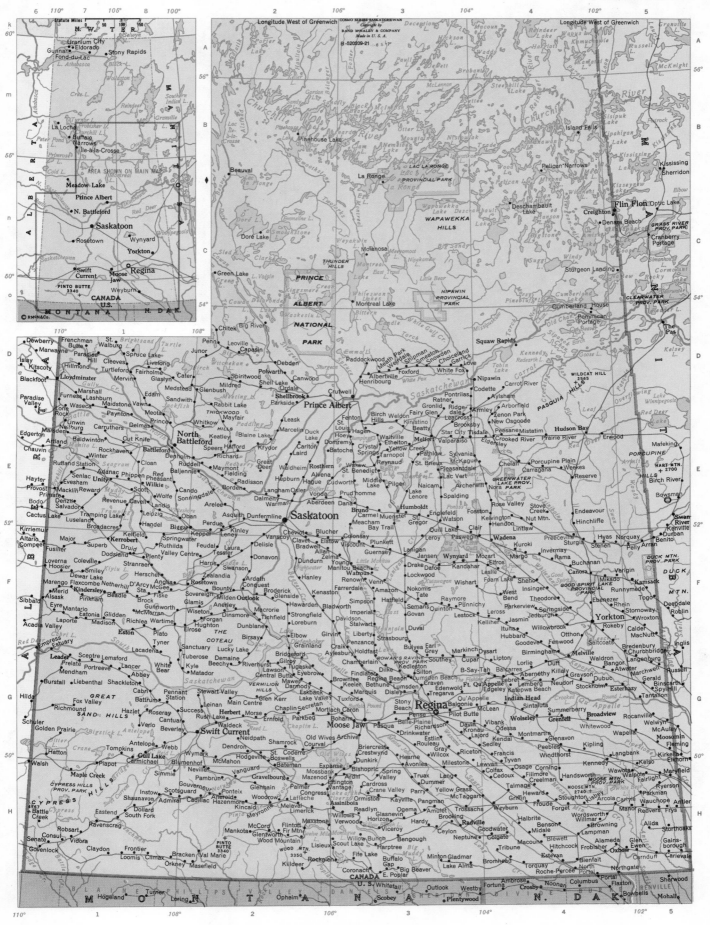

Oblique Cylindrical Projection

Statute Miles
Kilometers

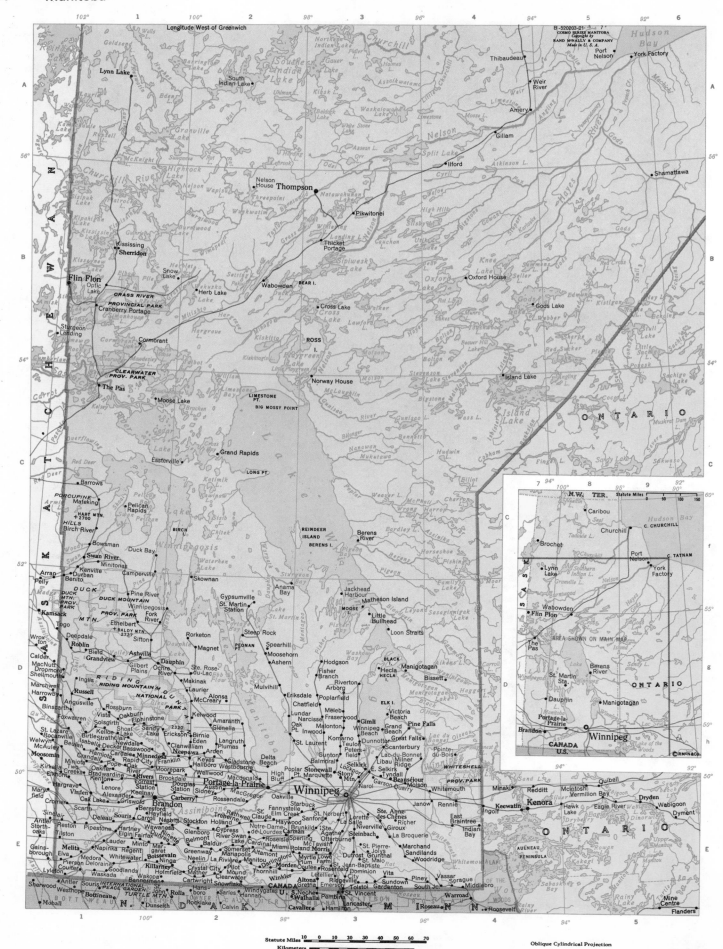

Longitude West of Greenwich

Statute Miles   10   0   10   20   30   40   50   60   70

Kilometers   10   0   10   20   40   60   80   100

Oblique Cylindrical Projection

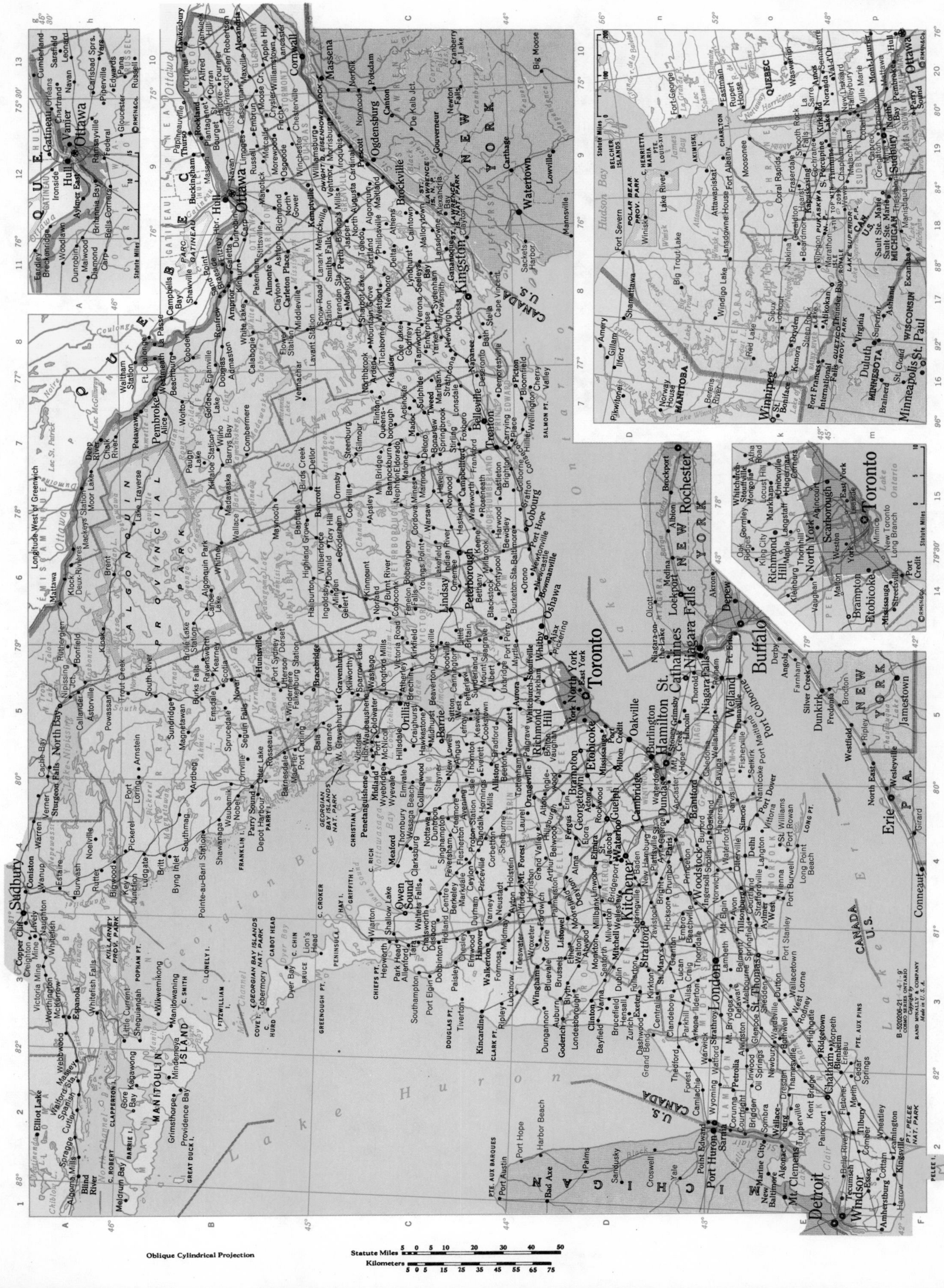

Oblique Cylindrical Projection

Statute Miles 5 0 5 10 20 30 40 50

Kilometers 5 0 5 15 25 35 45 55 75

B-502006-21
COPYRIGHT
RAND McNALLY & COMPANY
MADE IN ORLANDO
Made in U.S.A.

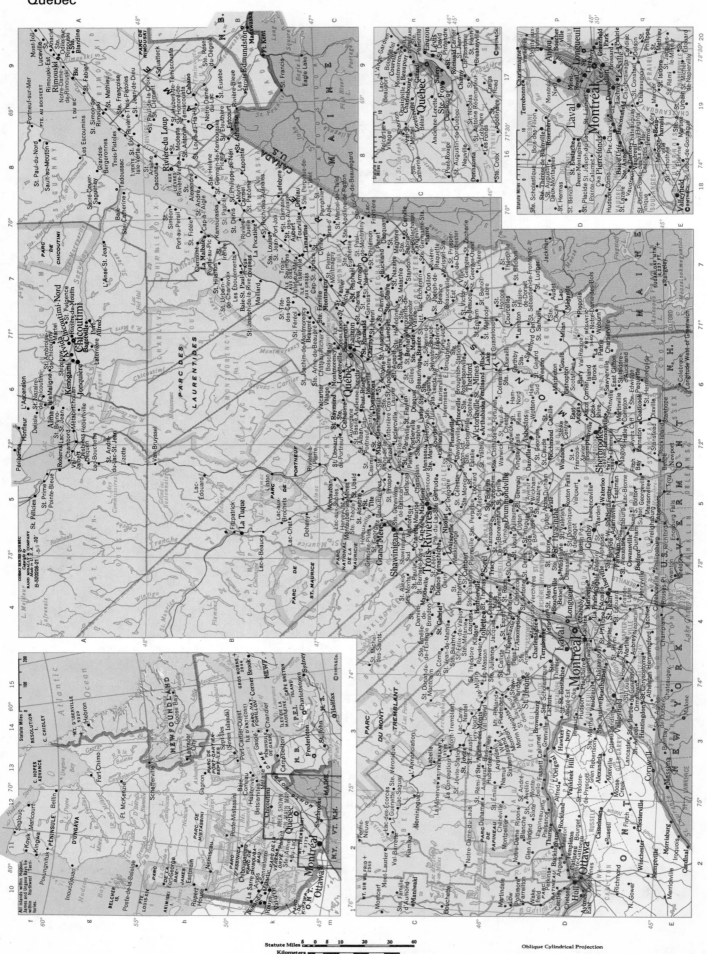

Statute Miles

Kilometers

Oblique Cylindrical Projection

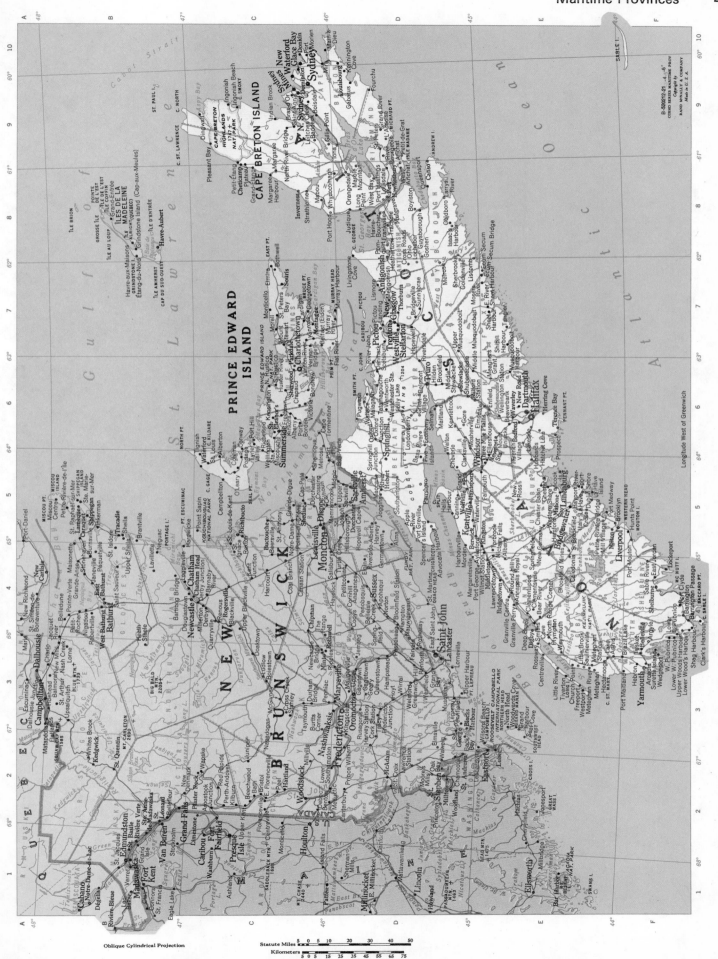

Oblique Cylindrical Projection

Statute Miles

Kilometers

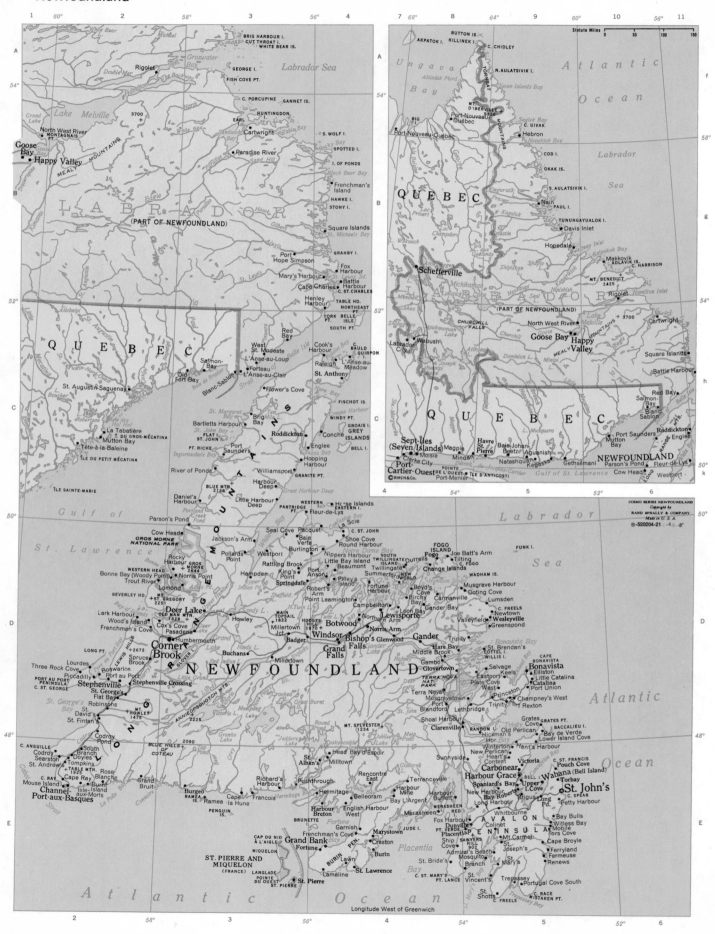

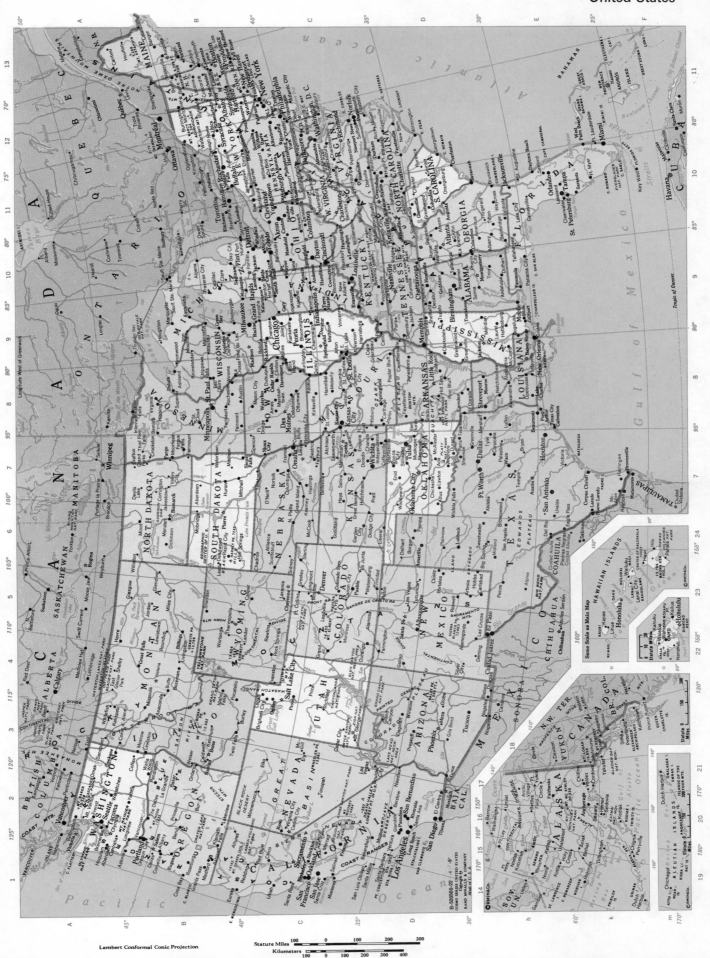

Lambert Conformal Conic Projection

Statute Miles 100 0 100 200 300

Kilometers
100 0 100 200 300 400

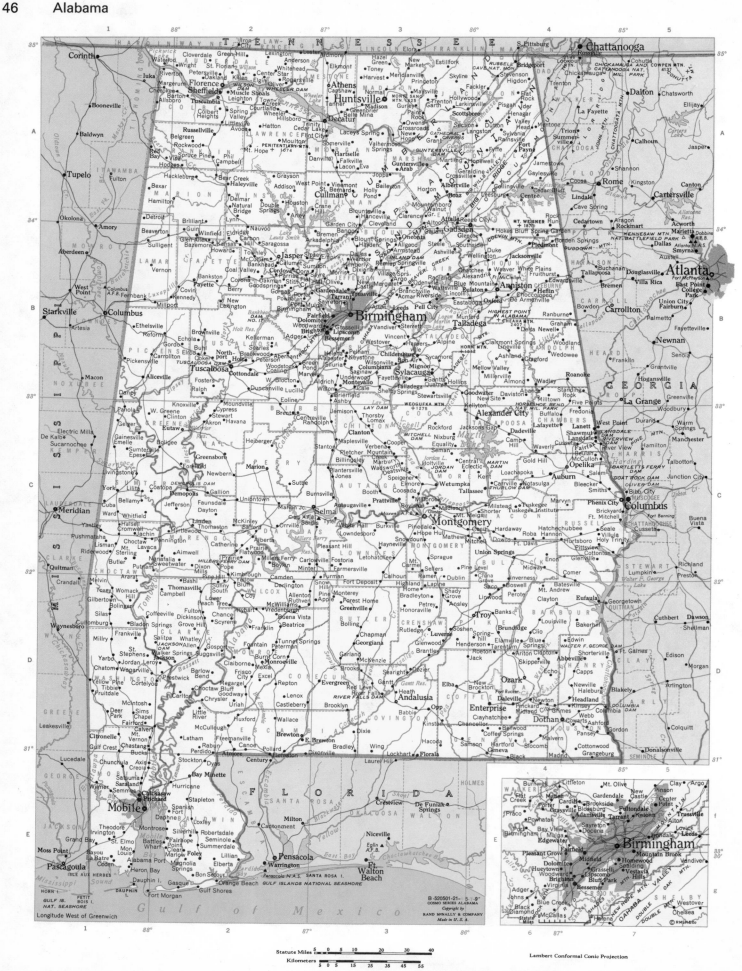

Statute Miles

Kilometers

B-520501-21- 5-7-9¹
COSMO SERIES ALABAMA
Copyright by
RAND McNALLY & COMPANY
Made in U.S.A.

Longitude West of Greenwich

Gulf of Mexico

Lambert Conformal Conic Projection

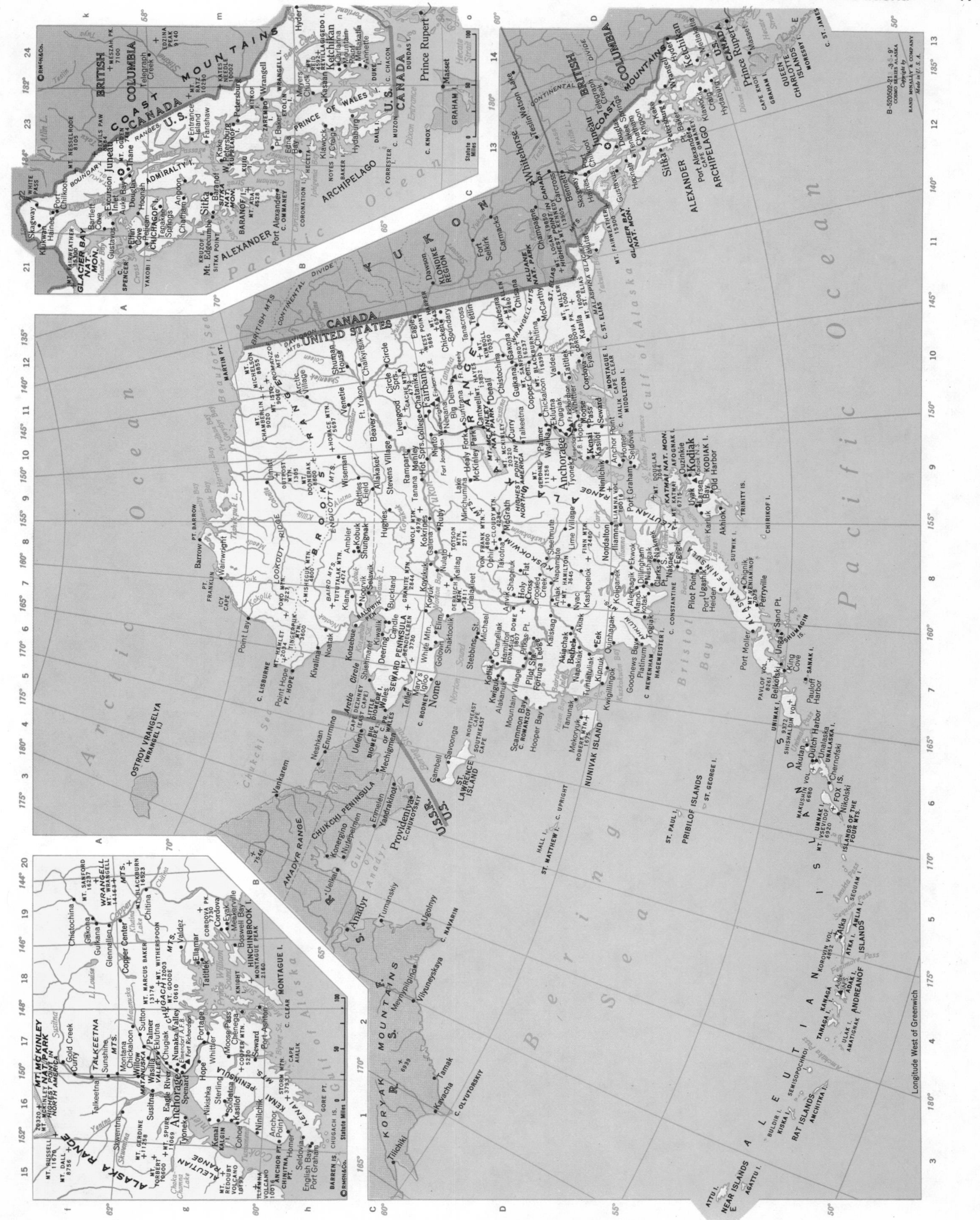

Polyconic Projection

Statute Miles 50 25 0 50 100 150 200 250

Kilometers 50 0 100 200 300

Longitude West of Greenwich

B-505602-21

COMMERCIAL ATLAS, ALASKA
Copyright by
RAND M°NALLY & COMPANY
Made in U. S. A.

Major labels

Arctic Ocean

Pacific Ocean

Bering Sea

Gulf of Alaska

Beaufort Sea

Chukchi Sea

Bristol Bay

BROOKS RANGE

ALASKA RANGE

ALEUTIAN RANGE

WRANGELL MTS.

ENDICOTT MTS.

BRITISH COLUMBIA

CANADA / UNITED STATES

YUKON

COAST MOUNTAINS

ALEUTIAN ISLANDS

ALEXANDER ARCHIPELAGO

SEWARD PENINSULA

ALASKA PENINSULA

KENAI PENINSULA

CHUKOTSKI PENINSULA

ANADYR RANGE

KORYAK MOUNTAINS

U.S.S.R.

OSTROV VRANGELYA (WRANGEL I.)

ST. LAWRENCE ISLAND

NUNIVAK ISLAND

PRIBILOF ISLANDS

KODIAK I.

NEAR ISLANDS

RAT ISLANDS

ANDREANOF ISLANDS

ISLANDS OF THE FOUR MTS.

Anchorage
Fairbanks
Juneau
Ketchikan
Sitka
Nome
Kodiak
Valdez
Cordova
Seward
Homer
Skagway
Haines
Wrangell
Petersburg
Prince Rupert
Whitehorse
Dawson
Barrow
Kotzebue
Bethel
Dillingham

MT. McKINLEY 20320 MT. McKINLEY NAT'L PARK

MT. ST. ELIAS

GLACIER BAY NAT. MON.

KATMAI NAT. MON.

MT. LOGAN (HIGHEST IN CANADA) 19850

KLONDIKE REGION

KLUANE NAT. PARK

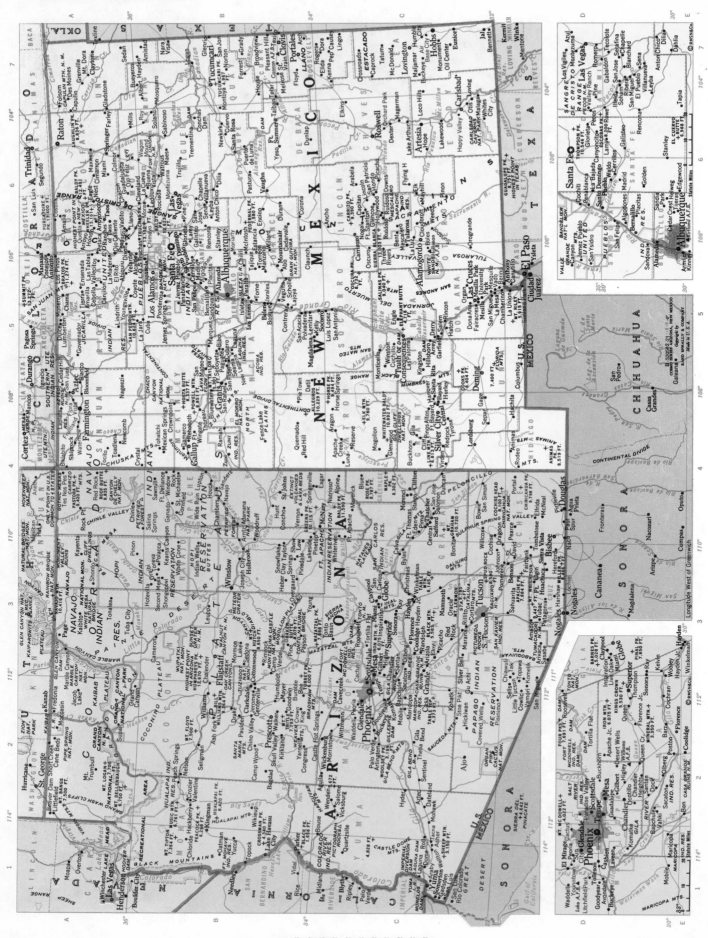

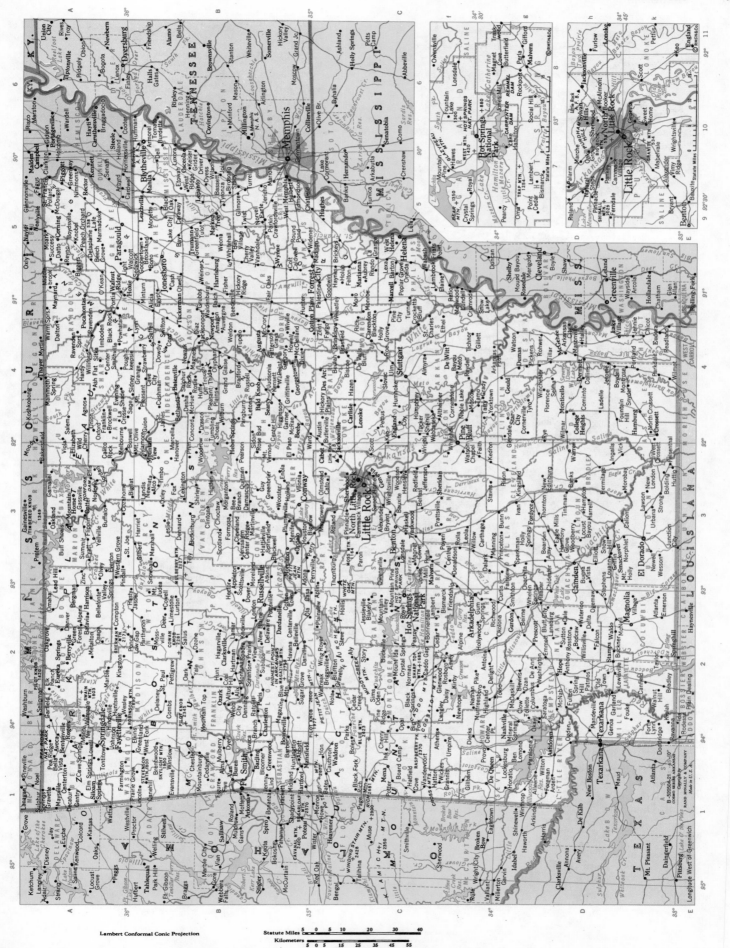

Lambert Conformal Conic Projection

Statute Miles 5 0 5 10 20 30 40

Kilometers 5 0 5 15 25 35 45 55

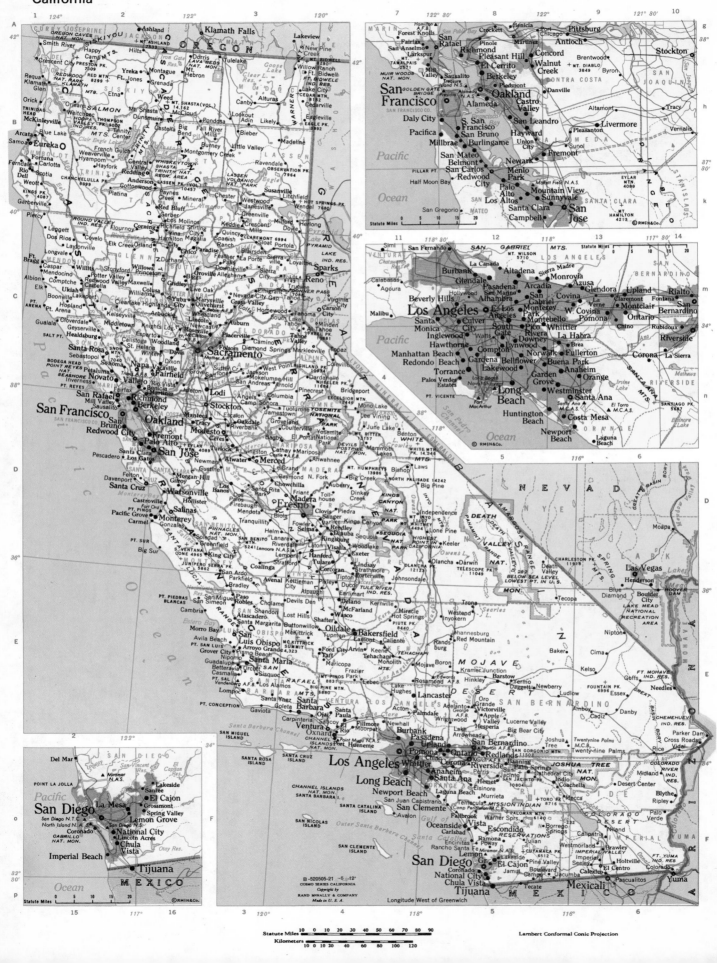

Statute Miles

Kilometers

Lambert Conformal Conic Projection

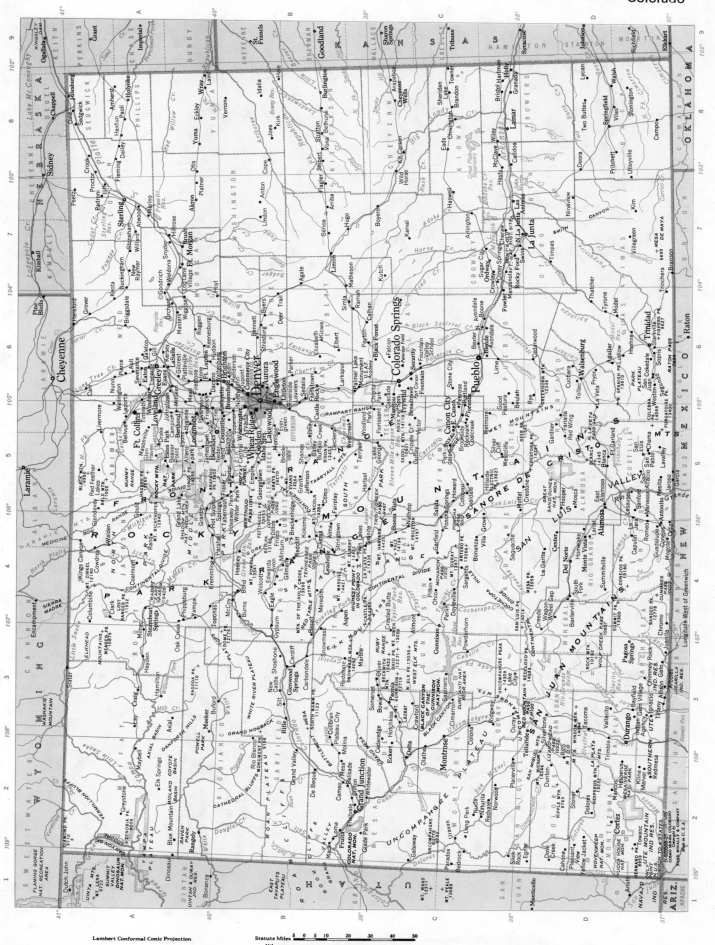

Lambert Conformal Conic Projection

Statute Miles 5 0 5 10 20 30 40 50

Kilometers 5 0 5 15 25 35 45 55 65 75

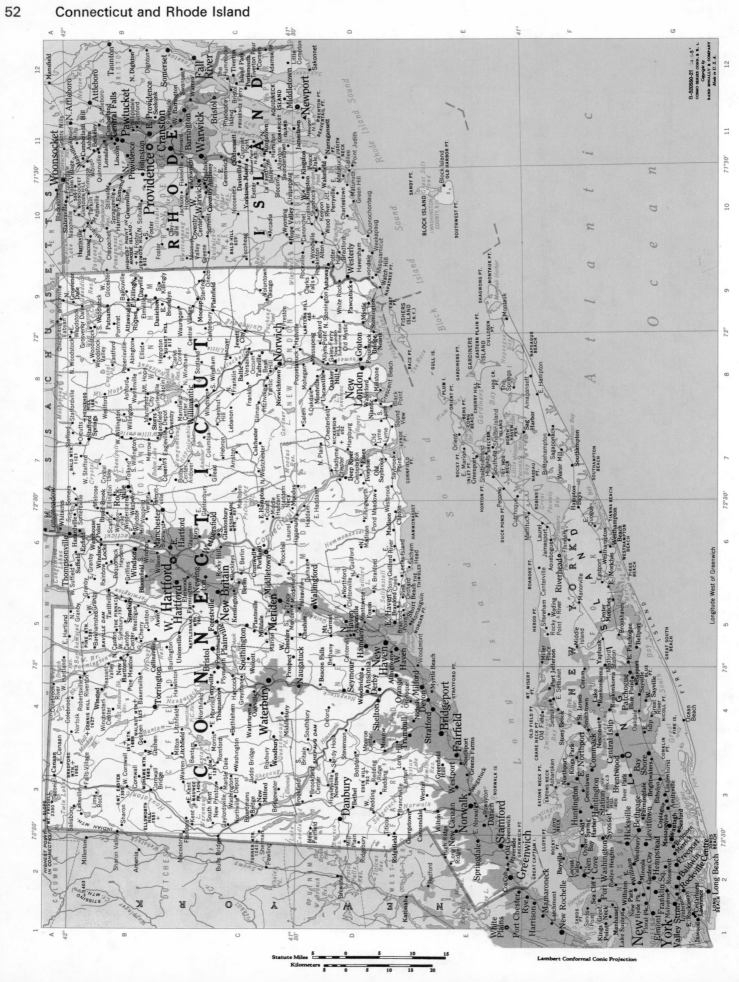

Statute Miles

Kilometers

Lambert Conformal Conic Projection

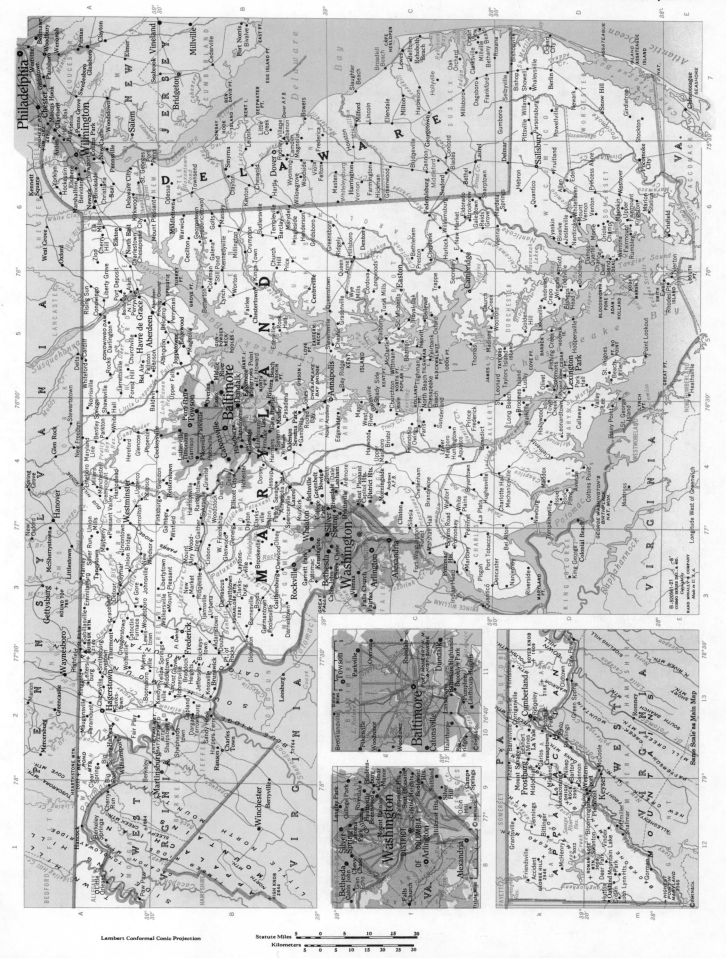

Lambert Conformal Conic Projection

Statute Miles 5   0   5   10   15   20
Kilometers   5   0   5   10   15   20   25   30

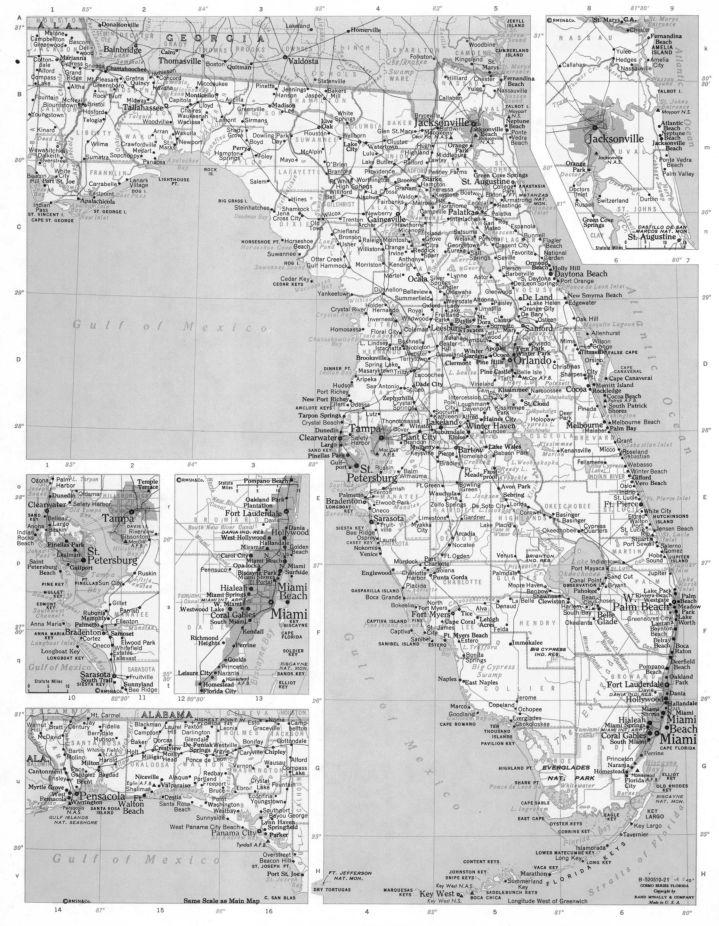

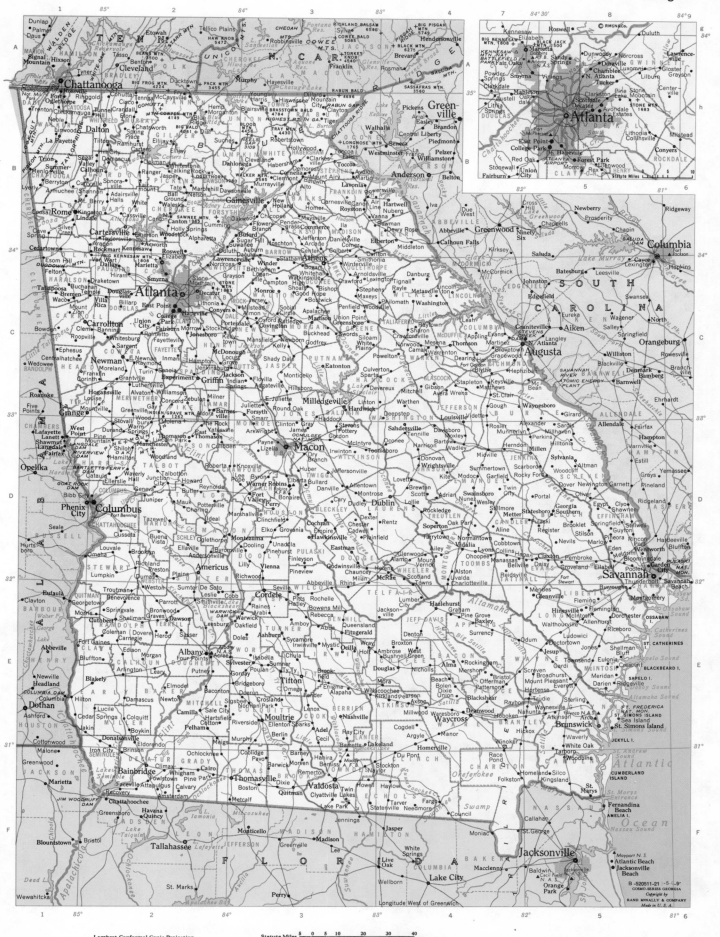

Lambert Conformal Conic Projection

Statute Miles
Kilometers

B-520511-21 -5- -9-
COSMO SERIES GEORGIA
Copyright by
RAND MCNALLY & COMPANY
Made in U.S.A.

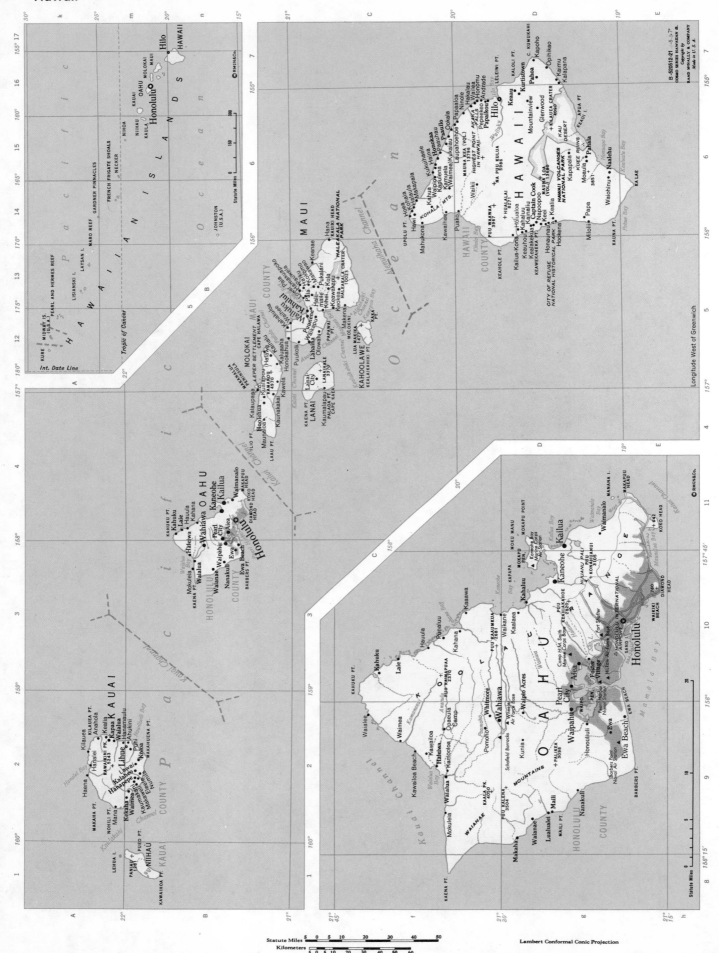

Statute Miles 5 0 5 10 20 30 40 50

Kilometers 5 0 5 10 20 30 40 50 60

Lambert Conformal Conic Projection

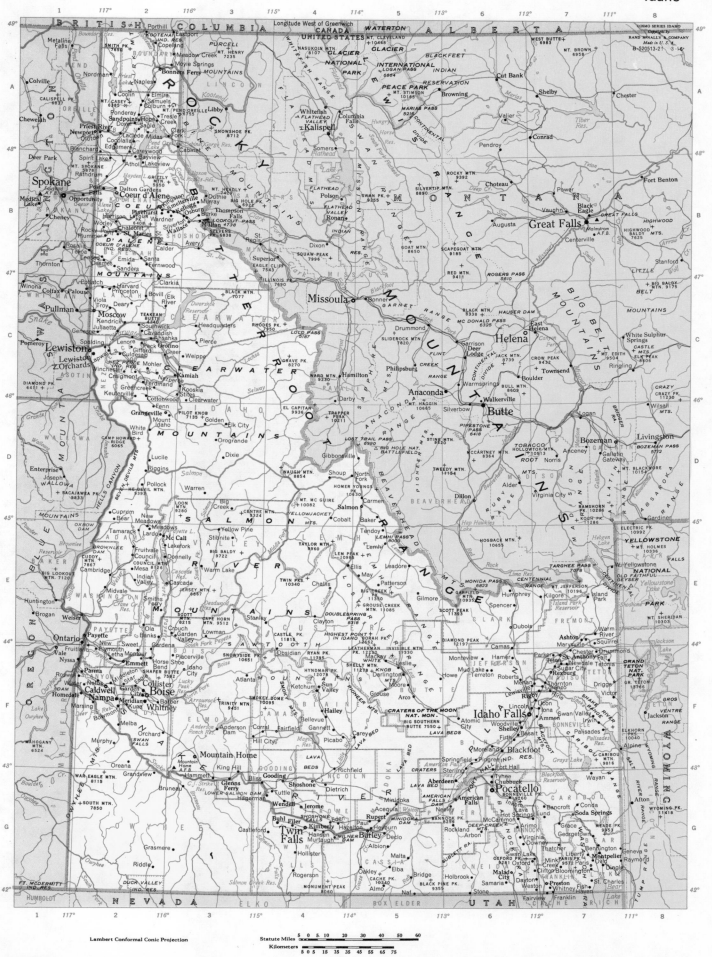

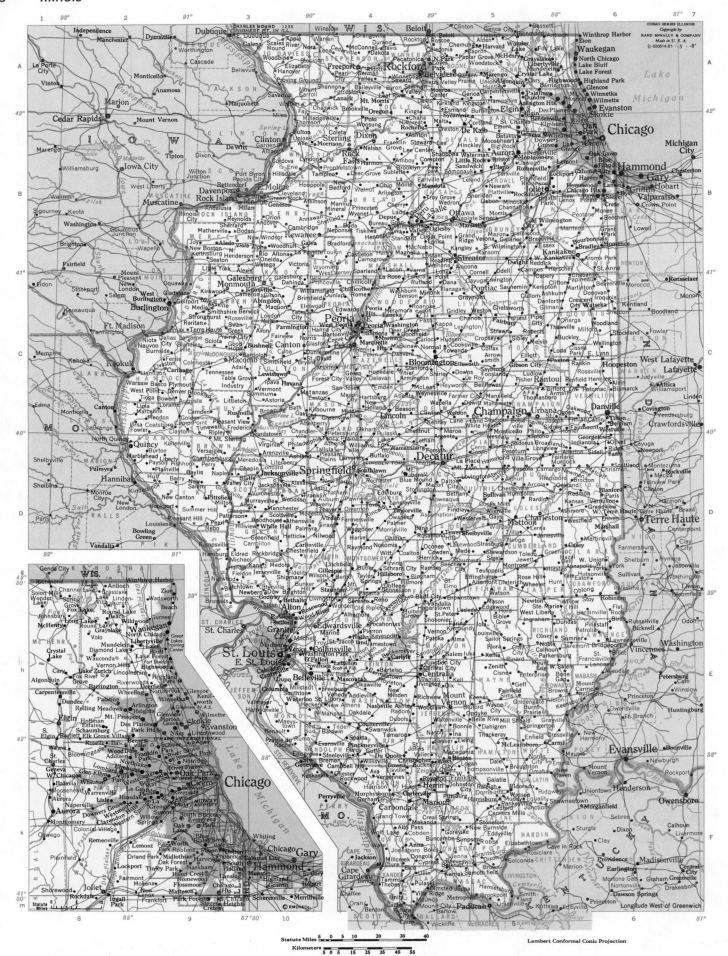

Statute Miles

Kilometers

Lambert Conformal Conic Projection

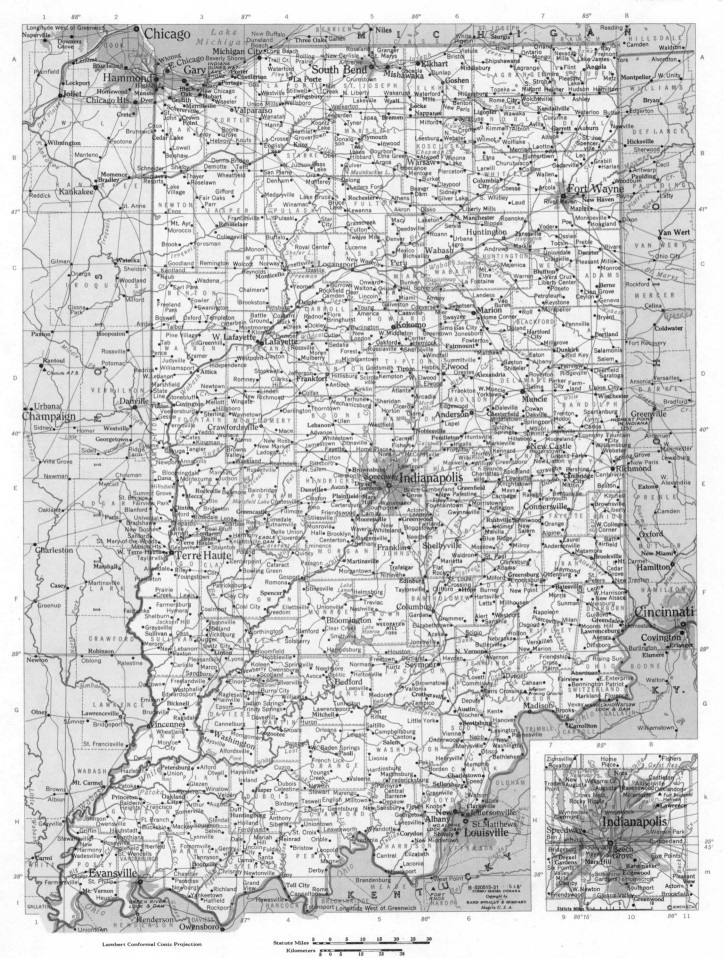

Lambert Conformal Conic Projection

Statute Miles

Kilometers

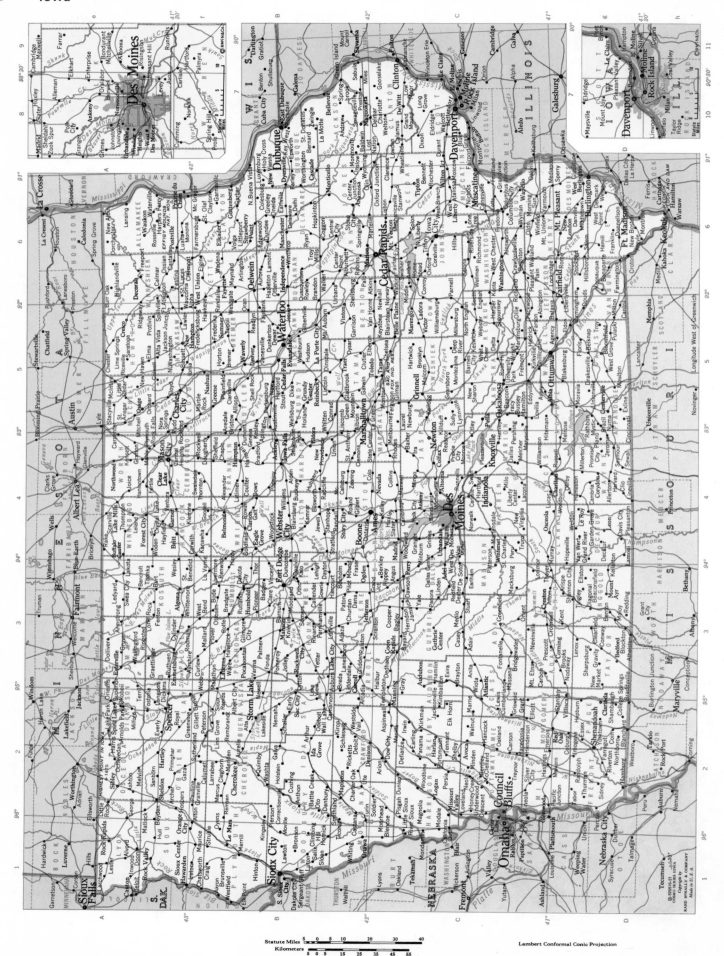

Statute Miles

Kilometers

Lambert Conformal Conic Projection

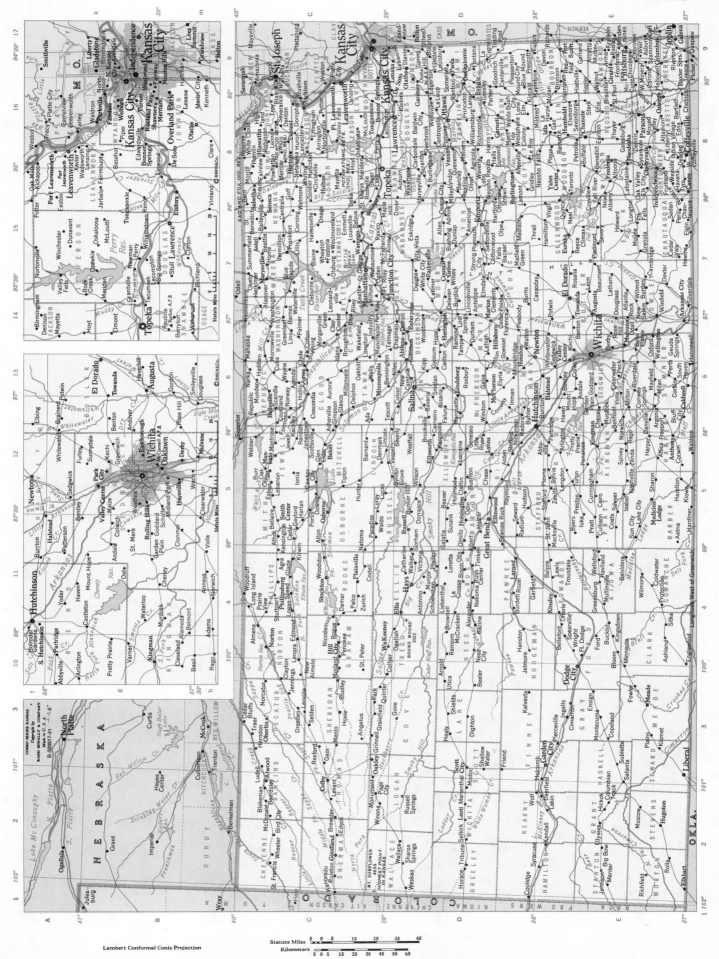

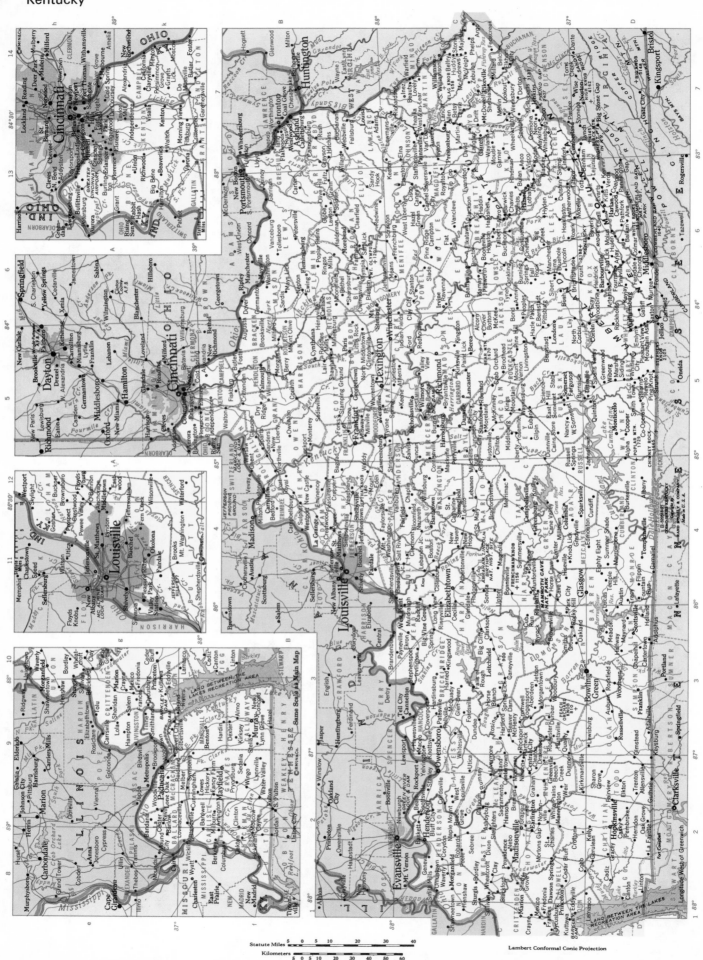

Statute Miles

Kilometers

Lambert Conformal Conic Projection

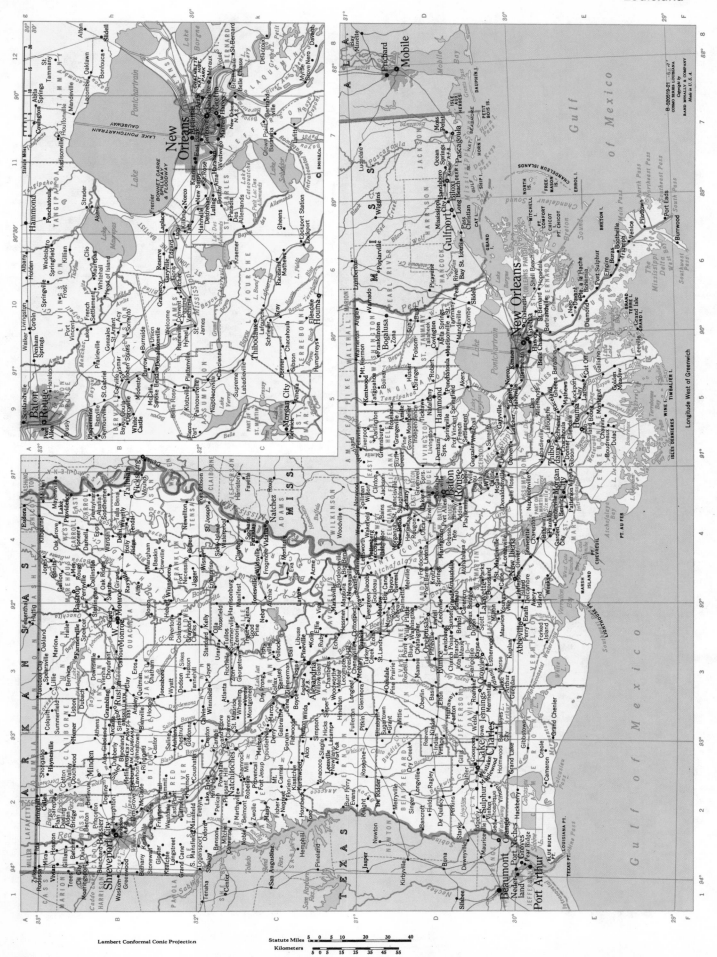

Lambert Conformal Conic Projection

Statute Miles 5 0 5 10   20   30   40

Kilometers 5 0 5 15 25 35 45 55

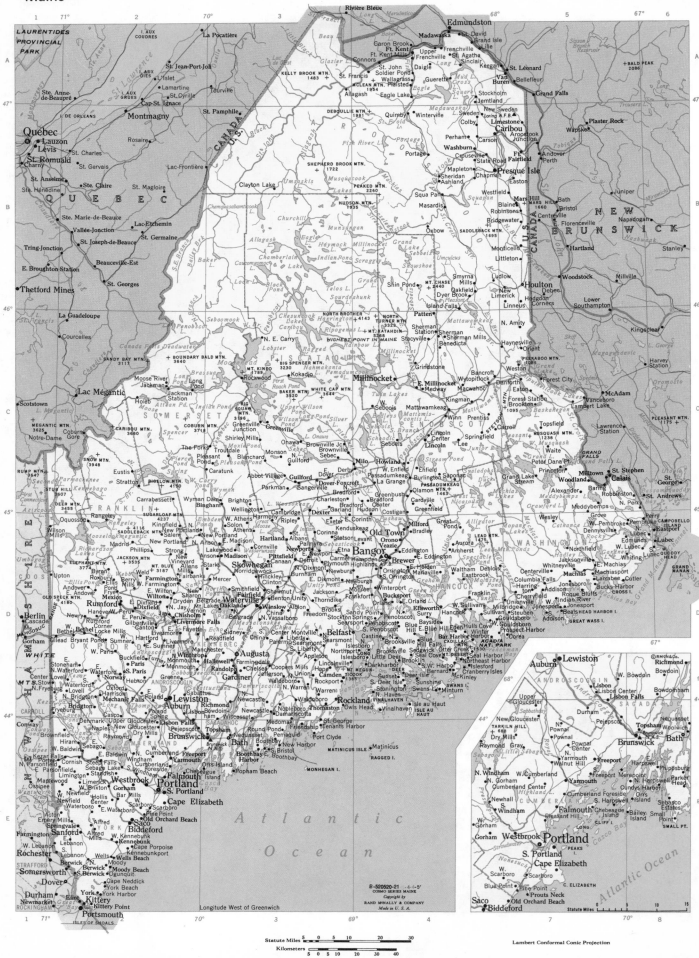

Longitude West of Greenwich

B-520520-21

COSMO SERIES MAINE

Copyright by
RAND McNALLY & COMPANY
Made in U.S.A.

Statute Miles 5 0 5 10 20 30

Kilometers 5 0 5 10 20 30 40

Lambert Conformal Conic Projection

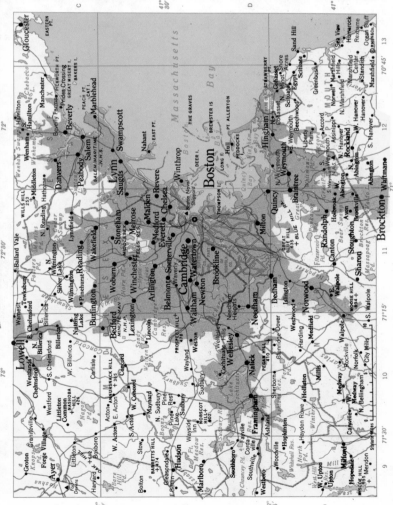

Lambert Conformal Conic Projection

Statute Miles

Kilometers

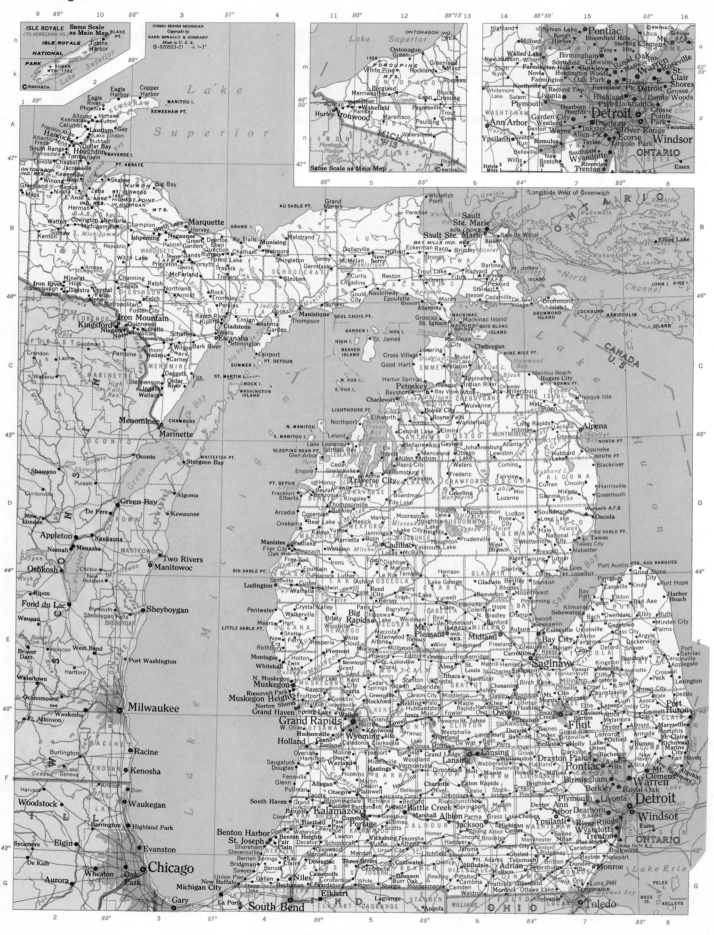

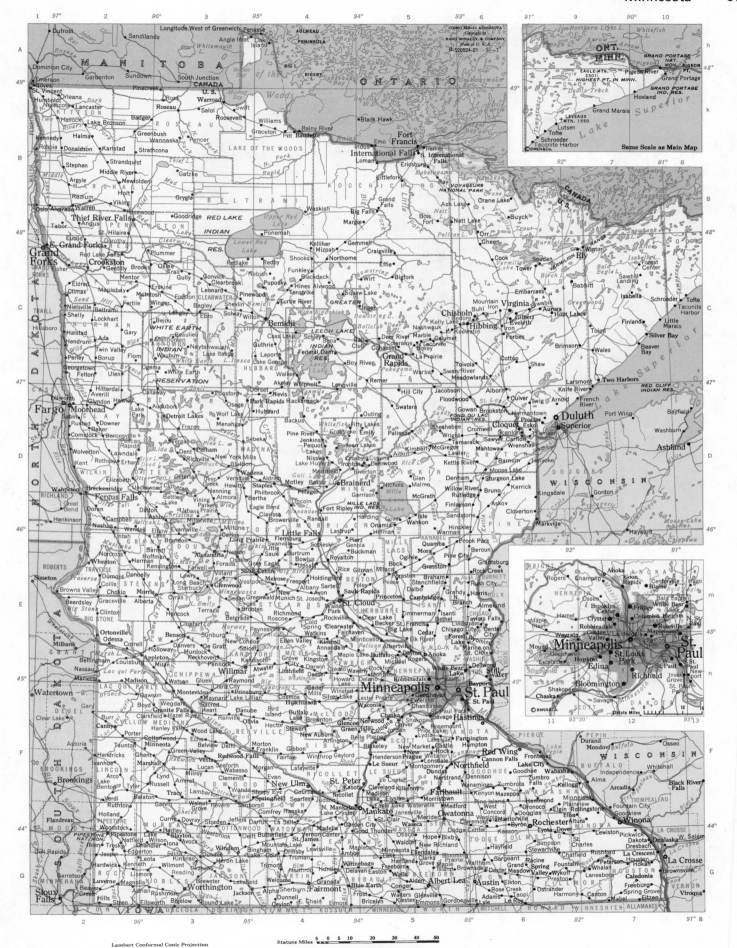

Lambert Conformal Conic Projection

Statute Miles

Kilometers

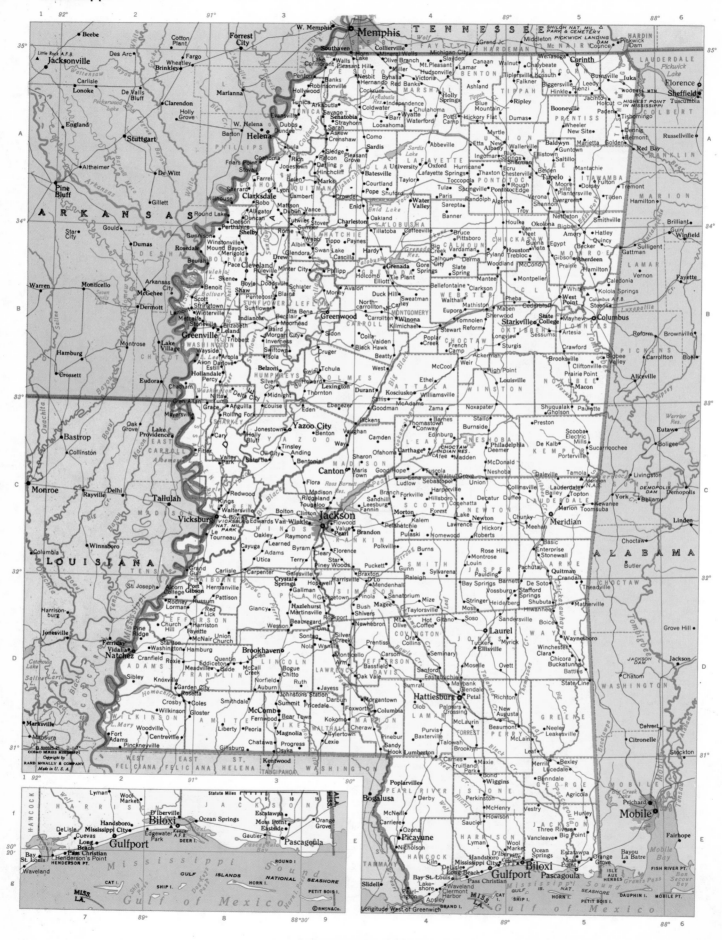

Statute Miles

Kilometers

Lambert Conformal Conic Projection

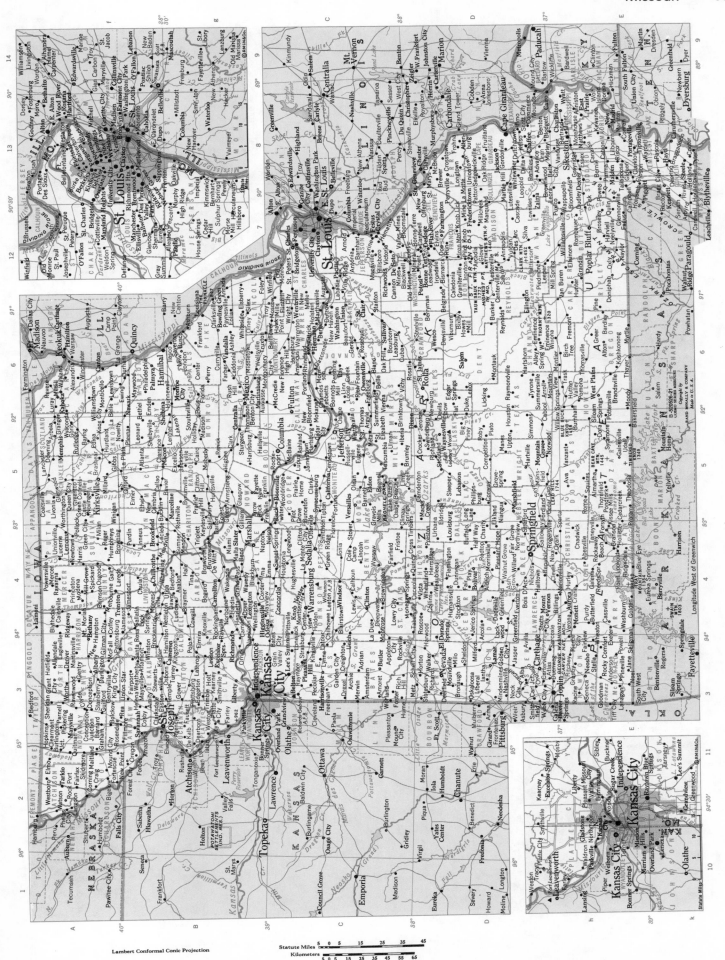

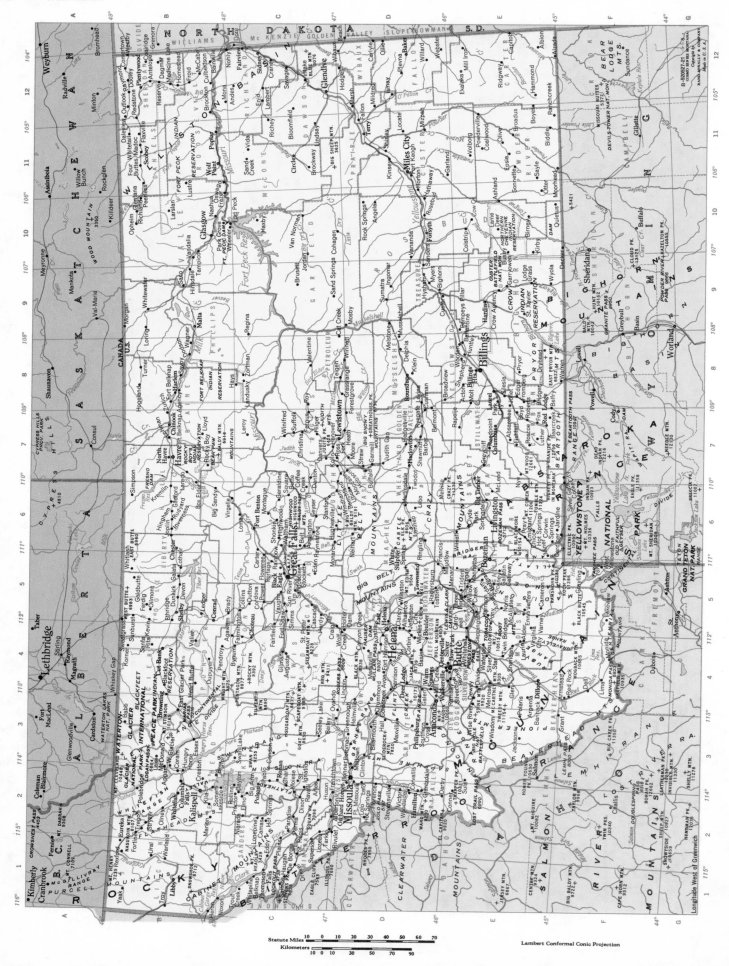

Statute Miles
Kilometers

Lambert Conformal Conic Projection

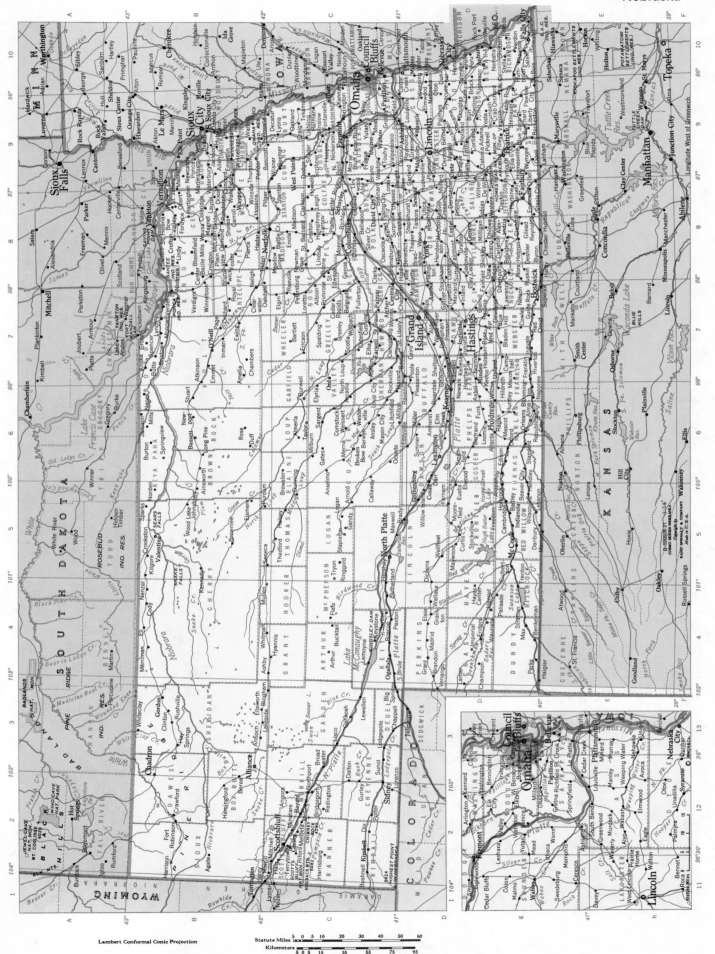

Lambert Conformal Conic Projection

Statute Miles

Kilometers

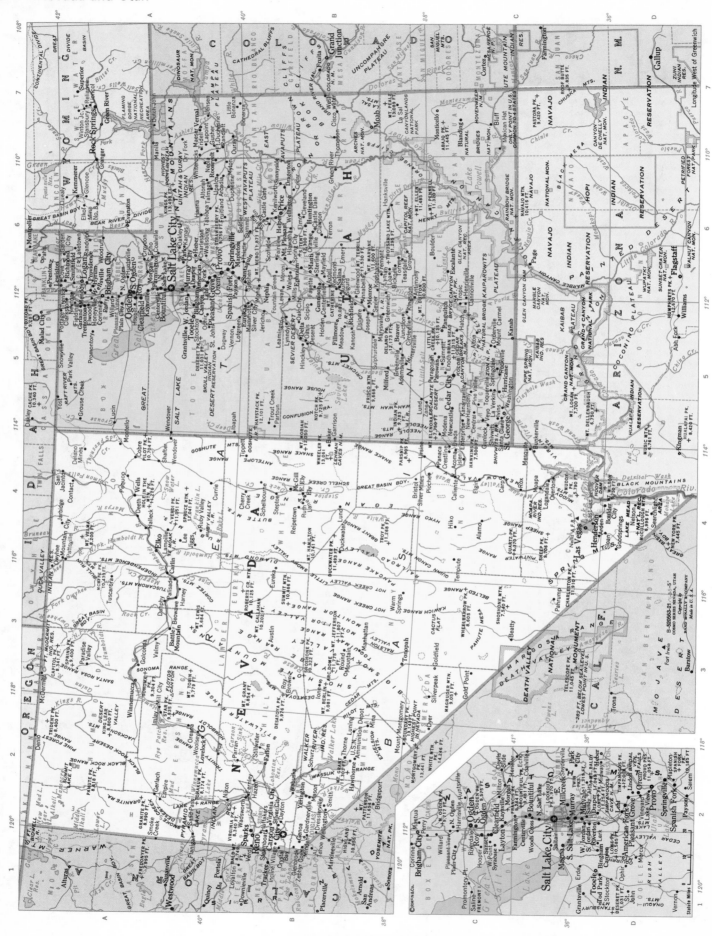

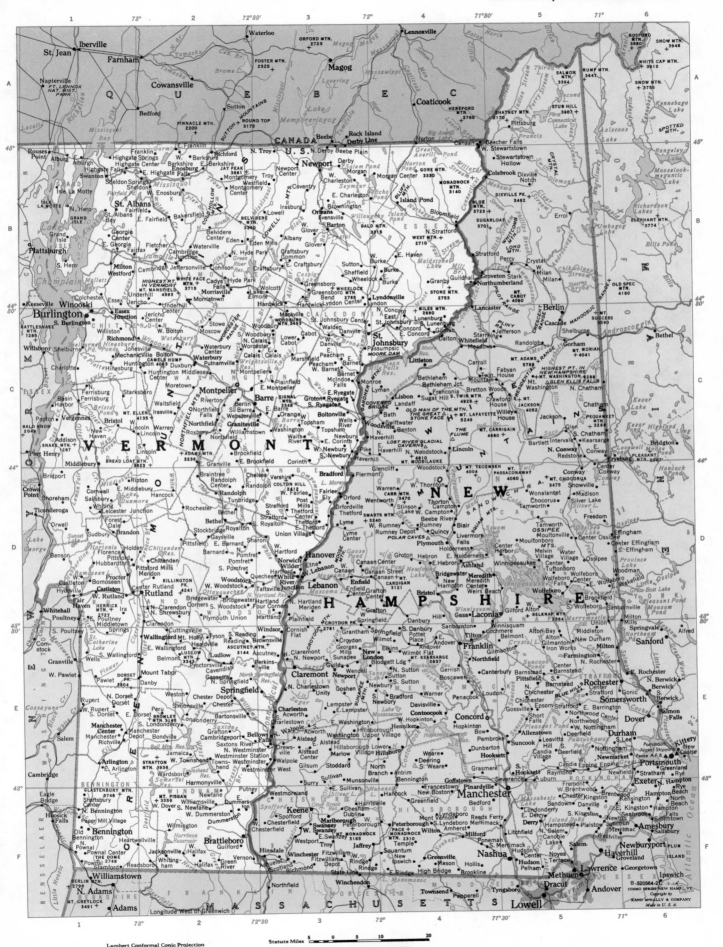

Lambert Conformal Conic Projection

Statute Miles

Kilometers

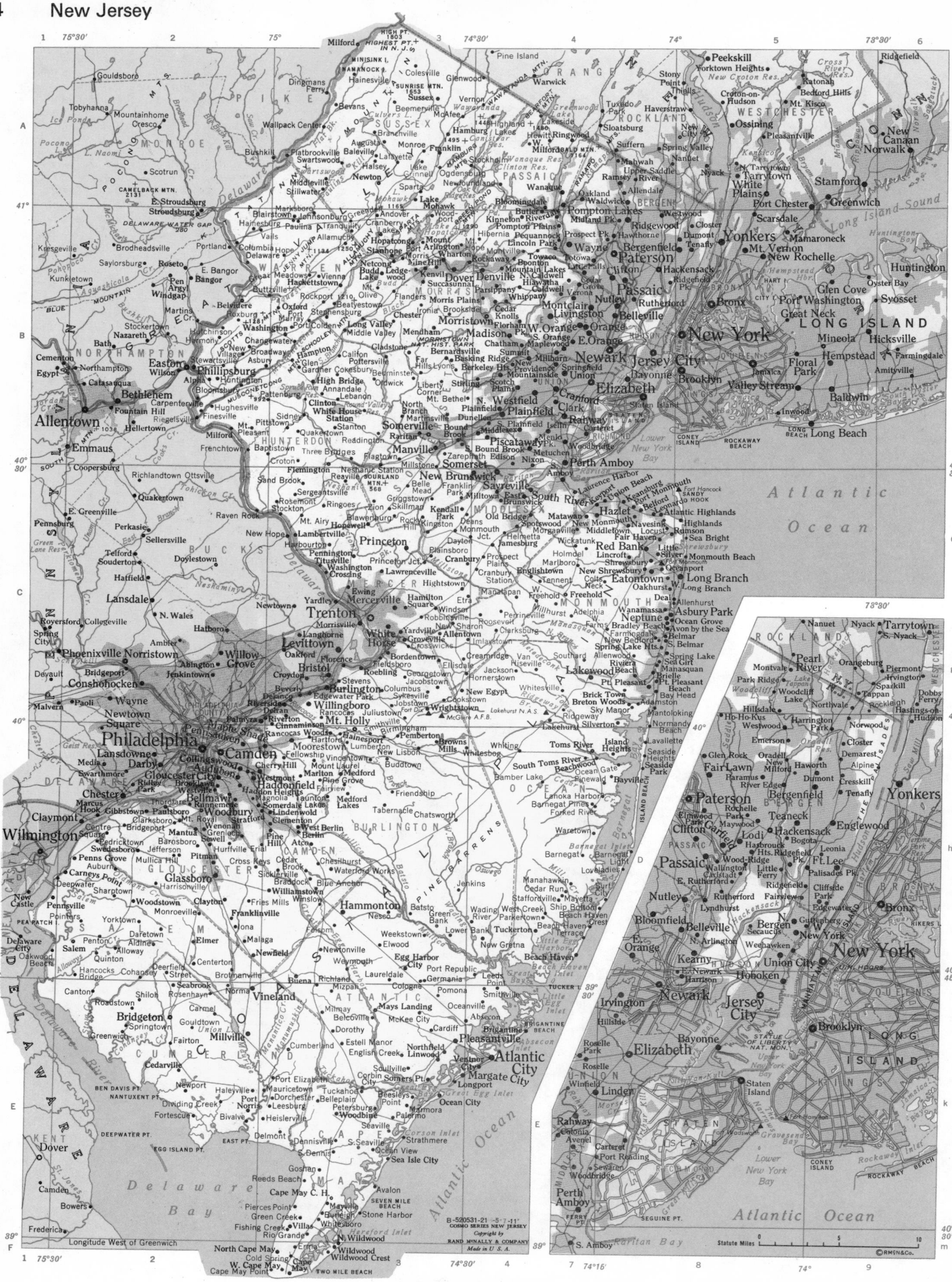

New Jersey

Longitude West of Greenwich

Statute Miles
Kilometers

Lambert Conformal Conic Projection

B-520531-21 —5-7-11
COSMO SERIES NEW JERSEY
Copyright by
RAND M^cNALLY & COMPANY
Made in U.S.A.

©RM&N&Co.

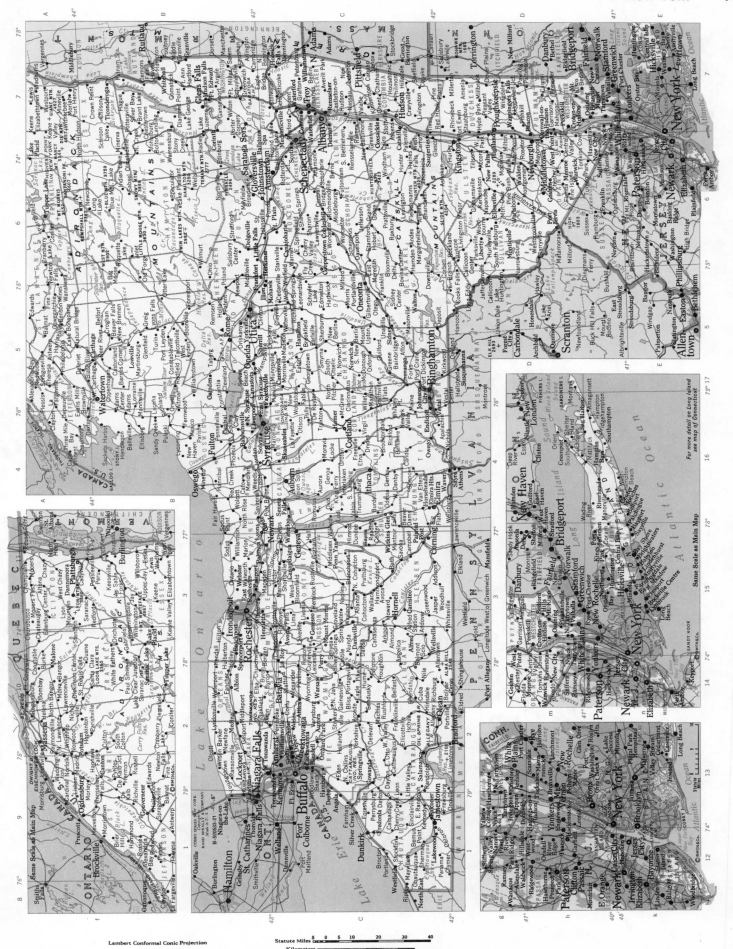

Lambert Conformal Conic Projection

Statute Miles 5 0 5 10 20 30 40

Kilometers 5 0 5 15 25 35 45 55

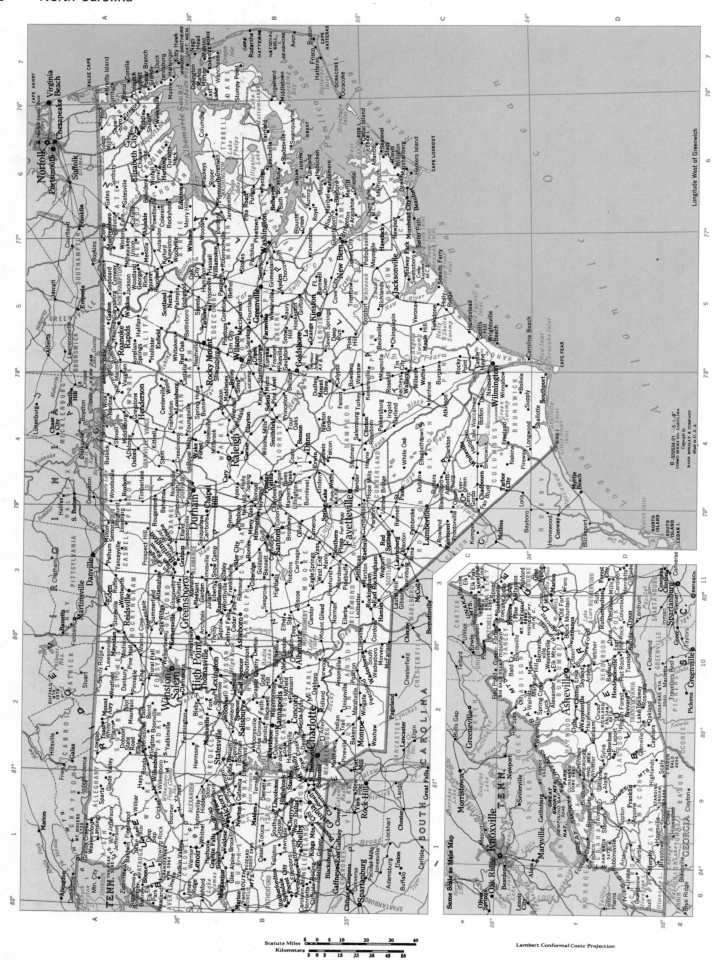

Statute Miles
Kilometers

Lambert Conformal Conic Projection

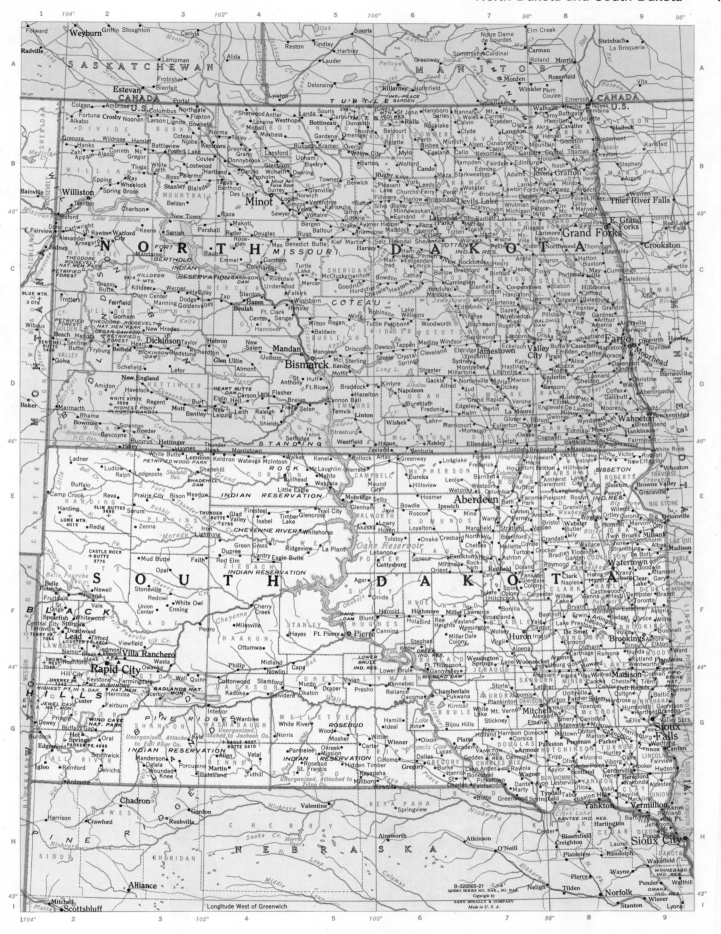

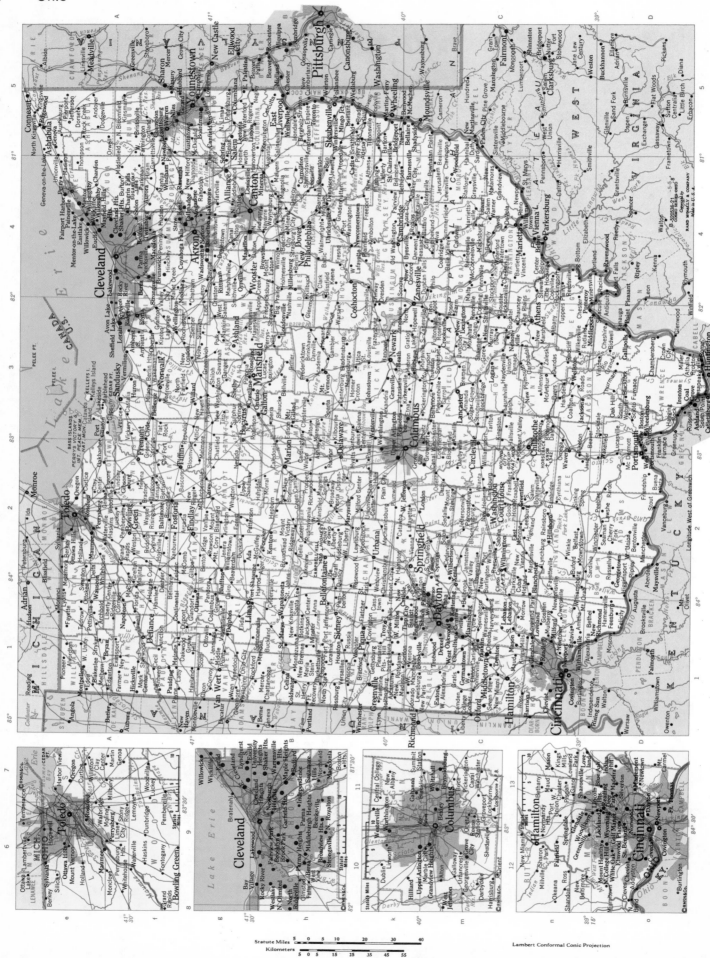

Statute Miles
Kilometers

Lambert Conformal Conic Projection

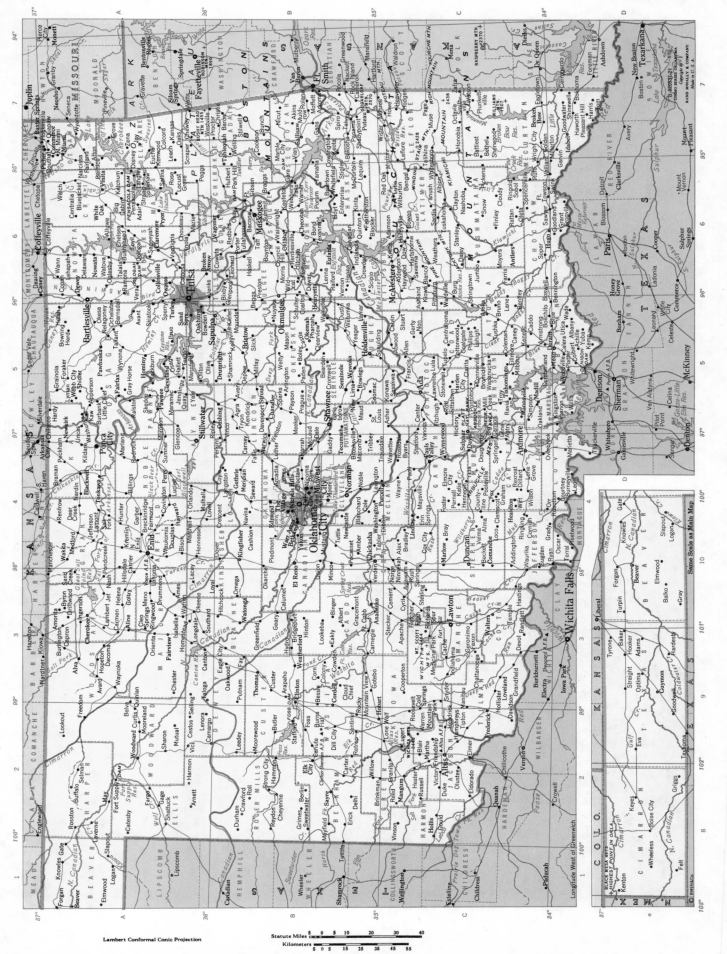

Lambert Conformal Conic Projection

Statute Miles
5 0 10   20   30   40

Kilometers
5 0 5   15   25   35   45   55

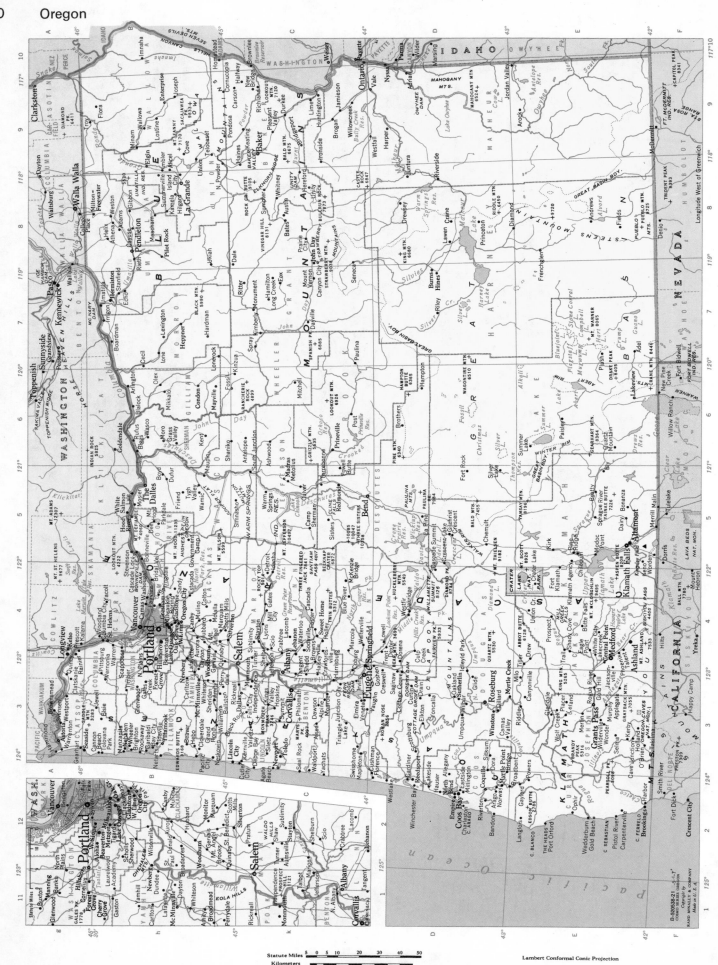

Statute Miles

Kilometers

Lambert Conformal Conic Projection

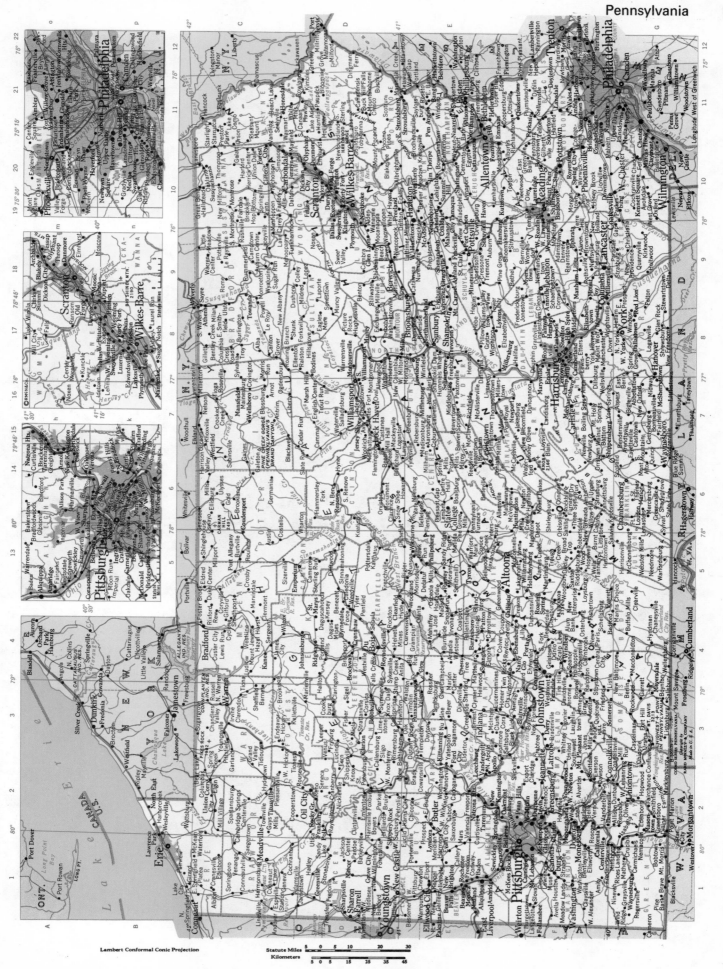

Lambert Conformal Conic Projection

Statute Miles
Kilometers

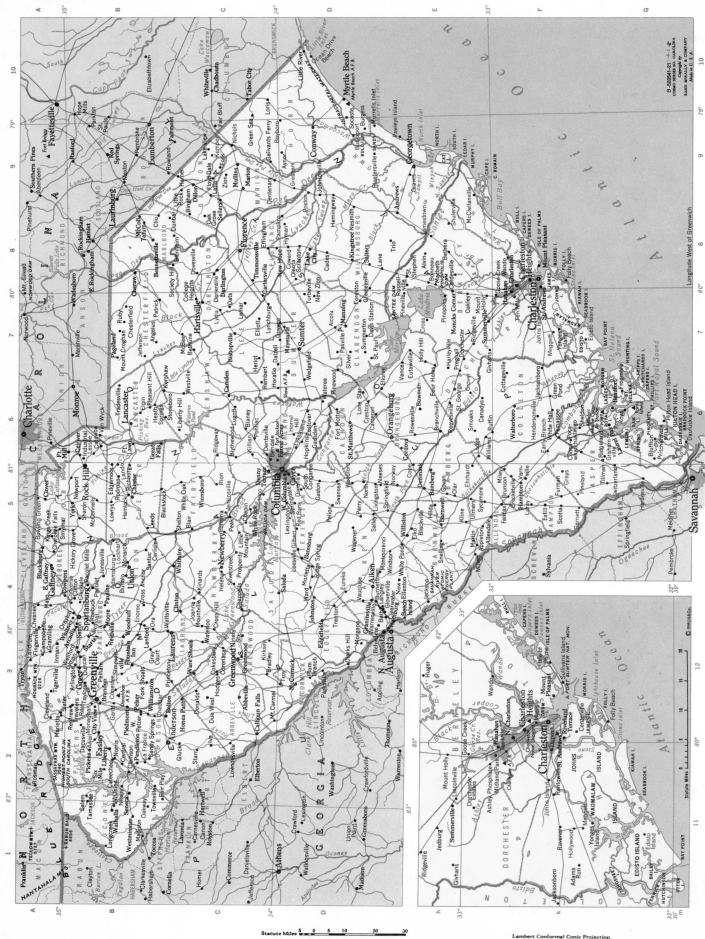

Statute Miles

Kilometers

Lambert Conformal Conic Projection

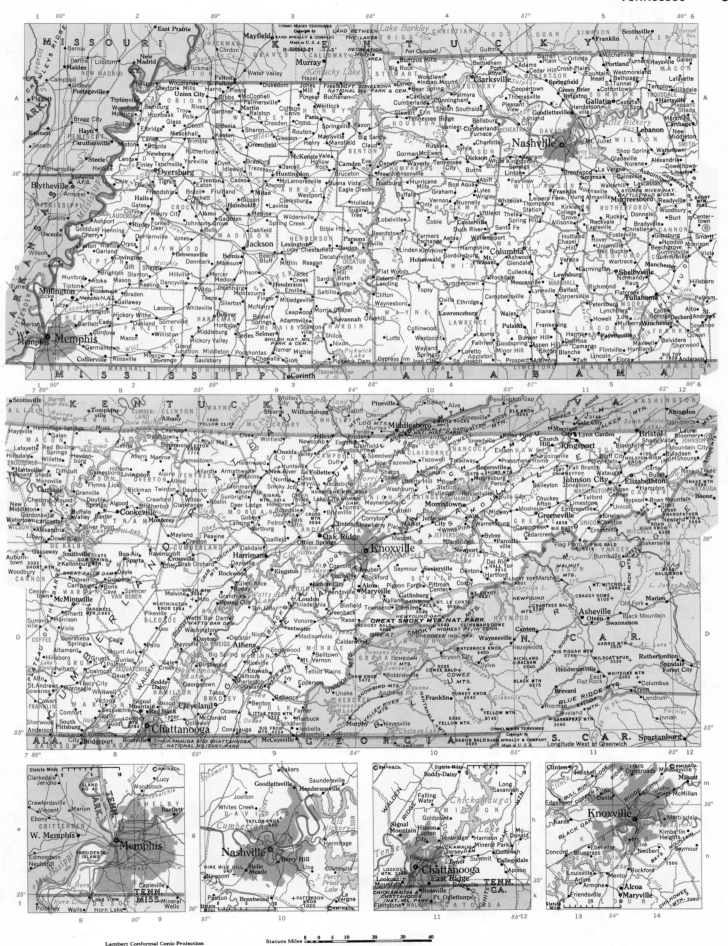

Lambert Conformal Conic Projection

Statute Miles

Kilometers

Statute Miles 10 0 10 20 30 40 50 60 70 80 90 100

Kilometers 10 0 10 20 40 60 80 100 120 140

Lambert Conformal Conic Projection

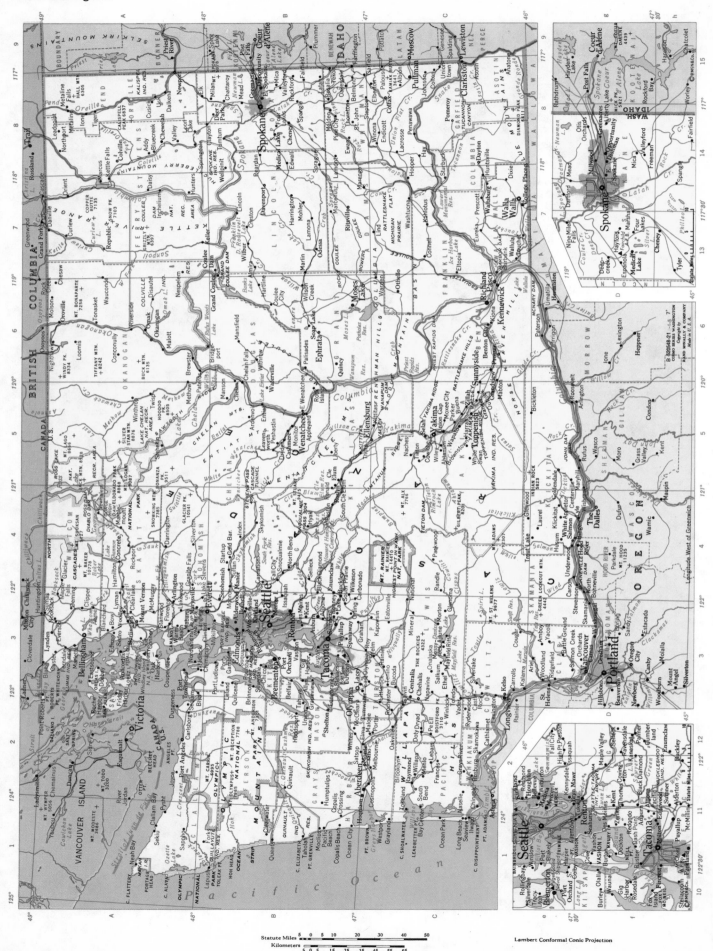

Statute Miles 5 0 5 10 20 30 40 50
Kilometers 5 0 5 15 25 35 45 55 65

Lambert Conformal Conic Projection

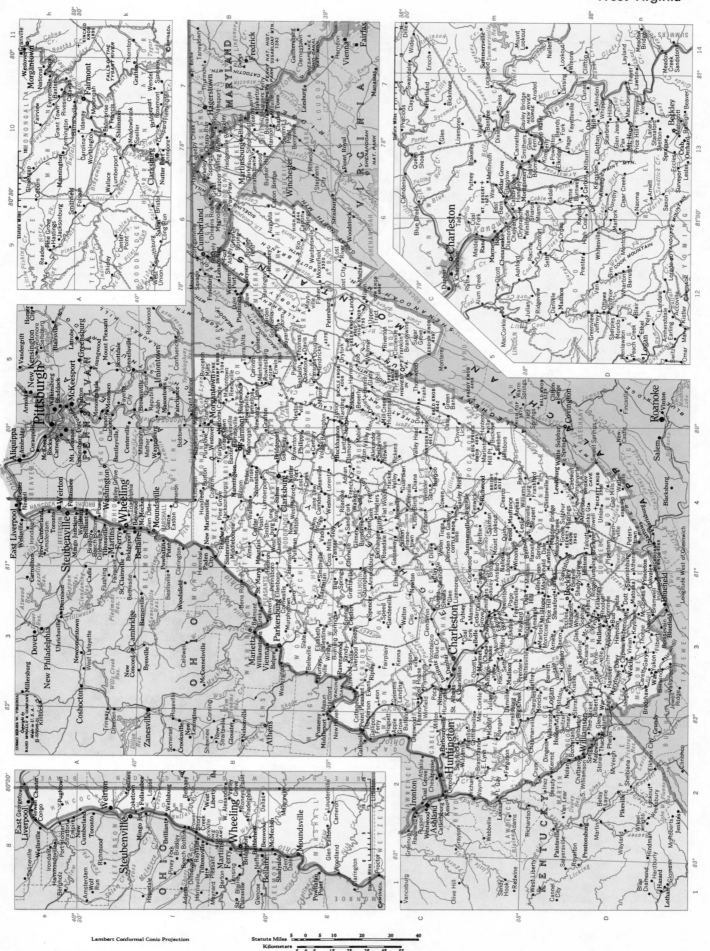

Lambert Conformal Conic Projection

Statute Miles 5 0 5 10 20 30 40

Kilometers 5 0 5 15 25 35 45 55

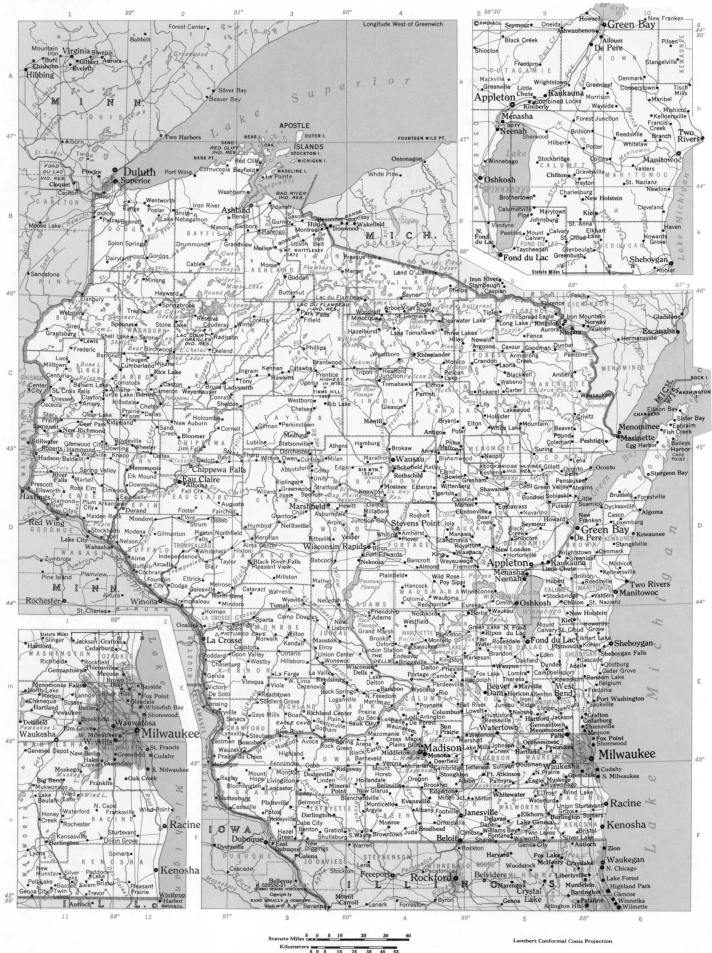

Statute Miles
Kilometers

Lambert Conformal Conic Projection

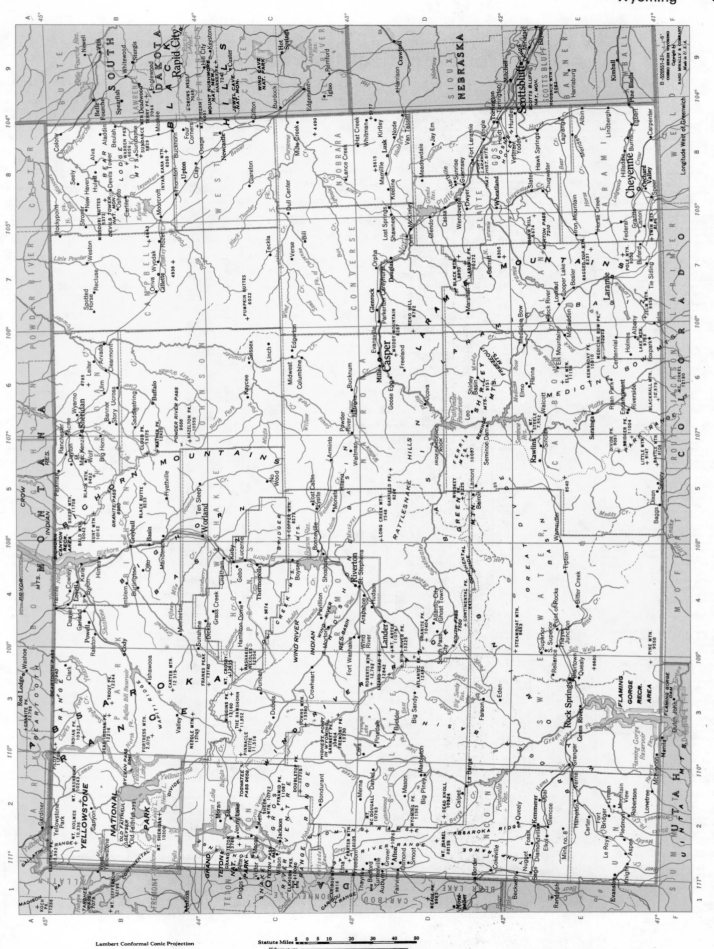

Lambert Conformal Conic Projection

Statute Miles 5 0 5 10 20 30 40 50

Kilometers 5 0 5 15 25 35 45 55 65 75

World Political Information Table

This table lists all countries and dependencies in the world, U.S. States, Canadian provinces, and other important regions and political subdivisions. Besides specifying the form of government for all political areas, the table classifies them into six groups according to their political status. Units labeled **A** are independent sovereign nations. (Several of these are designated as members of the British Commonwealth of Nations.) Units labeled **B** are independent as regards internal affairs, but for purposes of foreign affairs they are under the protection of another country. Areas under military government are also labeled **B**. Units labeled **C** are colonies, overseas territories, dependencies, etc., of other countries. Together the **A**, **B**, and **C** areas comprise practically the entire inhabited area of the world. The areas labeled **D** are physically separate units, such as groups of islands, which are *not* separate countries, but form part of a nation or dependency. Units labeled **E** are States, provinces, Soviet Republics, or similar major administrative subdivisions of important countries. Units in the table with no letter designation are regions or other areas that do not constitute separate political units by themselves.

Region or Political Division	Area in sq. miles	Estimated Population 1/1/1974	Pop. per sq. mi.	Form of Government and Ruling Power	Capital; Largest City (unless same)	Predominant Languages
Aden, see Yemen, P.D.R. of	....	....	......	....	....	....
Afars & Issas (French Somaliland)	8,900	95,000	11	Overseas Territory (France)...C	Djibouti	Somali, French
Afghanistan†	250,000	18,475,000	74	Republic...A	Kabul	Pushtu (Afghan), Persian
Africa	11,685,000	383,200,000	33	....	........; Cairo	....
Alabama	51,609	3,523,000	68	State (U.S.)...E	Montgomery; Birmingham	....
Alaska	586,412	337,000	0.6	State U.S.)...E	Juneau; Anchorage	English, Indian, Eskimo
Albania†	11,100	2,380,000	214	People's Republic...A	Tiranë	Albanian
Alberta	255,285	1,700,000	6.7	Province (Canada)...E	Edmonton	English
Algeria†	919,595	16,000,000	17	Republic...A	Algiers (Alger)	Arabic, French, Berber
American Samoa	76	30,000	395	Unincorporated Territory (U.S.)...C	Pago Pago	Polynesian, English
Andaman & Nicobar Is.	3,202	130,000	41	Territory (India)...D	Port Blair	Andaman, Nicobar Malay
Andorra	175	23,000	131	Principality...A	Andorra	Catalan
Angola	481,353	5,945,000	12	Overseas Province (Portugal)...C	Luanda	Bantu languages, Portuguese
Antarctica	5,100,000	....	....	....	....	....
Antigua (incl. Barbuda)	171	74,000	433	Associated State (U.K.)...B	St. Johns	English
Arabian Peninsula	1,145,636	18,785,000	16	....	........; Riyadh	Arabic
Argentina†	1,072,162	24,450,000	23	Federal Republic...A	Buenos Aires	Spanish
Arizona	113,909	2,064,000	18	State (U.S.)...E	Phoenix	....
Arkansas	53,104	1,994,000	38	State (U.S.)...E	Little Rock	....
Armenia (S.S.R.)	11,500	2,645,000	230	Soviet Socialist Republic (Sov. Un.)...E	Yerevan	Armenian, Russian
Aruba	69	63,000	913	Division of Netherlands Antilles (Neth.)...D	Oranjestad	Dutch, Spanish, English, Papiamento
Ascension I.	34	1,500	44	Dependency of St. Helena (U.K.)...D	Georgetown	English
Asia	17,085,000	2,273,200,000	133	....	........; Tōkyō	....
Australia†	2,967,909	13,335,000	4.5	Monarchy (Federal) (Br. Commonwealth of Nations)...A	Canberra; Sydney	English
Australian Capital Territory	939	170,000	181	Federal Territory (Australia)...E	Canberra	English
Austria†	32,374	7,550,000	233	Federal Republic...A	Vienna (Wien)	German
Azerbaidzhan (S.S.R.)	33,450	5,425,000	162	Soviet Socialist Republic (Sov. Un.)...E	Baku	Turkic languages, Russian, Armenian
Azores Is.	905	270,000	298	Part of Portugal (3 Districts)...D	........; Ponta Delgada	Portuguese
Baden-Wurttemberg	13,803	9,195,000	666	State (Federal Republic of Germany)...E	Stuttgart	German
Bahamas	5,380	205,000	38	Self-Governing Member (Br. Comm. of Nations)...A	Nassau	English
Bahrain†	231	235,000	1,017	Sheikdom...A	Manama	Arabic
Balearic Is.	1,936	650,000	336	Part of Spain (Baleares Province)...D	Palma de Mallorca	Catalan
Baltic Republics	67,150	7,150,000	106	Soviet Union........	........; Riga	Lithuanian, Latvian, Estonian, Russian
Bangladesh†	55,126	77,450,000	1,405	Republic (Br. Comm. of Nations)...A	Dacca	Bengali
Barbados†	166	250,000	1,506	Self-Governing Member (Br. Comm. of Nations)...A	Bridgetown	English
Basutoland, see Lesotho	....	....	....	....	....	....
Bavaria (Bayern)	27,239	10,810,000	397	State (Federal Republic of Germany)...E	Munich (München)	German
Bechuanaland, see Botswana	....	....	....	....	....	....
Belgium†	11,781	9,760,000	828	Monarchy...A	Brussels (Bruxelles)	Dutch, French
Belize (British Honduras)	8,867	130,000	15	Colony (U.K.)...C	Belmopan; Belize	English, Spanish, Indian languages
Benelux	28,549	23,660,000	829	....	Brussels (Bruxelles)	Dutch, French, Luxembourgeois
Berlin, West	185	2,050,000	11,081	State (Federal Republic of Germany)...E	Berlin (West)	German
Bermuda	21	56,000	2,667	Colony (U.K.)...C	Hamilton	English
Bhutan†	18,200	990,000	54	Monarchy (Indian protection)...B	Thimbu and Paro	Tibetan dialects
Bismarck Archipelago	18,965	250,000	13	Part of Australian Trust Ter. of New Guinea (3 Districts)...D	........; Rabaul	Malay-Polynesian and Papuan languages, English
Bolivia†	424,164	5,385,000	13	Republic...A	Sucre and La Paz; La Paz	Spanish, Quechua, Aymará, Guaraní
Borneo, Indonesian (Kalimantan)	208,286	5,385,000	26	Part of Indonesia (4 Provinces)...D	........; Bandjarmasin	Bahasa Indonesia (Indonesian)
Botswana (Bechuanaland)†	231,805	585,000	2.5	Republic (Br. Commonwealth of Nations)...A	Gaborone; Serowe	Bechuana, other Bantu languages, English
Brazil†	3,286,487	103,270,000	31	Federal Republic...A	Brasília; São Paulo	Portuguese
Bremen	156	745,000	4,776	State (Federal Republic of Germany)...E	Bremen	German
British Antarctic Territory (excl. Antarctic mainland)	2,040	Winter pop. 75	....	Colony (U.K.)...C	Stanley, Falkland Islands	....
British Columbia	366,255	2,330,000	6.4	Province (Canada)...E	Victoria; Vancouver	English
British Commonwealth of Nations	10,676,384	924,160,000	87	....	London	....
British Guiana, see Guyana	....	....	....	....	....	....
British Indian Ocean Territory	29	1,000	34	Colony (U.K.)...C	Victoria, Seychelles	Creole, English, French
Brunei	2,226	149,000	67	Sultanate (U.K. protection)...C	Bandar Seri Begawan (Brunei)	Malay-Polynesian languages, English
Bulgaria†	42,823	8,680,000	203	People's Republic...A	Sofia (Sofiya)	Bulgarian
Burma†	261,790	29,695,000	113	Federal Republic...A	Rangoon	Burmese, English
Burundi (Urundi)†	10,747	3,825,000	356	Republic...A	Bujumbura	Bantu and Hamitic languages, French
Byelorussia (Belorussia) (S.S.R.)†	80,150	9,320,000	116	Soviet Socialist Republic (Sov. Un.)...E	Minsk	Byelorussian, Polish, Russian
California	158,693	20,853,000	131	State (U.S.)...E	Sacramento; Los Angeles	....
Cambodia†	69,898	7,535,000	108	Republic...A	Phnom Penh	Cambodian (Khmer), French
Cameroon†	183,569	6,250,000	34	Federal Republic...A	Yaoundé; Douala	Native languages, French
Canada†	3,851,809	22,245,000	5.8	Monarchy (Federal) (Br. Commonwealth of Nations)...A	Ottawa; Montréal	English, French
Canal Zone	558	45,000	81	Under U.S. Jurisdiction...C	Balboa Heights; Balboa	Spanish, English
Canary Is.	2,808	1,290,000	459	Part of Spain (2 Provinces)...D	........; Las Palmas	Spanish
Canton & Enderbury	27	....	....	U.K.-U.S. Administration...C	Canton Island	Malay-Polynesian languages, English
Cape Verde Is.	1,557	285,000	183	Overseas Province (Portugal)...C	Praia; Mindelo	Portuguese
Caroline Is.	463	69,000	149	Part of U.S. Pacific Is. Trust Ter. (4 Districts)...D	....	Malay-Polynesian languages, English
Cayman Is.	100	12,000	120	Colony (U.K.)...C	Georgetown	English
Celebes (Sulawesi)	72,987	8,855,000	121	Part of Indonesia (2 Provinces)...D	........; Makasar	Bahasa Indonesia (Indonesian), Malay-Polynesian languages
Central African Republic†	240,535	1,715,000	7.1	Republic...A	Bangui	Bantu languages, French
Central America	202,063	18,405,000	91	....	........; Guatemala	Spanish, Indian languages
Central Asia, Soviet	493,950	21,375,000	43	Soviet Union........	........; Tashkent	Uzbek, Russian, Kirghiz, Turkoman, Tadzhik
Ceylon, see Sri Lanka	....	....	....	....	....	....
Chad†	495,800	3,915,000	7.9	Republic...A	Ndjamena (Fort Lamy)	Hamitic languages, Arabic, French
Channel Is. (Guernsey, Jersey, etc.)	75	130,000	1,733	....	........; St. Helier	English, French
Chile†	292,258	9,315,000	32	Republic...A	Santiago	Spanish
China (excl. Taiwan)†	3,691,500	821,010,000	222	People's Republic...A	Peking (Peiching); Shanghai	Chinese, Mongolian, Turkic, Tungus
China (Nationalist), see Taiwan	....	....	....	....	....	....

† *Member of the United Nations (1974).*

Region or Political Division	Area in sq. miles	Estimated Population 1/1/1974	Pop. per sq. mi.	Form of Government and Ruling Power	Capital; Largest City (unless same)	Predominant Languages
Christmas I. (Indian Ocean)	52	2,300	44	External Territory (Australia)........C	....	Chinese, Malay, English
Cocos (Keeling) Is.	5	600	120	External Territory (Australia)........C	....	Malay, English
Colombia†	439,737	23,530,000	54	Republic........A	Bogotá	Spanish
Colorado	104,247	2,486,000	24	State (U.S.)........E	Denver	....
Commonwealth of Nations, see Br. Commonwealth of Nations	....	....	....	....	....	....
Comoro Is.	838	295,000	352	Overseas Territory (France)........C	Moroni	Malagasy, French
Congo (Rep. of Congo; Capital Brazzaville)†	132,000	1,115,000	8.4	Republic........A	Brazzaville	Bantu languages, French
Congo, The, see Zaire	....	....	....	....	....	....
Connecticut	5,009	3,102,000	619	State (U.S.)........E	Hartford	....
Cook Is.	93	22,000	237	Self-Governing Territory, (New Zealand)........C	Avarua	Malay-Polynesian languages
Corsica	3,352	195,000	58	Part of France (Corse Department)........D	Ajaccio; Bastia	French, Italian
Costa Rica†	19,650	1,900,000	97	Republic........A	San José	Spanish
Cuba†	44,218	8,970,000	203	Republic........A	Havana (La Habana)	Spanish
Curaçao	173	152,000	879	Division of Netherlands Antilles (Neth.)........D	Willemstad	Dutch, Spanish, English, Papiamento
Cyprus †	3,572	655,000	183	Republic (Br. Commonwealth of Nations)........A	Nicosia	Greek, Turkish, English
Czechoslovakia†	49,373	14,590,000	296	People's Republic........A	Prague (Praha)	Czech, Slovak
Dahomey†	43,484	2,935,000	67	Republic........A	Porto Novo; Cotonou	Native languages, French
Delaware	2,057	573,000	279	State (U.S.)........E	Dover; Wilmington	....
Denmark†	16,629	5,035,000	303	Monarchy........A	Copenhagen (København)	Danish
Denmark and Possessions	857,169	5,128,000	6.0	....	Copenhagen (København)	Danish, Faeroese, Greenlandic
District of Columbia	67	740,000	11,045	District (U.S.)........E	Washington	....
Dominica	290	74,000	255	Associated State (U.K.)........B	Roseau	English, French
Dominican Republic†	18,816	4,470,000	238	Republic........A	Santo Domingo	Spanish
Ecuador†	109,483	6,825,000	62	Republic........A	Quito; Guayaquil	Spanish, Quechua
Egypt (United Arab Republic)†	386,900	35,975,000	93	Republic‡‡........A	Cairo (Al Qāhirah)	Arabic
El Salvador†	8,260	4,070,000	493	Republic........A	San Salvador	Spanish
England (excl. Monmouthshire)	50,332	46,745,000	929	United Kingdom........	........; London	English
England & Wales	58,348	49,520,000	849	Administrative division of United Kingdom........E	London	English, Welsh
Equatorial Guinea†	10,830	305,000	28	Republic........A	Malabo	Bantu languages, Spanish
Estonia (S.S.R.)	17,400	1,415,000	81	Soviet Socialist Republic (Sov. Un.)........E	Tallinn	Estonian, Russian
Ethiopia†	471,778	26,465,000	56	Monarchy........A	Addis Ababa	Amharic and other Semitic languages, English, various Hamitic languages
Eurasia	20,910,000	2,915,400,000	139	....	........; Tōkyō	....
Europe	3,825,000	642,200,000	168	....	........; London	....
Faeroe Is.	540	40,000	74	Self-Governing Territory (Denmark)........B	Tórshavn	Danish, Faeroese
Falkland Is. (excl. Deps)	4,618	2,000	0.4	Colony (U.K.)........C	Stanley	English
Fernando Poo	785	83,000	106	Part of Equatorial Guinea........D	Santa Isabel	Bantu languages, Spanish
Fiji†	7,055	560,000	79	Monarchy (Federal) (Br. Comm. of Nations)........A	Suva	Malaya-Polynesian languages, English, Hindi
Finland†	130,129	4,620,000	36	Republic........A	Helsinki	Finnish, Swedish
Florida	58,560	7,881,000	135	State (U.S.)........E	Tallahassee; Jacksonville	....
France†	210,039	52,430,000	250	Republic........A	Paris	French
France and Possessions	239,575	54,468,000	228	....	Paris	....
Franklin	549,253	9,500	0.02	District of Northwest Territories, Canada........E	........; Cambridge Bay	English, Eskimo, Indian
French Guiana	35,100	58,000	1.7	Overseas Department (France)........C	Cayenne	French
French Polynesia	1,550	132,000	85	Overseas Territory (France)........C	Papeete	Malay-Polynesian languages, French
French Somaliland see Afars & Issas	....	....	....	....	....	....
French Southern & Antarctic Ter. (excl. Adélie Coast)	2,918	300	0.1	Overseas Territory (France)........C	....	French
French West Indies	1,112	700,000	629	....	........; Fort-de-France	French
Gabon†	103,347	515,000	5.0	Republic........A	Libreville	Bantu languages, French
Galápagos Is. (Colon, Archipélago de)	3,075	4,000	1.3	Province (Ecuador)........D	Puerto Baquerizo	Spanish
Gambia†	4,361	400,000	92	Republic (Br. Comm. of Nations)........A	Banjul (Bathurst)	Mandingo, Fula, English
Georgia (S.S.R.)	26,900	4,880,000	181	Soviet Socialist Republic (Sov. Un.)........E	Tbilisi	Georgic, Armenian, Russian
Georgia	58,876	4,808,000	82	State (U.S.)........E	Atlanta	....
Germany (Entire)	137,727	79,105,000	574	....	........; Berlin	German
German Democratic Republic (East Germany)	41,768	16,990,000	407	People's Republic........A	Berlin (East)	German
Germany, Federal Republic of (West Germany)	95,959	62,115,000	647	Federal Republic........A	Bonn; Berlin (West)	German
Ghana†	92,100	9,430,000	102	Republic (Br. Commonwealth of Nations)........A	Accra	Twi, Fanti, Ewe-Fon, English
Gibraltar	2	29,000	14,500	Colony (U.K.)........C	Gibraltar	Spanish, English
Gilbert & Ellice Is.	283	60,000	212	Colony (U.K.)........C	Tarawa	Malay-Polynesian languages, English
Great Britain & Northern Ireland, see United Kingdom	....	....	....	....	....	....
Greece†	50,944	8,875,000	174	Republic........A	Athens (Athínai)	Greek
Greenland	840,000	53,000	0.06	Overseas Territory (Denmark)........C	Godthåb	Greenlandic, Danish, Eskimo
Grenada†	133	97,000	729	Self-Governing Member (Br. Comm. of Nations)........A	St. George's	English
Guadeloupe (incl. Dependencies)	687	345,000	502	Overseas Department (France)........C	Basse-Terre; Pointe-à-Pitre	French
Guam	212	92,000	434	Unincorporated Territory (U.S.)........C	Agana	English, Chamorro
Guatemala†	42,042	5,810,000	138	Republic........A	Guatemala	Spanish, Indian languages
Guernsey (incl. Dependencies)	30	55,000	1,833	Bailiwick (U.K.)........C	St. Peter Port	English, French
Guinea†	94,926	4,260,000	45	Republic........A	Conakry	Native languages, French
Guinea-Bissau†	13,948	475,000	34	Republic........A	Bissau	Native languages, Portuguese
Guyana†	83,000	770,000	9.3	Republic (Br. Comm. of Nations)........A	Georgetown	English
Haiti†	10,714	5,420,000	506	Republic........A	Port-au-Prince	Creole, French
Hamburg	288	1,800,000	6,250	State (Federal Republic of Germany)........E	Hamburg	German
Hawaii	6,450	842,000	131	State (U.S.)........E	Honolulu	English, Japanese, Hawaiian
Hesse (Hessen)	8,150	5,590,000	686	State (Federal Republic of Germany)........E	Wiesbaden; Frankfurt am Main	German
Hispaniola	29,530	9,890,000	335	....	........; Santo Domingo	French, Spanish
Holland, see Netherlands	....	....	....	....	....	....
Honduras†	43,277	2,765,000	64	Republic........A	Tegucigalpa	Spanish
Hong Kong	399	4,225,000	10,589	Colony (U.K.)........C	Victoria	Chinese, English
Hungary†	35,920	10,470,000	291	People's Republic........A	Budapest	Hungarian
Iceland†	39,800	210,000	5.3	Republic........A	Reykjavík	Icelandic
Idaho	83,557	742,000	8.9	State (U.S.)........E	Boise (Boise City)	....
Illinois	56,400	11,273,000	200	State (U.S.)........E	Springfield; Chicago	....
India (incl. part of Kashmir)†	1,226,466	581,200,000	474	Republic (Br. Commonwealth of Nations)........A	New Delhi; Calcutta	Hindi and other Indo-Aryan languages, Dravidian languages, English
Indiana	36,291	5,344,000	147	State (U.S.)........E	Indianapolis	....
Indonesia (incl. West Irian)	735,271	127,740,000	170	Republic........A	Djakarta	Bahasa Indonesia (Indonesian), Chinese, English
Iowa	56,290	2,891,000	51	State (U.S.)........E	Des Moines	....
Iran (Persia)†	636,300	31,830,000	50	Monarchy........A	Tehrān	Persian, Turkish dialects, Kurdish
Iraq†	167,925	10,410,000	62	Republic........A	Baghdād	Arabic, Kurdish
Ireland†	27,137	3,045,000	112	Republic........A	Dublin	English, Irish
Isle of Man	227	58,000	256	Possession (U.K.)........C	Douglas	English
Israel†	8,019	3,195,000	398	Republic‡‡........A	Jerusalem; Tel Aviv-Yafo	Hebrew, Arabic
Italy†	116,313	54,980,000	473	Republic........A	Rome (Roma); Milan (Milano)	Italian

† *Member of the United Nations (1974).*
‡‡ *As of late 1967, the Gaza Strip was under Israeli military occupation. Data for Egypt, Israel, Jordan and Syria do not reflect de facto changes which took place during 1967.*

Region or Political Division	Area in sq. miles	Estimated Population 1/1/1974	Pop. per sq. mi.	Form of Government and Ruling Power	Capital; Largest City (unless same)	Predominant Languages
Ivory Coast†	124,504	4,695,000	38	Republic ... A	Abidjan	French, native languages
Jamaica†	4,232	1,960,000	463	Self-Governing Member (Br. Comm. of Nations) ... A	Kingston	English
Japan†	143,706	108,960,000	758	Monarchy ... A	Tōkyō	Japanese
Java (Djawa) (incl. Madura)	51,040	79,000,000	1,548	Part of Indonesia (5 Provinces) ... D	........; Djakarta	Bahasa Indonesia (Indonesian), Chinese, English
Jersey	45	75,000	1,667	Bailiwick (U.K.) ... C	St. Helier	English, French
Jordan†	37,738	2,555,000	68	Monarchy‡‡ ... A	'Ammān	Arabic
Kansas	82,264	2,255,000	27	State (U.S.) ... E	Topeka; Wichita	....
Kashmir, Jammu &	86,024	6,135,000	71	In dispute (India & Pakistan)	Srinagar	Kashmiri, Punjabi
Kazakh S.S.R.	1,048,300	13,720,000	13	Soviet Socialist Republic (Sov. Un.) ... E	Alma-Ata	Turkic languages, Russian
Keewatin	228,160	4,000	0.02	District of Northwest Territories, Canada ... E	........; Baker Lake	English, Eskimo, Indian
Kentucky	40,395	3,322,000	82	State (U.S.) ... E	Frankfort; Louisville	....
Kenya†	224,960	12,690,000	56	Republic (Br. Comm. of Nations) ... A	Nairobi	Swahili and other Bantu languages, English
Kerguelen	2,700	85	0.03	Part of French Southern & Antarctic Ter. (Fr.) ... D	....	French
Kirghiz S.S.R.	76,650	3,130,000	41	Soviet Socialist Republic (Sov. Un.) ... E	Frunze	Turkic languages, Persian, Russian
Korea (Entire)	85,049‡	49,445,000	581	....	........; Seoul (Sŏul)	Korean
Korea, North	46,540	15,275,000	328	People's Republic ... A	Pyongyang	Korean
Korea, South	38,022	34,170,000	899	Republic ... A	Seoul (Sŏul)	Korean
Kuwait†	6,200	1,035,000	167	Sheikdom ... A	Kuwait (Al Kuwayt)	Arabic
Labrador	112,826	30,000	0.3	Part of Newfoundland Province, Canada ... D	........; Labrador City	English, Eskimo
Laos†	91,400	3,215,000	35	Monarchy ... A	Vientiane	Lao, French
Latin America	7,925,708	306,040,000	39	....	........; São Paulo	....
Latvia (S.S.R.)	24,600	2,455,000	100	Soviet Socialist Republic (Sov. Un.) ... E	Riga	Latvian, Russian
Lebanon†	3,950	3,115,000	789	Republic ... A	Beirut (Bayrūt)	Arabic, French, English
Lesotho (Basutoland)†	11,720	1,110,000	95	Monarchy (Br. Comm. of Nations) ... A	Maseru	Kaffir, other Bantu languages, English
Liberia†	43,000	1,695,000	39	Republic ... A	Monrovia	Native languages, English
Libya†	679,362	2,195,000	3.2	Republic ... A	Tripoli and Bengasi; Tripoli	Arabic
Liechtenstein	62	23,000	371	Principality ... A	Vaduz	German
Lithuania (S.S.R.)	25,150	3,280,000	130	Soviet Socialist Republic (Sov. Un.) ... E	Vilnius	Lithuanian, Polish, Russian
Louisiana	48,523	3,799,000	78	State (U.S.) ... E	Baton Rouge; New Orleans	....
Lower Saxony (Niedersachsen)	18,299	7,270,000	397	State (Federal Republic of Germany) ... E	Hannover (Hanover)	German
Luxembourg†	998	350,000	351	Grand Duchy ... A	Luxembourg	Luxembourgeois, French
Macao	6	285,000	47,500	Overseas Province (Portugal) ... C	Macao	Chinese, Portuguese
Mackenzie	527,490	26,500	0.05	District of Northwest Territories, Canada ... E	........; Yellowknife	English, Eskimo, Indian
Madagascar (Malagasy Republic)†	226,658	7,290,000	32	Republic ... A	Tananarive	French Malagasy
Madeira Is.	308	245,000	795	Part of Portugal (Funchal District) ... D	Funchal	Portuguese
Maine	33,215	1,045,000	31	State (U.S.) ... E	Augusta; Portland	....
Malawi (Nyasaland)†	45,747	4,845,000	106	Republic (Br. Comm. of Nations) ... A	Zomba; Blantyre	Bantu languages, English
Malaya	50,700	9,505,000	187	Part of Malaysia	Kuala Lumpur	Malay, Chinese, English
Malaysia†	128,430	11,295,000	88	Self-Governing Member (Br. Comm. of Nations) ... A	Kuala Lumpur	Malay, Chinese, English
Maldives†	115	126,000	1,096	Republic ... A	Male	Arabic, English
Mali†	478,655	5,425,000	11	Republic ... A	Bamako	Native languages, French, Arabic
Malta†	122	340,000	2,787	Self-Governing Member (Br. Comm. of Nations) ... A	Valletta	English, Maltese
Manitoba	251,000	1,010,000	4.0	Province (Canada) ... E	Winnipeg	English
Mariana Is. (excl. Guam)	184	13,000	71	District of U.S. Pacific Is. Trust Ter. ... D	Saipan	Malay-Polynesian languages, English
Maritime Provinces (excl.) Newfoundland)	51,963	1,580,000	30	Canada	........; Halifax	English
Marshall Is.	70	33,000	471	District of U.S. Pacific Is. Trust Ter ... D	Majuro	Malay-Polynesian languages, English
Martinique	425	355,000	835	Overseas Department (France) ... C	Fort-de-France	French
Maryland	10,577	4,113,000	389	State (U.S.) ... E	Annapolis; Baltimore	....
Massachusetts	8,257	5,822,000	705	State (U.S.) ... E	Boston	....
Mauritania†	397,950	1,275,000	3.2	Republic ... A	Nouakchott	Arabic, French
Mauritius (incl. Dependencies)†	789	875,000	1,109	Self-Governing Member (Br. Comm. of Nations) ... A	Port Louis	Indo-Aryan languages, French, Creole, English
Mexico†	761,604	55,310,000	73	Federal Republic ... A	Mexico City	Spanish
Michigan	58,216	9,101,000	156	State (U.S.) ... E	Lansing; Detroit	....
Middle America	1,055,708	100,540,000	95	....	........; Mexico City	....
Midway Is.	2	2,200	1,100	Possession (U.S.) ... C	....	English
Minnesota	84,068	3,947,000	47	State (U.S.) ... E	St. Paul; Minneapolis	....
Mississippi	47,716	2,288,000	48	State (U.S.) ... E	Jackson	....
Missouri	69,686	4,764,000	68	State (U.S.) ... E	Jefferson City; St. Louis	....
Moldavia (S.S.R.)	13,000	3,750,000	288	Soviet Socialist Republic (Sov. Un.) ... E	Kishinëv	Moldavian, Russian, Ukrainian
Monaco	0.6	26,000	43,333	Principality ... A	Monaco	French, Italian
Mongolia†	604,200	1,375,000	2.3	People's Republic ... A	Ulan Bator	Mongolian
Montana	147,138	726,000	4.9	State (U.S.) ... E	Helena; Billings	....
Montserrat	39	14,800	379	Colony (U.K.) ... C	Plymouth	English
Morocco†	172,415	16,495,000	96	Monarchy ... A	Rabat; Casablanca	Arabic, Berber, French
Mozambique	303,771	8,720,000	29	Overseas Province (Portugal) ... C	Lourenço Marques	Bantu Languages, Portuguese
Nauru	8	8,000	1,000	Republic (Br. Comm. of Nations) ... A	....	Malay-Polynesian languages, Chinese, English
Nebraska	77,227	1,543,000	20	State (U.S.) ... E	Lincoln; Omaha	....
Nepal†	54,362	11,745,000	216	Monarchy ... A	Kātmāndu	Nepali, Tibeto-Burman languages, English
Netherlands†	15,770	13,550,000	859	Monarchy ... A	Amsterdam and The Hague ('s Gravenhage); Amsterdam	Dutch
Netherlands and Possessions	79,178	14,230,000	180	....	Amsterdam and The Hague; Amsterdam	....
Netherlands Antilles	371	235,000	633	Self-Governing Territory (Netherlands) ... C	Willemstad	Dutch, Spanish, English, Papiamento
Netherlands Guiana, see Surinam	....	....	....	....	....	....
Nevada	110,540	583,000	5.3	State (U.S.) ... E	Carson City; Las Vegas	....
New Brunswick	28,354	655,000	23	Province (Canada) ... E	Fredericton; Saint John	English, French
New Caledonia (incl. Deps.)	7,358	130,000	18	Overseas Territory (France) ... C	Nouméa	Malay-Polynesian languages, French
New England	66,608	12,194,000	183	United States	........; Boston	English
Newfoundland	156,185	545,000	3.5	Province (Canada) ... E	St. John's	English
Newfoundland (excl. Labrador)	43,359	515,000	12	....	........; St. John's	English
New Guinea, North-East	69,095	1,620,000	23	Part of Australian Trust Ter. of New Guinea (3 Districts) ... D	........; Lae	Papuan and Negrito languages, English
New Guinea, Ter. of	92,160	1,955,000	21	Trust Territory (Austl.; administered from Papua) ... C	Port Moresby, Papua; Lae	Papuan and Negrito languages, English
New Hampshire	9,304	788,000	85	State (U.S.) ... E	Concord; Manchester	....
New Hebrides	5,700	88,000	15	Condominium (France-U.K.) ... C	Vila	Malay-Polynesian languages, French, English
New Jersey	7,836	7,361,000	939	State (U.S.) ... E	Trenton; Newark	....
New Mexico	121,666	1,090,000	9.0	State (U.S.) ... E	Santa Fe; Albuquerque	English, Spanish
New South Wales	309,433	4,780,000	15	State (Australia) ... E	Sydney	English
New York	49,576	18,292,000	369	State (U.S.) ... E	Albany; New York	....
New Zealand†	103,736	2,985,000	29	Monarchy (Br. Commonwealth of Nations) ... A	Wellington; Auckland	English
Nicaragua†	50,200	2,100,000	42	Republic ... A	Managua	Spanish
Niedersachsen, see Lower Saxony	....	....	....	....	....	....
Niger†	489,200	4,340,000	8.9	Republic ... A	Niamey	Hausa, Arabic, French

† *Member of the United Nations (1974).* ‡ *Includes 487 sq. miles of demilitarized zone, not included in North or South Korea figures.*
‡‡ *As of late 1967, the Gaza Area was under Israeli military occupation. Data for Egypt, Israel, Jordan, and Syria do not reflect de facto changes which took place during 1967.*

Region or Political Division	Area in sq. miles	Estimated Population 1/1/1974	Pop. per sq. mi.	Form of Government and Ruling Power	Capital; Largest City (unless same)	Predominant Languages
Nigeria†	356,669	60,260,000	169	Republic (Br. Commonwealth of Nations)............A	Lagos	Hausa, Ibo, Yoruba, English
Niue	100	4,900	49	Island Territory (New Zealand)............C	Alofi	Malay-Polynesian languages, English
Norfolk Island	14	1,600	114	External Territory (Australia)............C	Kingston	English
North America	9,420,000	334,200,000	35	....	.... ; New York	....
North Borneo, see Sabah	....	....	....			
North Carolina	52,586	5,274,000	100	State (U.S.)............E	Raleigh; Charlotte	....
North Dakota	70,665	632,000	8.9	State (U.S.)............E	Bismarck; Fargo	....
Northern Ireland	5,452	1,580,000	290	Administrative division of United Kingdom............E	Belfast	English
Northern Rhodesia, see Zambia						
Northern Territory	520,280	100,000	0.2	Territory (Australia)............E	Darwin	English, Aboriginal languages
North Polar Regions	....	....	....			
North Rhine-Westphalia (Nordrhein-Westfalen)	13,144	17,265,000	1,313	State (Federal Republic of Germany)............E	Düsseldorf; Cologne	German
Northwest Territories	1,304,903	40,000	0.03	Territory (Canada)............E	Yellowknife	English, Eskimo, Indian
Norway†	125,050	3,980,000	32	Monarchy............A	Oslo	Norwegian (Riksmål and Landsmål)
Nova Scotia	21,425	810,000	38	Province (Canada)............E	Halifax	English
Nyasaland, see Malawi	....					
Oceania (incl. Australia)	3,295,000	20,700,000	6.3		.... ; Sydney	....
Ohio	41,222	10,883,000	264	State (U.S.)............E	Columbus; Cleveland	....
Oklahoma	69,919	2,692,000	39	State (U.S.)............E	Oklahoma City	....
Oman†	82,030	725,000	8.8	Sultanate............A	Muscat; Maṭraḥ	Arabic
Ontario	412,582	7,990,000	19	Province (Canada)............E	Toronto	English
Oregon	96,981	2,227,000	23	State (U.S.)............E	Salem; Portland	English
Orkney Is.	376	16,900	46	Part of Scotland, U.K. (Orkney County)............D	Kirkwall	English
Pacific Islands Trust Territory	717	115,000	160	Trust Territory (U.S.)............C	Saipan	Malay-Polynesian languages, English
Pakistan (incl. part of Kashmir)	345,753	68,720,000	199	Federal Republic............A	Islamabad; Karachi	Urdu, English
Pakistan, East, see Bangladesh						
Palestine (Gaza Strip)	146	350,000	2,397	Military Government (Egypt)‡‡............B	Gaza (Ghazzah)	Arabic
Panama†	29,209	1,585,000	54	Republic............A	Panamá	Spanish
Papua (excl. New Guinea, Ter. of)	86,100	740,000	8.6	External Territory (Australia)............C	Port Moresby	Papuan and Negrito languages, English
Paraguay†	157,048	2,735,000	17	Republic............A	Asunción	Spanish, Guaraní
Pennsylvania	45,333	11,874,000	262	State (U.S.)............E	Harrisburg; Philadelphia	....
Persia, see Iran						
Peru†	496,224	14,140,000	28	Republic............A	Lima	Spanish, Quechua
Philippines†	115,831	40,665,000	351	Republic............A	Quezon City; Manila	Tagalog and other Malay-Polynesian languages, English
Pitcairn (excl. Dependencies)	2	100	50	Colony (U.K.)............C	Adamstown	English
Poland†	120,725	33,465,000	277	People's Republic............A	Warsaw (Warszawa)	Polish
Portugal†	35,553	8,770,000	247	Republic............A	Lisbon (Lisboa)	Portuguese
Portugal and Possessions	828,375	24,737,000	30		Lisbon (Lisboa)	
Portuguese Guinea, see Guinea-Bissau						
Portuguese Timor	5,763	655,000	114	Overseas Province (Portugal)............C	Dili	Malay, Papuan languages, Portuguese
Prairie Provinces	757,985	3,625,000	4.8	Canada	.... ; Winnipeg	English
Prince Edward Island	2,184	115,000	53	Province (Canada)............E	Charlottetown	English
Puerto Rico	3,435	2,875,000	837	Commonwealth (U.S.)............C	San Juan	Spanish, English
Qatar†	8,500	200,000	24	Sheikdom............A	Doha	Arabic
Quebec	594,860	6,115,000	10	Province (Canada)............E	Québec; Montréal	French, English
Queensland	667,000	1,930,000	2.9	State (Australia)............E	Brisbane	English
Reunion	969	580,000	599	Overseas Department (France)............C	St. Denis	French
Rhineland-Palatinate (Rhineland-Pfalz)	7,657	3,725,000	486	State (Federal Republic of Germany)............E	Mainz; Ludwigshafen am Rhein	German
Rhode Island	1,214	968,000	797	State (U.S.)............E	Providence	English
Rhodesia	150,804	5,975,000	40	Self-Governing Colony (U.K.)*............B	Salisbury	Bantu languages, English
Rio Muni, see Equatorial Guinea						
Rodrigues	42	26,000	619	Dependency of Mauritius (U.K.)............D	Port Mathurin	English, French
Romania†	91,699	21,190,000	231	People's Republic............A	Bucharest (București)	Romanian, Hungarian
Russian Soviet Federated Socialist Republic	6,592,850	133,975,000	20	Soviet Federated Socialist Republic (Sov. Un.)............E	Moscow (Moskva)	Russian, Finno-Ugric languages, various Turkic, Iranian, and Mongol languages
Russian S.F.S.R. in Europe	1,527,350	99,170,000	65	Soviet Union	.... ; Moscow	Russian, Finno-Ugric languages
Rwanda†	10,169	4,100,000	403	Republic............A	Kigali	Bantu and Hamitic languages, French
Saar (Saarland)	992	1,120,000	1,129	State (Federal Republic of Germany)............E	Saarbrücken	German
Sabah (North Borneo)	29,388	725,000	25	Administrative division of Malaysia............E	Kota Kinabalu; Sandakan	Malay, Chinese, English
St. Helena (incl. Dependencies)	162	6,000	37	Colony (U.K.)............C	Jamestown	English
St. Kitts-Nevis-Anguilla	138	67,000	486	Associated State (U.K.)............B	Basseterre	English
St. Lucia	238	107,000	450	Associated State (U.K.)............B	Castries	English
St. Pierre & Miquelon	93	5,500	59	Overseas Territory (France)............C	St. Pierre	French
St. Vincent	150	93,000	620	Associated State (U.K.)............B	Kingstown	English
Samoa (Entire)	1,173	180,000	153		.... ; Apia	Malay-Polynesian languages, English
San Marino	24	20,000	833	Republic............A	San Marino	Italian
Sao Tome & Principe	372	77,000	207	Overseas Province (Portugal)............C	São Tomé	Bantu languages, Portuguese
Sarawak	48,342	1,065,000	22	Administrative division of Malaysia............E	Kuching	Malay, Chinese, English
Sardinia	9,301	1,480,000	159	Part of Italy (3 Provinces)............D	.... ; Cagliari	Italian
Saskatchewan	251,700	915,000	3.6	Province (Canada)............E	Regina	English
Saudi Arabia†	830,000	8,530,000	10	Monarchy............A	Riyadh	Arabic
Scandinavia (incl. Finland and Iceland)	509,899	22,050,000	43		.... ; Copenhagen (København)	Swedish, Danish, Norwegian, Finnish, Icelandic
Schleswig-Holstein	6,046	2,545,000	421	State (Federal Republic of Germany)............E	Kiel	German
Scotland	30,414	5,240,000	172	Administrative division of United Kingdom............E	Edinburgh; Glasgow	English, Gaelic
Senegal†	75,955	4,265,000	56	Republic............A	Dakar	Wolof, Poular French
Seychelles	145	55,000	379	Colony (U.K.)............C	Victoria	French, Creole, English
Shetland Is.	550	16,900	31	Part of Scotland, U.K. (Zetland County)............D	Lerwick	English
Siam, see Thailand						
Sicily	9,926	4,655,000	469	Part of Italy (Sicilia Autonomous Region)............D	Palermo	Italian
Sierra Leone†	27,699	2,690,000	97	Republic (Br. Commonwealth of Nations)............A	Freetown	Temne, Mende, English
Sikkim	2,744	215,000	78	Monarchy (Indian protection)............B	Gangtok	Tibeto-Burman languages
Singapore†	224	2,265,000	10,112	Republic (Br. Comm. of Nations)............A	Singapore	Chinese, Malay, English
Solomon Is. (Austl. Trust)	4,100	85,000	21	Part of Australian Trust Ter. of New Guinea (Bougainville District)............D	Sohano; Kieta	Malay-Polynesian languages, English
Solomon Is., British	11,500	175,000	15	Protectorate (U.K.)............A	Honiara	Malay-Polynesian languages, English
Somalia†	246,201	3,055,000	12	Republic............A	Mogadiscio	Somali
South Africa (incl. Walvis Bay)†	471,879	23,910,000	51	Federal Republic............A	Pretoria and Cape Town; Johannesburg	English, Afrikaans, Bantu languages

† *Member of the United Nations (1974).*   * *Rhodesia unilaterally declared its independence from the United Kingdom on November 11, 1965.*
‡‡ *As of late 1967, the Gaza Strip was under Israeli military occupation. Data for Egypt, Israel, Jordan and Syria do not reflect de facto changes which took place during 1967.*

Region or Political Division	Area in sq. miles	Estimated Population 1/1/1974	Pop. per sq. mi.	Form of Government and Ruling Power	Capital; Largest City (unless same)	Predominant Languages
South America	6,870,000	205,500,000	30		......; Sao Paulo	
South Australia	380,070	1,220,000	3.2	State (Australia) ....E	Adelaide	English
South Carolina	31,055	2,700,000	87	State (U.S.) ....E	Columbia	....
South Dakota	77,047	680,000	8.8	State (U.S.) ....E	Pierre; Sioux Falls	....
Southern Rhodesia, see Rhodesia	....	....	....			
South Georgia	1,450	10	0.01	Dependency of Falkland Is. (U.K.) ....D	Grytviken	English, Norwegian
South Polar Regions						
South West Africa (excl. Walvis Bay)	317,827	800,000	2.5	Mandate (South Africa)** C	Windhoek	Bantu languages, Hottentot, Bushman, Afrikaans, English
Soviet Union (Union of Soviet Socialist Republics)†	8,600,350	251,050,000	29	Federal Soviet Republic ....A	Moscow (Moskva)	Russian and other Slavic languages, various Finno-Ugric, Turkic, and Mongol languages, Caucasian languages, Persian
Soviet Union in Europe	1,920,750	168,200,000	88	Soviet Union	......; Moscow (Moskva)	Russian and other Slavic languages, various Finno-Ugric and Caucasian languages
Spain†	194,885	34,905,000	179	Monarchy (Regency) ....A	Madrid	Spanish, Catalan, Galician, Basque
Spain and Possessions	297,597	35,141,000	118		Madrid	
Spanish Possessions in North Africa	12	130,000	10,833	Five Possessions (no central government) (Spain) C	......; Melilla	Spanish, Arabic, Berber
Spanish Sahara	102,700	106,000	1.0	African Province (Spain) C	El Aaiún	Arabic, Spanish
Spitsbergen, see Svalbard	....	....	....			
Sri Lanka (Ceylon)†	25,332	13,065,000	516	Republic (Br. Comm. of Nations) ....A	Colombo	Sinhalese, Tamil, English
Sudan†	967,500	17,085,000	18	Republic ....D	Khartoum	Arabic, native languages, English
Sumatra (Sumatera)	182,860	21,940,000	120	Part of Indonesia (6 Provinces) C	......; Medan	Bahasa Indonesia, English, Chinese
Surinam (Neth. Guiana)	63,037	445,000	7.1	Self-Governing Territory (Netherlands) C	Paramaribo	Dutch, Indo-Aryan languages
Svalbard (Spitsbergen)	24,102	Winter pop. 3,000		Dependency (Norway) C	Longyearbyen	Norwegian, Russian
Swaziland†	6,705	445,000	66	Monarchy (Br. Comm. of Nations) ....A	Mbabane	Swazi and other Bantu languages, English
Sweden†	173,649	8,165,000	47	Monarchy ....A	Stockholm	Swedish
Switzerland	15,941	6,550,000	411	Federal Republic ....A	Bern (Berne); Zürich	German, French, Italian
Syria†	71,498	7,015,000	98	Republic ....A	Damascus (Dimashq)	Arabic
Tadzhik S.S.R.	55,250	3,155,000	57	Soviet Socialist Republic (Sov. Un.) ....E	Dushanbe	Tadzhik, Turkic languages, Russian
Taiwan (Formosa) (Nationalist China)	13,885	16,370,000	1,179	Republic ....A	T'aipei	Chinese
Tanganyika, see Tanzania	....	....	....			
Tanzania (Tanganyika & Zanzibar)†	364,900	14,550,000	40	Republic (Br. Comm. of Nations) ....A	Dar es Salaam	Swahili and other Bantu languages, English, Arabic
Tasmania	26,383	405,000	15	State (Australia) ....E	Hobart	English
Tennessee	42,244	4,072,000	96	State (U.S.) ....E	Nashville; Memphis	....
Texas	267,339	11,885,000	44	State (U.S.) ....E	Austin; Houston	....
Thailand (Siam)†	198,500	37,715,000	190	Monarchy ....A	Bangkok (Krung Thep)	Thai, Chinese
Tibet	471,700	1,480,000	3.1	Autonomous Region (China) ....E	Lasa (Lhasa)	Tibetan
Togo†	21,600	2,175,000	101	Republic ....A	Lomé	Native languages, French
Tokelau (Union) Is.	4	1,500	375	Island Territory (New Zealand) C	......; Fakaofo	Malay-Polynesian languages, English
Tonga	270	95,000	352	Monarchy (Br. Comm. of Nations) ....A	Nukualofa	Malay-Polynesian languages, English
Transcaucasia	71,850	12,950,000	180	Soviet Union	......; Tbilisi	
Trinidad & Tobago†	1,980	1,110,000	561	Self-Governing Member (Br. Comm. of Nations) ......A	Port-of-Spain	English, Spanish
Tristan da Cunha	40	300	7.5	Dependency of St. Helena (U.K.) ....D	Edinburgh	English
Trucial States, see United Arab Emirates	....	....	....			
Tunisia†	63,379	5,575,000	88	Republic ....A	Tunis	Arabic, French
Turkey†	301,382	38,355,000	127	Republic ....A	Ankara; İstanbul	Turkish
Turkey in Europe	9,121	3,260,000	357	Turkey ....E	......; İstanbul	Turkish
Turkmen S.S.R.	188,450	2,330,000	12	Soviet Socialist Republic (Sov. Un.) ....E	Ashkhabad	Turkic languages, Russian
Turks & Caicos Is.	166	6,000	36	Colony (U.K.) C	Grand Turk	English
Uganda†	91,076	10,940,000	120	Republic (Br. Comm. of Nations) ....A	Kampala	Bantu languages, English
Ukraine (S.S.R.)†	233,100	48,810,000	209	Soviet Socialist Republic (Sov. Un.) ....E	Kiev	Ukrainian, Russian
Union of Soviet Socialist Republics, see Soviet Union	....	....	....			
United Arab Emirates	32,300	215,000	6.7	Self-Governing Union ....A	Abū Ẓaby	Arabic
United Arab Republic, see Egypt	....	....	....			
United Kingdom of Great Britain & Northern Ireland†	94,214	56,340,000	598	Monarchy (Br. Commonwealth of Nations) ....A	London	English, Welsh, Gaelic
United Kingdom & Possessions	288,205	68,241,000	237		London	English
United States†	*3,675,545	211,300,000	57	Federal Republic ....A	Washington; New York	English, Spanish
United States and Possessions	3,680,713	214,536,000	58		Washington; New York	
Upper Volta†	105,800	5,785,000	55	Republic ....A	Ouagadougou	Voltaic and Mande languages, French
Uruguay†	68,536	3,015,000	44	Republic ....A	Montevideo	Spanish
Utah	84,916	1,160,000	14	State (U.S.) ....E	Salt Lake City	English
Uzbek S.S.R.	173,600	12,760,000	74	Soviet Socialist Republic (Sov. Un.) ....E	Tashkent	Turkic languages, Sart, Russian
Vatican City (Holy See)	0.2	1,000	5,000	Ecclesiastical State ....A	Vatican City	Italian, Latin
Venezuela†	352,144	11,560,000	33	Federal Republic ....A	Caracas	Spanish
Vermont	9,609	469,000	49	State (U.S.) ....E	Montpelier; Burlington	English
Victoria	87,884	3,645,000	41	State (Australia) ....E	Melbourne	English
Vietnam (Entire)	128,402	42,760,000	333		......; Saigon	Annamese, Chinese
Vietnam, North	61,294	22,705,000	370	People's Republic ....A	Hanoi	Annamese, Chinese
Vietnam, South	67,108	20,055,000	299	Republic ....A	Saigon	Annamese, Chinese
Virginia	40,817	4,849,000	119	State (U.S.) ....E	Richmond; Norfolk	English
Virgin Is., British	59	11,000	186	Colony (U.K.) C	Road Town	English
Virgin Is. of the U.S.	133	74,000	556	Unincorporated Territory (U.S.) C	Charlotte Amalie	English
Wake I.	3	1,700	567	Possession (U.S.) C		English
Wales (incl. Monmouthshire)	8,016	2,775,000	346	United Kingdom	Cardiff	English, Welsh
Wallis & Futuna	98	12,000	122	Overseas Territory (France) C	Mata-Utu	Malay-Polynesian languages, French
Washington	68,192	3,423,000	50	State (U.S.) ....E	Olympia; Seattle	English
Western Australia	975,920	1,085,000	1.1	State (Australia) ....E	Perth	English
Western Samoa	1,097	150,000	137	Constitutional Monarchy (Br. Comm. of Nations) ......A	Apia	Malay-Polynesian languages, English
West Indies	92,041	26,825,000	291		......; Havana	
West Virginia	24,181	1,780,000	74	State (U.S.) ....E	Charleston; Huntington	....
White Russia, see Byelorussia	....	....	....			
Wisconsin	56,154	4,547,000	81	State (U.S.) ....E	Madison; Milwaukee	....
World	57,280,000	3,859,000,000	67		......; Tōkyō	
Wyoming	97,914	343,000	3.5	State (U.S.) ....E	Cheyenne	....
Yemen†	75,300	6,280,000	83	Republic ....A	Şan'ā'	Arabic
Yemen, People's Democratic Republic of,†	111,075	1,565,000	14	People's Republic ....A	Aden	Arabic; English
Yugoslavia†	98,766	21,055,000	213	Socialist Federal Republic ....A	Belgrade (Beograd)	Serbo-Croatian, Slovenian, Macedonian
Yukon	207,076	20,000	0.1	Territory (Canada) ....E	Whitehorse	English, Eskimo, Indian
Zaire (Congo The)†	905,567	23,600,000	26	Republic ....A	Kinshasa	Bantu languages, French
Zambia (Northern Rhodesia)†	290,586	4,600,000	16	Republic (Br. Comm. of Nations) ....A	Lusaka	Bantu languages, English
Zanzibar	950	405,000	426	Part of Tanzania ....D	......; Zanzibar	Arabic, English

† *Member of the United Nations (1974).* * *Total area of the United States includes 3,536,855 square miles of land, 78,268 square miles of inland water; and 60,422 square miles of Great Lakes area, not included in any State.* ** *The United Nations declared an end to the mandate of South Africa over South West Africa in October 1966. Administration of the territory by South Africa is not recognized by the United Nations.*
‡ *For 1970 census populations of the United States and each State, see table of Geographical Facts about the United States.*
‡‡ *As of late 1967, the Gaza Strip was under Israeli military occupation. Data for Egypt, Israel, Jordan and Syria do not reflect de facto changes which took place during 1967.*

World Facts and Comparisons

MOVEMENTS OF THE EARTH

The earth makes one complete revolution around the sun every 365 days, 5 hours, 48 minutes, and 46 seconds.

The earth makes one complete rotation on its axis in 23 hours and 56 minutes.

The earth revolves in its orbit around the sun at a speed of 66,700 miles per hour.

The earth rotates on its axis at an equatorial speed of more than 1,000 miles per hour.

MEASUREMENTS OF THE EARTH

Estimated age of the earth, at least 3 billion years.
Equatorial diameter of the earth, 7,926.68 miles.
Polar diameter of the earth, 7,899.99 miles.
Mean diameter of the earth, 7,918.78 miles.
Equatorial circumference of the earth, 24,902.45 miles.
Polar circumference of the earth, 24,818.60 miles.
Difference between equatorial and polar circumference of the earth, 83.85 miles.

Weight of the earth, 6,600,000,000,000,000,000,000 tons, or 6,600 billion billion tons.

Total area of the earth, 196,940,400 square miles.

Total land area of the earth (including inland water and Antarctica), 57,280,000 square miles.

THE EARTH'S INHABITANTS

Total population of the earth is estimated to be 3,791,000,000 (January 1, 1973).

Estimated population density of the earth, 66 per square mile.

THE EARTH'S SURFACE

Highest point on the earth's surface, Mount Everest, China (Tibet)–Nepal, 29,028 feet.

Lowest point on the earth's land surface, shores of the Dead Sea, Israel-Jordan, 1,299 feet below sea level.

Greatest ocean depth, the Marianas Trench, south of Guam, Pacific Ocean, 36,201 feet.

EXTREMES OF TEMPERATURE AND RAINFALL OF THE EARTH

Highest temperature ever recorded, 136.4°F. at Al 'Azīzīyah, Libya, Africa, on September 13, 1922.

Lowest temperature ever recorded, −126.9°F. at Vostok, Antarctica, on August 24, 1960.

Highest mean annual temperature, 88°F. at Lugh Ferrandi, Somalia.

Lowest mean annual temperature, −67°F. at Vostok, Antarctica.

At Cilaos, Réunion Island, in the Indian Ocean, 74 inches of rainfall was reported in a 24-hour period, March 15-16, 1952. This is believed to be the world's record for a 24-hour rainfall.

An authenticated rainfall of 366 inches in 1 month— July, 1861—was reported at Cherrapunji, India. More than 131 inches fell in a period of 7 consecutive days in June, 1931. Average annual rainfall at Cherrapunji is 450 inches.

The Continents

CONTINENT	Area (sq. mi.)	Population Estimated Jan. 1, 1974	Population per sq. mi.	Mean Elevation (feet)	Highest Elevation (Feet)	Lowest Elevation (Feet)	Highest Recorded Temperature	Lowest Recorded Temperature
North America	9,420,000	334,200,000	35	2,000	Mt. McKinley, United States (Alaska), 20,320	Death Valley, California, 282 below sea level	Death Valley, California, 134°F.	Snag, Yukon, Canada, −81°F.
South America	6,870,000	205,500,000	30	1,800	Mt. Aconcagua, Argentina, 2,831	Salinas Chicas, Argentina, 138 below sea level	Rivadavia, Argentina, 120°F.	Sarmiento, Argentina, −27.4°F.
Europe	3,825,000	642,200,000	168	980	Mt. Elbrus, Soviet Union, 18,481	Caspian Sea, Soviet Union— Iran, 92 below sea level	Sevilla (Seville), Spain, 122°F.	Ust-Shchugor, Soviet Union, −67°F.
Asia	17,085,000	2,273,200,000	133	3,000	Mt. Everest, China (Tibet)-Nepal, 29,028	Dead Sea, Israel-Jordan, 1,299 below sea level	Tirat Zvi, Israel, 129.2°F.	Oymyakon, Soviet Union, −89.9°F.
Africa	11,685,000	383,200,000	33	1,900	Mt. Kilimanjaro, Tanzania, 19,340	Lac Assal, Afars and Issas, 509 below sea level	A 'Azīzīyah, Libya, 136.4°F.	Ifrane, Morocco, −11.2°F.
Oceania, incl. Australia	3,295,000	20,700,000	6	.....	Mt. Wilhelm, New Guinea, Ter. of, 15,400	Lake Eyre, South Australia, 52 below sea level	Cloncurry, Queensland, Australia, 127.5°F.	Charlotte Pass, New South Wales, Australia, −8°F.
Australia	2,967,909	13,335,000	5	1,000	Mt. Kosciusko, New South Wales, 7,314	Lake Eyre, South Australia, 52 below sea level	Cloncurry, Queensland, 127.5°F.	Charlotte Pass, New South Wales, −8°F.
Antarctica	5,100,000	Uninhabited	...	6,000	Vinson Massif, 16,864	Unknown	Esperanza (Antarctic Peninsula), 58.3°F.	Vostok, −126.9°F.
World	57,280,000	3,859,000,000	67	.....	Mt. Everest, China (Tibet)-Nepal, 29,028	Dead Sea, Israel-Jordan, 1,299 below sea level	Al 'Azīzīyah, Libya, 136.4°F.	Vostok, −126.9°F.

Approximate Population of the World 1650-1974 *

AREA	1650	1750	1800	1850	1900	1914	1920	1939	1950	1974
North America	5,000,000	5,000,000	13,000,000	39,000,000	106,000,000	141,000,000	147,000,000	186,000,000	219,000,000	334,200,000
South America	8,000,000	7,000,000	12,000,000	20,000,000	38,000,000	55,000,000	61,000,000	90,000,000	111,000,000	205,500,000
Europe	100,000,000	140,000,000	190,000,000	265,000,000	400,000,000	470,000,000	453,000,000	526,000,000	530,000,000	642,200,000
Asia	335,000,000	476,000,000	593,000,000	754,000,000	932,000,000	1,006,000,000	1,000,000,000	1,247,000,000	1,418,000,000	2,273,200,000
Africa	100,000,000	95,000,000	90,000,000	95,000,000	118,000,000	130,000,000	140,000,000	170,000,000	199,000,000	383,200,000
Oceania, incl. Australia	} 2,000,000	2,000,000	2,000,000	2,000,000	{ 6,000,000	8,000,000	9,000,000	11,000,000	13,000,000	20,700,000
Australia					4,000,000	5,000,000	6,000,000	7,000,000	8,000,000	13,335,000
World	550,000,000	725,000,000	900,000,000	1,175,000,000	1,600,000,000	1,810,000,000	1,810,000,000	2,230,000,000	2,490,000,000	3,859,000,000

* Figures prior to 1974 are rounded to the nearest million.   Figures in italics represent very rough estimates.

Largest Countries of the World in Population

	Population 1/1/1974
1 China (excl. Taiwan)	821,010,000
2 India (incl. part of Kashmir)	581,200,000
3 Soviet Union	251,050,000
4 United States	211,300,000
5 Indonesia	127,740,000
6 Japan	108,960,000
7 Brazil	103,270,000
8 Bangladesh	77,450,000
9 Pakistan (incl. part of Kashmir)	68,720,000
10 Germany, Federal Republic of (incl. West Berlin)	62,115,000
11 Nigeria	60,260,000
12 United Kingdom (Great Britain)	56,340,000
13 Mexico	55,310,000
14 Italy	54,980,000
15 France	52,430,000
16 Philippines	40,665,000
17 Turkey	38,355,000
18 Thailand	37,715,000
19 Egypt (United Arab Republic)	35,975,000
20 Spain	34,905,000
21 Korea, South	34,170,000
22 Poland	33,465,000
23 Iran	31,830,000
24 Burma	29,695,000
25 Ethiopia	26,465,000

Largest Countries of the World in Area

	Area (sq. mi.)
1 Soviet Union	8,600,350
2 Canada	3,851,809
3 China (excl. Taiwan)	3,691,500
4 United States	3,675,545
5 Brazil	3,286,487
6 Australia	2,967,909
7 India (incl. part of Kashmir)	1,226,466
8 Argentina	1,072,162
9 Sudan	967,500
10 Algeria	919,595
11 Zaire (The Congo)	905,567
12 Greenland (Den.)	840,000
13 Saudi Arabia	830,000
14 Mexico	761,604
15 Indonesia	735,271
16 Libya	679,362
17 Iran	636,300
18 Mongolia	604,200
19 Peru	496,224
20 Chad	495,800
21 Niger	489,200
22 Angola (Port.)	481,353
23 Mali	478,655
24 South Africa (incl. Walvis Bay)	471,879
25 Ethiopia	471,778

Principal Mountains of the World

North America

Mountain	Height (Feet)
McKinley, △Alaska (△United States; △North America)	20,320
Logan, △Canada (△St. Elias Mts.)	19,850
Citlaltépetl (Orizaba), △Mexico	18,701
St. Elias, Alaska–Canada	18,008
Popocatépetl, Mexico	17,887
Foraker, Alaska	17,400
Ixtacihuatl, Mexico	17,343
Lucania, Yukon, Canada	17,147
Whitney, △California	14,494
Elbert, △Colorado (△Rocky Mts.)	14,443
Massive, Colorado	14,421
Harvard, Colorado	14,420
Rainier, △Washington (△Cascade Range)	14,410
Williamson, California	14,375
Blanca Pk., Colorado (△Sangre de Cristo Range)	14,345
Uncompahgre Pk., Colorado (△San Juan Mts.)	14,309
Grays Pk., Colorado (△Front Range)	14,270
Evans, Colorado	14,264
Longs Pk., Colorado	14,255
Wrangell, Alaska	14,163
Shasta, California	14,162
Pikes Peak, Colorado	14,110
Colima, Nevado de, Mexico	13,993
Tajumulco, △Guatemala (△Central America)	13,846
Gannett Pk., △Wyoming	13,804
Mauna Kea, △Hawaii (△Hawaii I.)	13,796
Grand Teton, Wyoming	13,766
Mauna Loa, Hawaii	13,680
Kings Pk., △Utah	13,528
Cloud Pk., Wyoming (△Big Horn Mts.)	13,175
Wheeler Pk., △New Mexico	13,161
Boundary Pk., △Nevada	13,143
Gunnbjörn, △Greenland	13,120
Waddington, Canada (△Coast Mts.)	13,104
Robson, Canada (△Canadian Rockies)	12,972
Granite Pk., △Montana	12,799
Borah Pk., △Idaho	12,662
Humphreys Pk., △Arizona	12,633
Chirripó Grande, △Coast Rica	12,533
Adams, Washington	12,307
San Gorgonio, California	11,502
Chiriquí, △Panama	11,411
Hood, △Oregon	11,235
Lassen Pk., California	10,457
Duarte, Pico, △Dominican Rep. (△West Indies)	10,417
Haleakala, Hawaii (△Maui)	10,023
Parícutin, Mexico	9,213
La Selle, Pic, △Haiti	8,773
Guadalupe Pk., △Texas	8,751
Olympus, Washington (△Olympic Mts.)	7,965
Monte Cristo, △El Salvador–Guatemala–Honduras	7,936
Blue Mountain Pk., △Jamaica	7,402
Harney Pk., △South Dakota (△Black Hills)	7,242
Mitchell, △North Carolina (△Appalachian Mts.)	6,684
Clingmans Dome, North Carolina–△Tennessee (△Great Smoky Mts.)	6,643
Turquino, Pico, △Cuba	6,542
Washington, △New Hampshire (△White Mts.)	6,288
Rogers, △Virginia	5,729
Marcy, △New York (△Adirondack Mts.)	5,344
Katahdin, △Maine	5,268
Kawaikini, Hawaii (△Kauai)	5,243
Spruce Knob, △West Virginia	4,862
Pelée, △Martinique	4,583
Mansfield, △Vermont (△Green Mts.)	4,393
Punta, Cerro de, △Puerto Rico	4,389
Black Mtn., △Kentucky	4,145
Kaala Pk., Hawaii (△Oahu)	4,050

South America

Mountain	Height (Feet)
Aconcagua, △Argentina (△Andes Mts.; △South America)	22,831
Ojos del Salado, Argentina–△Chile	22,516
Tupungato, Argentina–Chile	22,310
Pissis, Argentina	22,241
Mercedario, Argentina	22,211
Huascarán, △Peru	22,205
Llullaillaco, Argentina–Chile	22,057
Yerupaja, Peru	21,765
Incahuasi, Argentina–Chile	21,719
Sajama, Nevado, △Bolivia	21,391
Illimani, Bolivia	21,201
Chimborazo, △Ecuador	20,561
Cotopaxi, Ecuador	19,347
Misti, Peru	19,098
Cristóbal Colón, △Colombia	19,029
Huila, Colombia (△Cordillera Central)	18,865
Bolívar (La Columna), △Venezuela	16,411
Fitz Roy, Argentina	11,073
Neblina, Pico da, △Brazil	9,888

Europe

Mountain	Height (Feet)
Elbrus, Soviet Union (△Caucasus Mts.; △Europe)	18,481
Dykh-Tau, Soviet Union	17,070
Shkhara, Soviet Union	16,594
Kazbek, Soviet Union	16,512
Blanc, Mont, △France–△Italy (△Alps)	15,771
Rosa, Monte (Dufourspitze) △Switzerland	15,200
Weisshorn, Switzerland	14,803
Matterhorn, Italy–Switzerland	14,685
Finsteraarhorn, Switzerland	14,026
Jungfrau, Switzerland	13,668
Grossglockner, △Austria	12,457
Teide, Pico de, △Spain (△Canary Is.)	12,162
Mulhacén, △Spain (continental)	11,424
Aneto, Pico de, Spain (△Pyrenees)	11,168
Etna, Italy (△Sicily)	11,122
Perdido (Perdu), Spain	11,007
Clapier, France-Italy (△Maritime Alps)	9,993
Zugspitze, Austria–△Germany	9,721
Coma Pedrosa, Andorra	9,665
Musala, △Bulgaria	9,592
Corno, Italy (△Apennines)	9,560
Olympus, △Greece	9,550
Triglav, △Yugoslavia	9,393
Korab, △Albania–Yugoslavia	9,068
Ginto, France (△Corsica)	8,891
Gerlachovka, △Czechoslovakia (△Carpathian Mts.)	8,737
Moldoveanu, △Romania	8,343
Rysy, Czechoslovakia–△Poland	8,199
Glittertinden, △Norway (△Scandinavia)	8,110
Parnassós, Greece	8,061
Idhi (Ida), Greece (△Crete)	8,058
Pico, △Portugal (△Azores Is.)	7,713
Hvannadalshnúkur, △Iceland	6,952
Kebnekaise, △Sweden	6,926
Estrela, △Portugal (continental)	6,539
Narodnaya, Soviet Union (△Ural Mts.)	6,184
Marmora, Punta la, Italy (△Sardinia)	6,017
Hekla, Iceland	4,747
Nevis, Ben, △United Kingdom (△Scotland)	4,406
Haltia, △Finland–Norway	4,357
Vesuvius, Italy	3,842
Snowdon, △Wales	3,560
Carrantuohill, △Ireland	3,414
Kékes, △Hungary	3,330
Scafell Pikes, △England	3,210

Asia

Mountain	Height (Feet)
Everest, △China (△Tibet)–△Nepal (△Himalaya Mts.; △Asia; △World)	29,028
Godwin Austen (K²), China–△Pakistan (△Kashmir) (△Karakoram Range)	28,250
Kanchenjunga, Nepal–△Sikkim	28,208
Makalu, China (Tibet)–Nepal	27,824
Dhaulagiri, Nepal	26,810
Nanga Parbat, Pakistan (Kashmir)	26,650
Annapurna, Nepal	26,504
Gasherbrum, Pakistan (Kashmir)	26,470
Gosainthan, China (Tibet)	26,291
Nanda Devi, △India	25,645
Rakaposhi, Pakistan (Kashmir)	25,550
Kamet, India	25,447
Namcha Barwa, China (Tibet)	25,443
Gurla Mandhata, China (Tibet)	25,354
Ulugh Muztagh, China (△Kunlun Mts.)	25,338
Tirich Mir, Pakistan (△Hindu Kush)	25,230
Minya Konka, China	24,902
Muztagh Ata, China	24,787
Kula Kangri, △Bhutan	24,784
Communism Pk., △Soviet Union (△Pamir-Alay Mts.)	24,590
Pobeda Pk., China–Soviet Union (△Tien Shan)	24,406
Lenin Pk., Soviet Union	23,406
Api, Nepal	23,399
Khan-Tengri, Soviet Union	22,949
Kailas, China (Tibet)	22,031
Hkakabo Razi, △Burma–China	19,296
Demavend, △Iran	18,386
Ararat, △Turkey	17,011
Djaja Pk., △Indonesia (△New Guinea)	16,503
Klyuchevskaja Sopka, Soviet Union (△Kamchatka)	15,584
Trikora Pk., Indonesia	15,584
Belukha, Soviet Union	14,783
Tabun Bogdo (Khuitun), China–△Mongolia–Soviet Union (△Altai Mts.)	14,291
Turgun Uula, Mongolia	14,052
Kinabalu, △Malaysia (△Borneo)	13,455
Hsinkao, △Taiwan (Formosa)	13,113
Erciyeş, Turkey	12,848
Kerintji, Indonesia (△Sumatra)	12,467
Fuji, △Japan (△Honshu)	12,388
Hadūr Shu'ayb, △Yemen (△Arabian Peninsula)	12,336
Rindjani, Indonesia (△Lombok)	12,224
Semeru, Indonesia (△Java)	12,060
Munku-Sardyk, Mongolia–Soviet Union (△Sayan Mts.)	11,453
Rantekombola, Indonesia (△Celebes)	11,335
Sa'uda, Qurnet es, △Lebanon	10,131
Shām, Jabal ash, △Oman	9,957
Apo, △Philippines (△Mindanao)	9,692
Pulog, Philippines (△Luzon)	9,626
Bia, Phou, △Laos	9,242
Hermon, Lebanon–△Syria	9,232
Paektu-san, China–△Korea	9,003
Anai Mudi, △India (peninsular)	8,841
Inthanon, Doi, △Thailand	8,514
Pidurutalagala, △Sri Lanka	8,281
Mayon, Philippines (Luzon)	8,077
Asahi, Japan (△Hokkaido)	7,513
Tahan, Gunong, Malaysia (△Malaya)	7,174
Ólimbos, △Cyprus	6,401
Kuju-San, Japan (△Kyushu)	5,866
Meron, △Israel	3,963
Carmel, Israel	1,791

Africa

Mountain	Height (Feet)
Kilimanjaro (Kibo), △Tanzania (△Africa)	19,340
Kenya, △Kenya	17,058
Margherita Pk., △Zaire–△Uganda	16,763
Ras Dashen, △Ethiopia	15,158
Meru, Tanzania	14,978
Elgon, Kenya–Uganda	14,178
Toubkal, Jebel, △Morocco (△Atlas Mts.)	13,665
Cameroun, △Cameroon	13,353
Thabana Ntlenyana, △Lesotho	11,425
Koussi, Emi, △Chad (△Tibesti Mts.)	11,204
Injasuti, △South Africa	11,182
Neiges, Piton des, △Reunion	10,069
Santa Isabel, △Equatorial Guinea (△Fernando Poo)	9,868
Tahat, △Algeria (△Ahaggar Mts.)	9,852
Maromokotro, △Malagasy Republic	9,436
Pico, △Cape Verde Is.	9,281
Katrīnah, Jabal, △Egypt (United Arab Republic)	8,668
São Tomé, Pico de, △Sao Tome	6,640

Oceania

Mountain	Height (Feet)
Wilhelm, △New Guinea, Ter. of	15,400
Giluwe, △Papua	14,330
Bangeta, New Guinea, Ter. of	13,473
Victoria, Papua (△Owen Stanley Range)	13,363
Cook, △New Zealand (△South Island)	12,349
Ruapehu, New Zealand (△North Island)	9,175
Balbi, △Solomon Is. (△Bougainville)	9,000
Egmont, New Zealand	8,260
Sinewit, New Guinea, Ter. of (△Bismarck Archipelago)	8,000
Orohena, △Fr. Polynesia (△Tahiti)	7,352
Kosciusko, △Australia (△New South Wales)	7,314
Silisili, Mauga, △Western Samoa	6,095
Panié, △New Caledonia	5,341
Ossa, Australia (△Tasmania)	5,305
Bartle Frere, Australia (△Queensland)	5,287
Humboldt, New Caledonia	5,282
Woodroffe, Australia (△South Australia)	4,970
Tomaniivi (Victoria), △Fiji (△Viti Levu)	4,341
Bruce, Australia (△Western Australia)	4,024

Antarctica

Mountain	Height (Feet)
Vinson Massif (△Antarctica)	16,864
Kirkpatrick	14,856
Markham	14,272
Jackson	13,747
Sidley	13,717
Wade	13,396

△Highest mountain in state, country, range, or region named.

Great Oceans and Seas of the World

OCEANS AND SEAS	Area (sq. mi.)	Average Depth (feet)	Greatest Depth (feet)	OCEANS AND SEAS	Area (sq. mi.)	Average Depth (feet)	Greatest Depth (feet)	OCEANS AND SEAS	Area (sq. mi.)	Average Depth (feet)	Greatest Depth (feet)
Pacific Ocean	63,855,000	14,050	36,201	Bering Sea	876,000	4,710	16,800	Hudson Bay	476,000	402	850
Atlantic Ocean	31,744,000	12,690	27,651	Caribbean Sea	750,000	7,310	24,580	Japan, Sea of	389,000	4,490	12,280
Indian Ocean	28,371,000	13,000	24,442	Gulf of Mexico	596,000	4,960	14,360	North Sea	222,000	310	2,170
Arctic Ocean	5,427,000	5,010	17,880	Okhotsk, Sea of	590,000	2,760	11,400	Black Sea	178,000	3,610	7,360
Mediterranean Sea	967,000	4,780	16,420	East China Sea	482,000	620	9,840	Red Sea	169,000	1,610	7,370
South China Sea	895,000	5,420	18,090	Yellow Sea	480,000	150	300	Baltic Sea	163,000	180	1,440

Principal Lakes of the World

LAKES	Area (sq. mi.)	LAKES	Area (sq. mi.)	LAKES	Area (sq. mi.)
Caspian, Soviet Union–Iran (salt)	152,084	Ontario, United States–Canada	7,540	Torrens, Australia (salt)	△2,200
Superior, United States–Canada	31,820	Ladoga, Soviet Union	7,092	Albert, Uganda–Zaire	2,162
Victoria, Kenya–Uganda–Tanzania	26,828	Balkhash, Soviet Union	6,678	Vänern, Sweden	2,156
Aral, Soviet Union (salt)	26,518	Chad, Chad–Nigeria–Cameroon	△6,300	Winnipegosis, Canada	2,103
Huron, United States–Canada	23,010	Onega, Soviet Union	3,821	Bangweulu, Zambia	△1,900
Michigan, United States	22,400	Eyre, Australia (salt)	△3,700	Nipigon, Canada	1,870
Great Bear, Canada	12,275	Titicaca, Peru–Bolivia	3,500	Manitoba, Canada	1,817
Baykal, Soviet Union	12,159	Athabasca, Canada	3,120	Great Salt, United States (salt)	1,700
Great Slave, Canada	10,980	Nicaragua, Nicaragua	2,972	Koko Nor (Ching Hai), China	1,650
Tanganyika, Zaire–Tanzania–Burundi–Zambia	10,965	Rudolf, Kenya–Ethiopia (salt)	2,473	Dubawnt, Canada	1,600
Nyasa, Malawi–Tanzania–Mozambique	10,900	Reindeer, Canada	2,467	Gairdner, Australia (salt)	△1,500
Erie, United States–Canada	9,940	Issyk-Kul, Soviet Union	2,393	Lake of the Woods, United States–Canada	1,485
Winnipeg, Canada	9,465	Urmia, Iran (salt)	△2,229	Van, Turkey (salt)	1,470

△ Due to seasonal fluctuations in water level, areas of these lakes vary considerably.

Principal Rivers of the World

River	Length (miles)	River	Length (miles)	River	Length (miles)
Nile, Africa	4,132	Amu Darya, Asia	1,628	Si, Asia	930
Amazon (Amazonas), South America	3,900	Kolyma, Asia	1,615	Oka, Europe	920
Mississippi–Missouri–Red Rock, North America	3,860	Murray, Australia	1,600	Canadian, North America	906
Ob-Irtysh, Asia	3,461	Ganges, Asia	1,550	Dnestr, Europe	876
Yangtze (Chang), Asia	3,430	Pilcomayo, South America	1,550	Brazos, North America	870
Huang Ho (Yellow), Asia	2,903	Angara, Asia	1,549	Salado, South America	870
Congo, Africa	2,900	Ural, Asia	1,522	Fraser, North America	850
Amur, Asia	2,802	Vilyuy, Asia	1,513	Parnaíba, South America	850
Irtysh, Asia	2,747	Arkansas, North America	1,450	Colorado, North America (Texas)	840
Lena, Asia	2,653	Colorado, North America (U.S.–Mexico)	1,450	Rhine, Europe	820
Mackenzie, North America	2,635	Irrawaddy, Asia	1,425	Narbada, Asia	800
Mekong, Asia	2,600	Dnepr, Europe	1,420	Athabasca, North America	765
Niger, Africa	2,590	Aldan, Asia	1,392	Donets, Europe	735
Yenisey, Asia	2,566	Negro, South America	1,305	Pecos, North America	735
Missouri, North America	2,466	Paraguay, South America	1,290	Green, North America	730
Paraná, South America	2,450	Kama, Europe	1,261	Elbe, Europe	720
Mississippi, North America	2,348	Juruá, South America	1,250	James, North America	710
Plata-Paraguay, South America	2,300	Xingú, South America	1,230	Ottawa, North America	696
Volga, Europe	2,293	Don, Europe	1,224	White, North America	690
Madeira, South America	2,060	Ucayali, South America	1,220	Cumberland, North America	687
Indus, Asia	1,980	Columbia, North America	1,214	Gambia, Africa	680
Purús, South America	1,900	Saskatchewan, North America	1,205	Yellowstone, North America	671
St. Lawrence, North America	1,900	Peace, North America	1,195	Tennessee, North America	652
Rio Grande, North America	1,885	Orange, Africa	1,155	Gila, North America	630
Brahmaputra (Yalutsangpu), Asia	1,800	Tigris, Asia	1,150	Vistula (Wisła), Europe	630
Orinoco, South America	1,800	Sungari, Asia	1,140	Loire, Europe	625
São Francisco, South America	1,800	Pechora, Europe	1,118	Tagus (Tajo) (Tejo), Europe	625
Yukon, North America	1,800	Tobol, Asia	1,093	North Platte, North America	618
Danube, Europe	1,770	Snake, North America	1,038	Albany, North America	610
Darling, Australia	1,750	Uruguay, South America	1,025	Tisza (Tisa), Europe	607
Salween, Asia	1,730	Red, North America	1,018	Back, North America	605
Euphrates (Fırat), Asia	1,675	Churchill, North America	1,000	Ouachita, North America	605
Syr Darya, Asia	1,653	Marañón, South America	1,000	Cimarron, North America	600
Zambezi, Africa	1,650	Ohio, North America	981	Sava, Europe	585
Tocantins, South America	1,640	Magdalena, South America	950	Nemunas (Niemen), Europe	582
Araguaia, South America	1,630	Roosevelt (River of Doubt), South America	950	Branco, South America	580
		Godavari, Asia	930	Oder, Europe	565

Principal Islands of the World

Island	Area (sq. mi.)	Island	Area (sq. mi.)	Island	Area (sq. mi.)
Greenland, Arctic Region	840,000	Hispaniola, West Indies	29,530	Ceram, Indonesia	6,046
New Guinea, Oceania	316,856	Sakhalin, Soviet Union	29,344	New Caledonia, Oceania	5,671
Borneo, Indonesia	286,967	Tasmania, Australia	26,383	Flores, Indonesia	5,513
Madagascar, Indian Ocean	227,800	Ceylon, Indian Ocean	25,332	Samar, Philippines	5,124
Baffin, Canadian Arctic	183,810	Banks, Canadian Arctic	23,230	Negros, Philippines	4,903
Sumatra, Indonesia	182,860	Devon, Canadian Arctic	20,861	Palawan, Philippines	4,500
Honshū, Japan	88,930	Tierra del Fuego, Argentina-Chile	18,600	Panay, Philippines	4,448
Great Britain, North Atlantic Ocean	88,756	Kyūshū, Japan	16,215	Jamaica, West Indies	4,232
Ellesmere, Canadian Arctic	82,119	Melville, Canadian Arctic	16,141	Hawaii, Oceania	4,030
Victoria, Canadian Arctic	81,930	Southampton, Hudson Bay, Canada	15,700	Cape Breton, Canada	3,970
Celebes, Indonesia	72,986	West Spitsbergen, Arctic Region	15,260	Bougainville, Oceania	3,880
South Island, New Zealand	58,093	New Britain, Oceania	14,592	Mindoro, Philippines	3,794
Java, Indonesia	50,745	Formosa, China Sea	13,885	Cyprus, Mediterranean Sea	3,572
North Island, New Zealand	44,281	Hainan, South China Sea	13,127	Kodiak, Gulf of Alaska	3,569
Cuba, West Indies	44,218	Timor, Timor Sea	13,094	Puerto Rico, West Indies	3,435
Newfoundland, North Atlantic Ocean	43,359	Prince of Wales, Canadian Arctic	12,830	Corsica, Mediterranean Sea	3,352
Luzon, Philippines	40,814	Vancouver, Canada	12,408	Crete, Mediterranean Sea	3,217
Iceland, North Atlantic Ocean	39,800	Sicily, Mediterranean Sea	9,926	New Ireland, Oceania	3,205
Mindanao, Philippines	36,906	Somerset, Canadian Arctic	9,370	Leyte, Philippines	3,090
Ireland, North Atlantic Ocean	32,596	Sardinia, Mediterranean Sea	9,301	Wrangel, Soviet Arctic	2,819
Novaya Zemlya, Soviet Arctic	31,390	Shikoku, Japan	7,245	Guadalcanal, Oceania	2,500
Hokkaidō, Japan	29,950	North East Land, Svalbard Group	6,350	Long Island, United States	1,620

Largest Metropolitan Areas of the World, 1974

This table lists the major metropolitan areas of the world according to their estimated population on January 1, 1974. For convenience in reference, the areas are grouped by major region, and the number of areas in each region and size group is given.

For ease of comparison, each metropolitan area has been defined by Rand McNally & Company according to consistent rules. A metropolitan area includes a central city, neighboring communities linked to it by continuous built-up areas, and more distant communities if the bulk of their population is supported by commuters to the central city. Some metropolitan areas have more than one central city, for example Tōkyō–Yokohama or Detroit–Windsor.

POPULATION CLASSIFICATION	UNITED STATES and CANADA	LATIN AMERICA	EUROPE (excl. U.S.S.R.)	U.S.S.R.	ASIA	AFRICA–OCEANIA
Over 15,000,000 (2)	New York, U.S.				Tōkyō–Yokohama, Jap.	
10,000,000–15,000,000 (4)		Mexico City, Mex.	London, Eng.	Moscow	Ōsaka–Kōbe–Kyōto, Jap.	
5,000,000–10,000,000 (17)	Los Angeles, U.S. Chicago, U.S. Philadelphia, U.S.	Buenos Aires, Arg. São Paulo, Braz. Rio de Janeiro, Braz.	Paris, Fr. Essen–Dortmund– Duisburg (The Ruhr), Ger.		Calcutta, India Shanghai, China Bombay, India Seoul, Kor. Djakarta, Indon. Peking, China Delhi, India Manila, Phil.	Cairo, Eg.
3,000,000–5,000,000 (23)	Boston, U.S. Detroit, U.S.– Windsor, Can. San Francisco– Oakland– San Jose, U.S. Washington, U.S.	Lima, Peru Santiago, Chile	Barcelona, Sp. Berlin, Ger. Istanbul, Tur. Madrid, Sp. Milan, It. Rome, It.	Leningrad	Chungking, China Karāchi, Pak. Bangkok, Thai. Madras, India Nagoya, Jap. Mukden, China Taipei, Taiwan Tehrān, Iran Tientsin, China Victoria, Hong Kong	
2,000,000–3,000,000 (34)	Cleveland, U.S. Dallas– Fort Worth, U.S. Houston, U.S. Miami–Fort Lauderdale, U.S. Montréal, Can. Pittsburgh, U.S. St. Louis, U.S. Toronto, Can.	Bogotá, Col. Caracas, Ven. Recife, Braz.	Athens, Greece Birmingham, Eng. Brussels, Bel. Budapest, Hung. Hamburg, Ger. Katowice–Bytom– Gliwice, Pol. Manchester, Eng.	Kiev	Ahmādābād, India Baghdād, Iraq Canton, China Harbin, China Hyderābād, India Lahore, Pak. Pusan, Korea Rangoon, Bur. Saigon, Viet. Singapore, Singapore Wuhan, China	Alexandria, Eg. Johannesburg, S. Afr. Melbourne, Austl. Sydney, Austl.
1,500,000–2,000,000 (39)	Atlanta, U.S. Baltimore, U.S. Buffalo, U.S. Cincinnati, U.S. Minneapolis– St. Paul, U.S. San Diego, U.S.– Tijuana, Mex. Seattle– Tacoma, U.S.	Belo Horizonte, Braz. Guadalajara, Mex. Havana, Cuba Medellín, Col. Montevideo, Ur. Pôrto Alegre, Braz.	Amsterdam, Neth. Bucharest, Rom. Cologne, Ger. Frankfurt am Main, Ger. Glasgow, Scot. Leeds–Bradford, Eng. Lisbon, Port. Liverpool, Eng. Munich, Ger. Naples, It. Stuttgart, Ger. Turin, It. Vienna, Aus. Warsaw, Pol.	Baku Donetsk Gorki Kharkov Tashkent	Bangalore, India Chengtu, China Nanking, China Sian, China Surabaja, Indon. Taiyuan, China	Casablanca, Mor.
1,000,000–1,500,000 (66)	Denver, U.S. Hartford, U.S. Indianapolis, U.S. Kansas City, U.S. Milwaukee, U.S. New Orleans, U.S. Phoenix, U.S. Portland, U.S. Vancouver, Can.	Fortaleza, Braz. Monterrey, Mex. Salvador, Braz. San Juan, P.R.	Antwerp, Bel. Belgrade, Yugo. Copenhagen, Den. Düsseldorf, Ger. Lille, Fr. Lyon, Fr. Mannheim, Ger. Marseille, Fr. Newcastle– Sunderland, Eng. Prague, Czech. Rotterdam, Neth. Sofia, Bul. Stockholm, Swe. Valencia, Sp.	Chelyabinsk Dnepropetrovsk Kuybyshev Minsk Novosibirsk Odessa Saratov Sverdlovsk Tbilisi Volgograd	Ankara, Tur. Anshan, China Bandung, Indon. Beirut Leb. Chengchou, China Colombo, Sri Lanka Dacca, Bngl. Dairen, China Fukuoka, Jap. Fushun, China Hiroshima–Kure, Jap. Hsinking, China Kanpur, India Kaohsiung, Taiwan Kitakyūshū, Jap. Kunming, China Nāgpur, India Pune, India Pyŏngyang, Kor. Sapporo, Jap. Taegu, Kor. Tel Aviv–Yafo, Isr. Tsinan, China Tsingtao, China	Algiers, Alg. Cape Town, S. Afr. Durban, S. Afr. Kinshasa Zaire Lagos, Nig.
Total by Region (185)	32	19	44	18	61	11

Principal World Cities and Populations

The populations for all United States cities are estimates for January 1, 1975. For other cities, the populations are recent census figures or official estimates. Metropolitan populations are given for as many cities as possible, and identified by a star symbol (*). Some metropolitan areas, such as Minneapolis-St. Paul, include more than one large city. In such cases, the entry for the first named city carries the entire metropolitan population, and other cities in the metropolitan area carry a reference to the first-named city with a star symbol.

Aachen, Ger., Fed. Rep. of (*475,000)....239,619
Abidjan, Ivory Coast....510,000
Accra, Ghana (*736,718)....633,880
Addis Ababa, Ethiopia....912,090
Adelaide, Australia (*868,000)....15,000
Aden, Yemen, People's Democratic Republic of....250,000
Agra, India (*634,622)....591,917
Ahmadabad, India (*628,000)....1,585,544
Akron, Ohio (*745,000)....254,000
Albany, New York (*745,000)....109,000
Aleppo (Halab), Syria....639,361
Alexandria (Al Iskandarīyah), Egypt (*2,250,000)....2,032,000
Algiers (Algér), Algeria (*1,175,000)....1,000,000
Allahabad, India (*513,036)....490,622
Alma-Ata, Soviet Union....813,000
'Ammān, Jordan....520,720
Amritsar, India (*458,029)....407,628
Amsterdam, Netherlands (*1,800,000)....791,769
Ankara (Angora), Turkey (*1,270,000)....1,236,152
Anshan, China....1,050,000
Antwerp (Antwerpen), Belgium (*1,055,000)....222,775
Apia, Western Samoa....30,593
Asunción, Paraguay (*540,000)....392,753
Athens (Athínai), Greece (*2,540,241)....867,023
Atlanta, Georgia (*1,780,000)....455,000
Auckland, New Zealand (*745,000)....152,600

Baghdād, Iraq (*2,183,800)....1,300,000
Baku, Soviet Union (*1,525,000)....915,000
Baltimore, Maryland (*1,920,000)....847,000
Bamako, Mali....215,700
Bandung, Indonesia....1,201,730
Bangalore, India (*1,750,000)....1,540,741
Bangkok (Krung Thep), Thailand (*3,125,000)....1,867,297
Bangui, Central African Republic....187,000
Barcelona, Spain (*3,290,000)....1,781,561
Barranquilla, Colombia (*640,000)....590,300
Basel (Bâle), Switzerland (*565,000)....199,600
Beirut (Bayrūt), Lebanon (*1,010,000)....474,870
Belém (Pará), Brazil (*660,000)....565,097
Belfast, Northern Ireland (*720,000)....353,700
Belgrade (Beograd), Yugoslavia (*1,150,000)....770,140
Belo Horizonte, Brazil (*1,550,000)....1,235,001
Bengasi (Banghāzī), Libya....170,000
Berlin, East, Ger. Dem. Rep. (*Berlin)....1,088,828
Berlin, West, Ger., Fed. Rep. of (*3,875,000)....2,062,615
Bern (Berne), Switzerland (*287,000)....154,700
Bilbao, Spain (*850,000)....418,951
Birmingham, Alabama (*679,000)....281,000
Birmingham, England (*2,635,000)....1,006,760
Bogotá, Colombia (*2,250,000)....2,148,400
Bologna, Italy (*555,000)....493,639
Bombay, India (*6,750,000)....5,970,575
Bonn, Ger., Fed. Rep. of (*505,000)....281,089
Bordeaux, France (*560,000)....266,662
Boston, Massachusetts (*3,855,000)....601,000
Bradford, England (*Leeds)....294,370
Brasília, Brazil (*495,000)....272,002
Brazzaville, Congo....175,000
Bremen, Ger., Fed. Rep. of (*820,000)....589,825
Brighton, England (*435,000)....163,710
Brisbane, Australia (*911,000)....712,500
Bristol, England (*635,000)....421,580
Brussels (Bruxelles), Belgium (*2,010,000)....158,888
Bucharest (București), Romania (*1,642,651)....1,528,562
Budapest, Hungary (*2,360,000)....2,038,787
Buenos Aires, Argentina (*8,625,000)....2,972,453
Buffalo, New York (*1,572,000)....420,000
Bujumbura, Burundi....78,810

Cairo (Al Qāhirah), Egypt (*6,600,000)....4,961,000
Calcutta, India (*9,100,000)....3,148,746
Cali, Colombia....772,000
Canberra, Australia (*185,000)....166,101
Canton (Kuangchou), China....2,250,000
Cape Town (Kaapstad), South Africa (*1,125,000)....691,296
Caracas, Venezuela (*2,375,000)....1,625,000
Cardiff, Wales (*615,000)....274,920
Casablanca, Morocco (*1,575,000)....1,506,373
Changchiakou (Kalgan), China....350,000
Changchun (Hsinking), China....1,200,000
Changsha, China....750,000
Chelyabinsk, Soviet Union (*1,130,000)....947,000
Chengchou, China....900,000
Chengtu, China....1,450,000
Chicago, Illinois (*7,655,000)....3,115,000
Chichihaerh (Tsitsihar), China....825,000
Chilin (Kirin), China....583,000
Chittagong, Bangladesh....364,205
Chungking (Chungching), China....2,600,000
Cincinnati, Ohio (*1,422,000)....404,000
Cleveland, Ohio (*2,305,000)....660,000
Cologne (Köln), Ger., Fed. Rep. of (*1,700,000)....840,328
Colombo, Sri Lanka (*1,450,000)....607,000
Columbus, Ohio (*953,000)....582,000
Conakry, Guinea....197,267
Copenhagen (København), Denmark (*1,520,000)....578,403
Córdoba, Argentina (*825,000)....798,663
Coventry, England (*645,000)....336,370

Dacca, Bangladesh (*830,000)....362,006
Dakar, Senegal (*650,000)....581,000
Dallas, Texas (*2,465,000)....859,000
Damascus (Dimashq), Syria....836,179
Dar es Salaam, Tanzania....343,900
Dayton, Ohio (*938,000)....219,000
Delhi, India (*4,500,000)....3,706,558
Denver, Colorado (*1,285,000)....506,000
Detroit, Michigan (*4,800,000)....1,355,000
Dnepropetrovsk, Soviet Union (*1,340,000)....940,000
Donetsk (Stalino), Soviet Union (*1,950,000)....934,000
Dortmund, Ger., Fed. Rep. of (*Essen)....638,288
Dresden, Ger. Dem. Rep. (*640,000)....506,067
Dublin (Baile Átha Cliath), Ireland (*835,000)....567,866
Duisburg, Ger., Fed. Rep. of (*Essen)....441,452
Durban, South Africa (*1,040,000)....495,458
Düsseldorf, Ger., Fed. Rep. of (*1,135,000)....637,136

Edinburgh, Scotland (*650,000)....448,682
Edmonton, Canada (*495,702)....438,152
El Paso, Texas (*915,000)....370,000
Essen, Ger., Fed. Rep. of (*5,375,000)....682,336

Florence (Firenze), Italy (*645,000)....460,248
Fortaleza, Brazil (*910,000)....859,135
Fort Worth, Texas (*Dallas)....365,000
Frankfurt [am Main], Ger., Fed. Rep. of (*1,675,000)....667,451
Freetown, Sierra Leone (*225,000)....178,600
Fuchou (Foochow), China....700,000
Fukuoka, Japan (*1,285,000)....914,877
Fushun, China....1,350,000

Gdańsk (Danzig), Poland (*725,000)....397,700
Genève (Geneva), Switzerland (*400,000)....163,100
Genoa (Genova), Italy (*880,000)....815,708
Gent (Ghent), Belgium (*320,000)....148,166
Georgetown, Guyana (*100,855)....63,184
Glasgow, Scotland (*1,950,000)....835,622
Gorki (Gorkiy), Soviet Union (*1,740,000)....1,260,000
Göteborg, Sweden (*660,000)....441,522
Guadalajara, Mexico (*1,500,000)....1,193,601
Guatemala, Guatemala (*945,000)....717,322
Guayaquil, Ecuador....794,300

Halle [an der Saale], Ger. Dem. Rep. (*470,000)....245,681
Hamburg, Ger., Fed. Rep. of (*2,300,000)....1,766,214
Hamilton, Canada (*498,523)....309,173
Hangchou, China....875,000
Hannover (Hanover), Ger., Fed. Rep. of (*845,000)....511,298
Hanoi, Vietnam (North) (*643,576)....414,620
Harbin (Haerhpin), China....2,100,000
Hartford, Connecticut (*1,048,000)....146,500
Havana (La Habana), Cuba (*1,800,000)....1,755,400
Helsinki, Finland (*780,000)....512,305
Hiroshima, Japan (*1,175,000)....541,998
Honolulu, Hawaii (*685,000)....335,000
Houston, Texas (*2,110,000)....1,369,000
Howrah, India (*Calcutta)....737,877
Hsüchou (Süchow), China....825,000
Hyderabad, India (*2,000,000)....1,607,396
Hyderabad, Pakistan (*660,000)....600,000

Ibadan, Nigeria....758,000
Inchŏn, Korea (South)....646,013
Indianapolis, Indiana (*1,010,000)....741,000
Indore, India (*560,936)....543,381
Irkutsk, Soviet Union....485,000
İstanbul, Turkey (*2,825,000)....2,132,407
Ivanovo, Soviet Union....442,000
İzmir (Smyrna), Turkey (*760,000)....520,832

Jabalpur (Jubbulpore), India (*534,845)....426,224
Jacksonville, Florida (*595,000)....565,000
Jaipur, India....615,258
Jakarta (Djakarta), Indonesia....4,576,009
Jamshedpur, India (*456,146)....341,576
Jerusalem, Israel (*315,000)....304,500
Jerusalem, Jordan (*Jerusalem)....60,488
Johannesburg, South Africa (*2,550,000)....654,682
Juddah, Saudi Arabia....194,000

Kabul, Afghanistan (*498,800)....318,094
Kampala, Uganda....330,700
Kanpur, India (*1,320,000)....1,154,388
Kansas City, Missouri (*1,239,000)....475,000
Karachi, Pakistan (*3,500,000)....2,850,000
Karaganda, Soviet Union....559,000
Karl-Marx-Stadt (Chemnitz), Ger. Dem. Rep. (*460,000)....302,409
Katmandu, Nepal (*210,000)....153,405
Katowice, Poland (*2,140,000)....318,800
Kaunas, Soviet Union....332,000
Kawasaki, Japan (*Tōkyō)....1,001,368
Kazan, Soviet Union....931,000
Khabarovsk, Soviet Union....474,000
Kharkov, Soviet Union (*1,600,000)....1,330,000
Khartoum, Sudan (*675,000)....261,840
Kiev (Kiyev), Soviet Union (*2,070,000)....1,887,000
Kigali, Rwanda....60,000
Kingston, Jamaica....550,100
Kinshasa, Zaire....1,323,039
Kitakyūshū, Japan (*1,470,000)....1,051,076
Kōbe, Japan (*Ōsaka)....1,338,705
Kowloon, Hong Kong (*Victoria)....715,440
Kraków (Cracow), Poland....657,300
Krasnoyarsk, Soviet Union....728,000
Krivoy Rog, Soviet Union....620,000
Kuala Lumpur, Malaysia (*750,000)....451,810
Kueiyang, China....530,000
Kunming, China....1,100,000
Kuwait, Kuwait (*560,000)....80,405
Kuybyshev, Soviet Union (*1,345,000)....1,140,000
Kyōto, Japan (*Ōsaka)....1,435,254

Lagos, Nigeria (*1,250,000)....901,000
Lahore, Pakistan (*2,200,000)....2,050,000
Lanchou, China....875,000
La Paz, Bolivia....525,000
La Plata, Argentina (*510,000)....408,300
Leeds, England (*1,550,000)....498,790
Le Havre, France (*250,000)....208,379
Leicester, England (*480,000)....281,440
Leipzig, Ger. Dem. Rep. (*730,000)....574,432
Leningrad, Soviet Union (*4,925,000)....3,780,000
Libreville, Gabon....73,000
Liège, Belgium (*550,000)....144,875
Lille, France (*950,000)....190,546
Lima, Peru (*3,350,000)....340,339
Lisbon (Lisboa), Portugal (*1,735,000)....757,700
Liverpool, England (*1,615,000)....603,210
Łodź, Poland (*965,000)....780,900
Lomé, Togo....144,300
London, England (*10,675,000)....7,353,810
Los Angeles, California (*8,960,000)....2,750,000
Louisville, Kentucky (*867,000)....333,000
Lourenço Marques, Mozambique (383,775▲)....354,684
Loyang, China....500,000
Luanda, Angola....475,328
Lubumbashi, Zaire....318,000
Lucknow, India (*840,000)....749,239
Lusaka, Zambia....238,200
Lüta (Dairen), China (*1,200,000)....1,150,000
Luxembourg, Luxembourg (*100,000)....76,143
Lvov, Soviet Union....605,000
Lyon (Lyons), France (*1,100,000)....527,800

Macao, Macao (*248,636)....241,413
Madras, India (*3,200,000)....2,469,449
Madrid, Spain (*3,690,000)....3,209,246
Madurai, India (*725,000)....549,114
Magdeburg, Ger. Dem. Rep. (*385,000)....274,146
Managua, Nicaragua....398,514
Manchester, England (*2,880,000)....531,270
Manila, Philippines (*4,350,000)....1,330,788
Mannheim, Ger., Fed. Rep. of (*1,265,000)....328,411
Maracaibo, Venezuela....650,002
Marseille (Marseilles), France (*1,015,000)....889,029
Mecca (Makkah, Saudi Arabia....185,000
Medan, Indonesia....635,562
Medellín, Colombia (*1,240,000)....913,000
Melbourne, Australia (*2,583,900)....75,000
Memphis, Tennessee (*846,000)....660,000
Mexico City, Mexico (*9,000,000)....6,874,165
Miami, Florida (*2,345,000)....345,000
Middlesbrough (Teesside), England (*580,000)....393,960
Milan (Milano), Italy (*3,690,000)....1,738,487
Milwaukee, Wisconsin (*1,388,000)....685,000
Minneapolis, Minnesota (*1,935,000)....390,000
Minsk, Soviet Union (*1,105,000)....1,084,000
Mogadisho, Somalia....172,700
Monrovia, Liberia....100,000
Monterrey, Mexico (*1,200,000)....858,107
Montevideo, Uruguay (*1,300,000)....1,202,757
Montréal, Canada (*2,743,208)....1,214,352
Moscow (Moskva), Soviet Union (*10,525,000)....7,368,000
Munich (München), Ger., Fed. Rep. of (*1,885,000)....1,338,924

Nagasaki, Japan....421,114
Nagoya, Japan (*3,450,000)....2,075,249
Nagpur, India (*950,000)....866,076
Nairobi, Kenya....535,200
Nanchang, China....520,000
Nanking (Nanching), China....1,750,000
Naples (Napoli), Italy (*1,950,000)....1,223,659
Nashville, Tennessee (*562,000)....469,000
Ndjamena (Fort Lamy), Chad....179,000
Newark, New Jersey (*New York)....352,000
Newcastle-on-Tyne, England (*1,360,000)....217,220
New Delhi, India (*Delhi)....301,801
New Orleans, Louisiana (*1,131,000)....569,000
New York, New York (*17,150,000)....7,605,000
Niamey, Niger....79,000
Nice, France (*400,000)....322,442
Norfolk, Virginia (*768,000)....287,000
Nottingham, England (*650,000)....294,420
Novokuznetsk, Soviet Union....519,000
Novosibirsk, Soviet Union (*1,360,000)....1,243,000
Nürnberg (Nuremberg), Ger., Fed. Rep. of (*850,000)....514,976

Oakland, California (*San Francisco)....338,000
Odessa, Soviet Union....981,000
Oklahoma City, Oklahoma (*689,000)....378,000
Omaha, Nebraska (*558,000)....372,000
Omsk, Soviet Union....935,000
Ōsaka, Japan (*14,175,000)....2,841,937
Oslo, Norway (*720,000)....468,301
Ottawa, Canada (*602,510)....302,341
Ouagadougou, Upper Volta....110,000

Palembang, Indonesia....582,961
Palermo, Italy....650,113
Panamá, Panama (*465,000)....348,704
Paotou, China....490,000
Paris, France (*9,300,000)....2,425,000
Patna, India (*625,000)....473,001
Peking (Peiping), China (7,570,000▲)....*4,800,000
Perm, Soviet Union....920,000
Perth, Australia (*739,200)....94,300
Philadelphia, Pennsylvania (*5,275,000)....1,820,000
Phnom Penh, Cambodia....393,995
Phoenix, Arizona (*1,250,000)....705,000
Pinang (George Town), Malaysia (*450,000)....269,247
Pittsburgh, Pennsylvania (*2,075,000)....472,000
Port-au-Prince, Haiti (*493,932)....458,675
Portland, Oregon (*1,077,000)....363,000
Porto (Oporto), Portugal (*850,000)....304,000
Pôrto Alegre, Brazil (*1,375,000)....885,564
Port of Spain, Trinidad & Tobago (*310,000)....67,867
Porto Novo, Dahomey....74,500
Port Said (Būr Sa'īd), Egypt....282,977
Portsmouth, England (*495,000)....207,040
Poznań, Poland (*560,000)....499,000
Prague (Praha), Czechoslovakia (*1,215,000)....1,081,608
Pretoria, South Africa (*575,000)....543,950
Providence, Rhode Island (*898,000)....163,000
Pune (Poona), India (*1,175,000)....856,105
Pusan, Korea (South)....1,880,710
Pyŏngyang, Korea (North)....840,000

Québec, Canada (*480,502)....186,088
Quezon City, Philippines (*Manila)....754,452
Quito, Ecuador....528,100

Rabat, Morocco (*540,000)....367,620
Rangoon, Burma....1,717,600
Rawalpindi, Pakistan (*725,000)....375,000
Recife (Pernambuco), Brazil (*1,750,000)....1,060,752
Reykjavík, Iceland (*113,000)....84,333
Richmond, Virginia (*526,000)....233,000
Rīga, Soviet Union (*850,000)....776,000
Rio de Janeiro, Brazil (*7,000,000)....4,252,009
Riyadh (Ar Riyāḍ), Saudi Arabia....225,000
Rochester, New York (*838,000)....282,000
Rome (Roma), Italy (*3,030,000)....2,795,168
Rosario, Argentina (*875,000)....705,000
Rostov-na-Donu, Soviet Union (*1,000,000)....867,000
Rotterdam, Netherlands (*1,115,000)....654,024

Sacramento, California (*748,000)....262,000
Saigon, Vietnam (South) (*2,750,000)....1,804,880
St. Louis, Missouri (*2,270,000)....538,000
St. Paul, Minnesota (*Minneapolis)....291,000
St. Petersburg, Florida (*657,000)....236,000
Salisbury, Rhodesia (*503,000)....100,000
Salt Lake City, Utah (*561,000)....172,000
Salvador, Brazil (*1,020,000)....1,007,744
Ṣan'ā', Yemen....120,800
San Antonio, Texas (*925,000)....758,000
San Bernardino, California (*609,000)....107,000
San Diego, California (*1,790,000)....765,000
San Francisco, California (*4,450,000)....675,000
San Jose, California (*San Francisco)....535,000
San José, Costa Rica (*418,000)....216,200
San Juan, Puerto Rico (*1,185,000)....452,749
San Salvador, El Salvador (*600,000)....337,171
Santiago, Chile (*2,900,000)....510,246
Santo Domingo, Dominican Republic....673,470
Santos, Brazil (*610,000)....341,317
São Paulo, Brazil (*8,050,000)....5,921,796
Sapporo, Japan (*1,150,000)....1,130,828
Saratov, Soviet Union (*1,020,000)....820,000
Seattle, Washington (*1,788,000)....490,000
Semarang, Indonesia....646,590
Sendai, Japan (*690,000)....545,065
Seoul, Korea (South) (*5,900,000)....5,536,377
Sevilla (Seville), Spain (*645,000)....565,055
Shanghai, China (10,820,000▲)....*7,900,000
Sheffield, England (*725,000)....513,310
Shenyang (Mukden), China....3,000,000
Shihchiachuang, China....750,000
Shizuoka, Japan (*680,000)....416,378
Sian (Hsian), China....1,750,000
Singapore, Singapore (*2,225,000)....2,074,507
Sofia (Sofiya), Bulgaria (*1,035,480)....920,000
Southampton, England (*395,000)....213,710
Springfield, Massachusetts (*506,000)....158,000
Srinagar, India (*415,271)....403,413
Stockholm, Sweden (*1,350,929)....699,238
Stoke-on-Trent, England (*445,000)....262,120
Strasbourg, France (*355,000)....249,396
Stuttgart, Ger., Fed. Rep. of (*1,650,000)....630,390
Suchou (Soochow), China....725,000
Sucre, Bolivia....48,000
Surabaya, Indonesia....1,556,255
Sverdlovsk, Soviet Union (*1,320,000)....1,122,000
Sydney, Australia (*2,874,380)....57,770
Syracuse, New York (*549,000)....190,000
Szczecin (Stettin), Poland....358,000

Taegu, Korea (South)....1,082,750
Taipei, Taiwan (*2,490,000)....1,740,800
Taiyüan (Yangkü), China....1,350,000
Tallinn, Soviet Union....392,000
Tampa, Florida (*521,000)....279,000
Tananarive, Madagascar....366,530
Tanger (Tangier), Morocco....187,894
Tangshan, China....900,000
Tashkent, Soviet Union (*1,730,000)....1,552,000
Tbilisi, Soviet Union (*1,125,000)....984,000
Tegucigalpa, Honduras....232,300
Tehrān, Iran (*3,075,000)....2,719,730
Tel Aviv-Yafo, Israel (*1,150,000)....362,200
The Hague ('s Gravenhage), Netherlands (*810,000)....510,360
Thessaloníki (Salonika), Greece (*557,360)....345,799
Tientsin (Tienching), China (4,280,000▲)....*3,800,000
Tiranë, Albania....174,800
Tōkyō, Japan (*23,300,000)....8,738,997
Toledo, Ohio (*563,300)....366,000
Toronto, Canada (*2,628,043)....712,786
Toulouse, France (*440,000)....370,796
Tripoli (Tarābulus), Libya....264,000
Tsinan (Chinan), China....1,100,000
Tsingtao (Chingtao), China....1,350,000
Tula, Soviet Union (*575,000)....486,000
Tunis, Tunisia (*685,000)....468,997
Turin (Torino), Italy (*1,635,000)....1,172,476

Ufa, Soviet Union....871,000
Ulan Bator, Mongolia....267,400
Utrecht, Netherlands (*464,053)....269,574

Valencia, Spain (*950,000)....662,557
Valletta, Malta (*206,000)....15,600
Valparaíso, Chile (*540,000)....292,800
Vancouver, Canada (*1,082,352)....426,256
Varanasi (Benares), India (*606,271)....583,856
Venice (Venezia), Italy (*440,000)....363,540
Victoria, Hong Kong (*3,575,000)....521,612
Vienna (Wien), Austria (*1,940,000)....1,614,841
Vientiane, Laos....149,000
Vilnius, Soviet Union....420,000
Vladivostok, Soviet Union....481,000
Volgograd (Stalingrad), Soviet Union (*1,140,000)....885,000
Voronezh, Soviet Union....729,000

Warsaw (Warszawa), Poland (*1,850,000)....1,387,800
Washington, D.C. (*3,190,000)....715,000
Wellington, New Zealand (*346,900)....141,800
Wiesbaden, Ger., Fed. Rep. of (*640,000)....252,232
Winnipeg, Canada....548,573
Wrocław (Breslau), Poland....560,300
Wuhan, China....2,900,000
Wuhsi (Wusih), China....650,000
Wuppertal, Ger., Fed. Rep. of (*920,000)....413,153

Yaoundé, Cameroon....165,800
Yaroslavl, Soviet Union....558,000
Yerevan, Soviet Union....870,000
Yokohama, Japan (*Tōkyō)....2,494,975
Youngstown, Ohio (*500,000)....128,500

Zagreb, Yugoslavia....566,084
Zaporozhye, Soviet Union....729,000
Zürich, Switzerland (*785,000)....401,600

* *Population of metropolitan area, including suburbs. See headnote.*
▲ *Population of entire municipality or district, including rural area. Starred population in these entries refers to urban portion of municipality only.*

Geographical Facts about the United States

ELEVATION

The highest elevation in the United States is Mount McKinley, Alaska, 20,320 feet.

The lowest elevation in the United States is in Death Valley, California, 282 feet below sea level.

The average elevation of the United States is 2,500 feet.

EXTREMITIES

Direction	Location	Latitude	Longitude
North	Point Barrow, Alaska	71°23′N.	156°29′W.
South	South Cape, Hawaii	18°56′N.	155°41′W.
East	West Quoddy Head, Maine	44°49′N.	66°57′W.
West	Cape Wrangell, Alaska	52°55′N.	172°27′E.

The two places in the United States separated by the greatest distance are Kure Island, Hawaii, and Mangrove Point, Florida. These points are 5,848 miles apart.

LENGTH OF BOUNDARIES

The total length of the Canadian boundary of the United States is 5,525 miles.

The total length of the Mexican boundary of the United States is 1,933 miles.

The total length of the Atlantic coastline of the United States is 2,069 miles.

The total length of the Pacific and Arctic coastline of the United States is 8,683 miles.

The total length of the Gulf of Mexico coastline of the United States is 1,631 miles.

The total length of all coastlines and land boundaries of the United States is 19,841 miles.

The total length of the tidal shoreline and land boundaries of the United States is 96,091 miles.

GEOGRAPHIC CENTERS

The geographic center of the United States (including Alaska and Hawaii) is in Butte County, South Dakota at 44°58′N., 103°46′W.

The geographic center of North America is in North Dakota, a few miles west of Devils Lake, at 48°10′N., 100°10′W.

EXTREMES OF TEMPERATURE

The highest temperature ever recorded in the United States was 134°F., at Greenland Ranch, Death Valley, California, on July 10, 1913.

The lowest temperature ever recorded in the United States was —76°F., at Tanana, Alaska, in January, 1886.

PRECIPITATION

The average annual precipitation for the United States is approximately 29 inches.

Hawaii is the wettest state, with an average annual rainfall of 82.48 inches. Nevada, with an average annual rainfall of 8.81 inches, is the driest state.

The greatest local average annual rainfall in the United States is at Mt. Waialeale, Kauai, Hawaii, 460 inches.

Greatest 24-hour rainfall in the United States, 23.22 inches at New Smyrna, Florida, October 10–11, 1924.

Extreme minimum rainfall records in the United States include a total fall of only 3.93 inches at Bagdad, California, for a period of 5 years, 1909–13, and an annual average of 1.78 inches at Death Valley, California.

Heavy snowfall records include 76 inches at Silver Lake, Colorado, in 1 day; 42 inches at Angola, New York, in 2 days; 87 inches at Giant Forest, California, in 3 days; and 108 inches at Tahoe, California, in 4 days.

Greatest seasonal snowfall, 1,000.3 inches, more than 83 feet, at Paradise Ranger Station, Washington, during the winter of 1955–56.

Historical Facts about the United States

TERRITORIAL ACQUISITIONS

Accession	Date	Area (sq. mi.)	Cost in Dollars
Original territory of the Thirteen States	1790	888,685	....
Purchase of Louisiana Territory, from France	1803	827,192	$11,250,000.00
By treaty with Spain: Florida	1819	58,560	$ 5,000,000.00
Other areas	1819	13,443	
Annexation of Texas	1845	390,144	....
Oregon Territory, by treaty with Great Britain	1846	285,580	....
Mexican Cession	1848	529,017	$15,000,000.00
Gadsden Purchase, from Mexico	1853	29,640	$10,000,000.00
Purchase of Alaska, from Russia	1867	586,412	7,200,000.00
Annexation of Hawaiian Islands	1898	6,450	....
Puerto Rico, by treaty with Spain	1899	3,435	....
Guam, by treaty with Spain	1899	212	....
American Samoa, by treaty with Great Britain and Germany	1900	76	....
Panama Canal Zone, by treaty with Panama	1904	553	*$10,000,000.00
Virgin Islands, by purchase from Denmark	1917	133	$25,000,000.00
Total		3,619,532	$83,450,000.00

Note: The Philippines, ceded by Spain in 1898 for $20,000,000.00, were a territorial possession of the United States from 1898 to 1946. On July 4, 1946 they became the independent republic of the Philippines.

* $25,000,000.00 was also paid to the republic of Colombia, out of whose territory the republic of Panama was created. In addition, an annual payment of $1,930,000 is made to the republic of Panama.

WESTWARD MOVEMENT OF CENTER OF POPULATION

Year	U.S. Population Total at Census	Approximate Location
1790	3,929,214	23 miles east of Baltimore, Md.
1800	5,308,483	18 miles west of Baltimore, Md.
1810	7,239,881	40 miles northwest of Washington, D.C.
1820	9,638,453	16 miles east of Moorefield, W. Va.
1830	12,866,020	19 miles southwest of Moorefield, W. Va.
1840	17,069,453	16 miles south of Clarksburg, W. Va.
1850	23,191,876	23 miles southeast of Parkersburg, W. Va.
1860	31,443,321	20 miles southeast of Chillicothe, Ohio
1870	39,818,449	48 miles northeast of Cincinnati, Ohio
1880	50,155,783	8 miles southwest of Cincinnati, Ohio
1890	62,947,714	20 miles east of Columbus, Ind.
1900	75,994,575	6 miles southeast of Columbus, Ind.
1910	91,972,266	Bloomington, Ind.
1920	105,710,620	8 miles southeast of Spencer, Ind.
1930	122,775,046	3 miles northeast of Linton, Ind.
1940	131,669,275	2 miles southeast of Carlisle, Ind.
1950	150,697,361	8 miles northwest of Olney, Ill.
1960	179,323,175	6 miles northwest of Centralia, Ill.
1970	204,816,296	5 miles southeast of Mascoutah, Ill.

State Areas and Populations

STATE	Land Area (square miles)	Water Area (square miles)	Total Area (square miles)	Rank in Area	Apportionment Population in 1970‡	Resident Population in 1970	Population Per Square Mile in 1970	Population in 1960	Population in 1950	Rank in Population in 1970	in 1960	in 1950
Alabama	50,851	758	51,609	29	3,475,885	3,444,165	67	3,266,740	3,061,743	21	19	17
Alaska	566,432	19,980	586,412	1	304,067	302,173	0.5	226,167	128,643	50	50	50
Arizona	113,563	346	113,909	6	1,787,620	1,772,482	16	1,302,161	749,587	33	35	37
Arkansas	52,175	929	53,104	27	1,942,303	1,923,295	36	1,786,272	1,909,511	32	31	30
California	156,537	2,156	158,693	3	20,098,863	19,953,134	126	15,717,204	10,586,223	1	2	2
Colorado	103,794	453	104,247	8	2,226,771	2,207,259	21	1,753,947	1,325,089	30	33	34
Connecticut	4,870	139	5,009	48	3,050,693	3,032,217	605	2,535,234	2,007,280	24	25	28
Delaware	1,982	75	2,057	49	551,928	548,104	266	446,292	318,085	46	46	47
District of Columbia†	61	6	67	..	762,971‡	756,510	11,291	763,956	802,178	..	..	..
Florida	54,136	4,424	58,560	22	6,855,702	6,789,443	116	4,951,560	2,771,305	9	10	20
Georgia	58,197	679	58,876	21	4,627,306	4,589,575	78	3,943,116	3,444,578	15	16	13
Hawaii	6,425	25	6,450	47	784,901	769,913	119	632,772	499,794	40	43	45
Idaho	82,677	880	83,557	13	719,921	713,008	8.5	667,191	588,637	42	42	43
Illinois	55,875	525	56,400	24	11,184,320	11,113,976	197	10,081,158	8,712,176	5	4	4
Indiana	36,189	102	36,291	38	5,228,156	5,193,669	143	4,662,498	3,934,224	11	11	12
Iowa	56,043	247	56,290	25	2,846,920	2,825,041	50	2,757,537	2,621,073	25	24	22
Kansas	82,056	208	82,264	14	2,265,846	2,249,071	27	2,178,611	1,905,299	28	28	31
Kentucky	39,851	544	40,395	37	3,246,481	3,219,311	80	3,038,156	2,944,806	23	22	19
Louisiana	45,131	3,392	48,523	31	3,672,008	3,643,180	75	3,257,022	2,683,516	20	20	21
Maine	30,933	2,282	33,215	39	1,006,320	993,663	30	969,265	913,774	38	36	35
Maryland	9,891	686	10,577	42	3,953,698	3,922,399	371	3,100,689	2,343,001	18	21	23
Massachusetts	7,833	424	8,257	45	5,726,676	5,689,170	689	5,148,578	4,690,514	10	9	9
Michigan	56,817	1,399	58,216	23	8,937,196	8,875,083	152	7,823,194	6,371,766	7	7	7
Minnesota	79,289	4,779	84,068	12	3,833,173	3,805,069	45	3,413,864	2,982,483	19	18	18
Mississippi	47,358	358	47,716	32	2,233,848	2,216,912	46	2,178,141	2,178,914	29	29	26
Missouri	69,046	640	69,686	19	4,718,034	4,677,399	67	4,319,813	3,954,653	13	13	11
Montana	145,603	1,535	147,138	4	701,573	694,409	4.7	674,767	591,024	43	41	42
Nebraska	76,522	705	77,227	15	1,496,820	1,483,791	19	1,411,330	1,325,510	35	34	33
Nevada	109,889	651	110,540	7	492,396	488,738	4.4	285,278	160,083	47	49	49
New Hampshire	9,033	271	9,304	44	746,284	737,681	79	606,921	533,242	41	45	44
New Jersey	7,532	304	7,836	46	7,208,035	7,168,164	915	6,066,782	4,835,329	8	8	8
New Mexico	121,445	221	121,666	5	1,026,664	1,016,000	8.4	951,023	681,187	37	37	39
New York	47,869	1,707	49,576	30	18,338,055	18,241,266	368	16,782,304	14,830,192	2	1	1
North Carolina	48,880	3,706	52,586	28	5,125,230	5,082,059	97	4,556,155	4,061,929	12	12	10
North Dakota	69,280	1,385	70,665	17	624,181	617,761	8.7	632,446	619,636	45	44	41
Ohio	41,018	204	41,222	35	10,730,200	10,652,017	258	9,706,397	7,946,627	6	5	5
Oklahoma	68,983	936	69,919	18	2,585,486	2,559,253	37	2,328,284	2,233,351	27	27	25
Oregon	96,209	772	96,981	10	2,110,810	2,091,385	22	1,768,687	1,521,341	31	32	32
Pennsylvania	45,025	308	45,333	33	11,884,314	11,793,909	260	11,319,366	10,498,012	3	3	3
Rhode Island	1,049	165	1,214	50	957,798	949,723	782	859,488	791,896	39	39	36
South Carolina	30,280	775	31,055	40	2,617,320	2,590,516	83	2,382,594	2,117,027	26	26	27
South Dakota	75,956	1,091	77,047	16	673,247	666,257	8.6	680,514	652,740	44	40	40
Tennessee	41,367	878	42,244	34	3,961,060	3,924,164	93	3,567,089	3,291,718	17	17	16
Texas	262,970	4,369	267,339	2	11,298,787	11,196,730	42	9,579,677	7,711,194	4	6	6
Utah	82,381	2,535	84,916	11	1,067,810	1,059,273	12	890,627	688,862	36	38	38
Vermont	9,274	335	9,609	43	448,327	444,732	46	389,881	377,747	48	47	46
Virginia	39,841	976	40,817	36	4,690,742	4,648,494	114	3,966,949	3,318,680	14	14	15
Washington	66,683	1,529	68,192	20	3,443,487	3,409,169	50	2,853,214	2,378,963	22	23	24
West Virginia	24,084	97	24,181	41	1,763,331	1,744,237	72	1,860,421	2,005,552	34	30	29
Wisconsin	54,466	1,688	56,154	26	4,447,013	4,417,933	79	3,951,777	3,434,575	16	15	14
Wyoming	97,281	633	97,914	9	335,719	332,416	3.4	330,066	290,529	49	48	48
United States	3,540,911	74,212	3,675,545*	..	204,816,296‡	203,235,298	55	179,323,175	151,325,798	..	..	..

† District. * Includes the United States parts of the Great Lakes (60,422 square miles). These are not included in state figures.

‡ The apportionment population represents the resident population plus members of the armed forces overseas and other U. S. citizens who were abroad at the time of the census. A total U. S. apportionment population of 204,053,325 was used to compute the 1971 Congressional apportionment among the 50 States. This total excludes the District of Columbia, ignored in Congressional apportionment.

U.S. State General Information

STATE	CAPITAL	LARGEST CITY	ENTERED UNION AS STATE — Date of Entry	ENTERED UNION AS STATE — Rank of Entry	Greatest N-S Measurement (miles)	Greatest E-W Measurement (miles)	HIGHEST POINT — Location	HIGHEST POINT — Altitude (feet)	STATE FLOWER	STATE BIRD	STATE NICKNAME
Alabama	Montgomery	Birmingham	Dec. 14, 1819	22	330	200	Cheaha Mountain	2,407	Camellia	Yellowhammer	Yellowhammer
Alaska	Juneau	Anchorage	Jan. 3, 1959	49	1,332	2,250	Mt. McKinley	20,320	Forget-me-not	Willow Ptarmigan	Last Frontier
Arizona	Phoenix	Phoenix	Feb. 14, 1912	48	390	335	Humphreys Peak	12,633	Saguaro Cactus	Cactus Wren	Grand Canyon
Arkansas	Little Rock	Little Rock	June 15, 1836	25	240	275	Magazine Mtn.	2,753	Apple Blossom	Mockingbird	Land of Opportunity
California	Sacramento	Los Angeles	Sept. 9, 1850	31	800	375	Mt. Whitney	14,494	Golden Poppy	California Valley Quail	Golden
Colorado*	Denver	Denver	Aug. 1, 1876	38	270	380	Mt. Elbert	14,433	Rocky Mountain Columbine	Lark Bunting	Centennial
Connecticut*	Hartford	Hartford	Jan. 9, 1788	5	75	90	S. slope of Mt. Frissell	2,380	Mountain Laurel	American Robin	Constitution
Delaware*	Dover	Wilmington	Dec. 7, 1787	1	95	35	Ebright Road, New Castle Co.	442	Peach Blossom	Blue Hen Chicken	First
District of Columbia†	Washington	Washington	March 3, 1791	..	15	15	Tenleytown	410	American Beauty Rose	Wood Thrush	....
Florida	Tallahassee	Jacksonville	March 3, 1845	27	460	400	N. boundary, Walton Co.	345	Orange Blossom	Mockingbird	Sunshine
Georgia*	Atlanta	Atlanta	Jan. 2, 1788	4	315	250	Brasstown Bald (mtn.)	4,784	Cherokee Rose	Brown Thrasher	Peach State
Hawaii	Honolulu	Honolulu	Aug. 21, 1959	50	...	1,600	Mauna Kea	13,796	Red Hibiscus	Nene (Hawaiian Goose)	The Aloha
Idaho	Boise	Boise	July 3, 1890	43	480	305	Borah Peak	12,662	Syringa	Mountain Bluebird	Gem
Illinois	Springfield	Chicago	Dec. 3, 1818	21	380	205	Charles Mound	1,235	Native Violet	Cardinal	Prairie
Indiana	Indianapolis	Indianapolis	Dec. 11, 1816	19	265	160	Near Spartanburg	1,257	Peony	Cardinal	Hoosier
Iowa	Des Moines	Des Moines	Dec. 28, 1846	29	205	310	N. W. corner Osceola Co.	1,670	Wild Rose	Eastern Goldfinch	Hawkeye
Kansas	Topeka	Wichita	Jan. 29, 1861	34	205	410	Mt. Sunflower	4,039	Sunflower	Western Meadowlark	Sunflower
Kentucky	Frankfort	Louisville	June 1, 1792	15	175	350	Black Mountain	4,145	Goldenrod	Kentucky Cardinal	Bluegrass
Louisiana	Baton Rouge	New Orleans	April 30, 1812	18	275	300	Driskill Mountain	535	Magnolia	Eastern Brown Pelican**	Pelican
Maine	Augusta	Portland	March 15, 1820	23	310	210	Mt. Katahdin	5,268	White Pine Cone and Tassel	Chickadee	Pine Tree
Maryland*	Annapolis	Baltimore	April 28, 1788	7	120	200	Backbone Mountain	3,360	Black-eyed Susan	Baltimore Oriole	Free
Massachusetts*	Boston	Boston	Feb. 6, 1788	6	110	190	Mt. Greylock	3,491	Mayflower	Chickadee	Bay
Michigan	Lansing	Detroit	Jan. 26, 1837	26	400	310	Mt. Curwood	1,980	Apple Blossom	Robin	Wolverine
Minnesota	St. Paul	Minneapolis	May 11, 1858	32	400	350	Eagle Mtn.	2,301	Showy Lady's-slipper	Loon	Gopher
Mississippi	Jackson	Jackson	Dec. 10, 1817	20	340	180	Woodall Mountain	806	Magnolia	Mockingbird	Magnolia
Missouri	Jefferson City	St. Louis	Aug. 10, 1821	24	280	300	Taum Sauk Mountain	1,772	Hawthorne	Bluebird	Show Me
Montana	Helena	Billings	Nov. 8, 1889	41	315	570	Granite Peak	12,799	Bitterroot	Western Meadowlark	Treasure
Nebraska	Lincoln	Omaha	March 1, 1867	37	210	415	S.W. corner Kimball Co.	5,426	Goldenrod	Western Meadowlark	Cornhusker
Nevada	Carson City	Las Vegas	Oct. 31, 1864	36	485	315	Boundary Peak	13,143	Sagebrush	Mountain Bluebird**	Battle Born
New Hampshire*	Concord	Manchester	June 21, 1788	9	185	90	Mt. Washington	6,288	Purple Lilac	Purple Finch	Granite
New Jersey*	Trenton	Newark	Dec. 18, 1787	3	166	70	High Point	1,803	Purple Violet	Eastern Goldfinch	Garden
New Mexico	Santa Fe	Albuquerque	Jan. 6, 1912	47	390	350	Wheeler Peak	13,161	Yucca	Road Runner	Land of Enchantment
New York*	Albany	New York	July 26, 1788	11	310	330	Mt. Marcy	5,344	Rose	Bluebird**	Empire
North Carolina*	Raleigh	Charlotte	Nov. 21, 1789	12	200	520	Mt. Mitchell	6,684	Dogwood	Cardinal	Tar Heel
North Dakota	Bismarck	Fargo	Nov. 2, 1889	39	210	360	White Butte	3,506	Wild Prairie Rose	Western Meadowlark	Flickertail
Ohio	Columbus	Cleveland	March 1, 1803	17	230	205	Campbell Hill	1,550	Scarlet Carnation	Cardinal	Buckeye
Oklahoma	Oklahoma City	Oklahoma City	Nov. 16, 1907	46	210	460	Black Mesa	4,973	Mistletoe	Scissor-tailed Flycatcher	Sooner
Oregon	Salem	Portland	Feb. 14, 1859	33	290	375	Mt. Hood	11,235	Oregon Grape	Western Meadowlark	Beaver
Pennsylvania*	Harrisburg	Philadelphia	Dec. 12, 1787	2	180	310	Mt. Davis	3,213	Mountain Laurel	Ruffed Grouse	Keystone
Rhode Island*	Providence	Providence	May 29, 1790	13	50	35	Jerimoth Hill	812	Violet	Rhode Island Red	Little Rhody
South Carolina*	Columbia	Columbia	May 23, 1788	8	215	285	Sassafras Mountain	3,560	Carolina Jessamine	Carolina Wren	Palmetto
South Dakota	Pierre	Sioux Falls	Nov. 2, 1889	40	240	360	Harney Peak	7,242	Pasque	Ringnecked Pheasant	Coyote
Tennessee	Nashville	Memphis	June 1, 1796	16	120	430	Clingmans Dome	6,643	Iris	Mockingbird	Volunteer
Texas	Austin	Houston	Dec. 29, 1845	28	710	760	Guadalupe Peak	8,751	Bluebonnet	Mockingbird	Lone Star
Utah	Salt Lake City	Salt Lake City	Jan. 4, 1896	45	345	275	Kings Peak	13,528	Sego Lily	Seagull	Beehive
Vermont	Montpelier	Burlington	March 4, 1791	14	155	90	Mt. Mansfield	4,393	Red Clover	Hermit Thrush	Green Mountain
Virginia*	Richmond	Norfolk	June 25, 1788	10	205	425	Mt. Rogers	5,729	American Dogwood	Cardinal	Old Dominion
Washington	Olympia	Seattle	Nov. 11, 1889	42	230	340	Mt. Rainier	14,410	Rhododendron	Willow Goldfinch	Evergreen
West Virginia	Charleston	Huntington	June 20, 1863	35	200	225	Spruce Knob	4,862	Rhododendron	Cardinal	Mountain
Wisconsin	Madison	Milwaukee	May 29, 1848	30	300	290	Timms Hill	1,952	Violet	Robin	Badger
Wyoming	Cheyenne	Cheyenne	July 10, 1890	44	275	365	Gannett Peak	13,804	Indian Paint Brush	Meadowlark	Equality
United States	Washington, D.C.	New York	....	..	...	...	Mt. McKinley, Alaska	20,320		Bald Eagle	

*One of the Thirteen Original States.   **Unofficial.   †District.

U.S. Population by State or Colony 1650-1970

STATES	1970	1960	1950	1940	1930	1920	1900	1880	1860	1840	1820	1800	1790	1770	1750	1700	1650
Alabama	3,444,165	3,266,740	3,061,743	2,832,961	2,646,248	2,348,174	1,828,697	1,262,505	964,201	590,756	127,901						
Alaska	302,173	226,167	128,643	72,524	59,278	55,036	63,592	33,426									
Arizona	1,772,482	1,302,161	749,587	499,261	435,573	334,162	122,931	40,440									
Arkansas	1,923,295	1,786,272	1,909,511	1,949,387	1,854,482	1,752,204	1,311,564	802,525	435,450	97,574	14,273						
California	19,953,134	15,717,204	10,586,223	6,907,387	5,677,251	3,426,861	1,485,053	864,694	379,994								
Colorado	2,207,259	1,753,947	1,325,089	1,123,296	1,035,791	939,629	539,700	194,327	34,277								
Connecticut	3,032,217	2,535,234	2,007,280	1,709,242	1,606,903	1,380,631	908,420	622,700	460,147	309,978	275,248	251,002	237,946	183,881	111,280	25,970	4,139
Delaware	548,104	446,292	318,085	266,505	238,380	223,003	184,735	146,608	112,216	78,085	72,749	64,273	59,096	35,496	28,704	2,470	185
District of Columbia	756,510	763,956	802,178	663,091	486,869	437,571	278,718	177,624	75,080	43,712	23,336	8,144					
Florida	6,789,443	4,951,560	2,771,305	1,897,414	1,468,211	968,470	528,542	269,493	140,424	54,477							
Georgia	4,589,575	3,943,116	3,444,578	3,123,723	2,908,506	2,895,832	2,216,331	1,542,180	1,057,286	691,392	340,989	162,686	82,548	23,375	5,200		
Hawaii	769,913	632,772	499,794	422,770	368,300	255,881	154,001										
Idaho	713,008	667,191	588,637	524,873	445,032	431,866	161,772	32,610									
Illinois	11,113,976	10,081,158	8,712,176	7,897,241	7,630,654	6,485,280	4,821,550	3,077,871	1,711,951	476,183	55,211						
Indiana	5,193,669	4,662,498	3,934,224	3,427,796	3,238,503	2,930,390	2,516,462	1,978,301	1,350,428	685,866	147,178	5,641					
Iowa	2,825,041	2,757,537	2,621,073	2,538,268	2,470,939	2,404,021	2,231,853	1,624,615	674,913	43,112							
Kansas	2,249,071	2,178,611	1,905,299	1,801,028	1,880,999	1,769,257	1,470,495	996,096	107,206								
Kentucky	3,219,311	3,038,156	2,944,806	2,845,627	2,614,589	2,416,630	2,147,174	1,648,690	1,155,684	779,828	564,317	220,955	73,677	15,700			
Louisiana	3,643,180	3,257,022	2,683,516	2,363,880	2,101,593	1,798,509	1,381,625	939,946	708,002	352,411	153,407						
Maine[4]	993,663	969,265	913,774	847,226	797,423	768,014	694,466	648,936	628,279	501,793	298,335	151,719	96,540	31,257			
Maryland	3,922,399	3,100,689	2,343,001	1,821,244	1,631,526	1,449,661	1,188,044	934,943	687,049	470,019	407,350	341,548	319,728	202,599	141,073	29,604	4,504
Massachusetts[4]	5,689,170	5,148,578	4,690,514	4,316,721	4,249,614	3,852,356	2,805,346	1,783,085	1,231,066	737,699	523,287	422,845	378,787	235,308	188,000	55,941	16,603
Michigan	8,875,083	7,823,194	6,371,766	5,256,106	4,842,325	3,668,412	2,420,982	1,636,937	749,113	212,267	8,896						
Minnesota	3,805,069	3,413,864	2,982,483	2,792,300	2,563,953	2,387,125	1,751,394	780,773	172,023								
Mississippi	2,216,912	2,178,141	2,178,914	2,183,796	2,009,821	1,790,618	1,551,270	1,131,597	791,305	375,651	75,448	8,850					
Missouri	4,677,399	4,319,813	3,954,653	3,784,664	3,629,367	3,404,055	3,106,665	2,168,380	1,182,012	383,702	66,586						
Montana	694,409	674,767	591,024	559,456	537,606	548,889	243,329	39,159									
Nebraska	1,483,791	1,411,330	1,325,510	1,315,834	1,377,963	1,296,372	1,066,300	452,402	28,841								
Nevada	488,738	285,278	160,083	110,247	91,058	77,407	42,335	62,266	6,857								
New Hampshire	737,681	606,921	533,242	491,524	465,293	443,083	411,588	346,991	326,073	284,574	244,161	183,858	141,885	62,396	27,505	4,958	1,305
New Jersey	7,168,164	6,066,782	4,835,329	4,160,165	4,041,334	3,155,900	1,883,669	1,131,116	672,035	373,306	277,575	211,149	184,139	117,431	71,393	14,010	
New Mexico	1,016,000	951,023	681,187	531,818	423,317	360,350	195,310	119,565	93,516								
New York	18,241,266	16,782,304	14,830,192	13,479,142	12,588,066	10,385,227	7,268,894	5,082,871	3,880,735	2,428,921	1,372,812	589,051	340,120	162,920	76,696	19,107	4,116
North Carolina	5,082,059	4,556,155	4,061,929	3,571,623	3,170,276	2,559,123	1,893,810	1,399,750	992,622	753,419	638,829	478,103	393,751	197,200	72,984	10,720	785
North Dakota[3]	617,761	632,446	619,636	641,935	680,845	646,872	319,146	36,909									
Ohio	10,652,017	9,706,397	7,946,627	6,907,612	6,646,697	5,759,394	4,157,545	3,198,062	2,339,511	1,519,467	581,434	45,365					
Oklahoma[5]	2,559,253	2,328,284	2,233,351	2,336,434	2,396,040	2,028,283	790,391										
Oregon	2,091,385	1,768,687	1,521,341	1,089,684	953,786	783,389	413,536	174,768	52,465								
Pennsylvania	11,793,909	11,319,366	10,498,012	9,900,180	9,631,350	8,720,017	6,302,115	4,282,891	2,906,215	1,724,033	1,049,458	602,365	434,373	240,057	119,666	17,950	
Rhode Island	949,723	859,488	791,896	713,346	687,497	604,397	428,556	276,531	174,620	108,830	83,059	69,122	68,825	58,196	33,226	5,894	
South Carolina	2,590,516	2,382,594	2,117,027	1,899,804	1,738,765	1,683,724	1,340,316	995,577	703,708	594,398	502,741	345,591	249,073	124,244	64,000	5,704	
South Dakota[3]	666,257	680,514	652,740	642,961	692,849	636,547	401,570	98,268	4,837								
Tennessee	3,924,164	3,567,089	3,291,718	2,915,841	2,616,556	2,337,885	2,020,616	1,542,359	1,109,801	829,210	422,823	105,602	35,691	1,000			
Texas	11,196,730	9,579,677	7,711,194	6,414,824	5,824,715	4,663,228	3,048,710	1,591,749	604,215								
Utah	1,059,273	890,627	688,862	550,310	507,847	449,396	276,749	143,963	40,273								
Vermont	444,732	389,881	377,747	359,611	359,231	352,428	343,641	332,286	315,098	291,948	235,981	154,465	85,425	10,000			
Virginia[6]	4,648,494	3,966,949	3,318,680	2,677,773	2,421,851	2,309,187	1,854,184	1,512,565	1,219,630	1,025,227	938,261	807,557	691,737	447,016	231,033	58,560	18,731
Washington	3,409,169	2,853,214	2,378,963	1,736,191	1,563,396	1,356,621	518,103	75,116	11,594								
West Virginia[6]	1,744,237	1,860,421	2,005,552	1,901,974	1,729,205	1,463,701	958,800	618,457	376,688	224,537	136,808	78,592	55,873				
Wisconsin	4,417,933	3,951,777	3,434,575	3,137,587	2,939,006	2,632,067	2,069,042	1,315,497	775,881	30,945							
Wyoming	332,416	330,066	290,529	250,742	225,565	194,402	92,531	20,789									
Total[1]	203,235,298	179,323,175	151,325,798	132,164,569	123,202,624	106,021,537	76,212,168	50,189,209	31,443,321	17,069,453[2]	9,638,453	5,308,483	3,929,214	2,148,076	1,170,760	250,888	50,368

[1] All figures prior to 1890 exclude uncivilized Indians. Figures for 1650 through 1770 include only the British colonies that later became the United States. No areas are included prior to their annexation to the United States. However, many of the figures refer to territories prior to their admission as States. U.S. total includes Alaska from 1880 through 1970 and Hawaii from 1900 through 1970.

[2] U.S. total for 1840 includes 6,100 persons on public ships in service of the United States, not credited to any State.

[3] South Dakota figure for 1860 represents entire Dakota Territory. North and South Dakota figures for 1880 are for the parts of Dakota Territory which later constituted the respective States.

[4] Maine figures for 1770 through 1800 are for that area of Massachusetts which became the State of Maine in 1820. Massachusetts figures exclude Maine from 1770 through 1800, but include it from 1650 through 1750. Massachusetts figure for 1650 also includes population of Plymouth (1,566), a separate colony until 1691.

[5] Oklahoma figure for 1900 includes population of Indian Territory (392,060).

[6] West Virginia figures for 1790 through 1860 are for that area of Virginia which became West Virginia in 1863. These figures are excluded from the figures for Virginia from 1790 through 1860.

Glossary of Foreign Geographical Terms

Arab....Arabic
Bantu...Bantu
Bur.....Burmese
Camb...Cambodian
Celt.....Celtic
Chn.....Chinese
Czech...Czech
Dan.....Danish
Du......Dutch
Fin.....Finnish
Fr......French
Ger.....German
Grc.....Greek
Hung...Hungarian
Ice.....Icelandic
India...India
Indian..American
        Indian
It......Italian
Jap.....Japanese

Kor.....Korean
Lao.....Laotian
Lapp....Lappish
Mal.....Malayan
Mong...Mongolian
Nor.....Norwegian
Per.....Persian
Pol.....Polish
Port....Portuguese
Rom.....Romanian
Rus.....Russian
Siam....Siamese
So. Slav..Southern
        Slavonic
Sp......Spanish
Swe.....Swedish
Tib.....Tibetan
Tur.....Turkic
Viet.....Vietnamese

A

å, Dan., Nor.....river
aan, Du.....at, on
abad, India, Per.....dwelling, town
abu, abou, Arab.....father
ålen, Nor.....spit
alf, elf, Swe.....river
alp, Ger.....mountain
alt, Ger.....old
alta, -o, It., Port., Sp.....high
altipiano, It.....plateau
älv, älven, Swe.....river
amarillo, Sp.....yellow
arquipélago, Port.....archipelago
arroyo, Sp.....brook, dry bed of stream
as, Dan,. Nor., Swe.....hill, ridge
austral, Sp.....southern

B

baai, Du.....bay
bab, Arab.....gate, strait
bach, Ger.....brook, stream
backe, Swe.....hill
bad, Ger.....bath
bahía, Port., Sp.....bay, gulf
bahr, Arab.....bay, river
baia, It.....bay, gulf
baie, Fr.....bay, gulf
bajo, Sp.....low, lower
bakke, Dan., Nor.....hill
balkan, Tur.....mountain range
ban, Lao, Mal.....village
ban, Siam.....house
bana, Jap.....cape
bandar, Per.....harbor
batang, Mal.....river
belyy, belaya, Rus.....white
ben, Celt.....mountain, summit
bender, bandar, Arab., India
.....market town, port
beni, bani, Arab.....sons of, tribe of
berg, Du., Ger., Nor., Swe..mountain, hill
bir, bi'r, Arab.....well
birkat, Arab.....pool, well
bjeli, -a, -o, So. Slav.....white
bjerg, bjaerg, Dan., Nor.....mountain
blanc, Fr.....white
blanco, Sp.....white
blau, Ger.....blue
bleu, Fr.....blue
bodden, Ger.....ground
bogaz, bogazi, Tur.....strait
bois, Fr.....forest, wood
boloto, Rus.....marsh
bolshoy, bolshoye, Rus.....great
boreal, Sp.....northern
borg, Dan., Nor., Swe.....castle
borgo, It.....town
bosch, Du.....forest, wood
bouche, Fr.....river, mouth
bourg, Fr.....town, borough
bro, Dan., Nor., Swe.....bridge
brücke, brücken, Ger.....bridge, bridges
brun, Fr.....brown
bucht, Ger.....bay, bight
bugt, Dan., Nor.....bay, gulf
bukt, bukten, Swe.....bay, gulf
bulak, Tur.....spring
būr, Arab.....port
burg, Du., Ger.....castle, town
buri, Siam.....city

burun, burnu, Tur.....cape
büyük, Tur.....great
by, Dan., Nor., Swe.....town, village

C

cabeza, Sp.....summit
cabo, Port., Sp.....cape
cairn, carn, Celt.....rocky headland
campo, It., Port., Sp.....field
campos, Port. (Brazil).....plains
cañon, Sp.....canyon
cap, Fr.....cape
capo, It.....cape
casa, It., Port., Sp.....house
castello, It., Port.....castle, fort
castillo, Sp.....castle, fort
catingas, Port. (Brazil)...open brushlands
cayo, Sp.....rock, shoal, islet
central, Fr.....middle
cerro, Sp.....hill
chai, ciai, Tur.....river
champ, Fr.....field
chapada, Port. (Brazil).....hills, ridge
chateau, Fr.....castle
cherniy, chernyaya, Rus.....black
chin, Chn.....market town
chott, shat, Arab.....salt river or lake
chou, Chn.....island
cidade, Port.....city
città, It.....town, city
ciudad, Sp.....town, city
col, Fr.....pass
colina, Sp.....hill
colorado, Sp.....red
cordillera, Sp.....mountain chain
costa, It., Port., Sp.....coast
côte, côtes, Fr....coast, hills, peak, ridge
crkva, So. Slav.....church
crni, So. Slav.....black
cuchilla, Sp.....mountain range
cumbre, Sp.....peak, ridge

D

daal, dal, Du.....valley
dag, Tur.....mountain
daglari, Tur.....mountains, range
dake, take, Jap.....peak, ridge
dal, Dan., Du., Nor., Swe.....valley
dalay, Mong.....lake
dar, Arab.....land, country
darya, daria, Per.....river, sea
dasht, Per.....plain, desert
dawhat, Arab.....bay, inlet
deccan, India.....south
deir, Arab.....convent
denis, -z, Tur.....sea, lake
désert, Fr.....desert
deserto, It.....desert
desierto, Sp.....desert
détroit, Fr.....strait
djebel, jebel, Arab.....mountain
dolok, Mal.....mountain
dorf, Ger.....village
dorp, Du.....village
drift, Du., Ger.....current
duinen, Du.....dunes
dun, Celt.....fortified hill
dyk, Du.....dam, dyke
dzong, Tib...fort, administrative capital

E

eau, Fr.....water
ecuador, Sp.....equator
eiland, Du.....island
elf, älf, Swe.....river
elv, Dan., Nor.....river
erg, Arab.....dune, region of dunes
eski, Tur.....old
est, Fr.....east
estado, Sp.....state
este, It., Port., Sp.....east
estrecho, Sp.....strait
étang, Fr.....pond, lake
état, Fr.....state
étroit, Fr.....narrow

F

feld, Ger.....field, plain
fels, Ger.....rock
festung, Ger.....fort
firth, Scotch.....estuary
fiume, It.....river
fjäll, fjället, Swe.....mountain
fjärd, Swe.....bay, inlet
fjeld, Nor.....mountain, hill
fjell, Nor.....mountain
fjord, fjorden, Dan., Nor.....fiord, inlet
fjördhur, Ice.....fiord, inlet
fleuve, Fr.....river
flod, Dan., Swe.....river
flói, Ice.....bay
fluss, Ger.....river
foce, It.....river mouth
fontein, Du.....a spring
fors, Swe.....waterfall, torrent
forst, Ger.....forest
fos, Dan., Nor.....waterfall
fuente, Sp.....spring, fountain
fuerte, Sp.....fort
furt, Ger.....ford

G

gamla, Swe.....old
gamle, Dan., Nor.....old
gat, Dan., Nor.....passage, channel
gavan', Rus.....harbor
gebel, Arab.....mountain
gebergte, Du.....mountain range
gebiet, Ger.....district, territory
gebirge, Ger.....range, mountains
ghat, India..mountain pass, river passage
gobi, Mong.....desert
göl, gölu, Tur.....lake
golf, Du., Ger.....gulf, bay
golfe, Fr.....gulf, bay
golfo, It., Port., Sp.....gulf, bay
gong, India.....village
gora, Pol., Rus., So. Slav.....mountain
gornji, -a, -o, So. Slav.....upper
gorny, Pol.....upper
gorod, grad, Rus., So. Slav.....town
grand, grande, Fr.....large, great
grande, It., Port., Sp.....large, great
grod, gorod, Pol., Rus.....town
grön, Dan.....green
groot, Du.....great
gross, Ger.....great
guba, Rus.....bay, gulf
gunto, Jap.....archipelago

H

haf, Swe.....sea
hafen, Ger.....port, harbor
haff, Ger.....gulf, inland sea
hai, Chn.....sea, lake
hamn, Swe.....harbor
hamun, Per.....swampy lake, plain
haus, hausen, Ger.....house, houses
haut, Fr.....high, summit, upper
havet, Nor.....bay
havn, Dan., Nor.....harbor, port
havre, Fr.....harbor, port
hawr, Arab.....lake, marsh
haz, -a, Hung.....house, dwelling of
heim, Ger.....hamlet
hem, Swe.....hamlet
higashi, Jap.....east
hinterland, Ger.....back country
hissar, hisar, Tur.....castle, fort
ho, Chn.....river
hoch, Ger.....high
hoek, Du.....cape
hof, Ger.....court, farm house
höfn, Ice.....harbor
hoku, Jap.....north
holm, Dan., Nor., Swe.....island
hora, Czech.....mountain
horn, Ger.....peak
hoved, Dan., Nor.....cape, headland
hsien, Chn.....district, district capital
hügel, Ger.....hill

huk, Dan., Nor., Swe.....point
hus, Dan., Nor., Swe.....house
hwang, Chn.....yellow

I

ile, Fr.....island
ilha, Port.....island
indre, Dan., Nor.....inner
indsö, Dan., Nor.....lake
inférieur, Fr.....lower
insel, Ger.....island
insjö, Swe.....lake
irmak, Tur.....river
isla, Sp.....island
isola, It.....island
istmo, It., Sp.....isthmus

J

jabal, Arab.....mountain, plateau, ridge
järvi, Fin.....lake
jebel, djebel, Arab.....mountain
jima, shima, Jap.....island
jökel, jökelen, Nor.....glacier
joki, Fin.....river
jökull, Ice.....ice-covered mountain
juzna, So. Slav.....south, southern

K

kaap, Du.....cape
kafr, kefr, Arab.....village
kaikyo, Jap.....strait
kaise, Lapp.....mountain
kala, kalat, Arab., Per
.....castle, fortress, village
kale, Tur.....castle, fort
kamen', Rus.....rock
kang, Chn.....village
kap, Chn.....cape
kapp, Nor.....cape
kara, Tur.....black
kaupunki, Fin.....town, city
kavir, Per.....salt desert
kebir, Arab.....great
kefr, kafr, Arab.....village
ken, Jap.....prefecture
kend, kand, Per.....village
khalij, Arab.....bay, gulf
khrebet, Rus.....mountain range
ki, Jap.....tree, forest
kil, cill, Celt.....church, cell
kirche, Ger.....church
kirchen, Ger.....parish
kio, kyo, Jap.....town, capital
kis, Hung.....little, small
klein, Du., Ger.....small
köbstad, Dan.....city
köl, Mong., Tur.....lake, marsh
kompong, Camb.....village
kong, Chn.....river
kopf, Ger.....head, summit, peak
köping, Swe.....market, borough
kraal, Du.....native village
krasniy, krasnaya, Rus.
.....beautiful, fair, red
kuala, Mal.....junction, river mouth
kuchuk, Tur.....small
kuh, koh, Per.....mountain
kul, Mong., Tur.....lake
kum, qum, Tur.....desert
kuppe, Ger.....summit
küste, Ger.....coast
kyzyl, kizil, Tur.....red

L

laag, Du.....low
lac, Fr.....lake
lago, It., Sp.....lake
lâgoa, Port.....lagoon
laguna, It., Port., Sp.....lagoon, lake
lahti, Fin.....bay, gulf
län, Swe.....county
landsby, Dan., Nor.....village
lao, Viet.....island
lilla, Swe.....small

Glossary of Foreign Geographical Terms *Continued*

lille, *Dan., Nor*....small
liman, *Tur*....bay, port
ling, *Chn*....mountain, range
llanos, *Sp*....prairies, plains
loch, *Celt*....lake, bay (Scotland)
lough, *Celt*....lake, bay (Ireland)

M

maha, *India*....great
malyy, malaya, *Rus*....small
mar, *Port., Sp*....sea
mare, *It., Rom*....sea
mare, *Rom*....great
mark, *Ger*....boundary, limit
massif, *Fr*....mountain range
mato, *Port*....jungle, copse
medio, *Sp*....middle
meer, *Du., Ger*....lake, sea
mer, *Fr*....sea
mesa, *Sp*....flat-topped mountain
meseta, *Sp*....hill
midden, *Du*....middle
mina, *Port., Sp*....mine
mittel, *Ger*....middle
mont, *Fr*....mount, mountain
montagna, *It*....mountain
montagna, *Fr*....mountain
montaña, *Sp*....mountain
monte, *It., Port., Sp*....mount, mountain
more, *Rus., So. Slav*....sea
morro, *Port., Sp*....hill
moyen, *Fr*....middle
mühle, *Ger*....mill
mund, munde, *Ger*....river mouth
mündung, *Ger*....river mouth
muong, *Lao*....town, village
mura, *Jap*....village
muz, *Tur*....ice
mys, *Rus*....cape, point

N

nada, *Jap*....sea
nadi, *India*....river, creek
naes, näs, *Dan., Nor., Swe*....cape
nagar, nagon, *India*....town, city
nagy, *Hung*....large, great
naka, *Jap*....middle
neder, *Du*....low
nedre, *Nor*....lower
negro, *It., Port., Sp*....black
nejd, *Arab*....highland
neu, *Ger*....new
nevado, *Sp*....mountain
nez, *Fr*....point, cape
nieder, *Ger*....low, lower
nieuw, *Du*....new
nizhne, nizhniy, nizhnyaya, *Rus*....lower
noir, *Fr*....black
nong, *Siam*....marsh, pond, lake
noord, *Du*....north
nor, *Tib*....lake
nord, *Dan., Fr., Ger., It., Nor*....north
norr, norra, *Swe*....north
norte, *Port., Sp*....north
nos, *Rus*....cape
nouvelle, *Fr*....new
novi, -a, -o, *So. Slav*....new
novo, *Port*....new
novy, -e, -a, *Czech*....new
novyy, novyye, novaya, novo, *Rus*....new
nowa, nowy, Pol....new
nuevo, *Sp*....new
nuovo, *It*....new
nuur, *Mong*....lake
ny, *Dan., Swe*....new
nyasa, *Bantu*....lake

O

o, *Jap*....great, large
ö, *Dan., Nor., Swe*....island
ober, *Ger*....upper
occidental, *Sp*....western
odde, *Dan., Nor*....point, cape
oedjoeng, *Mal*....cape
oeste, *Port., Sp*....west
ojo, *Sp*....spring
oost, *Du*....east
op, *Du*....on
oriental, *Sp*....eastern
oro, *Sp*....gold
óros, *Grc*....mountain
ost, *Ger., Swe*....east
öst, öster, östre, *Dan., Nor., Swe.*
....east, eastern
ostrog, *Rus*....fort
ostrov, *Rus*....island
ouadi, *Arab*....intermittent stream
ouest, *Fr*....west
öy, *Nor*....island
ozero, *Rus*....lake

P

paa, *Fin*....mountain
padang, *Mal*....plain, field
pampas, *Sp. (Argentina)*....grassy plains
para, *Indian (Brazil)*....river
pas, *Fr*....channel, strait, pass
paso, *Sp*....mountain pass
passo, *It., Port*....mountain pass
patam, *India*....city, town
pequeño, *Sp*....small
peresheyek, *Rus*....isthmus
pertuis, *Fr*....strait
peski, *Rus*....desert, sands
petit, petite, *Fr*....small, little
pic, *Fr*....mountain peak
piccolo, *It*....small
pico, *Port., Sp*....mountain peak
piedra, *Sp*....stone, rock
pik, *Rus*....peak
planalto, *Port*....plateau
plata, *Sp*....silver
plato, *Rus*....plateau
playa, *Sp*....shore, beach
po, *Chn*....lake
pointe, *Fr*....point
polder, *Du., Ger*....reclaimed marsh
polje, *So. Slav*....field
poluostrov, *Rus*....peninsula
pont, *Fr*....bridge
ponta, *Port*....point, headland
ponte, *It., Port*....bridge
pore, pur, *India*....city, town
porto, *It*....port, harbor
pôrto, *Port*....port, harbor
prado, *Sp*....field, meadow
presqu'île, *Fr*....peninsula
proliv, *Rus*....strait
pu, *Chn*....commercial village
pueblo, *Sp*....town, village
puerto, *Sp*....port, harbor
pulau, *Mal*....island
punkt, *Ger*....point
punt, *Du*....point
punta, *It., Sp*....point
pur, pura, *India*....city, town
puy, *Fr*....peak

R

rann, *India*....wasteland
ra's, *Arab*....cape, summit
reg, *Arab*....coarse gravel desert
reka, *Rus., So. Slav*....river
represa, *Port*....reservoir
retto, *Jap*....archipelago
ria, *Sp*....river mouth
ribeira, -ão, *Port*....stream, river
rio, *It., Port*....river
río, *Sp*....river
rivière, *Fr*....river
roca, *Sp*....rock
rochedos, *Port. (Brazil)*....rocks in water
rouge, *Fr*....red
rud, *Per*....river

S

saari, *Fin*....island
sable, *Fr*....sand
sahra, *Arab*....desert
sal, *Sp*....salt
samar, *Mong*....path, route
san, *Chn., Jap., Kor*....mountain, hill
san, santa, santo, *It., Port., Sp*....saint
são, *Port*....saint
sat, satu, *Rom*....village
schloss, *Ger*....castle, fort
sebkha, *Arab*....salt marsh
see, *Ger*....lake, sea
sehir, shehr, *Tur*....town
selat, *Mal*....channel, strait
selatan, *Mal*....south, southern
selvas, *Port. (Brazil)*
....tropical rain forests
seno, *Sp*....bay
serra, *It., Port*....pass, mountain ridge
serranía, *Sp*....mountain ridge
seto, *Jap*....strait, channel
severnaya, *Rus*....north
shahr, shehr, *Per*....town
sha'īb, *Arab*
....depression, intermittent stream
shan, *Chn*....range, mountain, hill
shatt, chott, *Arab*....salt river or lake
shima, sima, *Jap*....island
shimo, *Jap*....lower
shiu, *Chn., Jap*....province
shoto, *Jap*....archipelago
si, *Chn*....west, western
sierra, *Sp*....mountain range
sint, *Du*....saint
sjö, *Nor., Swe*....lake, sea
sö, *Dan., Nor*....lake, sea
söder, *Swe*....south
soengai, sungei, *Mal*....river
sopka, *Rus*....extinct volcano
source, *Fr*....spring
spitze, *Ger*....summit, point
sredniy, sredne, srednyaya, *Rus*....middle
staat, *Ger*....state
stad, *Dan., Du., Nor., Swe*....city, town
stadt, *Ger*....city, town
stari, -a, -o, *So. Slav*....old
stary, *Czech., Pol*....old
staryy, staraya, *Rus*....old
stato, *It*....state
sten, *Dan., Nor., Swe*....stone
step, *Rus*....treeless plain, steppe
stor, *Dan., Nor., Swe*....great, large
straat, *Du*....strait
strand, *Dan., Du., Ger., Nor., Swe*
....shore, beach
stretto, *It*....strait
strom, *Ger*....stream
ström, *Dan., Nor., Swe*....river
stroom, *Du*....stream, river
su, suyu, *Tur*....water, river
sud, *Fr., Sp*....south
süd, *Ger*....south
sul, *Port*....south, southern
sund, *Dan., Nor., Swe*....sound
supérieure, *Fr*....upper
sur, *Fr*....on
sur, *Sp*....south
syd, *Dan., Nor., Swe*....south

T

tafelland, *Du., Ger*....plateau, tableland
tagh, *Mong., Tur*....mountain
tai, *Jap*....large, great
taiga, *Rus*....northern coniferous forest
take, dake, *Jap*....peak, ridge
tandjung, tanjong, *Mal*....cape
tao, -u, *Chn*....island
targ, targu, *Rom*....market, town
tash, *Per., Tur*....rock, stone
tau, *Tur*....mountain range
tell, tel, *Arab*....hill
terra, *It*....land
terre, *Fr*....earth, land
thal, *Ger*....valley
tierra, *Sp*....earth, land
torp, *Swe*....village, cottage
torre, *It., Port., Sp*....tower
tsi, *Chn*....village, borough
tsu, *Jap*....port
tundra, *Rus*....marshy arctic plains
tung, *Chn*....east, eastern
turn, turnu, *Rom*....tower
tuz, *Tur*....salt

U

udd, udde, *Swe*....cape
ufer, *Ger*....beach, shore, river bank
uj, *Hung*....new
ulan, *Mong*....red
umi, *Jap*....sea, gulf
unter, *Ger*....lower
ura, *Jap*....bay, shore, creek
ust, *Rus*....river mouth
uula, *Mong*....mountain, range
utara, *Mal*....north, northern

V

vall, *Swe*....coast
valle, *Port., Sp*....valley
vallée, *Fr*....valley
valli, *It*....lake, lagoon
var, *Hung*....fortress
varos, *Hung., So. Slav*....town
varre, *Lapp*....mountain
vecchio, *It*....old
veld, *Du*....open plain, field
velho, *Port*....old
velikiy, *Rus., So. Slav*....great
verde, *It., Port., Sp*....green
verkhniy, verkhnyaya, *Rus*
....upper, higher
vert, *Fr*....green
ves, *Czech*....village
vest, *Dan., Nor., Swe*....west
viejo, *Sp*....old
vieux, *Fr*....old
vik, viken, *Swe*....bay
villa, *Port., Sp*....small town
villar, *Sp*....village, hamlet
ville, *Fr*....town, city
vinh, *Viet*....bay
vishni, visni, *Rus*....high
vostok, *Rus*....east
volcán, *Sp*....volcano

W

wadi, wādī, wad, *Arab*
....intermittent stream
wald, *Ger*....forest, woodland
wan, *Chn., Jap*....bay, gulf
weiler, *Ger*....hamlet, village
weiss, *Ger*....white
westersch, *Du*....western
wiek, *Ger*....bay
wüste, *Ger*....desert

Y

yama, *Jap*....mountain
yang, *Chn*....channel
yeni, *Tur*....new
yokara, *Tur*....upper
yoma, *Bur*....mountain range
yug, *Rus*....south
yuzhno, *Rus*....south, southern

Z

zaki, saki, *Jap*....cape
zaliv, *Rus*....bay, gulf
zapad, zapadnyy, *Rus*....west
zapadni, -a, -o, *So. Slav*....west, western
zee, *Du*....sea
zemlya, *Rus*....land
zuid, *Du*....south

Abbreviations

admin	administered
Afg	Afghanistan
Afr	Africa
A. & I.	Afars & Issas
Ala	Alabama
Alb	Albania
Alg	Algeria
Alsk	Alaska
Alta	Alberta
Am	American
Am. Sam	American Samoa
And	Andorra
Ang	Angola
Ant	Antarctica
Arc	Arctic
arch	archipelago
Arg	Argentina
Ariz	Arizona
Ark	Arkansas
Atl. O.	Atlantic Ocean
Aus	Austria
Austl	Australia, Australian
auton	autonomous
Az. Is	Azores Islands
Ba	Bahamas
Barb	Barbados
B. C.	British Columbia
Bel	Belgium, Belgian
Bhu	Bhutan
Bis. Arch	Bismarck Archipelago
Bngl	Bangladesh
Bol	Bolivia
Bots	Botswana
Br	British
Braz	Brazil
Bru	Brunei
Bul	Bulgaria
Bur	Burma
Calif	California
Cam	Cameroon
Camb	Cambodia
Can	Canada
Can. Is	Canary Islands
Cen. Afr. Rep	Central African Republic
Cen. Am	Central America
co	county
Col	Colombia
Colo	Colorado
Con	Congo
Conn	Connecticut
cont	continent
C. R.	Costa Rica
C. V. Is	Cape Verde Islands
Cyp	Cyprus
C.Z.	Canal Zone
Czech	Czechoslovakia
Dah	Dahomey
D.C.	District of Columbia
Del	Delaware
Den	Denmark
dep	dependency, dependencies
dept	department
dist	district
div	division
Dom. Rep	Dominican Republic
Ec	Ecuador
Eg	Egypt
Eng	England
Equat. Gui	Equatorial Guinea
Eth	Ethiopia
Eur	Europe
Falk. Is	Falkland Islands
Fed	Federation
Fin	Finland
Fla	Florida
Fr	France, French
Fr. Gu	French Guiana
Ga	Georgia
Gam	Gambia
Ger., Fed. Rep. of	Federal Republic of Germany
Ger. Dem. Rep	German Democratic Republic
Gib	Gibraltar
Grc	Greece
Grnld	Greenland
Guad	Guadeloupe
Guat	Guatemala
Guy	Guyana
Hai	Haiti
Haw	Hawaii
Hond	Honduras
Hung	Hungary
I.	Island
I.C.	Ivory Coast
Ice	Iceland
Ill	Illinois
incl	includes, including
Ind	Indiana
Indian res	Indian reservation
Indon	Indonesia
I. of Man	Isle of Man
Ire	Ireland
is	islands
isl	island
Isr	Israel
It	Italy
Jam	Jamaica
Jap	Japan
Kans	Kansas
Ken	Kenya
Kor	Korea
Kuw	Kuwait
Ky	Kentucky
La	Louisiana
Leb	Lebanon
Le. Is	Leeward Islands
Leso	Lesotho
Lib	Liberia
Liech	Liechtenstein
Lux	Luxembourg
Mad	Madagascar
Mad. Is	Madeira Islands
Mala	Malaysia
Man	Manitoba
Mart	Martinique
Mass	Massachusetts
Maur	Mauritania
Md	Maryland
Medit	Mediterranean
Mex	Mexico
Mich	Michigan
Minn	Minnesota
Miss	Mississippi
Mo	Missouri
Mong	Mongolia
Mont	Montana
Mor	Morocco
Moz	Mozambique
mtn	mount, mountain
mts	mountains
mun	municipality
N.A.	North America
nat. mon	national monument
nat. park	national park
N.B.	New Brunswick
N.C.	North Carolina
N. Cal	New Caledonia
N. Dak	North Dakota
Nebr	Nebraska
Nep	Nepal
Neth	Netherlands
Nev	Nevada
Newf	Newfoundland
New Hebr	New Hebrides
N. Gui	New Guinea Territory
N.H.	New Hampshire
Nic	Nicaragua
Nig	Nigeria
N. Ire	Northern Ireland
N.J.	New Jersey
N. Mex	New Mexico
Nor	Norway, Norwegian
N.S.	Nova Scotia
N.W. Ter	Northwest Territories
N.Y.	New York
N.Z.	New Zealand
occ	occupied area
Okla	Oklahoma
Om	Oman
Ont	Ontario
Oreg	Oregon
Pa	Pennsylvania
Pac. O	Pacific Ocean
Pak	Pakistan
Pan	Panama
Pap	Papua
Par	Paraguay
par	parish
P.D.R. of Yem	Yemen, People's Democratic Republic of
P.E.I	Prince Edward Island
pen	peninsula
Phil	Philippines
Pol	Poland
pol. dist	political district
pop	population
Port	Portugal, Portuguese
Port. Timor	Portuguese Timor
poss	possession
P.R.	Puerto Rico
pref	prefecture
prot	protectorate
prov	province, provincial
pt	point
Que	Quebec
reg	region
rep	republic
res	reservation, reservoir
Rh	Rhodesia
R.I.	Rhode Island
riv	river
Rom	Romania
S. A	South America
S. Afr	South Africa
Sal	El Salvador
Sask	Saskatchewan
Sau. Ar	Saudi Arabia
S.C.	South Carolina
Scot	Scotland
S. Dak	South Dakota
Sen	Senegal
S.L.	Sierra Leone
Sol. Is	Solomon Islands
Som	Somalia
Sov. Un	Soviet Union
Sp	Spain, Spanish
St., Ste	Saint, Sainte
Sud	Sudan
Sur	Surinam
S. W. Afr	South West Africa
Swaz	Swaziland
Swe	Sweden
Switz	Switzerland
Syr	Syria
Tan	Tanzania
Tenn	Tennessee
ter	territories, territory
Tex	Texas
Thai	Thailand
Trin	Trinidad & Tobago
trust	trusteeship
Tun	Tunisia
Tur	Turkey
U.A.E	United Arab Emirates
Ug	Uganda
U.K.	United Kingdom
Ur	Uruguay
U.S.	United States
Va	Virginia
Ven	Venezuela
Viet	Vietnam
Vir. Is	Virgin Islands
vol	volcano
Vt	Vermont
Wash	Washington
W.I.	West Indies
Win. Is	Windward Islands
Wis	Wisconsin
W. Sam	Western Samoa
W. Va	West Virginia
Wyo	Wyoming
Yugo	Yugoslavia

Explanation of the Map Index

This universal index includes in a single alphabetical list all important names that appear on the reference maps. Each place name is followed by its location; the population figure, when available; the map index key; and the page number of the map.

State locations are given for all places in the United States. Province and country locations are given for all places in Canada. All other place name entries show only country locations.

United States populations, including counties, metropolitan areas, and incorporated cities are final 1970 census figures. Populations for the States, foreign countries, dependencies and other major regions and political divisions are estimates for January 1, 1974. Populations for individual foreign cities and minor political divisions are from the latest available official census figures and estimates. A triangle symbol (▲) denotes a population figure for an *entire* township, district, or other minor civil division. For some larger cities a second population figure is given accompanied by a star (*). The second figure indicates the population of the city's entire metropolitan area including suburbs, as: Chicago, 3,369,357 (*7,582,700).

The index reference key, always a letter and figure combination, and the map page number are the last items in each entry. Because some places are shown on both a main map and an inset map, more than one index key may be given for a single map page number. Reference also may be made to more than a single map. In each case, however, the index key *letter and figure* precede

the map page number to which reference is made. A lower case key letter indicates reference to an inset map which has been keyed separately.

All major and minor political divisions are followed by both a descriptive term (co., dist., region, prov., dept., state, etc.), indicating political status, and by the country in which they are located. U. S. counties are listed with state locations; all others are given with county references.

The more important physical names that are shown on the maps are listed in the index. Each entry is followed by a descriptive term (bay, hill, range, riv., mtn., isl., etc.), to indicate its nature.

Country locations are given for each name, except for features entirely within States of the United States or provinces of Canada, in which case these divisions are also given.

Some names are included in the index that were omitted from the maps because of scale size or lack of space. These entries are identified by an asterisk (*) and reference is given to the approximate location on the map.

A long name may appear on the map in a shortened form, with the full name given in the index. The part of the name not on the map then appears in brackets, thus: St. Gabriel [-de-Brandon].

The system of alphabetizing used in the index is standard. When more than one name with the same spelling is shown, place names are listed *first* and political divisions *second*.

Index

A

B

Booneville, Ark., 3,239.....B2 49
Booneville, Miss., 5,895....A5 68
Boonsboro, Md., 1,410....A2 53
Boon Terrace, Pa., 400...*F1 81
Boonton, N.J., 9,261......B4 74
Boonville, Calif., 950......C2 50
Boonville, Ind., 5,736.....H3 59
Boonville, Mo., 7,514......C5 69
Boonville, N.Y., 2,488.....B5 75
Boothbay Harbor, Maine, 1,800 (2,320 ▲).........E3 64
Boothwyn, Pa., 6,500....*G11 81
Boppard, Ger., Fed. Rep. of, 8,600..............C3 6
Boquerón, dept., Par., 40,405.................D3 29
Borah, pk., Idaho.........E3 57
Borås, Swe., 72,099 (*94,643)...............I5 11
Bordeaux, Fr., 266,662 (*560,000).............E3 5
Borden, co., Tex., 888....C2 84
Borden Springs, Ala., 60...B4 46
Bordentown, N.J., 4,490...C3 74
Bordighera, It., 9,700.....C1 9
Borgå, Fin., 11,800......G11 11
Borger, Tex., 14,195.......B2 84
Borgomanero, It., 7,900....B2 9
Borgo Val di Taro, It., 11,809................B2 9
Borislav, Sov. Un., 34,000..G7 12
Borisoglebsk, Sov. Un., 64,000...............F13 12
Borisov, Sov. Un., 84,000..D7 12
Borispol, Sov. Un., 32,000..F8 12
Borja, Sp., 4,381..........B5 8
Borkou, reg., Chad........E1 23
Borlänge, Swe., 45,194....G6 11
Borneo (Kalimantan), isl., Asia..................E4 19
Bornholm, co., Den., 48,500...............*A3 7
Bornos, Sp., 8,697........D3 8
Boromlya, Sov. Un., 10,000................F10 12
Borovan, Bul., 5,905......D6 10
Borovichi, Sov. Un., 55,000.................B9 12
Borovskoye, Sov. Un., 5,000.................q21 12
Borsod-Abauj-Zemplen, co., Hung., 608,368.......*A5 10
Bort-les-Orgues, Fr., 5,115..E5 5
Borūjerd, Iran, 71,486.....C4 15
Borzna, Sov. Un., 10,000...F9 12
Bosa, It., 8,169...........D2 9
Bosanska Gradiska, Yugo., 6,373.................C3 10
Bosanska Kostajnica, Yugo., 2,037.................C3 10
Bosanski Novi, Yugo., 7,082.................C3 10
Boscobel, Wis., 2,510......E3 88
Boskovice, Czech., 6,396...D4 7
Bosnia, reg., Yugo.........C3 10
Bosnia-Hercegovina, rep., Yugo., 3,277,948.......*C3 10
Bosque, co., Tex. 10,966...D4 84
Bossier, par. La., 63,703...B2 63
Bossier City, La., 41,595...B2 63
Boston, Eng., 26,030......D6 4
Boston, Ga., 1,443........F3 55
Boston, Mass., 641,071 (*3,762,900).......B5, g11 65
Boston, Pa., 1,200........*E1 81
Boswell, Ind., 998.........C3 59
Botetourt, co., Va. 18,193..C3 85
Botevgrad, Bul., 5,925.....D6 10
Bothwell, Ont., Can., 819..E3 41
Botkins, Ohio, 1,057.......B1 78
Botosani, Rom., 35,200....E8 10
Botswana, country, Afr., 585,000................E4 24
Bottineau, N. Dak., 2,760..A5 77
Bottineau, co., N. Dak., 9,496.................B5 77
Botucatu, Braz., 42,252............C3, m7 30
Botwood, Newf., Can., 4,115.................D4 44
Bouaké, I.C., 53,000......G3 22
Boucherville, Que., Can., 19,997...........D4, p20 42
Bouches-du-Rhône, dept., Fr., 1,470,271.........*F6 5
Bougie, see Bejaïa, Alg.
Boulder, Colo., 66,870 (*80,100).............A5 51
Boulder, Mont., 1,342.....D4 70
Boulder, co., Colo., 131,889...............A5 51
Boulder City, Nev., 5,223..D4 72
Boulder Creek, Calif., 1,306...............*D2 50
Boulogne-Billancourt, Fr., 109,008...............C5 5
Boulogne-sur-Mer, Fr., 49,276 (*106,000).......B4 5
Boundary, co., Idaho, 5,484.................A2 57
Boundary, pk., Nev........C2 72
Bound Brook, N.J., 10,450..B3 74
Bountiful, Utah, 27,751............A6, C2 72
Bourbon, Ind., 1,606......B5 59
Bourbon, co., Kans., 15,215.................E9 61
Bourbon, co., Ky., 18,476..B5 62
Bourbonnais, Ill., 5,909....B6 58
Bourbonnais, former prov., Fr....................D5 5
Bourg, La., 900...........E5 63
Bourg-de-Péage, Fr., 8,597.................E6 5
Bourg [-de-Bresse], Fr., 37,887.................D6 5
Bourges, Fr., 70,814.......D5 5
Bourg-la-Reine, Fr., 18,711................g10 5
Bourgoin [-Jallieu], Fr., 19,941.................E6 5
Bournemouth, Eng., 148,990 (*298,000)......E6 4
Bovey, Minn., 858........C5 67
Bovina, Tex., 1,428.......B1 84
Bowdon, Ga., 1,753.......C1 55
Bowie, Md., 35,028.......B4 53
Bowie, Tex., 5,185........C4 84
Bowie, co., Tex., 67,813...C5 84
Bow Island, Alta., Can., 1,122.................E5 38
Bowling Green, Fla., 1,357.................E5 54
Bowling Green, Ky., 36,705.................D3 62
Bowling Green, Mo., 2,936.................B6 69
Bowling Green, Ohio, 21,760.............A2, f6 78
Bowling Green, S.C., 700..A5 82
Bowman, N. Dak., 1,762...D2 77
Bowman, S.C., 1,095......E6 82
Bowman, co., N. Dak., 3,901.................D2 77
Bowmanstown, Pa., 864...E10 81
Bowmanville, Ont., Can., 8,947.................D6 41
Bowral, Austl., 5,913......G8 26
Box Butte, co., Nebr., 10,094.................B2 71
Box Elder, co., Utah, 28,129.................A5 72
Boxtel, Neth., 16,370......B6 5
Boyacá, dept., Col., 1,144,400.............B3 32
Boyce, La., 1,240.........C3 63
Boyd, co., Ky., 52,376.....B7 62
Boyd, co., Nebr., 3,752....B7 71
Boyertown, Pa., 4,428....F10 81
Boyes Hot Springs, Calif., 2,462.................*C2 50
Boyle, co., Ky., 21,090....C5 62
Boylston, Ala., 1,500......C3 46
Boyne City, Mich., 2,969..C5 66
Boynton Beach, Fla., 18,115.................F6 54
Boys Town, Nebr., 989....g12 71
Bozeman, Mont., 18,670...E5 70
Bozüyük, Tur., 13,307.....C8 14
Bra, It., 16,400...........B1 9
Brabant, prov., Bel., 2,157,300.............*B6 5
Bracciano, It., 6,460.......g8 9
Bracebridge, Ont., Can., 6,903.................B5 41
Bracken, co., Ky., 7,227...B5 62
Brackenridge, Pa., 4,796..h15 81
Brackettville, Tex., 1,539...E2 84
Brad, Sov. Un., 9,963.....B6 10
Bradbury Heights, Md., 1,000.................*C3 53
Braddock, Pa., 8,795.....k14 81
Braddock Heights, Md., 800...................B2 53
Braddock Hills, Pa., 2,459.................*E1 81
Bradenton, Fla., 21,040...........E4, q10 54
Bradenton Beach, Fla., 1,370.................*E4 54
Bradenville, Pa., 1,200.....F3 81
Bradford, Ont., Can., 3,401.................C5 41
Bradford, Eng., 294,740...D6 4
Bradford, Ill., 885.........B4 58
Bradford, Ohio, 2,163.....B1 78
Bradford, Pa., 12,672......C4 81
Bradford, R.I., 1,333.....D10 52
Bradford, co., Fla., 14,625..C4 54
Bradford, co., Pa., 57,962..C8 81
Bradfordwoods, Pa., 970..h13 81
Bradley, Fla., 1,035.......E5 54
Bradley, Ill., 9,881........B6 58
Bradley, co., Ark., 12,778..D3 49
Bradley, co., Tenn., 50,686.................D9 83
Bradley Beach, N.J., 4,163.................C4 74
Bradley Gardens, N.J., 3,250.................*B3 74
Bradner, Ohio, 1,140......A2 78
Bradshaw, W. Va., 1,048..D3 87
Brady, Tex., 5,557........D3 84
Braga, Port., 40,977.......B1 8
Bragado, Arg., 22,000..B4, g6 28
Bragança, Braz., 16,642..*D6 27
Bragança, Port., 8,075.....B2 8
Bragança Paulista, Braz., 39,573.......C3, m8 30
Brahmaputra, riv., Asia....C9 20
Braidwood, Ill., 2,323.....B5 58
Brăila, Rom., 138,600 (144,300 ▲)...........C8 10
Brainerd, Minn., 11,667...D4 67
Braintree, Mass., 35,050...........B5, h11 65
Brampton, Ont., Can., 41,211..........D5, m14 41
Bramwell, W. Va., 1,125..D3 87
Branch, co., Mich., 37,906.................G5 66
Branchville, N.J., 911.....A3 74
Branchville, S.C., 1,011....E6 82
Branco, riv., Braz.........C5 32
Brandenburg, Ger. Dem. Rep., 94,240...........B6 6
Brandenburg, Ky., 1,637...B3 62
Brandenburg, former state, Ger. Dem. Rep., 2,527,492.............B6 6
Brandenburg, reg., Ger. Dem. Rep. B6 6
Brandon, Man., Can., 31,150.............E2, h7 40
Brandon, Fla., 3,000......E4 54
Brandon, Miss., 2,685.....C4 68
Brandon, S.C., 2,200......B3 82
Brandon, Vt., 1,720.......D1 73
Brandys [nad Labem], Czech., 14,596........n18 7
Branford, Conn., 2,080....D5 52
Branson, Mo., 2,175.......E4 69
Brant, co., Ont., Can., 90,945................D4 41
Brantford, Ont., Can., 64,421 (*80,284).......D4 41
Brant Lake, N.Y., 800.....B7 75
Brantley, Ala., 1,066......D3 46
Brantley, co., Ga., 5,940...E4 55
Bras-d'or, N.S., Can., 947..C9 43
Brasília, Braz., 272,002....B3 30
Brasilia (Federal District), Braz., 546,015..........B3 30
Braşov, Rom., 163,300 (263,200 ▲)...........C7 10
Bratenahl, Ohio, 1,613.....g9 78
Bratislava, Czech., 283,539.................D4 7
Bratsk, Sov. Un., 155,000 ....*D13 13
Bratslav, Sov. Un., 10,000.................G7 12
Brattleboro, Vt., 12,239...F2 73
Braunau [am Inn], Aus., 16,414.................D6 6
Braunschweig, Ger., Fed. Rep. of, 220,244 (*355,000).............B5 6
Brawley, Calif., 13,746.....F6 50
Braxton, co., W. Va., 12,666................C4 87
Bray, Ire., 14,467.........D3 4
Braymer, Mo., 919........B4 69
Brazil, Ind., 8,163........E3 59
Brazil, country, S.A., 103,270,000............C3 30
Brazoria, Tex., 1,681......r14 84
Brazoria, co., Tex., 108,312.E5 84
Brazos, co., Tex., 57,978..D4 84
Brazzaville, Con., 175,000..A3 24
Brčko, Yugo., 25,422......C4 10
Brea, Calif., 18,447.......n13 50
Breathitt, co., Ky., 14,221................C6 62
Breaux Bridge, La., 4,942..D4 63
Brechin, Scot., 6,702......B5 4
Breckenridge, Mich., 1,257................E6 66
Breckenridge, Minn., 4,200.................D2 67
Breckenridge, Tex., 5,944..C3 84
Breckenridge Hills, Mo., 7,011.................*C7 69
Breckenridge, co., Ky., 14,789.................C3 62
Brecknock, co., Wales, 54,400.................*E5 4
Brecksville, Ohio, 9,137...............A4, h9 78
Břeclav, Czech., 13,131....D4 7
Brecon, Wales, 6,260......E5 4
Breda, Neth., 121,181.....B6 5
Breese, Ill., 2,885.........E4 58
Bregenz, Aus., 23,171......E4 6
Bregovo, Bul., 5,271.......C6 10
Bremen, Ga., 3,484.......C1 55
Bremen, Ger., Fed. Rep. of, 589,825 (*820,000)......B4 6
Bremen, Ind., 3,487........B5 59
Bremen, Ohio, 1,413......C3 78
Bremen, state, Ger., Fed. Rep. of, 745,000.......*B4 6
Bremer, co., Iowa, 22,737..B5 60
Bremerhaven, Ger., Fed Rep. of, 144,505 (*198,000).............B4 6
Bremerton, Wash., 35,307 (*87,700)....B3, e10 86
Bremerton East (Enetai), Wash., 2,539..........*B3 86
Bremond, Tex., 822.......D4 84
Brenham, Tex., 8,922.....D4 84
Brent, Ala., 2,093.........C2 46
Brent, Fla., 4,100........u14 54
Brenton, W. Va., 500.....D3 87
Brentwood, Calif., 2,649...h9 50
Brentwood, Md., 3,426....F9 53
Brentwood, Mo., 11,248...f13 69
Brentwood, N.Y., 54,186...F4 52
Brentwood, Pa., 13,732...k14 81
Brescia, It., 204,400.......B3 9
Breslau, see Wroclaw, Pol.
Bressanone, It., 11,300.....A3 9
Bressler, Pa., 850.........*F8 81
Bressuire, Fr., 6,528.......D3 5
Brest, Fr., 154,023........C1 5
Brest, Sov. Un., 122,000...E4 12
Breton Woods, N.J., 1,200..C4 74
Brevard, co., Fla., 230,006.E6 54
Brevard, N.C., 5,243......f10 76
Brewer, Maine, 9,300.....D4 64
Brestwer, N.Y., 1,638............D7, m15 75
Brewster, Ohio, 2,020......B4 78
Brewster, Wash., 1,059....A6 86
Brewster, co., Tex., 7,780..p13 84
Brewton, Ala., 6,747.....D2 46
Brezno [nad Hronom], Czech., 12,726.........D5 7
Briançon, Fr., 8,215.......E7 5
Briarcliff, Pa., 9,000.....*G11 81
Briarcliff Manor, N.Y., 6,521................D7 75
Briceville, Tenn., 800......C9 83
Bridge City, Tex., 4,677..*D6 84
Bridgehampton, N.Y., 900....................n16 75
Bridgeport, Ala., 2,908....A4 46
Bridgeport, Ont., Can., 2,375...............*D4 41
Bridgeport, Conn., 156,542 (*457,200).........E4 52
Bridgeport, Ill., 2,262.....E6 58
Bridgeport, Mich., 1,900...E7 66
Bridgeport, Nebr., 1,490...C2 71
Bridgeport, Ohio, 3,001....B5 78
Bridgeport, Pa., 5,630.............F11, o20 81
Bridgeport, Tex., 3,614....C4 84
Bridgeport, Wash., 952....B6 86
Bridgeport, W. Va., 4,777.............B4, k10 87
Bridgeton, Mo., 19,992............C7, f13 69
Bridgeton, N.J., 20,435 (*35,800).............E2 74
Bridgetown, Barb, 8,789 (*115,000)............J15 35
Bridgetown, N.S., Can., 1,043.................E4 43
Bridgetown, Ohio, 7,350..*C1 78
Bridgeview, Ill., 12,522...*B6 58
Bridgeville, Del., 1,317....C6 53
Bridgeville, Pa., 6,717.....k13 81
Bridgewater, N.S., Can., 5,231.................E5 43
Bridgewater, Mass., 4,032 (11,829 ▲)............C6 65
Bridgewater, Va., 2,828....B4 85
Bridgman, Mich., 1,621...G4 66
Bridgton, Maine, 1,779 (2,967 ▲)..............D2 64
Bridgwater, Eng., 26,740..E5 4
Bridlington, Eng., 26,770..C6 4
Brielle, N.J., 3,594........C4 74
Brigantine, N.J., 6,741.....E4 74
Brigham City, Utah, 14,007.............A5, C2 72
Brighton, Ala., 2,277...B3, g7 46
Brighton, Colo., 8,309....B6 51
Brighton, Eng., 163,860 (*430,000)...............E6 4
Brighton, Ill., 1,889.......D3 58
Brighton, Mich., 2,457.....F7 66
Brighton, N.Y., 35,065....*B3 75
Brightwaters, N.Y., 3,808..n15 75
Brignoles, Fr., 5,347.......F7 5
Brilliant, Ohio, 2,178......B5 78
Brillion, Wis., 2,588...D5, h9 88
Brindisi, It., 80,400.......D6 9
Brinkley, Ark., 5,275......C4 49
Brioude, Fr., 7,195........E5 5

Burnley, Eng., 76,130
(*166,000)............D5   4
Burns, Oreg., 3,293......D7 80
Burns Flat, Okla., 988...B2 79
Burns Lake, B.C., Can.,
  1,259................B5 37
Burnsville, N.C., 1,348...f10 76
Burnwell, Ala., 200......f6 46
Burr Oak, Mich., 873....G5 66
Bursa, Tur., 275,953....B7 14
Burt, co., Nebr., 9,247...C9 71
Burton, Mich., 32,540...F7 66
Burton, Ohio, 1,214......A4 78
Burton-on-Trent, Eng.,
  50,540................D6   4
Burundi, country, Afr.,
  3,825,000.............I3 23
Büshehr, Iran, 23,547...G8 16
Buskerud, co., Nor.,
  194,500...............*H4 11

Busko, Pol., 11,100......C6   7
Bussum, Neth., 40,219....A6   5
Busto Arsizio, It., 75,600..B2   9
Buta, Zaire, 11,200......H2 23
Bute, co., Scot., 12,555...*C4   4
Butler, Ala., 2,064......C1 46
Butler, Ga., 1,589.......D2 55
Butler, Ind., 2,394......B8 59
Butler, Mo., 3,984.......C3 69
Butler, N.J., 7,051......B4 74
Butler, Ohio, 1,052......B3 78
Butler, Pa., 18,691......E2 81
Butler, Wis., 2,261......m11 88
Butler, co., Ala., 22,007...D3 46
Butler, co., Iowa, 16,953..B5 60
Butler, co., Kans., 38,658..E7 61
Butler, co., Ky., 9,723...C3 62
Butler, co., Mo., 33,529...E7 69
Butler, co., Nebr., 9,461...C8 71
Butler, co., Ohio, 226,207..C1 78

Butler, co., Pa., 127,941...E2 81
Butner, N.C., 3,538......*A4 76
Butte, Mont., 23,368
  (*40,000).............D4 70
Butte, co., Calif., 101,969..C3 50
Butte, co., Idaho, 2,925...F5 57
Butte, co., S. Dak., 7,825..F2 77
Butterworth, Mala.,
  61,187................D2 19
Buttonwillow, Calif., 950...E4 50
Butts, co., Ga., 10,560...C3 55
Butuan, Phil., 48,470
  (131,094 ▲)...........D7 19
Buturlinovka, Sov. Un.,
  22,000................F13 12
Bützow, Ger. Dem. Rep.,
  10,900................B5   6
Buxtehude, Ger., Fed.
  Rep. of, 29,611.......*B4   6

Buxton, Guy., 3,800......C5 27
Büyük Ağrı Dağı (Mt.
  Ararat), mtn., Tur....C15 14
Buzău, Rom., 56,400.....C8 10
Buzet, Yugo., 444.......C1 10
Buzzards Bay, Mass.,
  2,422................C6 65
Byala Slatina, Bul., 14,951.D6 10
Bydgoszcz, Pol., 280,400...B5   7
Byelorussia (S.S.R.), rep.,
  Sov. Un., 9,320,000...E5 12
Byesville, Ohio, 2,097...C4 78
Byfield, Mass., 850......A6 65
Bykovo, Sov. Un., 10,000.G15 12
Byron, Ga., 1,368.......D3 55
Byron, Ill., 1,749.......A4 58
Bystrzyca, Pol., 7,929...C4   7
Bytom, Pol., 186,900...C5, g9   7
Bytosh, Sov. Un., 10,000.E10 12

C

Caacupé, Par., 7,278......E4 29
Caaguazú, dept., Par.,
  125,138...............D4 29
Caapucú, Par., 6,608.....E4 29
Caazapá, Par., 16,588....E4 29
Caazapá, dept., Par.,
  92,401................E4 29
Cabaceiras, Braz., 581....*D4 27
Cabana, Peru, 2,560......C2 31
Cabanatuan, Phil.,
  24,313 (99,890 ▲)....o13 19
Cabano, Que., Can.,
  3,063................B9 42
Cabarrus, co., N.C.,
  74,629...............B2 76
Cabedelo, Braz., 12,811..*D7 27
Cabell, co., W. Vir.,
  106,918..............C2 87
Cabeza del Buey, Sp.,
  11,737...............C3   8
Cabimas, Ven., 118,037...A3 32
Cabinda, Ang., 1,554.....B2 24
Cabinda, dist., Ang.,
  58,453...............B2 24
Cabin John, Md.,
  2,500...............C3, f8 53
Cabo, Braz., 6,029......*D7 27
Cabo Frio, Braz., 25,211..C4 30
Cabool, Mo., 1,848......D5 69
Caboolture, Austl., 3,240..*E9 25
Caborca, Mex., 20,771...A2 34
Cabo Rojo, P.R., 7,181
  (26,060 ▲)..........*G11 35
Cabo San Lucas, Mex.,
  1,534................C3 34
Cabot, Ark., 2,903.......C3 49
Cacak, Yugo., 38,170....D5 10
Caçapava, Braz., 24,626...C3 30
Cacequi, Braz., 9,976....D2 30
Cáceres, Sp., 55,341.....C2   8
Cáceres, prov., Sp.,
  499,100..............C2   8
Cachan, Fr., 26,187.....G10   5
Cache, Okla., 1,106......C3 79
Cache, co., Utah, 42,331..A6 50
Cache, peak, Idaho......G5 57
Cache Bay, Ont.,
  Can., 810...........A5 41
Cachi, Arg., 491........E2 29
Cachoeira, Braz., 11,464..*E7 27
Cachoeira do Sul, Braz.,
  50,001...............E2 30
Cachoeiro de Itapemirim,
  Braz., 58,968........C4 30
Cacouna, Que., Can.,
  1,001................B8 42
Caddo, Okla., 886.......C5 79
Caddo, co., Okla., 28,931..B3 79
Caddo, par., La., 230,184..B2 63
Cadillac, Mich., 9,990...D5 66
Cadillac, mtn., Maine....D4 64
Cadiz, Ky., 1,987.......D2 62
Cadiz, Ohio, 3,060......B4 78
Cádiz, Sp., 134,342.....D2   8
Cádiz, prov., Sp.,
  893,500..............*D2   8
Cadott, Wis., 977.......D2 88
Cadyville, N.Y., 800....f11 75
Caen, Fr., 110,262
  (*155,000)...........C3   5
Caernarvon, Wales, 9,370.D4   4
Caernarvon, co., Wales,
  122,410..............*D4   4

Cagayan de Oro, Phil.,
  26,465 (128,319 ▲)....D6 19
Cagayan, prov., Phil.,
  445,289..............*B6 19
Cagli, It., 3,235........C4   9
Cagliari, It., 219,900
  (*260,000)...........E2   9
Cagnes-sur-Mer, Fr.,
  15,392...............F7   5
Caguas, P.R., 63,215
  (95,661).............G12 35
Cahaba Heights, Ala.,
  3,800................*B3 46
Cahokia, Ill., 20,649....E3 58
Cahors, Fr., 19,203......E4   5
Caibarién, Cuba, 27,000
  (31,200 ▲)...........C4 35
Caicedonia, Col., 16,327..C2 32
Caicó, Braz., 24,594.....*D7 27
Cailloma, Peru, 923......E3 31
Cairnbrook, Pa., 1,100...F4 81
Cairns, Austl., 30,059...C8 25
Cairo, Ga., 8,061.......F2 55
Cairo, Ill., 6,277.......F4 58
Cairo, Eg., 4,500,000
  (*5,900,000).........B4 23
Caithness, co., Scot.,
  27,779...............*A5   4
Cajabamba, Peru, 10,500..C2 31
Cajacay, Peru, 1,094.....D2 31
Cajamarca, Peru, 37,608..C2 31
Cajamarca, dept., Peru,
  786,599..............C2 31
Cajatambo, Peru, 2,561...D2 31
Cajázeiras, Braz., 24,079..*D7 27
Cakovec, Yugo., 11,736...B3 10
Calabria, pol. dist., It.,
  2,045,047............*E5   9
Calabria, reg., It.,
  2,067,100............E6   9
Calafat, Rom., 8,069.....D6 10
Calahorra, Sp., 14,462...A5   8
Calais, Fr., 74,624
  (*94,000)............B4   5
Calais, Maine, 4,044.....C5 64
Calamar, Col., 6,055.....A3 32
Calamba, Phil., 11,868...C6 19
Calañas, Sp., 4,059......D2   8
Calapan, Phil., 11,376...C6 19
Călărasi, Rom., 35,700...C8 10
Calarcá, Col., 30,342....C2 32
Calasparra, Sp., 8,155...C5   8
Calauag, Phil., 3,981....P14 19
Calaveras, co., Calif.,
  13,585...............C3 50
Calca, Peru, 3,037......D3 31
Calcasieu, par., La.,
  145,415..............D2 63
Calceta, Ec., 4,946......B1 31
Calcutta, India, 3,148,746
  (*9,100,000).........D8 20
Calcutta, Ohio, 1,500....B5 78
Caldas, dept., Col.,
  775,400..............B2 32
Caldas da Rainha, Port.,
  10,635...............C1   8
Caldwell, Idaho, 14,219..F2 57
Caldwell, Kans., 1,540...E6 61
Caldwell, N.J., 8,677....B4 74
Caldwell, Ohio, 2,082....C4 78
Caldwell, Tex., 2,308....D4 84
Caldwell, co., Ky., 13,179..C2 62

Caldwell, co., Mo., 8,351..B3 69
Caldwell, co., N.C.,
  56,699...............B1 76
Caldwell, co., Tex., 21,178.E4 84
Caldwell, par., La., 9,354..B3 63
Caledonia, Ont., Can.,
  3,183................D5 41
Caledonia, Minn., 2,619..G7 67
Caledonia, N.Y., 2,327...C3 75
Caledonia, Ohio, 792.....B3 78
Caledonia, co., Vt.,
  22,789...............C3 73
Calella, Sp., 7,947......B7   8
Calera, Ala., 1,655......B3 46
Calera, Chile, 13,047....A2 28
Calexico, Calif., 10,625..F6 50
Calgary, Alta., Can.,
  403,319.............D3, g8 38
Calhoun, Ga., 4,748.....B2 55
Calhoun, co., Ala.,
  103,092..............B4 46
Calhoun, co., Ark., 5,573..D3 49
Calhoun, co., Fla., 7,624..B1 54
Calhoun, co., Ga., 6,606..E2 55
Calhoun, co., Ill., 5,675..D3 58
Calhoun, co., Iowa,
  14,287...............B4 60
Calhoun, co., Mich.,
  141,963..............F5 66
Calhoun, co., Miss.,
  14,623...............B4 68
Calhoun, co., S.C., 10,780.D6 82
Calhoun, co., Tex.,
  17,831...............E4 84
Calhoun, co., W. Va.,
  7,046................C3 87
Calhoun City, Miss.,
  1,847................B4 68
Calhoun Falls, S.C., 2,234..C2 82
Cali, Col., 772,000......C2 32
Calico Rock, Ark., 723...A3 49
Calicut, India, 333,979...F6 20
Caliente, Nev., 916......C4 72
California, Mo., 3,105....C5 69
California, Pa., 6,635....F2 81
California, state, U.S.,
  20,853,000...........C2 50
Calipatria, Calif., 1,824..F6 50
Calispell, peak, Wash....A8 86
Calistoga, Calif., 1,882..C2 50
Callahan, co., Tex., 8,205..C3 84
Callander, Ont., Can.,
  1,236................A5 41
Callander, Scot., 1,750...B4   4
Callao, Peru, 196,919....D2 31
Callao, prov., Peru,
  219,420..............D2 31
Callaway, co., Mo.,
  25,950...............C6 69
Callicoon, N.Y., 800.....D5 75
Calloway, co., Ky.,
  27,692...............f9 62
Calmar, Alta., Can., 700..C4 38
Calmar, Iowa, 1,008......A6 60
Caloundra, Austl., 6,091..C9 26
Caltagirone, It., 37,000..F5   9
Caltanissetta, It., 52,800..F5   9
Caluire [-et-Cuire], Fr.,
  37,603...............E6   5
Calumet, Que., Can.,
  889.................D3 42
Calumet, Mich., 1,007....A2 66
Calumet, Pa., 800.......*F2 81

Calumet, co., Wis., 27,604..D5 88
Calumet City, Ill.,
  33,107.............B6, k9 58
Calumet Park, Ill.,
  10,069...............*B6 58
Calvados, dept., Fr.,
  519,695..............*C3   5
Calvert, Tex., 2,072.....D4 84
Calvert, co., Md., 20,682..C4 53
Calvert City, Ky., 2,104..e9 62
Calverton Park, Mo.,
  2,025................A8 69
Calvillo, Mex., 6,453....m12 34
Calwa, Calif., 8,000.....*D4 50
Camacho, Mex., 1,672....C4 34
Camagüey, Cuba,
  196,900..............D5 35
Camagüey, prov., Cuba,
  813,200..............D5 35
Camaná, Peru, 5,100.....E2 31
Camanche, Iowa, 3,470...C7 60
Camargo, see Ciudad
  Camargo, Mex.
Camarillo, Calif., 19,219..*E4 50
Camarines Norte, prov.,
  Phil., 188,091.......*C6 19
Camarines Sur, prov.,
  Phil., 819,565.......*C6 19
Camas, Wash., 5,790....D3 86
Camas, co., Idaho, 728...F4 57
Cambay, India, 62,133...*D5 20
Cambodia, country, Asia,
  7,535,000............C2 19
Camborne [-Redruth],
  Eng., 41,930.........E4   4
Cambrai, Fr., 37,532
  (*48,000)............B5   5
Cambria, Calif., 700.....E3 50
Cambria, co., Pa.,
  186,785..............E4 81
Cambrian Park, Calif.,
  4,000................*D3 50
Cambridge, Eng., 99,600..D7   4
Cambridge, Ill., 2,095...B3 58
Cambridge, Md., 11,595..C5 53
Cambridge, Mass.,
  100,361............B5, g11 65
Cambridge, Minn., 2,720..E5 67
Cambridge, Nebr., 1,145..D5 71
Cambridge, N.J., 1,000...*C3 74
Cambridge, N.Y., 1,769..B7 75
Cambridge, Ohio, 13,656..B4 78
Cambridge & Isle of Ely,
  co., Eng., 304,570...*D7   4
Cambridge City, Ind.,
  2,481................E7 59
Cambridge Springs, Pa.,
  1,998................C1 81
Camden, Ala., 1,742.....D2 46
Camden, Ark., 15,147....D3 49
Camden, Del., 1,241.....B6 53
Camden, Maine, 3,492
  (4,115 ▲)............D3 64
Camden, N.J., 102,551...D2 74
Camden, N.Y., 2,936.....B5 75
Camden, Ohio, 1,507....C1 78
Camden, S.C., 8,532.....C6 82
Camden, Tenn., 3,052....A3 83
Camden, Tex., 350......D5 84
Camden, co., Ga., 11,334..F5 55
Camden, co., Mo., 13,315..C5 69
Camden, co., N.J.,
  456,291..............D3 74

D

Daisetta, Tex., 1,084......D5 84
Daisytown, Pa., 371.............*F1 81
Dajabón, Dom. Rep., 6,000.............E8 35
Dakar, Sen., 581,000 (*650,000).......F1 22
Dakota, co., Minn., 139,808...........F5 67
Dakota, co., Nebr., 13,137............B9 71
Dakota City, Nebr., 1,057..B9 71
Da Lat, Viet., 83,700......C3 19
D'Albertis Dome, mtn., Austl.,.............k11 25
Dalby, Austl., 8,890.......E9 25
Dale, Ind., 1,113.........H4 59
Dale, Pa., 2,274.........*E4 81
Dale, co., Ala., 52,938...D4 46
Daleville, Ind., 1,548...D6 59
Dalhart, Tex., 5,705......A1 84
Dalhousie, N.B., Can., 6,255.............A3 43
Dall, mtn., Alsk.........fl5 47
Dallam, co., Tex., 6,012..A1 84
Dallas, Ga., 2,133........C2 55
Dallas, N.C., 4,059.......B1 76
Dallas, Oreg., 6,361......C3 80
Dallas, Pa., 2,398...D10, m17 81
Dallas, Tex., 844,401 (*1,580,600)......C4, n10 84
Dallas, co., Ala., 55,296...C2 46
Dallas, co., Ark., 10,022...D3 49
Dallas, co., Iowa, 26,085...C3 60
Dallas, co., Mo., 10,054...D4 69
Dallas, co., Tex., 1,327,321.........C4 84
Dallas Center, Iowa, 1,128.............C4 60
Dallas City, Ill., 1,284...C2 58
Dallastown, Pa., 3,560...G8 81
Dalmatia, reg., Yugo......D3 10
Dalmellington, Scot., 2,130.............C4 4
Dalnerechensk, Sov. Un., 28,000............E16 13
Dalnyaya, Sov. Un., 10,000.............D11 18
Dalrymple, mtn., Austl...D8 25
Dalton, Ga., 18,872......B2 55
Dalton, Mass., 7,505......B1 65
Dalton, Ohio, 1,177......B4 78
Dalton, Pa., 1,282.......C10 81
Daltonganj, India, 32,367...D7 20
Dalton Gardens, Idaho, 1,559.............B2 57
Daly City, Calif., 66,400...h8 50
Damān, India, 17,317....D5 20
Damanhûr, Eg., 146,079...G8 14
Damariscotta, Maine, 720, (1,264▲),......D3 64
Damascus, Md., 2,638.....B3 53
Damascus, Va., 13,857....f10 85
Damascus (Dimashq), Syr., 836,179............F11 14
Da Nang, Viet.,334,200...B3 19
Dana Point, Calif., 1,186..*F5 50
Danbury, Conn., 50,781 (*79,900)..........D3 52
Dane, co., Wis. 290,272...E4 88
Dania, Fla., 9,013....F6, r13 54
Daniels, co., Mont., 3,083.............B11 70
Danielson, Conn., 4,580...B9 52
Dannemora, N.Y., 3,735...fl1 75
Dannevirke, N.Z., 5,610..N16 26
Dans, mtn., Md.,.......k13 53
Dansalan, Phil., 4,882...*D6 19
Dansville, N.Y., 5,436...C3 75
Dante, Som..............F8 23
Dante, Va., 1,153.........f9 85
Danube, riv., Eur.,......F10 3
Danubyu, Bur., 10,000...*E10 20
Danvers, Mass., 26,151........A6, f12 65
Danville, Ark., 1,362....B2 49
Danville, Calif., 7,000...h9 50
Danville, Que., Can., 2,566.............D5 42
Danville, Ill., 42,570....C6 58
Danville, Ind., 3,771....E4 59
Danville, Ky., 11,542....C5 62
Danville, Ohio, 1,025....B3 78
Danville, Pa., 6,176.....E8 81
Danville (Independent City), Va., 46,391...D3 85
Danville East, Pa., 2,046..*D8 81
Danzig see Gdańsk, Pol.
Daphne, Ala., 2,382.....E2 46
Dar'ā, Syr., 27,673.....F11 14
Darabani, Rom., 11,379...A8 10
Darasun, Sov. Un., 18,000............D14 13
Darbhanga, India, 132,059...........C8 20
Darby, Pa., 13,729..G11, p20 81
Dardanelle, Ark., 3,297...B2 49
Dare, co., N.C., 6,995...B7 76

Darenbe, Tur., 7,929.....C11 14
Dar-es-Salaam, Tan., 272,821...........B7 24
Darien, Conn., 20,336...E3 52
Darien, Ga., 1,826.......E5 55
Darien, Wis., 839........F5 88
Darjeeling, India, 42,873..C8 20
Dark Cove, Newf., Can., 955...............*D4 44
Darke, co., Ohio, 49,141...B1 78
Darling Range, mts., Austl.,.............F2 25
Darling, riv., Austl.......E5 26
Darlington, Eng., 85,900...C6 4
Darlington, S.C., 6,990...C8 82
Darlington, Wis., 2,351...F3 88
Darlington, co., S.C., 53,442...........C7 82
Darłowo, Pol., 11,200....A4 7
Darmstadt, Ger., Fed. Rep. of, 140,865 (*265,000)..D4 6
Darnah (Derna), Libya, 21,400............B2 23
Darrah, mtn., Alta., Can.,...............E3 38
Darrington, Wash., 1,094..............A4 86
Darrow, La., 450........h10 63
Dartmouth, N.S., Can., 64,770............E6 43
Dartmouth, Eng., 6,570...E5 4
Daruvar, Yugo., 6,280...C3 10
Darwin, Austl., 31,687 (*36,828)..........B5 25
Dassel, Minn., 1,058....E4 67
Daugavpils, Sov. Un., 100,000............D6 12
Dauphin, Man., Can 8,891............D1, g7 40
Dauphin, co., Pa., 223,713...........F8 81
Dauphiné, former prov., Fr.................E6 5
Davao, Phil., 148,424 (392,473▲)........D7 19
Davao, prov., Phil., 893,023...........*D7 19
Davenport, Fla., 1,303...D5 54
Davenport, Iowa, 98,469 (*310,900).......C7, g10 60
Davenport, Okla., 831...B5 79
Davenport, Wash., 1,363..B7 86
David, Pan., 35,677.....B1 32
David City, Nebr., 2,380..C8 71
Davidson, Sask., Can., 928...............F3 39
Davidson, N.C., 2,931....B2 76
Davidson, co., N.C., 95,627............B2 76
Davidson, co., Tenn., 447,877...........A5 83
Davie, Fla., 5,859....F6, r13 54
Davie, co., N.C., 18,855...B2 76
Daviess, co., Ind., 26,602..G3 59
Daviess, co., Ky., 79,486...C2 62
Daviess, co., Mo., 8,420...B3 69
Davis, Calif., 23,448....C3 50
Davis, Okla., 2,223.....C4 79
Davis, W. Va., 868......B5 87
Davis, co., Iowa, 8,207...D4 60
Davis, co., Utah, 99,028...A5 72
Davis, mtn., Pa.,.......C3 81
Davison, Mich., 5,259....E7 66
Davison, co., S. Dak., 17,319...........G7 77
Davisville, R.I., 400....C11 52
Davos, Switz., 11,800....E4 6
Davy, W. Va., 993.......D3 87
Dawes, co., Nebr., 9,761...B2 71
Dawson, Yukon, Can., 762...............D6 36
Dawson, Ga., 5,383.....E2 55
Dawson, Minn., 1,699...F2 67
Dawson, Tex., 848.......D4 84
Dawson, co., Ga., 3,639...B2 55
Dawson, co., Mont., 11,269...........C11 70
Dawson, co., Nebr., 19,771...........D6 71
Dawson, co., Tex., 16,604...........C1 84
Dawson, mtn., B.C., Can.,..............D9 37
Dawson Creek, B.C., Can., 11,885.........B7, m8 37
Dawson Springs, Ky., 3,009.............C2 62
Dax, Fr., 19,348 (*26,000)..........F3 5
Day, co., S. Dak., 8,713...E8 77
Dayrût, Eg., 27,646........C4 23
Dayton, Ky., 8,751.....h14 62
Dayton, Ohio, 242,917 (*934,000).........C1 78
Dayton, Tenn., 4,361....D8 83
Dayton, Tex., 3,804..D5, q15 84
Dayton, Va., 978........B4 85

Dayton, Wash., 2,596.....C8 86
Daytona Beach, Fla., 45,327 (*103,000)...C5 54
Daytona Beach Shores, Fla., 768..........*C6 54
Dayville, Conn., 800....B9 52
De Aar, S. Afr., 17,823...G4 24
Dead Indian, peak, Wyo...B3 89
Dead Knoll, mtn., Wyo....D2 89
Deadwood, S. Dak., 2,409..F2 77
Deaf Smith, co., Tex., 18,999............B1 84
Deal, N.J., 2,401........C4 74
Deale, Md., 1,059.......C4 53
Deán Funes, Arg., 16,280..A4 28
Dearborn, Mich., 104,199.........F7, p15 66
Dearborn, co., Ind., 29,430...........F8 59
Dearborn Heights, Mich., 80,069...........p15 66
Death, valley, Calif......D5 50
Deauville, Fr., 5,232....C4 5
De Baca, co., N. Mex., 2,547............B6 48
Debaltsevo, Sov. Un., 35,000............q21 12
Debar, Yugo., 6,341.....E5 10
De Bary, Fla., 3,154....D5 54
Dębica, Pol., 22,900....C6 7
Dębno, Pol., 10,700....B3 7
Deboullie, mtn., Maine...B4 64
Debrecen, Hung., 155,122...B5 10
Decatur, Ala., 38,044....A3 46
Decatur, Ga., 21,943...C2, h8 55
Decatur, Ill., 90,397 (*115,900).........D5 58
Decatur, Ind., 8,445....C8 59
Decatur, Mich., 1,764....F5 66
Decatur, Miss., 1,311....C4 68
Decatur, Tex., 3,240....C4 84
Decatur, co., Ga., 22,310..F2 55
Decatur, co., Ind., 22,738..F6 59
Decatur, co., Iowa, 9,737.............D5 60
Decatur, co., Kans., 4,988..C3 61
Decatur, co., Tenn., 9,457..B3 83
Decazeville, Fr., 10,532 (*26,000).........E5 5
Deccan, reg., India......E6 20
Deception, mtn., Wash....B2 86
Decherd, Tenn., 2,148...B5 83
Děčín, Czech., 44,228....C3 7
Decorah, Iowa, 7,458....A6 60
Dededo, Guam, 2,247....*F6 2
Dedham, Mass., 26,938......B5, h11 65
Dedinovo, Sov. Un., 5,000.............n19 12
Deephaven, Minn., 3,853.........F5, n11 67
Deep River, Ont., Can., 5,671.............A7 41
Deep River, Conn., 2,333..D7 52
Deepwater, N.J., 650....D2 74
Deer, mtn., Maine.......C2 64
Deerfield, Ill., 18,876...h9 58
Deerfield, Mich., 834....G7 66
Deerfield Beach, Fla., 16,662...........F6 54
Deer Lake, Newf., Can., 4,421.............D3 44
Deer Lodge, Mont., 4,306..D4 70
Deer Lodge, co., Mont., 15,652............D3 70
Deer Park, N.Y., 32,000...*F3 75
Deer Park, Ohio, 7,415...o13 78
Deer Park, Tex., 12,773..*E5 84
Deer Park, Wash., 1,295...B8 86
Deer River, Minn., 815...C5 67
Defense Highway, Md., 1,000.............*C4 53
Defiance, Ohio, 16,281...A1 78
Defiance, co., Ohio 36,949............A1 78
Defiance, mtn., Oreg.....B5 80
De Forest, Wis., 1,911...E4 88
De Funiak Springs, Fla., 4,966............u15 54
Deggendorf, Ger., Fed. Rep. of, 22,426....D6 6
Dehiwala-Mount Lavinia, Sri Lanka, 154,785..*G7 20
Dehra Dūn, India, 166,073 (*203,464)........B6 20
Dej, Rom., 19,281......B6 10
De Kalb, Ill., 32,949....B5 58
De Kalb, Miss., 1,072...C5 68
De Kalb, Tex., 2,197....C5 84
De Kalb, co., Ala., 41,981............A4 46
De Kalb, co., Ga., 415,387...........C2 55
De Kalb, co., Ill., 71,654..B5 58
De Kalb, co., Ind., 30,837............B7 59
De Kalb, co., Mo., 7,305..B3 69

De Kalb, co., Tenn., 11,151...........D8 83
Delafield, Wis., 3,182...*E5 88
Del Aire, Calif., 5,000....*F4 50
Delanco, N.J., 4,011....C3 74
De Land, Fla., 11,641...C5 54
Delano, Calif., 14,559...E4 50
Delano, Minn., 1,851....E5 67
Delavan, Ill., 1,844....C4 58
Delavan, Wis., 5,526....F5 88
Delaware, Ohio, 15,008...B2 78
Delaware, co., Ind., 129,219...........D7 59
Delaware, co., Iowa, 18,770............B6 60
Delaware, co., N.Y., 44,718............C5 75
Delaware, co., Ohio, 42,908............B2 78
Delaware, co., Okla., 17,767............A7 79
Delaware, co., Pa., 601,715...........G11 81
Delaware, state, U.S., 573,000..........C11 45
Delaware, bay, Del.,.....B7 53
Delaware City, Del., 2,024.............A6 53
Delbarton, W. Va., 903...............D2 87
Delcambre, La., 1,975...E4 63
Del City, Okla., 27,133..B4 79
Delémont, Switz., 11,300..E3 6
De Leon, Tex., 2,170....C3 84
De Leon Springs, Fla., 900...............C5 54
Delft, Neth., 87,777....A6 5
Delfzijl, Neth., 22,771...A7 5
Delhi, Calif., 1,175....*D3 50
Delhi, Ont., Can., 3,894...E4 41
Delhi, India, 3,706,558 (*4,500,000).....C6 20
Delhi, ter., India, 4,065,698.........*C6 20
Delhi, La., 2,887......B4 63
Delhi, N.Y., 3,017.....C6 75
Delhi Hills, Ohio, 9,000...*C1 78
Delisle, Que., Can., 1,302..A6 42
Delitzsch, Ger. Dem. Rep., 24,300............C6 6
Dellenbaugh, mtn., Ariz...............A2 48
Dell Rapids, S. Dak., 1,991.............G9 77
Dellwood, Mo., 7,137....*C7 69
Del Mar, Calif., 3,956...o15 50
Delmar, Md., 1,191.....D6 53
Delmar, N.Y., 8,900....C7 75
Delmenhorst, Ger., Fed. Rep. of, 66,052....B4 6
Delmont, Pa., 1,934......*F2 81
Del Monte Park, Calif., 1,500.............*D3 50
Del Norte, Colo., 1,569...D4 51
Del Norte, co., Calif., 14,580...........B2 50
Deloraine, Man., Can., 916...............E1 40
Delphi, Ind., 2,582.....C4 59
Delphos, Ohio, 7,608....B1 78
Delran, N.J., 10,065....C3 74
Delray Beach, Fla., 19,915..F6 54
Del Rey Oaks, Calif., 1,823.............*D3 50
Del Rio, Tex., 21,330....E2 84
Delson, Que., Can., 2,941..q19 42
Delta, Colo., 3,694.....C2 51
Delta, Ohio, 2,544.....A2 78
Delta, Pa., 778.........G9 81
Delta, Utah, 1,610.....B5 72
Delta, co., Colo., 15,286..C3 51
Delta, co., Mich., 35,924..C3 66
Delta, co., Tex., 4,927...C5 84
Delta, peak, B.C., Can....A3 37
Delta Amacuro, ter., Ven., 33,979............B5 32
Deltaville, Va., 500....C6 85
Demarest, N.J., 5,133...h9 74
Demavend, mtn., Iran,...F8 16
Demidov, Sov. Un., 10,000............D8 12
Deming, N. Mex., 8,343...C5 48
Demirci, Tur., 13,007...C7 14
Demmin, Ger. Dem. Rep., 16,400............B6 6
Demopolis, Ala., 7,651...C2 46
Demorest, Ga., 1,070....B3 55
Demotte, Ind., 1,697....B3 59
Dempo, mtn., Indon......F2 19
Denain, Fr., 27,973 (*130,000).........B5 5
Denbigh, Wales, 8,340...D5 4
Denbigh, co., Wales, 184,830..........*D5 4
Denham Springs, La., 6,752..........D5, h10 63

E

F

Fredericksburg (Independent City), Va., 14,450......B5 85
Fredericktown, Mo., 3,799................D7 69
Fredericktown, Ohio, 1,935................B3 78
Fredericktown, Pa., 1,067................F1 81
Fredericton, N.B., Can., 24,254 (*37,684)......D3 43
Frederiksborg, co., Den., 236,800............*J5 11
Frederikshavn, Den., 24,800................I4 11
Frederiksted, Vir. Is., (U.S.), 277........H12 35
Fredonia, Kans., 3,080....E8 61
Fredonia, N.Y., 10,326....C1 75
Fredonia, Pa., 731........D1 81
Fredonia, Wis., 1,045....E6 88
Fredrikstad, Nor., 30,200 (*48,000)........H4, p28 11
Freeborn, co., Minn., 38,064................G5 67
Freeburg, Ill., 2,495......E4 58
Freedom, Calif., 4,206....*D3 50
Freedom, Pa., 2,643......E1 81
Freehold, N.J., 10,545....C4 74
Freel, peak, Calif.........C4 50
Freeland, Mich., 1,303....E6 66
Freeland, Pa., 4,784......D10 81
Freelandville, Ind., 650....G3 59
Freeman, S. Dak., 1,357....G8 77
Freemansburg, Pa., 1,681................E11 81
Freeport, Fla., 518......u15 54
Freeport, Ill., 27,736......A4 58
Freeport, Maine, 1,822, (4,781▲)........E2, g7 64
Freeport, Minn., 593......E4 67
Freeport, N.Y., 40,374....G2 52
Freeport, Pa., 2,375......E2 81
Freeport, Tex., 11,997..........E5, s14 84
Freer, Tex., 2,804........F3 84
Freestone, co., Tex., 11,116................D4 84
Freetown, N.Y., 1,543..............*m16 75
Freetown, S.L., 170,600 (*215,000)........G2 22
Fregenal de la Sierra, Sp., 10,498................C2 8
Freiberg, Ger. Dem. Rep., 50,689................C6 8
Freiburg [im Breisgau], Ger., Fed. Rep. of, 171,453 (*215,000).....D3 6
Freising, Ger., Fed. Rep. of, 30,705..........D5 6
Freistadt, Aus., 5,952.....D7 6
Fréjus, Fr., 23,629 (*41,500)............F3 5
Fremantle, Austl., 25,990..F2 25
Fremont, Calif., 100,869..........D2, h9 50

Fremont, Ind., 1,043......A8 59
Fremont, Mich., 3,465.....E5 66
Fremont, Nebr., 22,962...........C9, g11 71
Fremont, N.C., 1,596.....B5 76
Fremont, Ohio, 18,490.....A2 78
Freemont, co., Colo., 21,942................C5 51
Fremont, co., Idaho, 8,710................E7 57
Fremont, co., Iowa, 9,282................D2 60
Fremont, co., Wyo., 28,352................C4 89
French Camp, Calif., 2,500................*D3 50
French Guiana, dep., S.A., 58,000................C5 27
French Lick, Ind., 2,059...G4 59
French Polynesia, Fr. dep., Oceania, 132,000............*H11 2
French Somaliland, see Afars & Issas, Afr.
Frenchtown, N.J., 1,459...B2 74
Frenchville, Maine, 700 (1,375▲)............A4 64
Freshfield, mtn., Alta., Can................D9 37
Freshwater, Newf., Can., 1,562................*f9 44
Fresnillo [de González Echeverría], Mex., 44,475................C4 34
Fresno, Calif., 165,990 (*306,100)............D4 50
Fresno, co., Calif., 413,329................D4 50
Freudenstadt, Ger., Fed. Rep. of, 14,811......D4 6
Frewsburg, N.Y., 1,772...C1 75
Friant, Calif., 350........D4 50
Friars Point, Miss., 1,177..A3 68
Frias, Arg., 11,862........E2 29
Fribourg, Switz., 40,200 (*52,000)......E3 6
Fribourg, canton, Switz., 178,000............*E3 6
Friday Harbor, Wash., 803................A2 86
Fridley, Minn., 29,233...m12 67
Friedberg, Ger., Fed. Rep. of, 24,919......C4 6
Friedens, Pa., 900........F4 81
Friedland, Ger. Dem. Rep., 8,500........B6 6
Friedrichshafen, Ger., Fed. Rep. of, 52,920....E4 6
Friend, Nebr., 1,126......D8 71
Friendship, N.Y., 1,285...C2 75
Friern Barnet, Eng., 28,300................k12 4
Fries, Va., 885............D2 85
Friesland, prov., Neth., 516,400............*A6 5

Frio, co., Tex., 11,159....E3 84
Friona, Tex., 3,111.......B1 84
Frisco, Pa., 900..........*E1 81
Frisco, Tex., 1,845.......*C4 84
Frisco City, Ala., 1,286...D2 46
Fritch, Tex., 1,778.......B2 84
Fritzlar, Ger., Fed. Rep. of, 14,813............C4 6
Friuli-Venezia Giulia, reg., It., 1,225,900........*B4 9
Frontenac, Kans., 2,223...E9 61
Frontenac, Mo., 3,920....*C7 69
Frontenac, co., Ont., Can., 97,138................C8 41
Frontenac, co., Que., Can., 28,848................D7 42
Frontera, Mex., 10,066...D6 34
Frontier, co., Nebr., 3,982..D5 71
Frontignan, Fr., 5,341....F5 5
Frontino, peak, Col........B2 32
Front Royal, Va., 8,211...B4 85
Frosinone, It., 33,100.....D4 9
Frostburg, Md., 7,327...k13 53
Frostproof, Fla., 2,814....E5 54
Frouard, Fr., 7,419.......C7 5
Fruita, Colo., 1,822......B2 51
Fruitdale, Oreg., 2,655...*E3 80
Fruitland, Idaho, 1,576...F2 57
Fruitland, Ill., 800......*B3 58
Fruitland, Md., 2,315.....D6 53
Fruitland Park, Fla., 1,359..D5 54
Fruitport, Mich., 1,409...E4 66
Fruitvale, Wash., 3,275...*C5 86
Fruitville, Fla., 2,131..E4, q11 54
Frunze, Sov. Un., 442,000.E10 13
Frýdek-Místek, Czech., 37,025................D5 7
Fryeburg, Maine, 1,075 (2,208▲)............D2 64
Fthiotis (Phthiotis), prov., Grc., 154,720......*C4 14
Fuchin, China, 40,000....B11 17
Fuchou (Foochow), China, 700,000............F8 17
Fuchū, Jap., 163,173.....*I9 18
Fuente Álamo, Sp., 9,270..D5 8
Fuente de Cantos, Sp., 8,941................C2 8
Fuenteovejuna, Sp., 5,914..C3 8
Fuhai (Bulun Tokhoi), China, 10,000........B2 17
Fuji, Jap., 180,639 (*265,000)............n17 18
Fuji, vol., Jap.......I9, n17 18
Fujieda, Jap., 56,000, (78,750▲)............o17 18
Fujimi, Jap., 52,011.....n17 18
Fujinomiya, Jap., 69,000 (88,880▲)............n17 18
Fujisawa, Jap., 228,978...*I9 18
Fuji-yoshida, Jap., 50,046 .n17 18
Fukagawa, Jap., 22,000 (38,373▲)............E10 18
Fukien, prov., China, 14,650,000............F8 17

Fukuchiyama, Jap., 41,000 (57,174▲)....I7, n14 18
Fukui, Jap., 200,509.....H8 18
Fukui, pref., Jap., 744,230..............*H8 18
Fukuoka, Jap., 5,120.....F10 18
Fukuoka, Jap., 914,877 (*1,285,000)....J5 18
Fukuoka, pref., Jap., 4,027,416............*J5 18
Fukushima, Jap., 6,675..............I8, n16 18
Fukushima, Jap., 227,451............H10 18
Fukushima, pref., Jap., 1,946,077..........*H10 18
Fukuyama, Jap., 255,086...I6 18
Fulda, Ger., Fed. Rep. of, 60,293 (*92,000)....C4 6
Fulda, Minn., 1,226......G3 67
Fullerton, Calif., 85,987...n13 50
Fullerton, Ky., 500......B7 62
Fullerton, Nebr., 1,444....C8 71
Fulton, Ill., 3,630.......B3 58
Fulton, Ky., 3,250.......f9 62
Fulton, Miss., 2,999.....A5 68
Fulton, Mo., 12,248......C6 69
Fulton, N.Y., 14,003.....B4 75
Fulton, co., Ark., 7,699...A4 49
Fulton, co., Ga., 607,592..C2 55
Fulton, co., Ill., 41,890...C3 58
Fulton, co., Ind., 16,984..B5 59
Fulton, co., Ky., 10,183...B2 62
Fulton, co., N.Y., 52,637..B6 75
Fulton, co., Ohio, 33,071..A1 78
Fulton, co., Pa., 10,776...G5 81
Fultondale, Ala., 5,163...f7 46
Fumay, Fr., 6,426........C6 5
Funabashi, Jap., 325,940............n19 18
Funchal, Port., 43,301...h12 8
Fundación, Col., 14,128...A3 32
Funkstown, Md., 1,051...A2 53
Fuquay-Varina, N.C., 3,576................*B4 76
Furano, Jap., 20,000 (30,876▲)............E11 18
Furman University, S.C., 239................*B3 82
Furnas, co., Nebr., 6,897................D6 71
Fürstenfeld, Aus., 6,071...E8 6
Fürstenwalde, Ger. Dem. Rep., 31,191..........B7 6
Fürth, Ger., Fed. Rep. of, 103,942............D5 6
Furukawa, Jap., 30,000 (52,518▲)..H8, m16 18
Fusagasugá, Col., 18,755...C3 32
Fushun, China, 1,350,000............C9 17
Füssen, Ger., Fed. Rep. of, 10,405................E5 6
Fusung, China, 5,000.....E3 18
Fuyü, China, 45,000......B9 17
Fuyuan, China, 5,000.....B7 18

G

Gabès, Tun., 32,330......B7 22
Gabin, Pol., 3,339.......B5 7
Gabon (Gabun), country, Afr., 515,000........I7 22
Gaborone, Bots., 17,698...E5 24
Gabrovo, Bul., 57,805....D7 10
Gadag, India, 95,426.....E6 20
Gadsden, Ala., 53,928 (*81,500)............A3 46
Gadsden, co., Fla., 39,184..B2 54
Gadyach, Sov. Un., 10,000.F9 12
Găeşti, Rom., 7,179......C7 10
Gaeta, It., 22,800........D4 9
Gaffney, S.C., 13,253.....A4 82
Gafsa, Tun., 24,345......B6 22
Gage, co., Nebr., 25,731...D9 71
Gages Lake, Ill., 3,395...*A5 58
Gagnon, Que., Can., 3,787.h13 42
Gagny, Fr., 35,780.......g11 5
Gahanna, Ohio, 12,400...k11 78
Gaillac, Fr., 6,205.......F4 5
Gaines, co., Tex., 11,593...C1 84
Gainesboro, Tenn., 1,101..C8 83
Gainesville, Fla., 64,510 (*82,100)............C4 54
Gainesville, Ga., 15,459...B3 55

Gainesville, Tex., 13,830...C4 84
Gainsborough, Eng., 17,580................D6 4
Gairdner, lake, Austl......F6 25
Gairloch, Scot., 104......B4 4
Gaithersburg, Md., 8,344..B3 53
Galacz, see Galati, Rom.
Galápagos Is., see Colón, Archipiélago de, Ec.
Galashiels, Scot., 12,560...C5 4
Galati, Rom., 151,300.....C8 10
Galatia, Ill., 792.........F5 58
Galatina, It., 20,900......D7 9
Galax (Independent City), Va., 6,278..........D2 85
Gáldar, Sp., 6,165......m14 8
Galeana, Mex., 710.......A3 34
Galena, Ill., 3,930.......A3 58
Galena, Kans., 3,712......E9 61
Galena Park, Tex., 10,479..............r14 84
Gales, peak, Oreg........g11 80
Galesburg, Ill., 36,290....C3 58
Galesburg, Mich., 1,355...F5 66
Galesville, Md., 625.....C4 53
Galesville, Wis., 1,162....D2 88

Galeton, Pa., 1,552......C6 81
Galeville, N.Y., 1,000....*B4 75
Galicia, reg., Pol., Sov. Un................D6 7
Galicia, reg., Sp., 2,692,100............A1 8
Galien, Mich., 691......G4 66
Galion, Ohio, 13,123.....B3 78
Gallarate, It., 41,200.....B1 9
Gallatin, Mo., 1,833......B4 69
Gallatin, Tenn., 13,253...A5 83
Gallatin, co., Ill., 7,418...F5 58
Gallatin, co., Ky., 4,134...B5 62
Gallatin, co., Mont., 32,505................E5 70
Galle, Sri Lanka, 72,720...G7 20
Gallia, co., Ohio, 25,239..D3 78
Gallipoli, It., 17,700.....D6 9
Gallipoli, see Gelibolu, Tur.
Gallipolis, Ohio, 7,490...D3 78
Gallitzin, Pa., 2,496.....F4 81
Gällivare, Swe., 22,119...D9 11
Galloway, W. Va., 300....B4 87
Gallup, N. Mex., 13,779...B4 48

Galt, Ont., Can., 38,897...D4 41
Galty, mts., Ire..........D2 4
Galva, Ill., 3,061........B3 58
Galveston, Tex., 61,809 (*132,500)......E5, r15 84
Galveston, co., Tex., 169,812............E5 84
Galway, Ire., 27,726.....D2 4
Galway, co., Ire., 148,340............*D2 4
Gamagori, Jap., 82,868...o16 18
Gamarra, Col., 4,664.....B3 32
Gambia, country, Afr., 400,000............F1 22
Gambia, riv., Afr.........F2 22
Gambier, Ohio, 1,571.....B3 78
Gamboa, C.Z., 2,102....*B2 32
Gambrills, Md., 600......B4 53
Ganado, Tex., 1,640......E4 84
Gananoque, Ont., Can., 5,212................C8 41
Gand, see Gent, Bel.
Gander, Newf., Can., 7,748................D4 44

Gandhinager, India, 24,055................D5 20
Gandía, Sp., 15,812.......C5 8
Gangaw, Bur., 3,800......D9 20
Ganges, riv., Asia.........D8 20
Gangtok, Sikkim, 6,848....C8 20
Gannat, Fr., 5,376........D5 5
Gannett, peak, Wyo.......C3 89
Gantt, S.C., 900..........B3 82
Gao, Mali, 6,500.........E5 22
Gap, Fr., 23,994..........E7 5
Gap, Pa., 1,022..........G9 81
Garanhuns, Braz., 49,579..............*D7 27
Garber, Okla., 1,011......A4 27
Garberville, Calif., 900....B2 50
Garça, Braz., 21,871.......C3 30
Garciasville, Tex., 350.....F3 84
Gard, dept., Fr., 478,544..*F6 5
Gardelegen, Ger. Dem. Rep., 12,400...........B5 6
Garden, co., Nebr., 2,929................C3 71
Gardena, Calif., 41,021...n12 50
Garden City, Ga., 5,790...D5 55
Garden City, Idaho, 2,368.................*F2 57
Garden City, Kans., 14,790.................E3 61
Garden City, Mich., 41,864...............p15 66
Graden City, Mo., 633....C3 69
Garden City, N.Y., 25,373................G2 52
Garden City, Pa., 745.................*G11 81
Garden City Park, N.Y., 7,488................*G2 52
Gardendale, Ala., 6,537...............B3, f7 46
Garden Grove, Calif., 122,524...............n13 50
Garden Home, Oreg., 4,700.................*B4 80
Garden Lakes, Ga., 2,500.................*B1 55
Garden View, Pa., 2,662..*D7 81
Gardez, Afg., 17,540......B4 20
Gardiner, Maine, 6,685....D3 64
Gardiner, Mont., 650......E6 70
Gardner, Ill., 1,212........B5 58
Gardner, Kans., 1,839.....D9 61
Gardner, Mass., 19,748...A4 65
Garfield, N.J., 30,797......h8 74
Garfield, Wash., 610......B8 86
Garfield, co., Colo., 14,821.................B2 51
Garfield, co., Mont., 1,796.................C9 70
Garfield, co., Nebr., 2,411.................C6 71
Garfield, co., Okla., 56,343.................A4 79
Garfield, co., Utah, 3,157..C6 72
Garfield, co., Wash., 2,911.................C8 86
Garfield Heights, Ohio, 41,417.................h9 78
Garfield peak, Wyo.......D5 89
Gargaliánoi, Grc., 5,888..D3 14
Garibaldi, Oreg., 1,083....B3 80
Garibaldi, mtn., B.C., Can.................E6 37
Garland, Md., 1,000.....*B4 53
Garland, N.C., 656.......C4 76
Garland, Tex., 81,437....n10 84
Garland, Utah, 1,187.....A5 72
Garland, co., Ark., 54,131..C2 49
Garmisch-Partenkirchen, Ger., Fed. Rep. of, 27,408.................E5 6
Garnavillo, Iowa, 634.....B6 60
Garner, Iowa, 2,257.......A4 60
Garner, N.C., 4,923.......B4 76
Garnett, Kans., 3,169.....D8 61
Garoua, Cam..............G7 22
Garrard, co., Ky., 9,457...C5 62
Garrett, Ind., 4,715.......B7 59
Garrett, Ky., 300........C7 62
Garrett, co., Md., 21,476................k12 53
Garrett Park, Md., 1,276...B3 53
Garrett Park Estates, Md., 3,000.................*B3 53
Garrettsville, Ohio, 1,718..A4 78
Garrison, Md., 600........B4 53
Garrison, N. Dak., 1,614...C4 77
Garrison, Tex., 1,082......D5 84
Garrovillas, Sp., 5,764.....C2 8
Garson, Ont., Can., 4,447................*p19 41
Gartok, see Kaerh, China
Garut, Indon., 81,234.....G3 19
Garvin, co., Okla., 24,874..C4 79
Garwolin, Pol., 6,910......C6 7
Garwood, N.J., 5,260.....*B4 74
Gary, Ind., 175,415.......A3 59
Gary, W. Va., 2,800......D3 87
Garyville, La., 2,389..D5, h10 63
Garza, co., Tex., 5,289....C2 84
Garzón, Col., 11,999......C2 32
Gas City, Ind., 5,742......D6 59
Gasconade, co., Mo., 11,878.................C6 69
Gascony (Gascogne), former prov., Fr........E3 5
Gaspé, Que., Can., 17,211.k14 42
Gaspe East, co., Que., Can., 41,250.........*k14 42
Gaspe West, co., Que., Can., 18,492.........*k13 42
Gasport, N.Y., 900........B2 75
Gassaway, W. Va., 1,253..C4 87
Gaston, Ind., 928.........D7 59
Gaston, N.C., 1,105.......A5 76
Gaston, co., N.C., 148,415..B1 76
Gastonia, N.C., 47,142 (*113,600)............B1 76
Gatchina, Sov. Un., 63,000...........H14, s31 11
Gate City, Va., 1,914......f9 85
Gates, N.Y., 26,442.......*B3 75
Gates, co., N.C., 8,524....A6 76
Gateshead, Eng., 94,680...C6 4
Gates Mills, Ohio, 2,378..*A4 78
Gatesville, Tex., 4,683.....D4 84
Gatineau, Que., Can., 22,321................D2 42
Gatineau, co., Que., Can., 50,979.................C2 42
Gatlinburg, Tenn., 2,329................D10 83
Gatton, Austl., 3,546......C9 26
Gatun, C.Z., 668.........*B2 32
Gauhāti, India, 123,783 (*200,377).............C9 20
Gauley Bridge, W. Va., 950..............C3, m13 87
Gävle, Swe., 84,537.......G7 11
Gävleborg, co., Swe., 294,100..............*G7 11
Gavrilovka, Sov. Un., 10,000...............G11 12
Gawler, Austl., 6,953......G2 26
Gaya, India, 179,884......D7 20
Gaylord, Mich., 3,012......C6 66
Gaylord, Minn., 1,720.....F4 67
Gaysin, Sov. Un., 24,000..G7 12
Gays Mills, Wis., 623......E3 88
Gaza (Ghazzah), Gaza Strip, 118,272..........C2 15
Gaza Strip, Israeli occ., Asia, 360,000...........C2 15
Gaziantep, Tur., 227,652..............D11 14
Gdańsk (Danzig), Pol., 364,200 (*670,000)......A5 7
Gdynia, Pol., 190,100.....A5 7
Gearhart, mtn., Oreg......E6 80
Geary, N.B., Can., 938....D3 43
Geary, Okla., 1,380.......B3 79
Geary, co., Kans., 28,111..D7 61
Geauga, co., Ohio, 62,977.................A4 78
Gediz, Tur., 10,651.......C7 14
Geelong, Austl., 17,775 (*121,966)........G7, n14 25
Geislingen, Ger., Fed. Rep. of, 29,774.........D4 6
Geistown, Pa., 3,633.......F4 81
Gela, It., 65,300..........F5 9
Gelderland, prov., Neth., 1,479,800.............*A6 5
Gelibolu, Tur., 14,716.....B6 14
Gelsenkirchen, Ger., Fed. Rep. of, 339,845.........C3 6
Gem, co., Idaho, 9,387.....E2 57
Gemlik, Tur., 16,915......B7 14
General Belgrano, Arg., 6,994.................B5 28
General Madariaga, Arg., 7,073.................B5 28
General Pico, Arg., 22,500..B4 28
General Roca, Arg., 32,000.................B3 28
Genesee, Idaho, 619........C2 57
Genesee, Mich., 800........E7 66
Genesee, co., Mich., 445,589................E7 66
Genesee, co., N.Y., 58,722..B2 75
Geneseo, Ill., 5,840.........B3 58
Geneseo, N.Y., 5,714.......C3 75
Geneva, Ala., 4,398........D4 46
Geneva, Ill., 9,115.........F1 58
Geneva, Ind., 1,100........C8 59
Geneva, Nebr., 2,275........D8 71
Geneva, N.Y., 16,793......C4 75
Geneva, Ohio, 6,449.......A5 78
Geneva-on-the-Lake, Ohio, 877..............A5 78
Geneva, co., Ala., 21,924..D4 46
Genève (Geneva), Switz., 169,200 (*390,000)......E3 6
Genève, canton, Switz., 329,400...............*E3 6
Genevia, Ark., 3,500..C3, k10 49
Genichesk, Sov. Un., 20,000................H10 12
Genk, Bel., 58,720.........B6 5
Gennevilliers, Fr., 46,074..g10 5
Genoa, Ill., 3,003.........A5 58
Genoa (Genova), It., 841,800 (*890,000)......B2 9
Genoa, Nebr., 1,174.......C8 71
Genoa, Ohio, 2,139....A2, e7 78
Genoa City, Wis., 1,085.............F5, n11 88
Genova, see Genoa, It.
Gent (Ghent), Bel., 148,166 (*320,000)......B5 5
Genthin, Ger. Dem. Rep., 15,200.................B6 6
Gentilly, Fr., 19,211......g10 5
Gentry, co., Mo., 8,060....A3 69
Genzano di Roma, It., 12,727.................h9 9
George, Iowa, 1,194.......A2 60
George, S. Afr., 24,395....G4 24
George, co., Miss., 12,459.................E5 68
George, hill, Md..........k12 53
George Town, Austl., 4,837.................o15 25
Georgetown, Ont., Can., 17,053.................D5 41
Georgetown, P.E.I., Can., 767.................C7 43
Georgetown, Conn., 1,600..D3 52
Georgetown, Del., 1,844...C7 53
Georgetown, Guy., 66,070 (*190,000).......C5 27
Georgetown, Idaho, 421...G7 57
Georgetown, Ill., 3,984....D6 58
Georgetown, Ind., 1,273...H6 59
Georgetown, Ky., 8,629....B5 62
Georgetown, Mass., 2,300..A6 65
Georgetown, Ohio, 3,087..D2 78
Georgetown, S.C., 10,449..E9 82
Georgetown, Tex., 6,395...D4 84
George Town, see Pinang, Mala.
Georgetown, co., S.C., 33,500.................E9 82
George West, Tex., 2,022..E3 84
Georgia (Georgian S.S.R.), rep., Sov. Un., 4,880,000..............*A3 15
Georgia, state, U.S., 4,808,000................ 55
Georgiana, Ala., 2,148....D3 46
Gera, Ger. Dem. Rep., 112,384.................C6 6
Geraldton, Austl., 15,330..E1 25
Geraldton, Ont., Can., 3,178.................o18 41
Gerber, Calif., 775........B2 50
Gering, Nebr., 5,639.......C2 71
Gerlachovka, mtn., Czech..D6 7
German Democratic Republic, country, Eur., 16,990,000...........E10 3
Germantown, Ill., 1,108...E4 58
Germantown, Ohio, 4,088..C1 78
Germantown, Tenn., 3,474.................B2 83
Germantown, Wis., 6,974.............E5, m11 88
Germany, East, see German Democratic Republic, country, Eur.
Germany, Federal Republic of, country, Eur., 62,115,000.............E9 3
Germany, West, see, Germany, Federal Republic of, country, Eur.
Germiston, S. Afr., 210,298.F5 24
Gero, Jap..................n16 18
Gerona, Sp., 47,747.......B7 8
Gerona, prov., Sp., 400,300...............*B7 8
Gers, dept., Fr., 181,577..*F4 5
Gertrudis Sánchez, Mex., 40,740.................h9 34
Getafe, Sp., 69,396....B4, p17 8
Gettysburg, Pa., 7,275.....G7 81
Gettysburg, S. Dak., 1,915.................E6 77
Geyserville, Calif., 750.....C2 50
Ghana, country, Afr., 9,430,000..............G4 22
Gharyān, Libya, 2,796.....B7 22
Ghazni, Afg., 27,084.......B4 20
Ghazzah, see Gaza, Gaza Strip
Ghent, see Gent, Bel.
Gheorgheni, Rom., 11,969.................B7 10
Gherla, Rom., 7,617.......B6 10
Gia Dinh, Viet. S., 151,100.................C3 19
Giamda, see Taichao, China
Giant, mtn., N.Y.,........A7 75
Gibara, Cuba, 12,100 (29,800 ▲)..............D5 35
Gibbon, Minn., 877........F4 67
Gibbon, Nebr., 1,388......D7 71
Gibbsboro, N.J., 2,634....*D3 74
Gibbstown, N.J., 5,676....D2 74
Gibraleón, Sp., 8,865......D2 8
Gibraltar, Gib., 25,300 (*102,000).......D3 8
Gibraltar, Mich., 3,842...*F7 66
Gibraltar, Br. dep., Eur., 29,000................*D3 8
Gibsland, La., 1,380......B2 63
Gibson, co., Ind., 30,444...H2 59
Gibson, co., Tenn., 47,871.................A3 83
Gibsonburg, Ohio, 2,585...............A2, e7 78
Gibson City, Ill., 3,454...C5 58
Gibsonia, Pa., 2,065......h14 81
Gibsons, B.C., Can., 1,934.................E6 37
Gibsonton, Fla., 2,500...p11 54
Gibsonville, N.C., 2,019...A3 76
Giddings, Tex., 2,783.....D4 84
Gideon, Mo., 1,112........E8 69
Gien, Fr., 8,812...........D5 5
Giessen, Ger., Fed. Rep. of, 77,537 (*155,000).......C4 6
Giffard, Que., Can., 13,135...............N17 42
Gifford, Fla., 3,509.......E6 54
Gifu, Jap., 385,727...I8, n15 18
Gifu, pref., Jap., 1,758,954..............*I8 18
Gigante, Col., 4,594.......C2 32
Gig Harbor, Wash., 1,657...............B3, f10 86
Gijon, Sp., 184,698.......A3 8
Gila, co., Ariz., 29,255....C3 48
Gila, riv., Ariz., N. Mex...D4 45
Gila Bend, Ariz., 1,795....C2 48
Gilbert, Ariz., 1,971..C3, D2 48
Gilbert, Minn., 2,287.....C6 67
Gilbert, peak, Wash.......C4 86
Gilbert & Ellice Is., Br. dep, Oceania, 60,000...*F8 2
Gilberton, Pa., 1,293....*E9 81
Gilbert Plains, Man., Can., 849..............D1 40
Gilbertsville, Pa., 900....F10 81
Gilbertville, Iowa, 665.....B5 60
Gilbertville, Mass., 1,247...B3 65
Gilchrist, co., Fla., 3,551...C4 54
Giles, co., Tenn., 22,138...B4 83
Giles, co., Va., 16,741.....C2 85
Gilford Park, N.J., 3,200................*D4 74
Gillespie, Ill., 3,457.......D4 58
Gillespie, co., Tex., 10,553.D3 84
Gillett, Wis., 1,288.......D5 88
Gillette, Wyo., 7,194.......B7 89
Gilliam, co., Oreg., 2,342..B6 80
Gillingham, Eng., 90,800..E7 4
Gilly, Bel., 23,531.........B6 5
Gilman, Ill., 1,786.........C5 58
Gilmer, Tex., 4,196.......C5 84
Gilmer, co., Ga., 8,956....B2 55
Gilmer, co., W. Va., 7,782.................C4 87
Gilmore City, Iowa, 766...B3 60
Gilpin, co., Colo., 1,272...B5 51
Gilroy, Calif., 12,665......D3 50
Gimli, Man., Can., 2,041..D3 40
Ginosa, It., 17,800........D6 9
Ginzo, Sp., 9,130..........A2 8
Gioia del Colle, It., 22,600................D6 9
Gioiosa Ionica, It., 5,002...E6 9
Girard, Ill., 1,881.........D4 58
Girard, Kans., 2,591.......E9 61
Girard, Ohio, 14,119.......A5 78
Girard, Pa., 2,613.........B1 81
Girardot, Col., 71,200 (82,300 ▲)..............C3 32
Girardville, Pa., 2,450.....E9 81
Giresun, Tur., 32,522.....B12 14
Giridih, India, 40,308.....D8 20
Girishk, Afg., 5,000........B3 20
Gironde, dept., Fr., 1,009,390..............*E3 5
Girvan, Scot., 7,396........C4 4
Gisborne, N.Z., 28,700 (*30,700)..............M17 26
Giscome, B.C., Can., 646...B6 37
Gisors, Fr., 7,329..........C4 5
Gitega, Burundi, 2,800.....I4 23
Giulianova, It., 9,100......C4 9
Giurgiu, Rom., 39,200.....D7 10
Giv'atayim, Isr., 48,500...*B2 15
Givet, Fr., 7,865...........B6 5
Givors, Fr., 19,048 (*34,000)...............E6 5
Gjinokaster, Alb., 15,600...B3 14
Gjinokaster, pref., Alb., 168,000..............*B3 14
Gjövik, Nor., 23,700.......G4 11

Groningen, prov., Neth.,
514,000............*A7   5
Grosse Ile, Mich., 8,306...*B7   66
Grossenhain, Ger. Dem.
Rep., 19,500...........C6   6
Grosse Pointe, Mich.,
6,637................p16   66
Grosse Pointe Farms,
Mich., 11,701.......*p16   66
Grosse Pointe Park, Mich.,
15,641...............p16   66
Grosse Pointe Shores,
Mich., 3,042.........*F8   66
Grosse Pointe Woods,
Mich., 21,878.........p16   66
Grosseto, It., 45,200......C3   9
Grossglockner, mtn., Aus..E6   6
Grossmont, Calif., 2,000...o16   50
Gros Ventre, range, Wyo..C2   89
Groton, Conn., 8,933
(38,244 ▲)............D8   52
Groton, Mass., 1,314...A4, f9   65
Groton, N.Y., 2,112.......C4   75
Groton, S. Dak., 1,021.....E7   77
Grottaferrata, It., 5,377....h9   9
Grottaglie, It., 24,800......D6   9
Grottoes, Va., 1,166.......B4   85
Grove, Okla., 2,000........A7   79
Grove City, Ohio,
13,911.............C2, m10   78
Grove City, Pa., 8,312....D1   81
Grove Hill, Ala., 1,825....D2   46
Groveland, Fla., 1,928.....D5   54
Groveland, Mass., 2,500...A5   65
Groveport, Ohio,
2,490.............C2, m11   78
Grover City, Calif., 5,939..E3   50
Groves, Tex., 18,067......E6   84
Groveton, N.H., 1,597....B4   73
Groveton, Pa., 640.......*E1   81
Groveton, Tex., 1,219.....D5   84
Groveton, Va., 11,750....g12   85
Grovetown, Ga., 3,169....C4   55
Groveville, N.J., 1,800....C3   74
Groznyy, Sov. Un.,
341,000.............E7   13
Grudziądz, Pol., 75,500...B5   7
Grulla, Tex., 1,500.......F3   84
Grundy, Va., 2,054.......e9   85
Grundy, co., Ill., 26,535...B5   58
Grundy, co., Iowa, 14,119..B5   60
Grundy, co., Mo., 11,819...A4   69
Grundy, co., Tenn.,
10,631.............D8   83
Grundy Center, Iowa,
2,712................B5   60
Gruver, Tex., 1,265......A2   84
Gruz, Yugo., 10,000......D4   10
Gryazi, Sov. Un., 41,000..E12   12
Guadalajara, Mex.,
1,193,601
(*1,500,000)......C4, m12   34
Guadalajara, Sp., 31,640..B4   8

Guadalajara, prov., Sp.,
159,000..............*B4   8
Guadalcanal, Sp., 6,931...C3   8
Guadalupe, Ariz., 4,000...D2   48
Guadalupe, Calif., 3,145...E3   50
Guadalupe, co., N. Mex.,
4,765................B6   48
Guadalupe, co., Tex.,
33,554................E4   84
Guadalupe, peak, Tex....o12   84
Guadeloupe, Fr. dep., N.A.,
345,000..............H14   35
Guaira, dept., Par., 114,949.E4   29
Gualeguay, Arg., 16,542...A5   28
Gualeguaychú, Arg.,
31,000................A5   28
Guam, U.S., dep.,
Oceania, 92,000......*F6   2
Guanabacoa, Cuba, 69,700.C2   35
Guanabara, state, Braz.,
4,315,746...........*C4   30
Guanacaste, prov., C.R.,
171,700.............*E8   34
Guanajay, Cuba, 18,800
(22,000 ▲)...........C2   35
Guanajuato, Mex.,
36,809...........C4, m13   34
Guanajuato, state, Mex.,
1,957,900............C4   34
Guanare, Ven., 37,715....B4   32
Guane, Cuba, 8,300
(24,700 ▲)...........C1   35
Guánica, P.R., 8,979
(14,889 ▲)..........*G11   35
Guantánamo, Cuba,
130,100 (131,500 ▲)...D6   35
Guarabira, Braz., 22,627..*D7   27
Guaranda, Ec., 9,900......B2   31
Guarapuava, Braz.,
14,419................D2   30
Guaratinguetá, Braz.,
55,069................C3   30
Guarda, Port., 9,094......B2   8
Guareña, Sp., 9,742......C2   8
Guárico, state, Ven.,
244,966..............B4   32
Guarujá, Braz., 30,741....n8   30
Guatemala, Guat.,
717,322 (*945,000)......E6   34
Guatemala, country, N.A.,
5,810,000.............D6   34
Guaxupé, Braz., 17,319 .C3, k8   30
Guayabal, Cuba, 9,000....D5   35
Guayama, P.R., 20,318
(36,249 ▲)..........n13   36
Guayaquil, Ec., 738,600...B2   31
Guayas, prov., Ec.,
1,238,800.............B1   31
Guaymas, Mex., 57,492...B2   34
Gubakha, Sov. Un.,
33,000.............*D8   13

Gubat, Phil., 8,392.......*C6   19
Gubbio, It., 9,200.........C4   9
Gūdūr, India, 33,778.....F6   20
Guebwiller, Fr., 10,840
(*20,500)............D7   5
Guecho, Sp., 22,951......A4   8
Guelma, Alg., 39,817.....A6   22
Guelph, Ont., Can.,
60,087 (*62,659)......D4   41
Güemes, Arg., 5,688......D2   29
Guéret, Fr., 12,849.......D4   5
Guerneville, Calif., 900...*C2   50
Guernsey, Wyo., 793......D8   89
Guernsey, Br. dep., Eur.,
55,000................F5   4
Guernsey, co., Ohio,
37,665................B4   78
Guerrero, state, Mex.,
1,331,000.............D5   34
Gueydan, La., 1,984......D3   63
Guiana, French, see French
Guiana, dep., S.A.
Guiana, Netherlands,
see Surinam,
Neth. dep., S.A.
Guidonia, It., 22,205 ...D4, h9   9
Guildford, Eng.,
58,090............E6, m11   4
Guilford, Conn., 3,632....D6   52
Guilford, Maine, 1,216....C3   64
Guilford, N.C., 61.......*A3   76
Guilford, co., N.C.,
288,590...............A3   76
Guimarães, Port., 23,229..B1   8
Guin, Ala., 2,220.........B2   46
Guinea, country, Afr.,
4,260,000.............F2   22
Guinea-Bissau, country,
Afr., 475,000.........E4   21
Güines, Cuba, 41,400
(45,300 ▲)...........C2   35
Guingamp, Fr., 9,232.....C2   5
Guipúzcoa, prov., Sp.,
591,900.............*A4   8
Güira de Melena, Cuba,
19,900 (26,700 ▲)......C2   35
Güiria, Ven., 10,061......A5   32
Guise, Fr., 6,805.........C5   5
Gujarat, state, India,
26,697,475...........D5   20
Gujrānwāla, Pak.,
366,000..............B5   20
Gujrāt, Pak., 100,000.....*B5   20
Gulbarga, India, 145,588..E6   20
Gulf, co., Fla., 10,096.....C1   54
Gulf Hammock, Fla.,
350.................C4   54
Gulfport, Fla.,
9,976.............E4, p10   54
Gulfport, Miss., 40,791
(*151,300)........E4, f7   68
Gull Lake, Sask., Can.,
1,038.................G1   39

Gulyay-Pole, Sov. Un.,
10,000..............H11   12
Gumma, pref., Jap.,
1,658,909.............*H9   18
Gummersbach, Ger., Fed.
Rep. of, 45,361.......*C3   6
Gunnedah, Austl., 8,219...E8   26
Gunnison, Colo., 4,613....C4   51
Gunnison, Utah, 1,073....B6   72
Gunnison, co., Colo., 7,578 .C3   51
Guntersville, Ala., 6,491...A3   46
Guntūr, India, 269,991....E7   20
Gurabo, P.R., 6,290
(18,289 ▲)..........*G11   35
Gurdon, Ark., 2,075......D2   49
Gurnee, Ill., 2,738.......E2   58
Guryev, Sov. Un., 114,000.E8   13
Gusav, Nig., 69,231......F6   22
Gusev, Sov. Un., 20,000...A7   7
Gusinje, Yugo., 2,757....D4   10
Gus-Khrustalnyy,
Sov. Un., 65,000.....D13   12
Gustavo A. Madero, Mex.,
11,773................h9   34
Gustine, Calif., 2,793....D3   50
Güstrow, Ger. Dem. Rep.,
36,882................B6   6
Gütersloh, Ger., Fed. Rep.
of, 77,599............C4   6
Guthrie, Ky., 1,200......D2   62
Guthrie, Okla., 9,575.....B4   79
Guthrie, co., Iowa, 12,243 ..C3   60
Guthrie Center, Iowa,
1,834................C3   60
Guttenberg, Iowa, 2,177..B6   60
Guttenberg, N.J., 5,754....h8   74
Guyana, country, S.A.,
770,000..............C5   27
Guyenne, former prov.,
Fr..................E4   5
Guymon, Okla.,
7,674................e9   79
Guysborough, co., N.S.,
Can., 12,830..........D8   43
Gvardeysk, Sov. Un.,
5,000................A6   7
Gwādar, Pak., 8,146....C3   20
Gwalior, India, 384,772
(*406,140)...........C6   20
Gwelo, Rh., 34,000
(*41,000)............D5   24
Gwinn, Mich., 1,054.....B3   66
Gwinnett, co., Ga.,
72,349...............C2   55
Gyangtse, see Chiangtzu,
China
Gympie, Austl., 11,131....E9   25
Gyöngyös, Hung.,
33,149...............B4   10
Győr, Hung., 100,065.....B3   10
Gyor-Sopron, co., Hung.,
404,698.............*B3   10
Gyula, Hung., 22,880
(26,266 ▲)............B5   10

H

Haakon, co., S. Dak., 2,802.F4   77
Haapsalu, Sov. Un., 10,000.B4   12
Haarlem, Neth., 170,667...A6   5
Habersham, Ga., 200......B3   55
Habersham, co., Ga.,
20,691...............B3   55
Haboru, Jap., 11,650.....D10   18
Hachiman, Jap., 8,680....n15   18
Hachinohe, Jap., 208,801.F10   18
Hachioji, Jap., 253,527.I9, n18   18
Hackberry, La., 800......E2   63
Hackensack, N.J.,
36,008..............B4, h8   74
Hackettstown, N.J., 9,472..B3   74
Haddonfield, N.J., 13,118..D2   74
Haddon Heights, N.J.,
9,365................D2   74
Hadera, Isr., 31,900....B2, g5   15
Haderslev, co., Den.,
74,600.............*J3   11
Hadramawt, reg., P.D.R.
of Yem...............G4   15
Hadley, Mass., 800
(3,750 ▲)............B2   65
Haeju, Kor., 82,135......G2   18
Haerhpin (Harbin), China,
2,100,000............E15   16
Hagaman, N.Y., 1,410...*C6   75

Hagar Shores (Lake
Michigan Beach),
Mich., 1,201.........*F4   66
Hagen, Ger., Fed. Rep. of,
197,870..............C3   6
Hagerman, N. Mex., 953 ..C6   48
Hagerstown, Ind., 2,059...E7   59
Hagerstown, Md., 35,862
(*83,400)............A2   53
Hagersville, Ont., Can.,
2,292................E4   41
Hagi, Jap., 42,000
(52,541 ▲)............I5   18
Ha Giang, Viet., 25,000...G6   17
Haguenau, Fr., 22,944....C7   5
Hague, The ('s Gravenhage),
see The Hague, Neth.
Hahira, Ga., 1,326........F3   55
Hahnville, La., 1,297..E5, k11   63
Haicheng, China, 80,000..*C9   17
Hai Duong, Viet.,
24,752..............*A3   19
Haifa (Hefa), Isr., 217,400
(*370,000)........B3, g5   15
Hā'il, Sau, Ar., 30,000....D3   15
Hailaerh (Hulun), China,
60,000...............B8   17
Hailey, Idaho, 1,425......F4   57

Haileybury, Ont., Can.,
5,280 (*12,965).......p20   41
Haileyville, Okla., 928.....C6   79
Hailun, China, 48,000.....C3   18
Hailung, China, 20,000....E2   18
Hainan, isl., China.......B4   19
Hainaut, prov., Bel.,
1,332,500............*B5   5
Haines City, Fla., 8,956...D5   54
Haines Falls, N.Y., 700...C6   75
Hainesport, N.J., 900.....D3   74
Haiphong, Viet.,
182,496 (369,248 ▲).....A3   19
Haiti, country, N.A.,
5,420,000.............E7   35
Hajdu-Bihar, co., Hung.,
375,371.............*B5   10
Hajduhadház, Hung.,
11,221...............B5   10
Hajdunánás, Hung.,
16,100 (17,824 ▲).....B5   10
Hajduszoboszló, Hung.,
20,789 (21,793 ▲).....B5   10
Hakalau, Haw., 742......D6   56
Hakodate, Jap., 241,663.F10   18
Halawa Heights, Haw.,
5,809................g10   56

Halberstadt, Ger. Dem.
Rep., 46,812..........C5   6
Halden, Nor., 26,700.....H4   11
Haldensleben, Ger. Dem.
Rep., 19,490..........B5   6
Haldimand, co., Ont.,
Can., 30,020..........E5   41
Hale, co., Ala., 15,888....C2   46
Hale, co., Tex., 34,137....B2   84
Haleakala, crater, Haw....C5   56
Hale Center, Tex., 1,964..B2   84
Haledon, N.J., 6,767....*B4   74
Haleiwa, Haw., 2,626..B3, f9   56
Hales Corners, Wis.,
7,771................n11   88
Halesite, N.Y., 4,400....*n15   75
Halethorpe, Md.,
24,000.............B4, h10   53
Haleyville, Ala., 4,190....A2   46
Half Moon Bay, Calif.,
4,038.................k8   50
Halfway, Md., 6,106.....A2   53
Haliburton, Ont., Can.,
853.................B6   41
Haliburton, co., Ont., Can.,
7,768................B6   41
Halifax, N.S., Can., 122,035
(*222,637)...........E6   43

Halifax, Eng., 91,040
(*164,000)..........D6 4
Halifax, N.C., 335.......A5 76
Halifax, Mass., 600
(1,599▲)...........C6 65
Halifax, Pa., 907.......F8 81
Halifax, Va., 899.......D4 85
Halifax, co., N.C.,
53,884.............A5 76
Halifax, co., N.S., Can.,
244,948............E7 43
Halifax, co., Va., 30,076...D4 85
Hall, Aus., 10,016.......E5 6
Hall, co., Ga., 59,405....B3 55
Hall, co., Nebr., 42,851...D7 71
Hall, co., Tex., 6,015....B2 84
Halland, co., Swe.,
189,300............I15 11
Hallandale, Fla.,
23,849.........G6, s13 54
Halle, Ger. Dem. Rep.,
245,681 (*470,000)...C5 6
Hallein, Aus., 14,090....E6 6
Hallettsville, Tex., 2,712...E4 84
Hallock, Minn., 1,477....B2 67
Hallowell, Maine, 2,814...D3 64
Halls, Tenn., 2,323......B2 83
Hallstead, Pa., 1,447....C10 81
Hallsville, Tex., 1,038...C5 84
Halmstad, Swe., 46,912
(*62,526)..........I5 11
Halstad, Minn., 598......C2 67
Halstead, Kans.,
1,716.........E6, g11 61
Haltia, mtn., Fin........C9 11
Haltom City, Tex.,
28,127...........*C4 84
Halton, co., Ont., Can.,
140,800............D4 41
Hamada, Jap., 49,407....I6 18
Hamadān, Iran, 124,167..F7 16
Ḥamāh, Syr., 137,584...E11 14
Hamamatsu, Jap.,
432,221........I8, o16 18
Hamar, Nor., 15,000.....G4 11
Hama-tombetsu, Jap.....D11 18
Hambantota, Sri Lanka,
6,908.............G7 20
Hamblen, co., Tenn.,
38,696............C10 83
Hamburg, Ark., 3,102....D4 49
Hamburg, Ger.,
Fed. Rep. of,
1,766,214 (*2,300,000)..B5 6
Hamburg, Iowa, 1,649....D2 60
Hamburg, N.J., 1,820....A3 74
Hamburg, N.Y., 10,215...C2 75
Hamburg, Pa., 3,909....E10 81
Hamburg, state, Ger., Fed.
Rep. of, 1,800,000...*B5 6
Hamburg, mts., N.J......A3 74
Hamden, Conn., 49,357...D6 52
Hamden, Ohio, 953......C3 78
Häme, prov., Fin.,
619,200..........*G11 11
Hämeenlinna, Fin.,
38,380............G11 11
Hamel, Minn., 2,396....*E5 67
Hameln, Ger., Fed. Rep.
of, 62,845 (*77,000)...B4 6
Hamhung, Kor., 112,184..G3 18
Hami (Kumul) (Qomul),
China, 30,000.......C3 17
Hamilton, Ala., 3,088....A2 46
Hamilton, Austl., 9,662...G7 25
Hamilton, Bermuda,
2,060 (*13,757).......p20 35
Hamilton, Ont., Can.,
309,173 (*498,523)...D5 41
Hamilton, Ill., 2,764....C2 58
Hamilton, Mass., 900
(6,373▲)........A6, f12 65
Hamilton, Mich., 700....F4 66
Hamilton, Mo., 1,645....B3 69
Hamilton, Mont., 2,499...D2 70
Hamilton, N.Y., 3,636....C5 75
Hamilton, N.Z., 77,600
(*83,800)..........L15 26
Hamilton, Ohio, 67,865...C1 78
Hamilton, Scot., 46,376...C4 4
Hamilton, Tex., 2,760....D3 84
Hamilton, co., Fla., 7,787..B3 54
Hamilton, co., Ill., 8,665...E5 58
Hamilton, co., Ind.,
54,532............D5 59
Hamilton, co., Iowa,
18,383............B4 60
Hamilton, co., Kans., 2,747.E2 61
Hamilton, co., Nebr.,
8,867.............D7 71
Hamilton, co., N.Y.,
4,714.............C5 75
Hamilton, co., Ohio,
923,205............C1 78
Hamilton, co., Tenn.,
254,236............D8 83
Hamilton, co., Tex., 7,198..D3 84
Hamilton, mtn., N.Y......B6 75

Hamilton Park, Pa.,
3,800............*G9 81
Hamilton Square, N.J.,
10,000............C3 74
Hamina, Fin., 9,800.....G12 11
Hamiota, Man., Can.,
779...............D1 40
Hamīrpur, India, 10,000...C7 20
Hamlet, N.C., 4,627.....C3 76
Hamlin, Tex., 3,325.....C2 84
Hamlin, co., S. Dak.,
5,520.............F8 77
Hamm [in Westfalen], Ger.,
Fed. Rep. of, 84,370
(*166,000).........C3 6
Hammon, Okla., 677.....B2 79
Hammond, Ind., 107,885..A2 59
Hammond, La.,
12,487.........D5, h11 63
Hammond, Wis., 768.....D1 88
Hammond East, La.,
1,342...........*D5 63
Hammondsport, N.Y.,
1,066.............C3 75
Hammonton, N.J., 11,464..D3 74
Hampden, Newf., Can.,
682...............D3 44
Hampden, Maine, 1,400
(4,693▲).........*D4 64
Hampden, co., Mass.,
459,050............B2 65
Hampden Highlands,
Maine, 800.........D4 64
Hampshire, Ill., 1,611....A5 58
Hampshire, co., Eng.,
1,687,010.........*E6 4
Hampshire, co., Mass.,
123,981............B2 65
Hampshire, co., W. Va.,
11,710............B6 87
Hampstead, Que., Can.,
7,033...........*D4 42
Hampton, Ark., 1,252....D3 49
Hampton, Ga., 1,551....C2 55
Hampton, Iowa, 4,376....B4 60
Hampton, N.H., 5,407....F6 73
Hampton, N.J., 1,380....B3 74
Hampton, S.C., 2,845....F5 82
Hampton, Tenn., 1,000..C11 83
Hampton
(Independent City)
Va., 120,779.....C6, h15 85
Hampton, co., S.C.,
15,878............F5 82
Hampton Bays, N.Y.,
1,862.............n16 75
Hamtramck, Mich.,
27,245............p15 66
Hana, Haw., 459.......C6 56
Hanahan, S.C.,
8,376.........F7, k11 82
Hanamaki, Jap., 37,000
(63,753▲).........G10 18
Hanamaulu, Haw., 2,461..B2 56
Hanapepe, Haw., 1,388...B2 56
Hanau, Ger., Fed. Rep.
of, 57,073..........C4 6
Hanceville, Ala., 2,027....A3 46
Hanchung, China, 70,000..E6 17
Hancock, Md., 1,832.....A1 53
Hancock, Mich., 4,820....A2 66
Hancock, Minn., 806.....B3 67
Hancock, N.Y., 1,688....D5 75
Hancock, co., Ga., 9,019...C3 55
Hancock, co., Ill., 23,645...C2 58
Hancock, co., Ind.,
35,096............E6 59
Hancock, co., Iowa,
13,330............A4 60
Hancock, co., Ky., 7,080...C3 62
Hancock, co., Maine,
34,590............D4 64
Hancock, co., Mich., 4,820..A2 66
Hancock, co., Miss.,
17,387............E4 68
Hancock, co., Ohio,
61,217............A2 78
Hancock, co., Tenn.,
6,719............C10 83
Hancock, co., W. Va.,
39,749............A4 87
Hand, co., S. Dak., 5,883..F6 77
Handa, Jap., 80,663.....o15 18
Handley, W. Va., 460...m13 87
Haney, B.C., Can.,
3,221.........E6, f13 37
Hanford, Calif., 15,179...D4 50
Hanford Northwest, Calif.,
1,364...........*D4 50
Hangchou, China,
875,000............E9 17
Hangö, Fin., 8,200.....H10 11
Hankinson, N. Dak.,
1,125.............D9 77
Hanley Hills, Mo.,
2,807...........*C7 69
Hanna, Alta., Can.,
2,545.............D5 38

Hanna, Wyo., 460.......E6 89
Hanna City, Ill., 1,282....C4 58
Hannibal, Mo., 18,609...B6 69
Hannibal, N.Y., 686.....B4 75
Hannover (Hanover),
Ger., Fed. Rep. of,
511,298 (*845,000)....B4 6
Hanover, Ont., Can.,
5,063.............C3 41
Hanover, Ill., 1,243.....A3 58
Hanover, Ind., 3,018....G7 59
Hanover, Kan., 793......C7 61
Hanover, Mass., 1,500
(10,107▲).......B6, h12 65
Hanover, N.H., 6,147....D3 73
Hanover, N.J., 7,734...*B4 74
Hanover, Pa., 15,623....G8 81
Hanover, co., Va., 37,479..C5 85
Hanover, reg., Ger.,
Fed. Rep. of.........B4 6
Hanover Green, Pa., 700..*D9 81
Hansford, co., Tex., 6,351..A2 84
Hanson, Mass., 800
(7,148▲)..........B6 65
Hanson, co., S. Dak.,
3,781.............G8 77
Hantan, China, 380,000...D7 17
Hants, co., N.S., Can.,
26,893............D6 43
Hantsport, N.S., Can.,
1,381.............D5 43
Haoching, China.......C11 20
Haoli, China, 200,000....C5 18
Hapeville, Ga., 9,567..C2, h8 55
Happy Valley, Newf., Can.,
4,937 (*6,528)....B1, h9 44
Harahan, La., 13,037....k11 63
Haralson, co., Ga., 15,927..C1 55
Harar, Eth., 48,440.....G6 23
Harbin, see Haehpin, China
Harbor Beach, Mich.,
2,134.............E8 66
Harborcreek, Pa., 800...B2 81
Harbor Isle, N.Y., 1,300..*E7 75
Harbor Springs, Mich.,
1,662.............C6 66
Harbour Breton, Newf.,
Can., 2,196........E4 44
Harbour Grace, Newf.,
Can., 2,771........E5 44
Harbour Main, Newf.,
Can., 469..........E5 44
Hardee, co., Fla., 14,889..E5 54
Hardeeville, S.C., 853....G5 82
Hardeman, co., Tenn.,
22,435............B2 83
Hardeman, co., Tex.,
6,795.............B3 84
Hardin, Ill., 1,035......D3 58
Hardin, Mo., 683.......B4 69
Hardin, co., Ill., 4,914....F5 58
Hardin, co., Iowa, 22,248..B4 60
Hardin, co., Ky., 78,421...C3 62
Hardin, co., Mont., 2,733..E9 70
Hardin, co., Ohio, 30,813..B2 78
Hardin, co., Tenn.,
18,212............B3 83
Hardin, co., Tex., 29,996..D5 84
Harding, co., N. Mex.,
1,348.............B7 48
Harding, co., S. Dak.,
1,855.............E2 77
Hardinsburg, Ky., 1,547...C3 62
Hardshell, Ky., 350.....C6 62
Hardwār, India, 77,864
(*79,277)..........C6 20
Hardwick, Ga., 6,000....C3 55
Hardwick, Vt., 1,503....B3 73
Hardy, co., W. Va., 8,855..B6 87
Hare Bay, Newf., Can.,
1,467.............D4 44
Harfleur, Fr., 10,514....C4 5
Harford, co., Md.,
115,378............A5 53
Hargeisa, Som., 42,000..G6 23
Harihar, India, 33,888....F6 20
Harkers Island, N.C.,
1,633.............C6 76
Harlan, Iowa, 5,049.....C2 60
Harlan, Ky., 3,318......D6 62
Harlan, co., Ky., 37,370...D6 62
Harlan, co., Nebr., 4,357..D6 71
Harlem, Fla., 1,256.....F6 54
Harlem, Ga., 1,540.....C4 55
Harlem, Mont., 1,094....B8 70
Harlingen, Neth., 13,853..A6 5
Harlingen, Tex., 33,503
(*56,800)..........F4 84
Harlow, Eng., 77,920...k13 4
Harlowton, Mont.,
1,375.............D7 70
Harmarville, Pa., 1,300..h14 81
Harmon, co., Okla.,
5,136.............C2 79
Harmony, Ind., 750.....E3 59
Harmony, Minn., 1,130...G6 67

Harmony, Pa., 1,207.....E1 81
Harnett, co., N.C., 49,667..B4 76
Harney, co., Oreg., 7,215..D7 80
Harney, peak, S. Dak....F2 77
Harnösand, Swe., 24,128..F8 11
Haro, Sp., 8,554........A4 8
Harper, Kans., 1,665....E5 61
Harper, Lib., 8,000.....H3 22
Harper, co., Kans.,
7,871.............E5 61
Harper, co., Okla., 5,151..A2 79
Harper Woods, Mich.,
20,186..........*F7 66
Harrah, Okla., 1,931....B4 79
Harriman, Tenn., 8,734...D1 83
Harrington, Del., 2,407...C6 53
Harrington Park, N.J.,
4,841.............h9 74
Harris, co., Ga., 11,520...D1 55
Harris, co., Tex.,
1,741,912...........E5 84
Harris, hill, Mass.......A3 65
Harrisburg, Ark., 1,931...B5 49
Harrisburg, Ill., 9,535....F5 58
Harrisburg, Oreg., 1,311..C3 80
Harrisburg, Pa., 68,061
(*355,100)..........F8 81
Harris Hill, N.Y., 5,000..*C2 75
Harrison, Ark., 7,239....A2 49
Harrison, Mich., 1,460...D6 66
Harrison, N.J., 11,811....k8 74
Harrison, N.Y.,
13,000........D2, h13 75
Harrison, Ohio, 4,408....C3 78
Harrison, co., Ind.,
20,423............H5 59
Harrison, co., Iowa,
16,240............C2 60
Harrison, co., Ky.,
14,158............B5 62
Harrison, co., Miss.,
134,582............E4 68
Harrison, co., Mo.,
10,257............A3 69
Harrison, co., Ohio,
17,013............B4 78
Harrison, co., Tex.,
44,841............C5 84
Harrison, co., W. Va.,
73,028............B4 87
Harrisonburg, La., 626...C4 63
Harrisonburg (Independent
City), Va., 14,605....B4 85
Harrisonville, Mo., 5,052..C3 69
Harriston, Ont., Can.,
1,631.............D4 41
Harrisville, Pa., 944.....D2 81
Harrisville, R.I., 1,053...B10 52
Harrisville, W. Va., 1,464..B3 87
Harrisville, N.Y., 836....A5 75
Harrodsburg, Ky., 6,741...C5 62
Harrogate, Eng., 63,470...C6 4
Harrow, Ont., Can.,
1,787.............E2 41
Hart, Mich., 2,139......E4 66
Hart, co., Ga., 15,814....B3 55
Hart, co., Ky., 13,980....C4 62
Hart, mtn., Man., Can....C1 40
Hartford, Ala., 2,648....D4 46
Hartford, Conn.,
158,017 (*1,036,900)..B6 52
Hartford, Ill., 2,243.....E3 58
Hartford, Ky., 1,868....C3 62
Hartford, Mich., 2,508...F4 66
Hartford, Wis.,
6,499.........E5, m11 88
Hartford, co., Conn.,
816,737............B5 52
Hartford City, Ind.,
8,207.............D7 59
Hartington, Nebr., 1,581..B8 71
Hartland, N.B., Can.,
1,025.............C2 43
Hartland, Maine, 950
(1,414▲)...........D3 64
Hartland, Wis.,
2,763.........E5, m11 88
Hartlepool, Eng., 97,110..C6 4
Hartley, Iowa, 1,694....A2 60
Hartley, co., Tex., 2,782..B1 84
Hartsdale, N.Y., 12,226..*D7 75
Hartselle, Ala., 7,355....A3 46
Hartshorne, Okla., 2,121..C6 79
Hartsville, S.C., 8,017....C7 82
Hartsville, Tenn., 2,243...A5 83
Hartville, Ohio, 1,752....B4 78
Hartwell, Ga., 4,865....B4 55
Hartwick, N.Y., 600.....C5 75
Harvard, Ill., 5,177.....A5 58
Harvard, Nebr., 1,230...D7 71
Harvard, mtn., Colo.....C4 51
Harvey, Ill., 34,636...B6, k9 58
Harvey, La., 10,000...E5, k11 63
Harvey, Mich., 900.....B3 66
Harvey, N. Dak., 2,361...C6 77
Harvey, co., Kans.,
27,236............D6 61
Harvey, mtn., Mass......B1 65

I

Iserlohn, Ger., Fed. Rep.
of, 57,078 (*97,000).... *C3   6
Isernia, It., 8,600...........D5   9
Isesaki, Jap., 91,277..H9, m18   18
Iseyin, Nig., 95,220........G5   22
Ishikawa, pref., Jap.,
1,002,420............*H8   18
Ishim, Sov. Un., 56,000....D9   13
Ishimbay, Sov. Un.,
54,000.............*D8   13
Ishinomaki, Jap.,
106,681.............G10   18
Ishioka, Jap., 27,500
(39,508*)............m19   18
Ishpeming, Mich., 8,245...B3   66
Isigny-sur-Mer, Fr., 2,391..C3   5
Isiro (Paulis), Zaire,
9,700...............H3   23
İskenderun (Alexandretta),
Tur., 79,297........D11   14
İskilip, Tur., 16,129......B10   14
Isla Cristina, Sp., 8,276....D2   8
Islāmābād, Pak., 77,000...B5   20
Islamorada, Fla., 700......H6   54
Island, co., Wash., 27,011..A3   86
Island Falls, Maine, 800
(913 ▲)...........B4   64
Island Heights, N.J.,
1,397.............D4   74
Island Lake, Ill., 1,973...*E2   58
Island Park, N.Y., 5,396..*E7   75
Island Pond, Vt., 1,123....B4   73
Islay, isl., U.K..........C3   4
Isle, Minn., 551.........D5   67
Isle-aux-Morts, Newf.,
Can., 884..........E2   44
Isle of Ely, co., Eng.,
89,112............*D7   4
Isle of Man, Br. dep; Eur.,
58,000............*C4   4
Isle of Man, isl., U.K......C4   4
Isle of Palms, S.C.,
2,657............k12   82

Isle of Wight, co., Eng.,
102,100...........*E6   4
Isle of Wight, co., Va.,
18,285.............D6   85
Isle of Wight, isl., U.K.....E6   4
Isle Royale, isl., Mich.....h9   66
Isleton, Calif., 909.......C3   50
Isle-Verte, Que., Can.,
1,360.............A8   42
Islington, Mass., 4,500....h11   65
Islip, N.Y., 12,100.......n15   75
Islip Terrace, N.Y.,
5,100............*n15   75
Isola Capo Rizzuto, It.,
9,218.............E6   9
Isparta, Tur., 50,905......D8   14
Israel, country, Asia,
3,195,000...........C2   15
Issaquah, Wash., 4,313....e11   86
Issaquena, co., Miss.,
2,737.............C2   68
Issoire, Fr., 11,886.......E5   5
Issoudun, Fr., 13,900......D4   5
Issyk-kul, lake, Sov. Un...E10   13
Issy [les-Moulineaux], Fr.,
50,442............g10   5
İstanbul (Constantinople),
Tur., 2,132,407
(*2,825,000)........B7   14
Istmina, Col., 3,996......B2   32
Itá, Par., 18,777.........E4   29
Itabaiana, Braz.,
16,425............*E7   27
Itabaiana, Braz.,
14,148............*D7   27
Itaberaba, Braz., 16,003..*E6   27
Itabira, Braz., 40,143.....B4   30
Itabuna, Braz., 89,928....E7   27
Itajaí, Braz., 54,135......D3   30
Itajubá, Braz., 42,485.....C3   30
Italy, Tex., 1,309.........C4   84
Italy, country, Eur.,
54,980,000..............   9

Itami, Jap., 153,763......o14   18
Itaperuna, Braz., 26,508...C4   30
Itapetininga, Braz.,
42,331...........C3, m7   30
Itapeva, Braz., 24,220.....C3   30
Itápolis, Braz., 9,372......k7   30
Itapúa, dept., Par.,
149,821............E4   29
Itaqui, Braz., 17,262......D1   30
Itararé, Braz., 15,696.....C3   30
Itasca, Ill., 4,638........k8   58
Itasca, Tex., 1,483.......C4   84
Itasca, co., Minn.,
35,530.............C5   67
Itatiba, Braz., 20,765.....m8   30
Itaúna, Braz., 32,731.....C4   30
Itawamba, co., Miss.,
16,847.............A5   68
Ithaca, Mich., 2,749......E6   66
Ithaca, N.Y., 26,226......C4   75
Itō, Jap., 63,003.........o18   18
Itoigawa, Jap., 22,000
(38,395 ▲)..........H8   18
Itta Bena, Miss., 2,489....B3   68
Itu, Braz., 35,907.....C3, m8   30
Ituango, Col., 3,466......B2   32
Ituiutaba, Braz., 46,784...B3   30
Ituna, Sask., Can., 837....F4   39
Itzehoe, Ger., Fed. Rep.
of, 36,178..........B4   6
Iuka, Miss., 2,389........A5   68
Iva, S.C., 1,114.........C2   82
Ivanhoe, Calif., 1,595....*D4   50
Ivanhoe, Minn., 738......F2   67
Ivanhoe, Va., 500........D2   85
Ivano-Frankovsk, Sov. Un.,
105,000............G5   12
Ivanovka, Sov. Un.,
5,000.............q21   12
Ivanovo, Sov. Un.,
420,000............C13   12
Ivanteyevka, Sov. Un.,
36,000............n17   12

Ivory Coast, country, Afr.,
4,695,000...........G3   22
Ivoryton, Conn., 950......D7   52
Ivrea, It., 28,600........B1   9
Ivry-sur-Seine, Fr.,
60,455............g10   5
Ivywild, Colo., 4,000.....C6   51
Iwaki (Tairi), Jap.,
260,000 (327,164 ▲)....H10   18
Iwaki-yama, mtn., Jap...F10   18
Iwakuni, Jap., 106,116....I6   18
Iwamizawa, Jap., 54,000
(68,712▲).........E10   18
Iwanai, Jap., 25,799....E10   18
Iwate, pref., Jap.,
1,371,383..........*G10   18
Iwate-yama, mtn., Jap...G10   18
Iwo, Nig., 158,583......G5   22
Ixmiquilpan, Mex.,
6,048.............m14   34
Ixtacalco, Mex., 48,954...h9   34
Ixtacihuatl, mtn., Mex.....n14   34
Ixtapalapa, Mex., 41,243...h9   34
Ixtlán de Juárez, Mex.,
1,396.............o15   34
Ixtlán del Río, Mex.,
10,986.........C4, m11   34
Izamal, Mex., 9,749......C7   34
Izard, co., Ark., 7,381....A4   49
Izhevsk, Sov. Un.,
422,000............D8   13
Izmail, Sov. Un., 70,000...I7   12
İzmir (Smyrna), Tur.,
520,832 (*760,000)....C6   14
İzmit (Kocaeli), Tur.,
120,694............B7   14
Izúcar de Matamoros,
Mex., 21,164......n14   34
Izuhara, Jap., 9,131......I4   18
Izumo, Jap., 46,000
(69,078▲)...........I6   18
Izyum, Sov. Un., 52,000..G11   12

J

Jabalpur (Jubbulpore),
India, 426,224
(*534,845)...........D6   20
Jaboatão, Braz., 52,537...*D7   27
Jaboticabal, Braz.,
29,019..........C3, k7   30
Jaca, Sp., 9,856.........A5   8
Jacala de Ledesma,
Mex., 2,160........m14   34
Jacareí, Braz., 48,684.....m9   30
Jacarèzinho, Braz.,
19,161............C3   30
Jáchymov, Czech., 6,806...C2   7
Jacinto City, Tex., 9,563...r14   84
Jack, co., Tex., 6,711.....C3   84
Jack, mtn., Mont........D4   70
Jack, mtn., Va..........B3   85
Jackfork, mtn., Okla......C6   79
Jacks, mtn., Pa.........E6   81
Jacksboro, Tex., 3,554....C3   84
Jackson, Ala., 5,957......D2   46
Jackson, Calif., 1,924.....C3   50
Jackson, Ga., 3,778......C3   55
Jackson, Ky., 1,887......C6   62
Jackson, La., 4,697......D4   63
Jackson, Mich., 45,484
(*131,100)...........F6   66
Jackson, Minn., 3,550.....G3   67
Jackson, Miss., 153,968
(*239,100)..........C3   68
Jackson, Mo., 5,896......D8   69
Jackson, N.C., 762.......A5   76
Jackson, Ohio, 6,843......C3   78
Jackson, S.C., 1,928......E4   82
Jackson, Tenn., 39,996
(*52,300)..........B3   83
Jackson, Wyo., 2,688.....C2   89
Jackson, co., Ala., 39,202..A3   46
Jackson, co., Ark., 20,452..B4   49
Jackson, co., Colo., 1,811..A4   51
Jackson, co., Fla., 34,434..B1   54
Jackson, co., Ga., 21,093..B3   55
Jackson, co., Ill., 55,008...F4   58
Jackson, co., Ind., 33,187..G5   59
Jackson, co., Iowa,
20,839............B7   60
Jackson, co., Kans.,
10,342............C8   61
Jackson, co., Ky., 10,005...C5   62

Jackson, co., Mich.,
143,274............F6   66
Jackson, co., Minn.,
14,352............G3   67
Jackson, co., Miss.,
87,975.............E5   68
Jackson, co., Mo.,
654,558............C3   69
Jackson, co., N.C., 21,593..f9   76
Jackson, co., Ohio,
27,174.............C3   78
Jackson, co., Okla.,
30,902.............C2   79
Jackson, co., Oreg.,
94,533.............E3   80
Jackson, co., S. Dak.,
1,531.............G4   77
Jackson, co., Tenn., 8,141..C8   83
Jackson, co., Tex.,
12,975.............E4   84
Jackson, co., W. Va.,
20,903.............C3   87
Jackson, co., Wis., 15,325..D3   88
Jackson, par., La., 15,963..B3   63
Jackson, mtn., Maine.....D2   64
Jackson Center, Ohio,
1,119.............B1   78
Jacksonville, Ala., 7,715...B4   46
Jacksonville, Ark.,
19,832..........C3, h10   49
Jacksonville, Fla., 528,865
(*548,500).......B5, m8   54
Jacksonville, Ill., 20,553...D3   58
Jacksonville, N.C.,
16,289.............C5   76
Jacksonville, Oreg., 1,611..E4   80
Jacksonville, Tex., 9,734...D5   84
Jacksonville Beach, Fla.B5, m9   54
Jacmel, Hai., 11,391......E7   35
Jacobābād, Pak., 35,278...C4   20
Jacobina, Braz., 18,892...*E6   27
Jacomino, Cuba, 6,121...*C2   35
Jacques Cartier, mtn.,
Que..............k13   42
Jaén, Sp., 77,317........D4   8
Jaén, prov., Sp., 702,900..*D4   8
Jaffna, Sri Lanka, 107,663.G7   20
Jaffrey, N.H., 1,922
(3,353▲)...........F3   73

Jaguarão, Braz., 16,541....E2   30
Jagüey Grande, Cuba,
8,700 (17,100 ▲).......C3   35
Jaipur, India, 615,258.....C6   20
Jaisalmer, India, 16,578...C5   20
Jajce, Yugo., 6,853.......C3   10
Jājpur, India, 16,707......D8   20
Jakarta (Djakarta), Indon.,
4,576,009...........G3   19
Jakobstad (Pietersaari)
Fin., 19,333........F10   11
Jal, N. Mex., 2,602.......C7   48
Jalalabad, Afg., 14,756....B5   20
Jalapa, Guat., 13,819....*F6   34
Jalapa Enríquez, Mex.,
122,377........D5, n15   34
Jalca Grande, Peru,
1,189.............C2   31
Jālgaon, India, 106,711....D6   20
Jalisco, state, Mex.,
2,857,200........C4, m12   34
Jālna, India, 91,099.......E6   20
Jalpa, Mex., 9,904...C4, m12   34
Jalpan, Mex., 1,878..C5, m14   34
Jamaica, country, N.A.,
1,960,000...........E5   35
Jambi, Indon., 158,559....F2   19
James, riv., S. Dak.......F7   77
Jamesburg, N.J., 4,584....C4   74
James City, N.C., 500.....B5   76
James City, co., Va.,
17,853.............C6   85
Jamesport, Mo., 614......B4   69
Jamestown, Calif., 950....D3   50
Jamestown, Ind., 938.....E4   59
Jamestown, Ky., 1,027....D4   62
Jamestown, N.Y., 39,795..C1   75
Jamestown, N.C., 1,297...B3   76
Jamestown, N. Dak.,
15,385............D7   77
Jamestown, Ohio, 1,790...C2   78
Jamestown, Pa., 937......D1   81
Jamestown, R.I., 2,911...D11   52
Jamestown, Tenn.,
1,899.............C9   83
Jamestown, N.Y., 1,000...*C4   75
Jamiltepec, Mex., 5,280...D5   34
Jammu, India,
155,338 (*164,207)....B5   20

Jammu and Kashmir,
Disputed reg., India,
Pak., 4,616,632........B6   20
Jāmnagar, India, 199,709
(*277,640)..........D5   20
Jamshedpur, India,
341,576 (*456,146).....D8   20
Jämtland, co., Swe.,
127,900............*F6   11
Janesville, Iowa., 741.....B5   60
Janesville, Minn., 1,557...F5   67
Janesville, Wis., 46,426
(*59,200)...........F4   88
Janīn, Jordan, 13,365.....B3   15
Janos, Mex., 1,178.......A3   34
Jánoshalma, Hung.,
10,767............B4   10
Janów Lubelski, Pol.,
4,708.............C7   7
Januária, Braz., 13,605....B4   30
Jaoho (Tuanshantzu), China,
30,000............B11   17
Japan, country, Asia.,
108,960,000..........I6   18
Japan, sea, Asia..........F6   18
Jaral [del Progreso], Mex.,
8,689.............m13   34
Jarales, N. Mex., 300.....B5   48
Jarocin, Pol., 18,100......C4   7
Jarosław, Pol., 26,500....C7   7
Jarvis, Ont., Can., 783....E4   41
Jarvisburg, N.C., 150.....A7   76
Jasonville, Ind., 2,335.....F3   59
Jasper, Ala., 10,798......B2   46
Jasper, Alta., Can., 2,932..C1   38
Jasper, Fla., 2,221.......B4   54
Jasper, Ga., 1,202.......B2   55
Jasper, Ind., 8,641.......H4   59
Jasper, Minn., 754.......G2   67
Jasper, Mo., 796........D3   69
Jasper, Tenn., 1,839......D8   83
Jasper, Tex., 6,251.......D6   84
Jasper, co., Ga., 5,760....C3   55
Jasper, co., Ill., 10,741....D5   58
Jasper, co., Ind., 20,429...B3   59
Jasper, co., Iowa, 35,425..C4   60
Jasper, co., Miss., 15,994..C4   68
Jasper, co., Mo., 79,852...D3   69
Jasper, co., S.C., 11,885...G5   82
Jasper, co., Tex., 24,692...D5   84

K

Kingston, Ohio, 1,157.....C3 78
Kingston, Okla., 710......D5 79
Kingston, Pa., 18,325..........D10, n17 81
Kingston, R.I., 5,601.....D10 52
Kingston, Tenn., 4,142....D9 83
Kingston, W. Va., 400..............D3, n13 87
Kingstree, S.C., 3,381.....D8 82
Kingsville, Ont., Can., 4,076................E2 41
Kingsville, Ohio, 1,129....A5 78
Kingsville, Tex., 28,915....F4 84
King William, co., Va., 7,497................C5 85
King William's Town, S. Afr., 15,429.........G5 24
Kingwood, W. Va., 2,550..B5 87
Kinistino, Sask., Can., 764..................E3 39
Kinloch, Mo., 5,629......f13 69
Kinmundy, Ill., 759.......E5 58
Kinnaird, B.C., Can., 2,846................E9 37
Kinnelon, N.J., 7,600.....B4 74
Kinney, co., Tex., 2,006...E2 84
Kinomoto, Jap..........n15 18
Kinross, co., Scot., 6,371..*B5 4
Kinshasa (Leopoldville), Zaire, 901,500.........A3 24
Kinsley, Kans., 2,212.....E4 61
Kinsman, Ohio, 700......A5 78
Kinston, N.C., 23,020.....B5 76
Kinwood, Tex., 1,800....*E5 84
Kiowa, Kans., 1,414......E5 61
Kiowa, Okla., 754........C6 79
Kiowa, co., Colo., 2,029...C8 51
Kiowa, co., Kans., 4,088...E4 61
Kiowa, co., Okla., 12,532................C2 79
Kiparissia, Grc., 3,882.....D3 14
Kipling, Sask., Can., 773..G4 39
Kippens, Newf., Can., 1,079...............*D2 44
Kipushi, Zaire, 15,100.....C5 24
Kirbyville, Tex., 1,869....D6 84
Kirensk, Sov. Un., 14,500...............D13 13
Kirghiz, S.S.R., rep., Sov. Un., 3,130,000....E10 16
Kırıkkale, Tur., 91,658...*C9 14
Kirin, prov., China, 12,550,000............C9 17
Kirkağaç, Tur., 14,072....C6 14
Kirkcaldy, Scot., 50,091 (*138,000)............B5 4
Kirkcudbright, co., Scot., 27,448...............*C4 4
Kirkland, Ill., 1,138.......A5 58
Kirkland, Wash., 14,970...........B3, e11 86
Kirkland Lake, Ont., Can., 13,599...............o19 41
Kirklareli, Tur., 27,431....B6 14
Kirklin, Ind., 736.........D5 59
Kirksville, Mo., 15,560....A5 69
Kirkūk, Iraq, 167,413....E15 14
Kirkwood, Md., 2,500....*C3 53
Kirkwood, Mo., 31,890....f13 69
Kirn, Ger., Fed. Rep. of, 10,545................D3 6
Kirov, Sov. Un., 333,000..D7 13
Kirovabad, Sov. Un., 190,000...............E7 13
Kirovograd, Sov. Un., 189,000...............G9 12
Kirovsk, Sov. Un., 45,000...............C6 13
Kirsanov, Sov. Un., 22,000...............E14 12
Kirşehir, Tur., 33,173....C10 14
Kirtland, Ohio, 5,530....*A4 78
Kiruna, Swe., 26,160......D9 11
Kiryū, Jap., 132,000..........H9, m18 18
Kisangani (Stanleyville), Zaire, 149,900.........H3 23
Kisarazu, Jap., 73,319....n18 18
Kiselevsk, Sov. Un., 127,000.............*D11 13
Kishangarh, India, 37,405...............C5 20
Kishinev, Sov. Un., 374,000...............H7 12
Kishiwada, Jap., 162,022...............o14 18
Kishorganj, Bngl., 19,067..D9 20
Kiskoros, Hung., 9,972....B4 10
Kiskundorozsma, Hung., 8,705................B5 10
Kiskunfelegyháza, Hung., 25,871 (34,127 ▲).......B4 10
Kiskunhalas, Hung., 20,787 (28,447 ▲).......B4 10
Kiskunmajsa, Hung., 7,611................B4 10
Kislovodsk, Sov. Un., 90,000...............*E7 13
Kiso-sammyaku, mts., Jap...................n16 18
Kissimmee, Fla., 7,119....D5 54
Kistler, W. Va., 500...D3, D5 87
Kisújszállás, Hung., 11,802 (13,391 ▲).......B5 10
Kisumu, Ken., 23,526......I4 23
Kisvárda, Hung., 13,759...A6 10
Kita-dake, mtn., Jap.......I9 18
Kitakyūshū, Jap., 1,051,076 (*1,470,000)...J5 18
Kitale, Ken., 9,342.......H4 23
Kitami, Jap., 66,000 (82,727 ▲)...........E11 18
Kit Carson, co., Colo., 7,530..................B8 51
Kitchener, Ont., Can., 111,804 (*226,846)......D4 41
Kitimat, B.C., Can., 11,824................B3 37
Kitsap, co., Wash., 101,732................B3 86
Kittanning, Pa., 6,231.....E2 81
Kittery, Maine, 7,363 (11,028▲)...............E2 64
Kittery Point, Maine, 1,172.................E2 64
Kittitas, co., Wash., 25,039................B5 86
Kitts, Ky., 500..........D6 62
Kittson, co., Minn., 6,853..................B2 67
Kitwe, Zam., 146,000....*C5 24
Kitzbühel, Aus., 8,003......E6 6
Kitzingen, Ger., Fed. Rep. of, 17,775........D5 6
Kitzmiller, Md., 443.....m12 53
Kizel, Sov. Un., 46,000...*D8 13
Kizyl-Arvat, Sov. Un., 22,000...............F8 13
Kladno, Czech., 56,935 (*73,000)...C3, n17 7
Klagenfurt, Aus., 82,512...E7 6
Klaipeda (Memel), Sov. Un., 140,000.......D3 12
Klamath, co., Oreg., 50,021................E4 80
Klamath, mts., Calif.......B2 50
Klamath Falls, Oreg., 15,775................E5 80
Klamath Glen, Calif., 600...................B2 50
Klatovy, Czech., 16,852...D2 7
Kleberg, Tex., 4,768.....*C4 84
Kleberg, co., Tex., 33,166................F4 84
Klemme, Iowa, 554.......A4 60
Kletnya, Sov. Un., 10,000................E9 12
Kletsk, Sov. Un., 10,000...E6 12
Kleve, Ger., Fed. Rep. of, 43,481................C3 6
Klickitat, Wash., 700......D4 86
Klickitat, co., Wash., 12,138................D5 86
Klintsy, Sov. Un., 58,000..E9 12
Ključ, Yugo., 2,322........C3 10
Kłobuck, Pol., 12,600......C5 7
Kłodzko, Pol., 26,000......C4 7
Klosterneuburg, Aus., 21,989................D8 6
Kluczbork, Pol., 18,000....C5 7
Klyuchevskaya, vol., Sov. Un.............D19 13
Knezha, Bul., 14,049......D7 10
Knightdale, N.C., 815.....B4 76
Knights Landing, Calif., 900....................C3 50
Knightstown, Ind., 2,456..E6 59
Knightsville, Ind., 788.....E3 59
Knittlefeld, Aus., 14,494...E7 6
Knob Noster, Mo., 2,264..C4 69
Knockmealdown, mts., Ire.D2 4
Knollwood, Ohio, 5,353..*C2 78
Knoolwood Park, Mich., 350.................*F6 66
Knott, co., Ky., 14,698....C6 62
Knox, Ind., 3,519.........B4 59
Knox, Pa., 1,306........*E1 81
Knox, co., Ill., 61,280.....B3 58
Knox, co., Ind., 41,546....G3 59
Knox, co., Ky., 23,689.....D6 62
Knox, co., Maine, 29,013..D4 64
Knox, co., Mo., 5,692......A5 69
Knox, co., Nebr., 11,723...B8 71
Knox, co., Ohio, 41,795...B3 78
Knox, co., Tenn., 276,293 ....C10 83
Knox, co., Tex., 5,972......C3 84
Knox City, Tex., 1,536.....C3 84
Knoxville, Ill., 2,930......C3 58
Knoxville, Iowa, 7,755....C4 60
Knoxville, Tenn., 174,587 (*415,800).......D10, n14 83
Knysna, S. Afr., 13,304....G4 24
Kōbe, Jap., 1,338,705.....o14 18
Kobelyaki, Sov. Un., 10,000...............G10 12
København (Copenhagen), co., Den., 1,467,200....*J5 11
Koblenz, Ger., Fed. Rep. of, 119,781 (*172,000)...C3 6
Kobrin, Sov. Un., 25,000..E5 12
Kočani, Yugo., 17,237......E6 10
Koch, mtn., Mont.........E5 70
Kochi, Jap., 240,481.......J6 18
Kochi, pref., Jap., 786,882.*J6 18
Kochiu, China, 180,000...G5 17
Kodaira, Jap., 137,373..*n18 18
Kodak, Ky., 90..........C6 62
Kodiak, Alsk., 3,798......D9 47
Kodiak, isl., Alsk.........D9 47
Koforidua, Ghana, 34,900.G4 22
Kofu, Jap., 182,669...I9, n17 18
Koga, Jap., 54,173......m18 18
Kohala, Haw., 237........C6 56
Kohāt, Pak., 36,016 (*49,854)..............B5 20
Kohler, Wis., 1,738...E5, k10 88
Kokand, Sov. Un., 133,000...............E10 13
Kokchetav, Sov. Un., 81,000...............D9 13
Kokkola, Fin., 21,347....F10 11
Kokomo, Ind., 44,042 (*81,200)..............D5 59
Kokonor, lake, China.....D4 17
Kokstad, S. Afr., 9,268....G5 24
Kolār Gold Fields, India 76,112 (*118,861).......F6 20
Kolarovo, Bul., 31,169....D8 10
Kolárovo, Czech., 10,829..E4 7
Kolhāpur, India, 259,050 (*267,513)..............E5 20
Kolín, Czech., 26,519.....C3 7
Köln, see Cologne, Ger.
Koło, Pol., 13,100........B5 7
Koloa, Haw., 1,368.......B2 56
Kolomna, Sov. Un., 136,000..........D12, n18 12
Kolomyya, Sov. Un., 41,000...............G5 12
Kolonodale, Indon.........F6 19
Kolpino, Sov. Un., 62,000...............s31 11
Kolwezi, Zaire, 48,000....C5 24
Kolyberovo, Sov. Un., 10,000................n18 12
Kolyma, riv., Sov. Un....C18 16
Komádi, Hung., 7,362.....B5 10
Komandorski Village, Calif., 900...........*D2 50
Komárno, Czech., 27,282..E5 7
Komarno, Sov. Un., 5,000.D7 7
Komárom, Hung., 11,271..B4 10
Komárom, co., Hung., 301,853...............*B4 10
Komatsu, Jap., 95,684....H8 18
Komatsushima, Jap., 31,000 (40,507 ▲)........I7 18
Kommunarsk, Sov. Un., 123,000.........G12, q21 12
Komotiní, Grc., 28,896....B5 14
Kompong Cham, Camb., 28,000...............*C2 19
Kompong Chhnang, Camb., 12,900.........*C2 19
Kompong Kleang, Camb., 10,000...............*C2 19
Kompong Speu, Camb., 7,500...............*C2 19
Kompong Thom, Camb., 9,600................C2 19
Komrat, Sov. Un., 21,400.H7 12
Komsomolsk [-na Amure], Sov. Un., 218,000.......D16 13
Konawa, Okla., 1,719.....C5 79
Kondoa, Tan., 2,816......A7 24
Kondopoga, Sov. Un., 5,000.................F16 11
Kong, reg., I.C...........G4 22
Kongju, Kor., 27,500 (33,210 ▲).......H3 18
Kongsberg, Nor., 18,100...H3 11
Konin, Pol., 40,600.......B5 7
Konosha, Sov. Un., 10,000..............A13 12
Konotop, Sov. Un., 68,000................F9 12
Końskie, Pol., 13,100.....C6 7
Konstantinovka, Sov. Un., 105,000................q20 12
Konstanz, Ger., Fed. Rep. of, 65,203................E4 6
Kontum, Viet., 8,760......C3 19
Konya, Tur., 200,464.....D9 14
Konyang, Kor., 2,300 (10,760 ▲).............I3 18
Koochiching, co., Minn., 17,131.................B4 67
Koontz Lake, Ind., 900...B5 59
Kooskia, Idaho, 809.......C3 57
Kootenai, co., Idaho, 35,332...............B2 57
Kopeysk, Sov. Un., 156,000...............*D9 13
Köping, Swe., 22,155..H6, t33 11
Kopparberg, co., Swe., 280,000..............*G6 11
Koppel, Pa., 1,312........E1 81
Koprivnica, Yugo., 16,469..B3 10
Kopychintsy, Sov. Un., 10,000................G5 12
Korçë, Alb., 45,900.......B3 14
Korçë, pref., Alb., 175,000...............*B3 14
Korea, North, country, Asia, 15,275,000........F4 18
Korea, South, country, Asia, 34,170,000........H4 18
Korets, Sov. Un., 10,000...F6 12
Korhogo, I.C., 14,000.....G3 22
Kórinthos (Corinth), Grc., 20,773................D4 14
Kóriyama, Jap., 165,000 (241,673▲)...........H10 18
Korkino, Sov. Un., 71,000.*D9 13
Korla, see Kuerhlo, China
Körmend, Hung., 7,581....B3 10
Korneuburg, Aus., 8,751...D8 6
Koropí, Grc., 9,367......h11 14
Korosten, Sov. Un., 56,000.................F7 12
Korsakov, Sov., Un., 38,000...............E17 13
Kortrijk, Bel., 45,040 (*168,000)............B5 5
Kos, Grc., 7,828..........D6 14
Kościan, Pol., 18,700.......B4 7
Kościerzyna, Pol., 14,900...A4 7
Kosciusko, Miss., 6,800....B4 68
Kosciusko, co., Ind., 48,127................B6 59
Kosciusko, mtn., Austl. ...G8 25
Koshan, China, 25,000...B10 17
Košice, Czech., 142,233...D6 7
Kosong, Kor., 14,842......G4 18
Kosove (Kosovo), pref., Alb., 53,000...........*A3 14
Kosovska Mitrovica, Yugo., 42,241................D5 10
Kossuth, co., Iowa, 22,937................A3 60
Kostroma, Sov. Un., 223,000...............C13 12
Kostrzyn, Pol., 11,200.....B3 7
Koszalin, Pol., 64,400.....A4 7
Koszeg, Hung., 10,164.....B3 10
Kota, India, 212,991......C6 20
Kota Baharu, Mala., 55,124 (*69,812).......D2 19
Kotabaru, Indon., 330.....F5 19
Kota Kinabalu, Mala., 40,939...............I14 19
Kotelnikovskiy, Sov. Un., 17,605...............H14 12
Köthen, Ger. Dem. Rep., 35,723................C5 6
Kotka, Fin., 33,862.......G12 11
Kotlas, Sov. Un., 56,000...C7 13
Kotor, Yugo., 4,833.......D4 10
Kotovsk, Sov. Un., 33,000................H7 12
Kotung, China, 5,000.....B7 18
Kotzebue, Alsk., 1,696....*B7 47
Koudougou, Upper Volta, 8,000................F4 22
Kountze, Tex., 2,173......D5 84
Kouts, Ind., 1,388.........B3 59
Kouvola, Fin., 27,148....G12 11
Kovel, Sov. Un., 33,000...F5 12
Kovrov, Sov. Un., 123,000...............C13 12
Kowa, Jap., 10,300.......o15 18
Kowloon, Hong Kong, 715,440...............G7 17
Kowon, Kor., 5,000.......G3 18
Kozan, Tur., 26,097.....D10 14
Kozáni, Grc., 23,240......B3 14
Kozáni, prov., Grc., 135,619...............*B3 14
Kozienice, Pol., 6,109.....C6 7
Koźle, Pol., 13,100.......C5 7
Kozloduy, Bul., 7,422.....D6 10
Kożuchów, Pol., 7,419.....C3 7
Kragujevac, Yugo., 71,180................D5 10
Kraków, Pol., 583,400.....C5 7
Kraljevo, Yugo., 27,817...D5 10
Kralupy [nad Vltavou], Czech., 14,777.........n17 7
Kramatorsk, Sov. Un., 150,000 (*375,000).......G11, q20 12
Kranj, Yugo., 27,209......B2 10
Kraslice, Czech., 6,294....C2 7
Kraśnik Lubelski, Pol., 14,600................C7 7
Krasnoarmeysk, Sov. Un., 55,000 (*135,000)......F15 12
Krasnodar, Sov. Un., 464,000...............I12 12
Krasnograd, Sov. Un., 18,000...............G10 12

L

Lansdowne, Pa., 14,090...G11, p20 81
Lansdowne House, Ont., Can., 612...n18 41
L'Anse, Mich., 2,538...B2 66
Lansford, Pa., 5,168...E10 81
Lansing, Ill., 25,805...B6, k9 58
Lansing, Iowa, 1,227...A6 60
Lansing, Kans., 3,797...B8 61
Lansing, Mich., 131,403 (*303,200)...F6 66
Lansing, Ohio, 1,200...*C4 78
Lantana, Fla., 7,126...F6 54
Lanús, Arg., 449,824...*A5 28
Laoag, Phil., 30,938...B6 19
Laoighis, co., Ire., 44,595...*D3 4
Lao Kay, Viet., 25,000...*G13 16
Laon, Fr., 26,316...C5 5
Laona, Wis., 700...C5 88
La Oroya, Peru, 24,724...D2 31
Laos, country, Asia, 3,215,000...B2 19
Lapa, Braz., 9,502...D3 30
La Palma, Sp., 8,669...D2 8
La Pampa, prov., Arg., 158,746...B3 28
La Paz, Arg., 11,028...A5 28
La Paz, Bol., 525,000...C2 29
La Paz, Col., 4,278...A3 32
La Paz, Mex., 46,011...C2 34
La Paz, Mex., 3,735...C4 34
La Paz, dept., Bol., 1,176,300...C2 29
Lapeer, Mich., 6,314...E7 66
Lapeer, co., Mich., 52,361...E7 56
Lapel, Ind., 1,796...D6 59
La Piedad [Cavadas], Mex., 34,963...m12 34
Laplace, La., 5,953...h11 63
Lapland, reg., Eur...C12 11
La Plata, Arg., 408,300 (*510,000)...A5, g8 28
La Plata, Col., 5,863...C2 32
La Plata, Md., 1,561...C4 53
La Plata, Mo., 1,377...A5 69
La Plata, co., Colo., 19,199...D3 51
La Pocatière, Que., Can., 4,256...B7 42
La Pola, Sp., 5,430...A3 8
La Porte, Ind., 22,140...A4 59
La Porte, Tex., 7,149...r14 84
La Porte, co., Ind., 105,342...A4 59
La Porte City, Iowa, 2,256...B5 60
Lappeenranta, Fin., 51,203...G13 11
Lappi, prov., Fin., 221,200...*D11 11
La Prairie, Que., Can., 8,309...D4, q20 42
Laprairie, co., Que., Can., 44,980...D4, q20 42
La Presa, Calif....*F5 50
La Providence, Que., Can., 4,709...*D5 42
La Pryor, Tex., 900...E3 84
La Puebla, Sp., 9,931...C7 8
La Puebla de Montalbán, Sp., 7,700...C3 8
La Puente, Calif., 31,092...*F4 50
La Purisima, Mex., 377...B2 34
La Quiaca, Arg., 6,290...D2 29
L'Aquila, It., 46,500...C4 9
Lara, state, Ven., 489,140...A3 32
Larache, Mor., 45,710...A3 22
Laramie, Wyo., 23,143...E7 89
Laramie, co., Wyo., 56,360...E8 89
Laramie, peak, Wyo...D7 89
Larchmont, N.Y., 7,203...h13 75
Laredo, Sp., 6,206...A4 8
Laredo, Tex., 69,024 (*220,000)...F3 84
Largo, Fla., 22,031...E4, p10 54
Lariat, Colo...D4 51
La Ricamarie, Fr., 11,902...E6 5
Larimer, Pa., 550...*F2 81
Larimer, co., Colo., 89,900...A5 51
Larimore, N. Dak., 1,469...C8 77
Larino, It., 8,678...D5 9
La Rioja, Arg., 43,000...E2 29
La Rioja, prov., Arg., 136,237...E2 29
La Rioja, Cuba, 1,818...D5 35
Lárisa (Larissa), Grc., 72,336...C4 14
Lárisa (Larissa), prov., Grc., 232,157...*C4 14
Lārkāna, Pak., 48,008...C4 20
Larkspur, Calif., 10,487...h7 50
Larksville, Pa., 3,937...n17 81
Larne, N. Ire., 18,242...C4 4
Larned, Kans., 4,567...D4 61
La Rochelle, Fr., 73,347 (*88,000)...D3 5
La Roche-sur-Yon, Fr., 36,067...D3 5
La Roda, Sp., 12,190...C4 8
La Romana, Dom. Rep., 36,700...E9 35
La Ronge, Sask., Can., 707.B3 39
Larose, La., 4,267...E5 63
La Rue, Ohio, 867...B2 78
Larue, co., Ky., 10,672...C4 62
Larvik, Nor., 10,500 (*18,000)...H4, p28 11
Larwill, Ind., 324...B6 59
Lasa, see Lhasa, China
La Salle, Que., Can., 72,912...q19 42
La Salle, Colo., 1,227...A6 51
La Salle, Ill., 10,736...B4 58
La Salle, co., Ill., 111,409...B5 58
La Salle, co., Tex., 5,014...E3 84
La Salle, par., La., 13,295...C3 63
Las Animas, Colo., 3,148...C7 51
Las Animas, co., Colo., 15,744...D6 51
La Sarre, Que., Can., 5,185...o20 41
Lascahobas, Hai., 3,132...E8 35
L'Ascension, Que., Can., 1,197...A6 42
La Scie, Newf., Can., 939...D4 44
Las conchas, Arg., 24,809...g7 28
Las Cruces, N. Mex., 37,857 (*48,000)...C5 48
La Selle, peak, Hai...E8 37
La Serena, Chile, 40,854...E1 29
La Seyne [-sur-Mer], Fr., 43,783...F6 5
Las Flores, Arg., 14,838...B5 28
La Sierra, Calif...n14 50
Lasithi (Lasithion), prov., Grc., 66,105...*E5 14
Las Matas de Farfan, Dom. Rep., 3,585...*E8 35
La Solana, Sp., 14,948...C4 8
Las Palmas [de Gran Canaria], Sp., 254,800...m14 8
Las Palmas, prov., Sp., 554,200...m14 8
La Spezia, It., 129,200 (*196,000)...B2 9
Las Piedras, Ur., 40,658...E1 30
Lassen, co., Calif., 16,796...B3 50
Lassen, peak, Calif...B3 50
L'Assomption, Que., Can., 4,915...D4 42
L'Assomption, co., Que., Can., 49,839...D4 42
Las Varillas, Arg., 7,405...A4 28
Las Vegas, Nev., 125,787 (*261,900)...C4 72
Las Vegas, N. Mex., 6,307...B6, D7 48
Las Villas, prov., Cuba, 1,362,200...C3 35
Latacunga, Ec., 16,400...B2 31
Latah, co., Idaho, 24,891...C2 57
Latakia (Al Lādhiqīyah), Syr., 125,657...E10 14
Laterrière, Que., Can., 651...A6 42
La Teste-de-Buch, Fr., 11,842...E3 5
Latham, N.Y., 9,661...*C7 75
Lathrop, Calif., 2,137...*D3 50
Lathrop, Mo., 1,268...B3 69
Lathrup Village, Mich., 4,676...*F7 66
Latimer, co., Okla., 8,601...C6 79
Latina, It., 47,800...D4, k9 9
Latium, reg., It...C4 9
Laton, Calif., 1,071...D4 50
Latour, peak, Idaho...B2 57
La Trinité, Mart., 3,631...I14 35
Latrobe, Pa., 11,749...F3 81
Latta, S.C., 1,764...C9 82
Lattimer Mines, Pa., 650...E10 81
Lattingtown, N.Y., 1,773...*E7 75
La Tuque, Que., Can., 13,009...B5 42
Latvia (S.S.R.), rep., Sov. Un., 2,455,000...C4 12
Lauderdale, Minn., 2,530...n12 67
Lauderdale, co., Ala., 68,111...A2 46
Lauderdale, co., Miss., 67,087...C5 68
Lauderdale, co., Tenn., 20,271...B2 83
Lauderdale-by-the-Sea, Fla., 2,879...*F6 54
Launceston, Austl., 35,001 (*62,181)...o15 25
Launceston, Eng., 4,780...E4 4
La Unión, Chile, 11,600...C5 28
La Unión, Col., 3,875...C2 32
La Unión, Mex., 1,385...D4, o13 34
La Unión, Peru, 1,672...C2 31
La Unión, Sal., 17,207...E7 34
La Unión, Sp., 11,687...D5 8
La Union, prov., Phil., 293,300...*B6 19
Laupheim, Ger., Fed. Rep. of, 13,592...D4 6
Laurel, Del., 2,408...C6 53
Laurel, Fla., 1,200...E4 54
Laurel, Ind., 753...F7 59
Laurel, Md., 10,525...B4 53
Laurel, Miss., 24,145...D4 68
Laurel, Mont., 4,454...E8 70
Laurel, Nebr., 1,009...B8 71
Laurel, Va., 900...C5 85
Laurel, co., Ky., 27,386...C5 62
Laurel Bay, S.C., 4,490...G6 82
Laureldale, Pa., 4,519...F10 81
Laurel Gardens, Pa., 1,800...*E1 81
Laurel Heights, Wash...*B3 86
Laurel Hill, N.C., 1,215...C3 76
Laurel Run, Pa., 327...n17 81
Laurel Springs, N.J., 2,566...*D3 74
Laurence Harbor, N.J., 3,500...C4 74
Laurens, Iowa, 1,792...B3 60
Laurens, S.C., 10,298...B3 82
Laurens, co., Ga., 32,738...D3 55
Laurens, co., S.C., 49,713...C3 82
Laurentides, Que., Can., 1,746...D4 42
Laurier, Que., Can., 653...C6 42
Laurierville, Que., Can., 872...C6 42
Laurinburg, N.C., 8,859...C3 76
Laurium, Mich., 2,868...A2 66
Lausanne, Switz., 134,900 (*225,800)...E3 6
Lautaro, Chile, 10,400...B2 28
Lauzon, Que., Can., 12,809...C6, n17 42
Lavaca, co., Tex., 17,903...E4 84
Lava Hot Springs, Idaho, 516...G6 57
Laval, Fr., 45,674...C3 5
Laval, Que., Can., 228,010...D4 42
Laval-des-Rapides, Que., Can., 19,227...*D4 42
La Vale, Md., 3,971...k13 53
Lavalleja, dept., Ur., 65,525...*E1 30
Lavallette, N.J., 1,509...D4 74
Laval-Ouest, Que., Can., 5,440...*p19 42
Lavaltrie, Que., Can., 1,261...D4 42
Lavaur, Fr., 4,137...F4 5
La Vega, Dom. Rep., 31,100...E8 35
Lavello, It., 13,745...D5 9
La Verne, Calif., 12,965...m13 50
Laverne, Okla., 1,373...A2 79
Laviana, Sp., 12,455...A3 8
La Victoria, Ven., 41,889...A4 32
La Villa, Tex., 1,255...*F4 84
La Vista, Ga., 5,200...C2 55
La Vista, Nebr., 4,807...g13 71
La Viuda, mtn., Peru...C2 31
Lavonia, Ga., 2,044...B3 55
Lavras da Mangabeira, Braz., 4,111...*D7 27
Lawn, Newf., Can., 716...E4 44
Lawndale, Calif., 24,825...*F4 50
Lawndale, N.C., 544...B1 76
Lawnside, N.J., 2,757...*D2 74
Lawnton, Pa., 1,500...*F8 81
Lawrence, Ind., 16,917...E5, k10 59
Lawrence, Kans., 45,698 (*46,500)...D9, m15 61
Lawrence, Mass., 66,915...A5 65
Lawrence, Mich., 790...F4 66
Lawrence, N.Y., 6,566...G2 52
Lawrence, Pa., 970...F1 81
Lawrence, co., Ala., 27,281...A2 46
Lawrence, co., Ark., 16,320...A4 49
Lawrence, co., Ill., 17,522...E6 58
Lawrence, co., Ind., 38,038...G4 59
Lawrence, co., Ky., 10,726...B7 62
Lawrence, co., Miss., 11,137...D3 68
Lawrence, co., Mo., 24,585...D4 69
Lawrence, co., Ohio, 56,868...D3 78
Lawrence, co., Pa., 107,374...E1 81
Lawrence, co., S. Dak., 17,453...F2 77
Lawrence, co., Tenn., 29,097...B4 83
Lawrenceburg, Ind., 4,636...F8 59
Lawrenceburg, Ky., 3,579...B5 62
Lawrenceburg, Tenn., 8,899...B4 83
Lawrence Park, Pa., 4,517...B1 81
Lawrenceville, Ga., 5,115...C3, h9 55
Lawrenceville, Ill., 5,863...E6 58
Lawrenceville, N.J., 1,800...C3 74
Lawrenceville, Va., 1,636...D5 85
Lawson, Mo., 1,034...B3 69
Lawtey, Fla., 636...B4 54
Lawton, Mich., 1,358...F5 66
Lawton, Okla., 74,470 (*96,500)...C3 79
Layland, W. Va., 400...n14 87
Layton, Utah, 13,603...C2 72
Laytonville, Calif., 900...C2 50
Lazio, reg., It., 4,565,400.*D4 9
Lea, co., N. Mex., 49,554...C7 48
Leachville, Ark., 1,582...B5 49
Lead, S. Dak., 5,420...F2 77
Lead, mtn., Maine...D4 64
Leader, Sask., Can., 1,211...G1 39
Leadville, Colo., 4,314...B4 51
Leadwood, Mo., 1,397...D7 69
League City, Tex., 10,818.*E5 84
Leake, co., Miss., 17,085...C4 68
Leakesville, Miss., 1,090...D5 68
Leakey, Tex., 393...E3 84
Leaksville, N.C...A3 76
Lealman, Fla., 16,000...p10 54
Leamington, Ont., Can., 10,435...E2 41
Leamington, Eng., 45,010...D6 4
Leaside, Ont., Can., 21,250...m15 41
Leatherhead, Eng., 41,050...m12 4
Leatherwood, Ky., 250...C6 62
Leavenworth, Kans., 25,147 (*42,400)...C9, k16 61
Leavenworth, Wash., 1,322...B5 86
Leavenworth, co., Kans., 53,340...C8 61
Leavittsburg, Ohio, 3,000...A5 78
Leawood, Kans., 10,349...D9 61
Lebanon, Ill., 3,564...E4 58
Lebanon, Ind., 9,766...D5 59
Lebanon, Ky., 5,528...C4 62
Lebanon, Mo., 8,616...D5 69
Lebanon, N.H., 9,725...D3 73
Lebanon, N.J., 885...B3 74
Lebanon, Ohio, 7,934...G1 78
Lebanon, Oreg., 6,636...C4, k12 80
Lebanon, Pa., 28,572...F9 81
Lebanon, Tenn., 12,492...A5 83
Lebanon, Va., 2,272...f9 85
Lebanon, co., Pa., 99,665...F9 81
Lebanon, country, Asia, 3,115,000...F10 14
Lebanon Junction, Ky., 1,571...C4 62
Lebedyan, Sov. Un., 10,000...E12 12
Le Blanc, Fr., 5,279...D4 5
Le Blanc-Mesnil, Fr., 48,487...g10 5
Lębork, Pol., 25,000...A4 7
Le Bourget, Fr., 9,648...g10 5
Le Bouscat, Fr., 22,550...E3 5
Lebrija, Sp., 12,297...D2 8
Le Cateau, Fr., 9,114...B5 5
Lecce, It., 81,000...D7 9
Lecco, It., 52,000...B2 9
Le Center, Minn., 1,890...F5 67
Le Chambon-Feugerolles, Fr., 21,937...E6 5
Le Chesnay, Fr., 13,249...g9 5
Le Claire, Iowa, 2,520...C7, g11 60
Lecompte, La., 1,518...C3 63
Le Coteau, Fr., 6,571...D6 5
Le Creusot, Fr., 34,102...D6 5
Łęczyca, Pol., 12,600...B5 7
Ledgewood, N.J., 1,100...B3 74
Ledo, India...C10 20
Leduc, Alta., Can., 4,000...C4 38
Lee, Mass., 3,389 (6,426 ▲)...B1 65
Lee, co., Ala., 61,268...C4 46
Lee, co., Ark., 18,884...C5 49
Lee, co., Fla., 105,216...F5 54

Limestone, Maine, 1,572...B5 64
Limestone, co., Ala., 41,699...A2 46
Limestone, co., Tex., 18,100...D4 84
Limoeiro do Norte, Braz., 6,179...*D7 27
Limoges, Fr., 132,935...E4 5
Limon, Colo., 1,814...B7 51
Limón, C.R., 22,000...F8 34
Limón, prov., C.R., 79,300...*I12 33
Limousin, former prov., Fr...E4 5
Limoux, Fr., 9,603...F5 5
Linares, Chile, 27,568...B2 28
Linares, Col., 1,344...C2 32
Linares, Mex., 24,456...C5 34
Linares, Sp., 43,000 (51,883 ▲)...C4 8
Linares, prov., Chile, 197,500...B2 28
Linch, Wyo., 300...*C6 89
Linchuan, China, 10,000...F8 17
Lincoln, Arg., 15,477...A4 28
Lincoln, Calif., 3,176...C3 50
Lincoln, Ont., Can., 14,247...D5 41
Lincoln, Eng., 74,090...D6 4
Lincoln, Ill., 17,582...C4 58
Lincoln, Kans., 1,582...C5 61
Lincoln, Maine, 3,482...C4 64
Lincoln, Mass., 2,400...g10 65
Lincoln, Nebr., 149,518 (*158,100).D9, h11 71
Lincoln, N.H., 800 (1,341 ▲)...*C4 73
Lincoln, Pa., 1,885...*E1 81
Lincoln, R.I...B11 52
Lincoln, co., Ark., 12,913..D4 49
Lincoln, co., Colo., 4,836..C7 51
Lincoln, co., Eng., 812,310...*D6 4
Lincoln, co., Ga., 5,895...C4 55
Lincoln, co., Idaho, 3,057..G4 57
Lincoln, co., Kans., 4,582..C5 61
Lincoln, co., Ky., 16,663...C5 62
Lincoln, co., Maine, 20,537...D3 64
Lincoln, co., Minn., 8,143..F2 67
Lincoln, co., Miss., 26,198..D3 68
Lincoln, co., Mo., 18,041..B6 69
Lincoln, co., Mont., 18,063...B1 70
Lincoln, co., Nebr., 29,538.D5 71
Lincoln, co., Nev., 2,557...C4 72
Lincoln, co., N. Mex., 7,560...C6 48
Lincoln, co., N.C., 32,682..B1 76
Lincoln, co., Okla., 19,482.B5 79
Lincoln, co., Oreg., 25,755...C3 80
Lincoln, co., S.Dak., 11,761...G9 77
Lincoln, co., Tenn., 24,318...B5 83
Lincoln, co., Wash., 9,572...B7 86
Lincoln, co., W. Va., 18,912...C2 87
Lincoln, co., Wis., 23,499..C4 88
Lincoln, co., Wyo., 8,640..D2 89
Lincoln, par., La., 33,800..B3 63
Lincoln Acres, Calif., 1,000...o15 50
Lincoln City, Oreg., 4,198...C3 80
Lincoln Heights, Ohio, 6,099...o13 78
Lincoln Highway, Nebr..*C5 71
Lincoln Park, Colo., 2,984...*C5 51
Lincoln Park, Ga., 1,852...D2 55
Lincoln Park, Mich., 52,984...p15 66
Lincoln Park, N.J., 9,034..B4 74
Lincoln Park, N.Y., 1,100...*D6 75
Lincoln Park, Pa., 1,500..*F9 81
Lincolnton, Ga., 1,442...C4 55
Lincolnton, N.C., 5,293...B1 76
Lincoln Village, Calif., 6,112...*D3 50
Lincoln Village, Ohio, 11,215...*C3 78
Lincolnwood, Ill., 12,929..h9 58
Lincroft, N.J., 4,100...C4 74
Lind, Wash., 622...C7 86
Linda, Calif., 7,731...*C3 50
Lindale, Ga., 2,768...B1 55
Lindale, Tex., 1,631...C5 84
Lindau, Ger., Fed. Rep. of, 25,395...E4 6
Linden, Ala., 2,697...C2 46
Linden, Ind., 713...D4 59
Linden, Mich., 1,546...F7 66
Linden, N.J., 41,409...k8 74
Linden, Tenn., 1,062...B4 83
Linden, Tex., 2,264...C5 84
Lindenhurst, Ill., 3,141...h8 58
Lindenhurst, N.Y., 28,359...G3 52
Lindenwold, N.J., 12,199..D3 74
Lindesberg, Swe., 10,749..H6 11
Lindi, Tan, 10,315...B7 24
Lindon, Utah, 1,644...*A6 72
Lindsay, Calif., 5,206...D4 50
Lindsay, Ont., Can., 12,746...C6 41
Lindsay, Okla., 3,705...C4 79
Lindsborg, Kans., 2,764...D6 61
Lindstrom, Minn., 1,260...E6 67
Linesville, Pa., 1,265...C1 81
Lineville, Ala., 1,984...B4 46
Lingayen, Phil., 8,221...B6 19
Lingen, Ger., Fed. Rep. of, 31,984...B3 6
Linglestown, Pa., 3,000...F8 81
Lingyuan, China, 20,000..C8 17
Linhai, China, 26,000...F9 17
Lini, China, 40,000...D8 17
Linière, Que., Can., 1,269..C7 42
Linköping, Swe., 106,628..H6 11
Linn, Mo., 1,289...C6 69
Linn, co., Iowa, 163,213...B6 60
Linn, co., Kans., 7,770...D9 61
Linn, co., Mo., 15,125...B4 69
Linn, co., Oreg., 71,914...C4 80
Linntown, Pa., 1,851...*E7 81
Lino Lakes, Minn., 3,692..*E5 67
Lins, Braz., 38,080...C3 30
Linthicum Heights, Md., 12,700...B4, h11 53
Linton, Ind., 5,450...F3 59
Linton, N. Dak., 1,695...D5 77
Linwood, Mass., 1,100...B4 65
Linwood, Mich., 650...E7 66
Linwood, N.J., 6,159...E3 74
Linwood, Pa., 4,009...*G11 81
Linworth, Ohio, 500...k10 78
Linz, Aus., 204,627 (*275,000)...D7 6
Lipa, Phil., 16,006..C6, p13 19
Lipari, It., 3,731...E5 9
Lipetsk, Sov. Un., 289,000...E12 12
Lipkany, Sov. Un., 10,000...A8 10
Lipno, Pol., 10,900...B5 7
Lipova, Rom., 10,064...B5 10
Lippstadt, Ger., Fed. Rep. of, 42,191...C4 6
Lipscomb, Ala., 3,225..B3, g7 46
Lipscomb, co., Tex., 3,486...A2 84
Liria, Sp., 9,723...C5 8
Lisboa, see Lisbon, Port.
Lisbon, Iowa, 1,329...C6 60
Lisbon, Maine, 1,100...D2, f7 64
Lisbon, N.H., 1,247 (1,480 ▲)...C4 73
Lisbon, N. Dak., 2,090...D8 77
Lisbon, Ohio, 3,521...B5 78
Lisbon (Lisboa), Port., 757,700 (*1,735,000)...C1, f9 8
Lisbon Falls, Maine, 3,257...D5, f7 64
Lisburn, N. Ire., 27,405...C3 4
Lishu, China, 5,000...E2 18
Lisichansk, Sov. Un., 118,000 (*320,000)...q21 12
Lisieux, Fr., 23,830...C4 5
Lisle, Ill., 5,329...k8 58
L'Islet, co., Que., Can., 24,382...B7 42
L'Islet-sur-Mer, Que., 1,195...B7 42
L'Isletville, Que., Can., 1,184...B7 42
Lisman, Ala., 628...C1 46
Lismore, Austl., 20,901...E9 25
Listowel, Ont., Can., 4,677...D4 41
Litchfield, Conn., 1,559 (6,264▲)...B4 52
Litchfield, Ill., 7,190...D4 58
Litchfield, Mich., 1,167...F6 66
Litchfield, Minn., 5,262...E4 67
Litchfield, co., Conn., 144,091...B3 52
Litchfield Park, Ariz., 1,664...D1 48
Lithgow, Austl., 13,135...F9 25
Lithonia, Ga., 2,270...C2, h8 55
Lithuania (S.S.R), rep., Sov. Un., 3,280,000...D4 12
Lititz, Pa., 7,072...F9 81
Litókhoron, Grc., 5,561...*B4 14
Litoměřice, Czech., 19,713...C3 7
Litomyšl, Czech., 6,384...D7 7
Little, mtn., Wyo...E5 89
Little Belt, mtn., Mont.,...D6 70
Little Canada, Minn., 3,481...*E5 67
Little Catalina, Newf., Can., 752...D5 44
Little Chute, Wis., 5,522...D5, h9 88
Little Current, Ont., Can., 1,527...B3 41
Little Falls, Minn., 7,467..E4 67
Little Falls, N.J., 11,727...B4 74
Little Falls, N.Y., 7,629...B6 75
Little Ferry, N.J., 9,064...h8 74
Littlefield, Tex., 6,738...C1 84
Littlefork, Minn., 824...B5 67
Little River, co., Ark., 11,194...D1 49
Little Rock, Ark., 132,483 (*293,700)...C3, k10 49
Little Rock, river, Iowa...A1 70
Little Silver, N.J., 6,010...C4 74
Littlestown, Pa., 3,026...G7 81
Littleton, Colo., 26,466...B6 51
Littleton, Mass., 2,764 (6,380 ▲)...f9 65
Littleton, N.H., 4,180 (5,290 ▲)...C4 73
Littleton, N.C., 903...A5 76
Littleton Common, Mass..f10 65
Little Valley, N.Y., 1,340..C2 75
Liuho, China., 5,000...E2 18
Lively, Ont., Can., 3,000..A3 41
Live Oak, Calif., 2,654...C3 50
Live Oak, Fla., 6,830...B4 54
Live Oak, co., Tex., 6,697..E3 84
Livermore, Calif., 37,703..h9 50
Livermore, Ky., 1,594...C2 62
Livermore, peak, Tex...o12 84
Livermore Falls, Maine, 2,378...D2 64
Liverpool, N.S., Can., 3,654...E5 43
Liverpool, Eng., 603,210 (*1,615,000)...D5 4
Liverpool, N.Y., 3,307...B4 75
Liverpool, Pa., 847...E7 81
Livingston, Ala., 2,358...C1 46
Livingston, Calif., 2,588...D3 50
Livingston, Guat., 2,606...D7 34
Livingston, Ill., 916...E4 58
Livingston, La., 1,398...D5, g10 63
Livingston, Mont., 6,883...E6 70
Livingston, N.J., 30,127...B4 74
Livingston, Tenn., 3,050...C8 83
Livingston, Tex., 3,965...D5 84
Livingstone, Zambia, 33,600...D5 24
Livingston, co., Ill., 40,690...C5 58
Livingston, co., Ky., 7,596...e9 62
Livingston, co., Mich., 58,967...F6 66
Livingston, co., Mo., 15,368...B4 69
Livingston, co., N.Y., 54,041...C3 75
Livingston, par., La., 36,511...D5 63
Livingston Manor, N.Y., 1,522...D6 75
Livno, Yugo., 5,170...D3 10
Livny, Sov. Un., 37,000..E11 12
Livonia, Mich., 110,109...F7 66
Livonia, N.Y., 1,278...C3 75
Livorno (Leghorn), It., 172,800...C3 9
Livry-Gargan, Fr., 32,063...g11 5
Lizard Head, peak, Wyo...D3 89
Ljubljana, Yugo., 173,662...B2 10
Ljungby, Swe., 14,535...I5 11
Llandrindod Wells, Wales, 3,360...D5 4
Llandudno, Wales, 17,360...D5 4
Llanelli, Wales, 26,260...E4 4
Llanes, Sp., 20,421...A3 8
Llano, Tex., 2,608...D3 84
Llano, co., Tex., 6,979...D3 84
Llanquihue, prov., Chile, 201,800...C2 28
Lloyd, Ky., 400...B7 62
Lloyd Harbor, N.Y., 3,371...*G3 52
Lloydminster, Alta., Sask., Can., 8,691...D1 39
Lloyd Place, Va...*D6 85
Lluchmayor, Sp., 10,664...C7 8
Llullaillaco, vol., Chile...D2 29
Löbau, Ger. Dem. Rep., 16,800...C7 6
Lobería, Arg., 8,455...B5 28
Lobito, Ang., 50,164...C2 24
Lobos, Arg., 10,352...B5, g7 28
Locarno, Switz., 14,700 (*38,500)...E4 6
Lochdale, B.C., Can...f12 37
Lochearn, Md., 5,000...*B4 53
Loches, Fr., 6,359...D4 5
Loch Raven, Md...*B4 53
Lockeport, N.S., Can., 1,231...F4 43
Lockhart, Tex., 6,489...E4, h8 84
Lock Haven, Pa., 11,427...D7 81
Lockland, Ohio, 5,288...o13 78
Lockney, Tex., 2,094...B2 84
Lockport, Ill., 9,985...B5, k8 58
Lockport, La., 2,398..E5, k10 63
Lockport, N.Y., 25,399...B2 75
Lockwood, Mo., 887...D4 69
Locumba, Peru, 634...E3 31
Locust, N.J., 700...C4 74
Locust Grove, Okla., 1,090...A6 79
Locust Valley, N.Y., 3,900...F2 52
Lod (Lydda), Isr., 30,500...C2, h5 15
Lodève, Fr., 7,556...F5 5
Lodeynoye Pole, Sov. Un., 20,000...A9 12
Lodge Grass, Mont., 806...E9 70
Lodhrān, Pak., 6,663...C5 20
Lodi, Calif., 28,691...C3 50
Lodi, N.J., 25,163...h8 74
Lodi, Ohio, 2,399...A3 78
Lodi, Wis., 1,831...E4 88
Łódź, Pol., 761,700 (*930,000)...C5 7
Loei, Thai., 7,268...*B2 19
Logan, Iowa, 1,526...C2 60
Logan, Kans., 760...C4 61
Logan, Ohio, 6,269...C3 78
Logan, Utah, 22,333...A6 72
Logan, W. Va., 3,311.D3, n12 87
Logan, co., Ark., 16,789...B2 49
Logan, co., Colo., 18,852..A7 51
Logan, co., Ill., 33,538...C4 58
Logan, co., Kans., 3,814...D2 61
Logan, co., Ky., 21,793...D3 62
Logan, co., Nebr., 991...C5 71
Logan, co., N. Dak., 4,245...D6 77
Logan, co., Ohio, 35,072...B2 78
Logan, co., Okla., 19,645..B4 79
Logan, co., W. Va., 46,269...D3 87
Logan, mtn., Yukon, Can..D6 36
Logansport, Ind., 19,255...C5 59
Logansport, La., 1,330...C2 63
Loganville, Ga., 1,318...C3 55
Loggieville, N.B., Can., 691...B4 43
Logroño, Sp., 82,821...A4 8
Logroño, prov., Sp., 234,600...*A4 8
Logrosán, Sp., 6,595...C3 8
Lohārdaga, India, 17,087..D7 20
Lohrville, Iowa, 553...B3 60
Loire, dept., Fr., 722,383...*E6 5
Loire, riv., Fr...D3 5
Loire-Atlantique, dept., Fr., 861,452...*D3 5
Loiret, dept., Fr., 430,629...*D4 5
Loir-et-Cher, dept., Fr., 267,896...*D4 5
Loja, Ec., 33,900...B2 31
Loja, Sp., 11,441 (25,976 ▲)...D3 8
Loja, prov., Ec., 345,500...B2 31
Lokhvitsa, Sov. Un., 10,000...F9 12
Lom, Bul., 28,196...D6 10
Loma Linda, Calif., 10,100...*E5 50
Lomas de Zamora, Arg., 410,806...A5, g7 28
Lombard, Ill., 34,043...k8 58
Lombardia, reg., It., 8,231,700...*B2 9
Lombardy, reg., It...B2 9
Lomé, Togo, 90,600...G5 22
Lometa, Tex., 633...D3 84
Lomira, Wis., 1,084...E5 88
Lomita, Calif., 19,784...*E4 50
Lomonosov, Sov. Un., 40,000...s30 11
Lompoc, Calif., 25,284...E3 50
Łomża, Pol., 25,500...B7 7
Lonaconing, Md., 1,572...k13 53
London, Ont., Can., 223,222 (*286,011)...E3 41
London, Eng., 7,418,020 (*10,700,000)...E6, k12 4
London, Ky., 4,337...C5 62
London, Ohio, 6,481...C2 78
London, Greater, co., Eng., 7,418,020...*E6 4
Londonderry, N. Ire., 51,850 (*85,000)...C3 4

Lyle, Minn., 522........G6 67
Lyman, Nebr., 561.......C1 71
Lyman, S.C., 1,159......B3 82
Lyman, co., S. Dak., 4,060.G6 77
Lynbrook, N.Y., 23,151...G2 52
Lynch, Ky., 1,517.......D7 62
Lynchburg, Ohio, 1,186...C2 78
Lynchburg (Independent City), Va., 54,083 (*96,600)..............C3 85
Lynden, Wash., 2,808.....A3 86
Lyndhurst, N.J., 22,729...h8 74
Lyndhurst, Ohio, 19,749...g9 78
Lyndon, Kans., 958......D8 61
Lyndon, Ky., 460.......g11 62

Lyndonville, N.Y., 888....B2 75
Lyndonville, Vt., 1,415....B3 73
Lyndora, Pa., 5,700......E2 81
Lynn, Ind., 1,360........D8 59
Lynn, Mass., 90,294...B6, g12 65
Lynn, co., Tex., 9,107.....C2 84
Lynnfield, Mass., 10,826...f11 65
Lynn Garden, Tenn., 7,000..............C11 83
Lynn Haven, Fal., 4,044..u16 54
Lynn Lake, Man., Can., 2,931........A1, f7 40
Lynnville, Ky., 1,165......f9 62
Lynnwood, Pa., 1,800....*D9 81
Lynnwood, Wash., 16,919.*B3 86

Lynwood, Calif., 43,354...n12 50
Lyon, Fr., 527,800 (*1,100,000)..........E6 5
Lyon, co., Iowa, 13,340...A1 60
Lyon, co., Kans., 32,071...D7 61
Lyon, co., Ky., 5,562......C1 62
Lyon, co., Minn., 24,273...F3 67
Lyon, co., Nev., 8,221...B2 72
Lyon Mountain, N.Y., 950..............f11 75
Lyonnais, former prov., Fr..E6 5
Lyons, Ga., 3,739........D4 55
Lyons, Ill., 11,124......k9 58
Lyons, Ind., 702.........G3 59
Lyons, Kans., 4,355......D5 61

Lyons, Mich., 758.......F6 66
Lyons, Nebr., 1,177......C9 71
Lyons, N.Y., 4,496.......B4 75
Lyons Falls, N.Y., 852....B5 75
Lysá, Czech., 10,281....n18 7
Lysaya Gora, Sov. Un., 10,000.............G8 12
Lysekil, Swe., 6,783....H4 11
Lyster Station, Que., Can., 912..........C6 42
Lysva, Sov. Un., 73,000...D8 13
Lytle, Tex., 1,271.......E3 84
Lyubar, Sov. Un., 10,000..G6 12
Lyubertsy, Sov. Un., 139,000............N17 12

M

Ma'alot Tarshiha, Isr., 5,100.................A3 15
Maastricht, Neth., 111,931 (*145,277)......B6 5
Mabank, Tex., 1,239.....C4 84
Mabel, Minn., 888.......G7 67
Mableton, Ga., 12,900....h7 55
Mabscott, W. Va., 1,254........D3, n13 87
Mabton, Wash., 926......C5 86
McAdam, N.B., Can., 2,224..............D2 43
McAdenville, N.C., 950...*B1 76
McAdoo, Pa., 3,326......E9 81
Macaé, Braz., 29,348......C4 30
McAlester, Okla., 18,802...C6 79
McAllen, Tex., 37,636 (*86,700)............F3 84
Macamic, Que., Can., 1,614...............*o20 41
Macao, Port. dep., Asia, 285,000.............G7 17
Macapá, Braz., 51,563....C5 27
McArthur, Ohio, 1,543....C3 78
Macas Ec., 1,355........D3 27
Macau, Braz., 18,853....D7 27
McBee, S.C., 592........C7 82
McBride, B.C., Can., 658..C7 37
McCall, Idaho, 1,758.....E2 57
McCamey, Tex., 2,647....D1 84
McCarthy, mtn., Mont....E4 70
McCaysville, Ga., 1,619...B2 55
McChesneytown, Pa., 400.*F2 81
McClain, co., Okla., 14,157..............C4 79
McCleary, Wash., 1,265...B2 86
MacClenny, Fla., 2,733...B4 54
Macclesfield, Eng., 44,030.............D5 4
McCloud, Calif., 1,643...B2 50
McClure, Ohio, 699......A2 78
McClure, Pa., 1,094......E7 81
McColl, S.C., 2,524......B8 82
McComas, W. Va., 900...D3 87
McComb, Miss., 11,969...D3 68
McComb, Ohio, 1,329....A2 78
McCone, co., Mont., 2,875..............C11 70
McConnellsburg, Pa., 1,228..............G6 81
McConnelsville, Ohio, 2,107..............C4 78
McCook, Nebr., 8,285....D5 71
McCook, Co., S. Dak., 7,246..............G8 77
McCormick, S.C., 1,864...D3 82
McCormick, co., S.C., 7,955..............D3 82
McCracken, co., Ky., 58,281..............*e9 62
McCreary, Man., Can., 597...............D2 40
McCreary, co., Ky., 12,548.............D5 62
McCrory, Ark., 1,378.....B4 49
McCulloch, co., Tex., 8,571..............D3 84
McCurtain, Okla., 575...B7 79
McCurtain, co., Okla., 28,642.............C7 79
McDermott, Ohio, 900...D2 78
McDonald, Ohio, 3,177...A5 78
McDonald, Pa., 2,879....k13 81
MacDonald, W. Va., 300.............D3, D7 87
McDonald, co., Mo., 12,357.............*E3 69

McDonough, Ga., 2,675...C2 55
McDonough, co., Ill., 36,653.............C3 58
McDowell, co., N.C., 30,648.............f10 76
McDowell, co., W. Va., 50,606.............D3 87
McDuffie, co., Ga., 15,276.............C4 55
Macedon, N.Y., 1,168...B3 75
Macedonia, rep., Eur....*B4 14
Macedonia, rep., Yugo., 1,406,003.........*D5 10
Maceió, Braz., 242,867...D7 27
Macerata, It., 32,500....C4 9
McEwen, Tenn., 1,237...A4 83
McFarland, Calif., 4,177...E4 50
McFarland, Wis., 2,386...E4 88
McGehee, Ark., 4,683....D4 49
McGill, Nev., 2,164......B4 72
MacGillicuddy's Reeks, mts., Ire...........E2 4
McGrann, Pa., 500......*E2 81
McGraw, N.Y., 1,319.....C4 75
MacGregor, Man., Can., 642...............E2 40
McGregor, Iowa, 990.....A6 60
McGregor, Tex., 4,365...D4 84
McGuffey, Ohio, 704.....B2 78
McGuire, mtn., Idaho....D4 57
Machado, Braz., 11,119..........C3, k9 30
Machala, Ec., 46,100....B2 31
McHenry, Ill., 6,772...A5, h8 58
McHenry, co., Ill., 111,555.............A5 58
McHenry, co., N. Dak., 8,977.............B5 77
Machias, Maine, 1,368, (2,441 ▲)..........D5 64
Machida, Jap., 202,801..*n18 18
Machilipatnam (Bandar), India, 112,612.......E7 20
Macías Nguema Biyoga, reg., Equat. Gui., 83,000............*H6 22
Măcin, Rom., 6,533.....C9 10
McIntoch, Minn., 753....C3 67
McIntosh, co., Ga., 7,371..E5 55
McIntosh, co., N. Dak., 5,545.............D6 77
McIntosh, co., Okla., 12,472.............B6 79
Mack, Ohio, 6,000......*D2 78
Mackay, Austl., 19,101 (*28,416)...........D8 25
Mackay, Idaho, 539......F5 57
McKean, co., Pa., 51,915..C4 81
McKeesport, Pa., 37,977............F4, r14 81
McKees Rocks, Pa., 11,901.........F1, k13 81
McKenney, Va., 489......D5 85
McKenzie, Tenn., 4,873...A3 83
McKenzie, co., N. Dak., 6,127.............C2 77
Mackenzie, dist., N.W. Ter., Can., 26,500.....D11 36
Mackenzie, mts., Can....C7 33
Mackenzie, riv., N. W. Ter., Can.........C8 36
Mackinac, co., Mich., 9,660.............B5 66
Mackinac Island, Mich., 517...............C6 66
Mackinaw, Ill., 1,293....C4 58
Mackinaw City, Mich., 810...............C6 66

McKinley, Minn., 317.....C6 67
McKinley, co., N. Mex., 43,391.............B4 48
McKinley, mtn., Alsk.....C9 47
McKinley Heights, Ohio, 1,700............*A5 78
McKinleyville, Calif., 2,000..............B1 50
McKinney, Tex., 15,193...C4 84
McKittrick Summit, mtn., Calif..............E4 50
Macklin, Sask., Can., 829..E1 39
McKnight, Pa...........*E1 81
McKnownville, N.Y., 3,500............*C7 75
McLaughlin, S. Dak., 863...............E5 77
McLean, Tex., 1,183.....B2 84
McLean, Va., 17,698....g12 85
McLean, co., Ill., 104,389..C5 58
McLean, co., Ky., 9,062...C2 62
McLean, co., N. Dak., 11,252.............C4 77
McLean, mtn., Maine.....A4 64
McLeansboro, Ill., 2,630...E5 58
McLennan, Alta., Can., 1,090..............B2 38
McLennan, co., Tex., 147,553.............D4 84
McLeod, co., Minn., 27,662.............F4 67
McLeod Lake, B.C., Can., 123............B6, n18 37
McLoud, Okla., 2,159....B4 79
McLoughlin, mtn., Oreg...E4 80
McLouth, Kans., 623.............C8, k15 61
McMasterville, Que., Can., 2,518............*D4 42
McMechen, W. Va., 2,808...........B4, g8 87
McMillan Manor, Calif., 1,000............*E4 50
McMinn, co., Tenn., 35,462.............D9 83
McMinnville, Oreg., 10,125.........B3, h11 80
McMinnville, Tenn., 10,662.............D8 83
McMullen, co., Tex., 1,095..............E3 84
McMurray, Alta., Can., 1,186.........A5, f8 38
McNair, Tex., 2,039.....E5 84
McNairy, co., Tenn., 18,369.............B3 83
McNary, Ariz., 900......B4 48
McNeill, mtn., B.C., Can..B2 37
Macomb, Ill., 19,643....C3 58
Macomb, co., Mich., 625,309............F8 66
Macon, Fr., 33,445......D6 5
Macon, Ga., 122,423 (*212,800)..........D3 55
Macon, Ill., 1,249......D5 58
Macon, Miss., 2,614....B5 68
Macon, Mo., 15,432....B5 69
Macon, co., Ala., 24,841...C4 46
Macon, co., Ga., 12,933...D2 55
Macon, co., Ill., 125,010...D5 58
Macon, co., Mo., 5,301...B5 69
Macon, co., N.C., 15,788..f9 76
Macon, co., Tenn., 12,315..C7 83
Macoupin, co., Ill., 44,557.............D4 58
McPherson, Kans., 10,851.D6 61
McPherson, co., Kans., 24,778.............D6 61

McPherson, co., Nebr., 623...............C4 71
McPherson, co., S. Dak., 5,022..............E6 77
McRae, Ga., 3,151.......D4 55
McRoberts, Ky., 1,037...C7 62
McSherrystown, Pa., 2,773..............G7 81
Macksville, Kans., 484....E5 61
MacTier, Ont., Can., 851..B5 41
Macungie, Pa., 1,414....E10 81
McVeigh, Ky., 800......C7 62
Ma'dabā, Jordan, 11,224..C3 15
Madagascar, country, Afr., 7,290,000..........E9 24
Madawaska, Maine, 4,452 (5,585 ▲)......A4 64
Madawaska, co., N.B., Can., 37,306........B1 43
Madeira, Ohio, 6,713...o13 78
Madeira Beach, Fla., 4,177............*E4 54
Madeira Is., reg., Port. 245,000............B1 22
Madelia, Minn., 2,316...F4 67
Madera, Calif., 16,044...D3 50
Madera, Mex., 9,759.....B3 34
Madera, Pa., 900........E5 81
Madera, co., Calif., 41,519.............D4 50
Madgaon, India, 41,655 (*48,593)..........E5 20
Madhya Pradesh, state, India, 41,654,119.....D6 20
Madill, Okla., 2,875.....C5 79
Madīnat ash Sha'b, P.D.R. of Yem., 10,000..G4 15
Madison, Ala., 3,086....A3 46
Madison, Ala., 900......C3 46
Madison, Conn., 4,310...D6 52
Madison, Fla., 3,737.....B3 54
Madison, Ga., 2,890.....C3 55
Madison, Ill., 7,042.....E3 58
Madison, Ind., 13,081....G7 59
Madison, Kans., 1,061...D7 61
Madison, Maine, 2,920 (4,278 ▲)..........D3 64
Madison, Minn., 2,242...E2 67
Madison, Mo., 540......B5 69
Madison, Nebr., 1,595...C8 71
Madison, N.J., 16,710...B4 74
Madison, N.C., 2,018....A3 76
Madison, Ohio, 1,678....A4 78
Madison, S. Dak., 6,315..G9 77
Madison, W. Va., 2,342............C3, m12 87
Madison, Wis., 171,769 (*248,100)..........E4 88
Madison, co., Ala., 186,540............A3 46
Madison, co., Ark., 9,453..B2 49
Madison, co., Fla., 13,481..B3 54
Madison, co., Ga., 13,517..B3 55
Madison, co., Idaho, 13,452.............F7 57
Madison, co., Ill., 250,934..E4 58
Madison, co., Ind., 138,451............D6 59
Madison, co., Iowa, 11,558.............C3 60
Madison, co., Ky., 42,730..C5 62
Madison, co., Miss., 29,737.............C4 68
Madison, co., Mo., 8,641..D7 69
Madison, co., Mont., 5,014..............E4 70
Madison, co., Nebr., 27,402............C8 71

Maple Heights, Ohio, 34,093....h9 78
Maple Lake, Minn., 1,124....E4 67
Maple Lane, Ind....*A5 59
Maple Mount, Ky., 500....C2 62
Maple Plain, Minn., 1,169....m11 67
Maple Rapids, Mich., 683....E6 66
Maple Shade, N.J., 16,464....D2 74
Mapleton, Iowa, 1,647....B2 60
Mapleton, Maine, 500 (1,598 ▲)....B4 64
Mapleton, Minn., 1,307....G5 67
Mapleton, Oreg., 900....C3 80
Mapleton, Utah, 1,980....D2 72
Maplewood, La., 470....D2 63
Maplewood, Minn., 25,186....m12 67
Maplewood, Mo., 12,785....f13 69
Maplewood, N.J., 24,932....B4 74
Maplewood, N.Y., 650....*C7 75
Maplewood Park, Pa., 2,000....*G11 81
Maquoketa, Iowa, 5,677....B7 60
Marabá, Braz., 14,593....D6 27
Maracaibo, Ven., 650,002....A3 32
Maracaju, Braz., 3,410....F5 27
Maracay, Ven., 255,134....A4 32
Maradi, Niger, 10,100....F6 22
Marāgheh, Iran, 54,106....B4 15
Maragogipe, Braz., 12,769....*E7 27
Marana, Ariz., 500....C3 48
Maranguape, Braz., 8,715....*D7 27
Maranhão, state, Braz., 3,037,135....*D6 27
Marañón, riv., Peru....B2 31
Maraş, Tur., 110,761....D11 14
Marathon, Ont., Can., 2,409....o18 41
Marathon, Fla., 4,397....H5 54
Marathon, Iowa, 447....B3 60
Marathon, N.Y., 1,053....C4 75
Marathon, Tex., 750....D1, o13 84
Marathon, Wis., 1,214....D4 88
Marathon, co., Wis., 97,457....D4 88
Maravatío de Ocampo, Mex., 5,732....n13 34
Mara Vista, Mass....C6 65
Marawī, Sud., 1,620....E4 23
Marbella, Sp., 8,982....D3 8
Marble, Minn., 682....C5 67
Marble Cliff, Ohio, 715....m10 78
Marble Falls, Tex., 2,209....D3 84
Marblehead, Mass., 21,295....B6, f12 65
Marblehead, Ohio, 726....A3 78
Marbleton, Que., Can., 661....D6 42
Marburg, Ger., Fed. Rep. of, 48,031....C4 6
Marbury, Md., 500....C3 53
Marceline, Mo., 2,622....B5 69
Marcellus, Mich., 1,139....F5 66
Marcellus, N.Y., 2,017....C4 75
Marche, former prov., Fr....D4 5
Marche, pol. dist., It., 1,347,489....*C4 9
Marchena, Sp., 17,030....D3 8
Marches, reg., It., 1,358,100....C4 9
Marcola, Oreg., 500....C4 80
Marcos Juarez, Arg., 12,897....A4 28
Marcus, Iowa, 1,272....B2 60
Marcus Hook, Pa., 3,041....G11 81
Marcy, mtn., N.Y....A7 75
Mardān, Pak., 109,000....B5 20
Mar Del Plata, Arg., 302,000....B5 28
Mardin, Tur., 33,740....D13 14
Marechal Deodoro, Braz., 5,508....*D7 27
Marengo, Ill., 4,235....A5 58
Marengo, Ind., 767....H5 59
Marengo, Iowa, 2,235....C5 60
Marengo, co., Ala., 23,819....C2 46
Marenisco, Mich., 700....n12 66
Marfa, Tex., 2,647....o12 84
Margaret, Ala., 685....B3 46
Margaretville, N.Y., 816....C6 75
Margate, Eng., 49,680....E7 4
Margate, Fla., 8,867....*F6 54
Margate City, N.J., 10,576....E3 74
Margelan, Sov. Un., 95,000....E10 13
Margherita, mtn., Ug., Zaire....H3 23
Maria la Baja, Col., 5,739....A2 32
Mariana, is., Pac. O....E6 2
Marianao, Cuba (part of Havana)....D2 35
Marianna, Ark., 6,196....C5 49
Marianna, Fla., 6,741....B1 54
Marianna, Pa., 875....*F1 81
Mariánské Lázně, Czech., 13,581....D2 7
Maribo, co., Den., 127,700....*J4 11
Maribor, Yugo., 97,167....B2 10
Maricopa, Calif., 740....E4 50
Maricopa, co., Ariz., 968,487....C2 48
Mariemont, Ohio, 4,540....o13 78
Marienville, Pa., 900....D3 81
Maries, co., Mo., 6,851....C6 69
Mariestad, Swe., 20,379....H5 11
Marietta, Ga., 27,216....C2, h7 55
Marietta, Ohio, 16,861....C4 78
Marietta, Okla., 2,013....D4 79
Marietta, Pa., 2,838....F8 81
Marietta, S.C., 1,000....A2 82
Marieville, Que., Can., 4,563....D4 42
Marília, Braz., 73,165....C3 30
Marín, Sp., 7,261....A1 8
Marin, co., Calif., 206,758....C2 50
Marin City, Calif., 1,650....*C2 50
Marinduque, prov., Phil., 114,586....*C6 19
Marine, Ill., 882....E4 58
Marine City, Mich., 4,567....F8 66
Marinette, Wis., 12,696....C6 88
Marinette, co., Wis., 35,810....C5 88
Maringouin, La., 1,365....D4 63
Marinha Grande, Port., 4,698....C1 8
Marino, It., 33,700....H9 9
Marion, Ala., 4,289....C2 46
Marion, Ill., 11,724....F5 58
Marion, Ind., 39,607....C6 59
Marion, Iowa, 18,028....B6 60
Marion, Kans., 2,052....D6 61
Marion, Ky., 3,008....e9 62
Marion, La., 796....B3 63
Marion, Mass., 1,262 (3,466 ▲)....C6 65
Marion, Mich., 891....D5 66
Marion, N.Y., 850....B3 75
Marion, N.C., 3,335....B1, f10 76
Marion, Ohio, 38,646....B2 78
Marion, S.C., 7,435....C9 82
Marion, Va., 8,158....f10 85
Marion, Wis., 1,218....D5 88
Marion, co., Ala., 23,788....A2 46
Marion, co., Ark., 7,000....A3 49
Marion, co., Fla., 69,030....C4 54
Marion, co., Ga., 5,099....D2 55
Marion, co., Ill., 38,986....E5 58
Marion, co., Ind., 792,299....E5 59
Marion, co., Iowa, 26,352....C4 60
Marion, co., Kans., 13,935....D6 61
Marion, co., Ky., 16,714....C4 62
Marion, co., Miss., 22,871....D4 68
Marion, co., Mo., 28,121....B6 69
Marion, co., Ohio, 64,724....B2 78
Marion, co., Oreg., 151,309....C4 80
Marion, co., S.C., 30,270....C9 82
Marion, co., Tenn., 20,577....D8 83
Marion, co., Tex., 8,517....C5 84
Marion, co., W. Va., 61,356....B4 87
Marion Heights, Pa., 958....*D8 81
Marionville, Mo., 1,496....D4 69
Mariposa, Calif., 900....D4 50
Mariposa, co., Calif., 6,015....D3 50
Marissa, Ill., 2,004....E4 58
Maris Town, Miss....C3 68
Mariupol, see Zhdanov, Sov. Un.
Marka. Som., 17,700....H6 23
Markdale, Ont., Can., 1,090....C4 41
Marked Tree, Ark., 3,229....B5 49
Markesan, Wis., 1,285....E5 88
Markham, Ont., Can., 36,684....D5, k15 41
Markham, Ill., 15,987....k9 58
Markham, mtn., Ant....L7 2
Markle, Ind., 963....C7 59
Markovka, Sov. Un., 5,000....G12 12
Marks, Miss., 2,609....A3 68
Marksville, La., 4,519....C3 63
Marktredwitz, Ger., Fed. Rep. of, 16,209....C6 6
Marlbank, Ont., Can., 237....C7 41
Marlboro, Mass., 27,936....B4, g9 65
Marlboro, N.J., 900....C4 74
Marlboro, N.Y., 1,580....D6 75
Marlboro, co., S.C., 27,151....B8 82
Marlborough, N.H., 1,231....F3 73
Marlene Village, Oreg., 1,000....*B3 80
Marlette, Mich., 1,706....E7 66
Marley, Md., 2,500....B4 53
Marlin, Tex., 6,351....D4 84
Marlinton, W. Va., 1,286....C4 87
Marlow, Okla., 4,027....C4 79
Marlowe, W. Va., 700....B7 87
Marlton, N.J., 10,180....D3 74
Marmande, Fr., 10,199....E4 5
Marmet, W. Va., 2,339....C3, m12 87
Marmora, Ont., Can., 1,381....C7 41
Marmora, N.J., 500....E3 74
Marmora, peak, It....D2 9
Marne, Mich., 500....E5 66
Marne, dept., Fr., 485,388....*C6 5
Maroa, Ill., 1,467....C5 58
Maroantsetra, Mad., 5,300....D9 24
Maromokotro, mtn., Mad....C9 24
Maroochydore-Mooloolaba, Austl., 6,360....C9 26
Maroua, Cam....F7 22
Marovoay, Mad., 14,000....D9 24
Marquesas, is., Fr. Polynesia....G11 2
Marquette, Kans., 578....D6 61
Marquette, Mich., 21,967....B3 66
Marquette, co., Mich., 64,686....B3 66
Marquette, co., Wis., 8,865....E4 88
Marquette Heights, Ill., 2,758....C4 58
Marrakech, Mor., 332,741....B3 22
Marrero, La., 35,000....k11 63
Marromeu, Moz....D7 24
Mars, Pa., 1,488....E1 81
Mars, hill, Maine....g7 64
Marsala, It., 42,100....F4 9
Marseille, Fr., 889,029 (1,015,000)....F6 5
Marseilles, Ill., 4,320....B5 58
Marshall, Ark., 1,397....B3 49
Marshall, Ill., 3,468....D6 58
Marshall, Mich., 7,253....F6 66
Marshall, Minn., 9,886....F3 67
Marshall, Mo., 12,051....B4 69
Marshall, N.C., 982....F10 76
Marshall, Tex., 22,937....C5 84
Marshall, Va., 500....B5 85
Marshall, Wis., 1,034....E4 88
Marshall, co., Ala., 54,211....A3 46
Marshall, co., Ill., 13,302....B4 58
Marshall, co., Ind., 34,986....B5 59
Marshall, co., Iowa, 41,076....C4 60
Marshall, co., Kans., 13,139....C7 61
Marshall, co., Ky., 20,381....f9 62
Marshall, co., Minn., 13,060....B2 67
Marshall, co., Miss., 24,027....A4 68
Marshall, co., Okla., 7,682....C5 79
Marshall co., S. Dak., 5,965....E8 77
Marshall, co., Tenn., 17,319....B5 83
Marshall, co., W. Va., 37,598....B4 87
Marshallberg, N.C., 600....C6 76
Marshall Northeast, Tex....*C5 84
Marshallton, Del., 9,000....A6 35
Marshallton, Pa., 1,802....*D8 81
Marshalltown, Iowa, 26,219....B5 60
Marshallville, Ga., 1,376....D3 55
Marshallville, Ohio, 693....B4 78
Marshfield, Mass., 2,562 (15,223 ▲)....B6, h13 65
Marshfield, Mo., 2,961....D5 69
Marshfield, Wis., 15,619....D3 88
Marshfield Hills, Mass., 1,350....B6, h13 65
Mars Hill, Ind....E5, m10 59
Mars Hill, Maine, 1,384 (1,875 ▲)....B5 64
Mars Hill, N.C., 1,623....f10 76
Marshville, N.C., 1,405....C2 76
Marsing, Idaho, 610....F2 57
Marston, Mo., 666....E8 69
Mart, Tex., 2,183....D4 84
Martel, Que., Can., 1,009....A6 42
Martí, Cuba....D5 35
Martigues, Fr., 17,826....F6 5
Martin, Ky., 786....C7 62
Martin, Mich., 502....F5 66
Martin, S. Dak., 1,248....G4 77
Martin, Tenn., 7,781....A3 83
Martin, co., Fla., 28,035....E6 54
Martin, co., Ind., 10,909....G4 59
Martin, co., Ky., 9,377....C7 62
Martin, co., Minn., 24,316....G4 67
Martin, co., N.C., 24,730....B5 76
Martin, co., Tex., 4,774....C2 84
Martina [Franca], It., 28,500....D6 9
Martinez, Calif., 16,506....C2, h8 50
Martinez, Ga., 7,300....C4 55
Martinique, Fr. dep., N.A., 355,000....I14 35
Martinsburg, Pa., 2,088....F5 81
Martinsburg, W. Va., 14,626....B7 87
Martins Creek, Pa., 850....B2 81
Martins Ferry, Ohio, 10,757....B5 78
Martinsville, Ill., 1,374....D6 58
Martinsville, Ind., 9,723....F5 59
Martinsville, N.J., 900....B3 74
Martinsville (Independent City), Va., 19,653....D3 85
Martos, Sp., 16,442 (23,990 ▲)....D4 8
Marudi, Mala., 2,663....E5 19
Maruf, Afg., 5,000....B4 20
Marugame, Jap., 59,214....I6 18
Marvell, Ark., 1,980....C5 49
Mary, Sov. Un., 62,000....F9 13
Maryborough, Austl., 19,304....E9 25
Maryborough, Austl., 7,469....G7 25
Maryfield, Sask., Can., 476....H5 39
Maryland, state, U.S., 4,113,000.... 53
Maryland Heights, Mo., 6,000....f13 69
Maryport, Eng., 11,660....C5 4
Marys, peak, Oreg....C3 80
Mary's Harbour, Newf., Can., 264....B4 44
Marystown, Newf., Can., 4,960....E4 44
Marysville, Calif., 9,353....C3 50
Marysville, B.C., Can., 1,057....E10 37
Marysville, N. B., Can., 3,872....D3 43
Marysville, Kans., 3,588....C7 61
Marysville, Mich., 5,610....F8 66
Marysville, Ohio, 5,744....B2 78
Marysville, Pa., 2,328....F8 81
Marysville, Wash., 4,343....A3 86
Maryvale, Ariz....*C2 48
Maryville, Mo., 9,970....A3 69
Maryville, Tenn., 13,808....D10, n14 83
Masan, Kor., 190,992....I4 18
Masaya, Nic., 30,753....E7 34
Masbate, Phil., 17,749....C6 19
Masbate, prov., Phil., 335,971....*H7 19
Mascara, Alg., 36,930....A5 22
Mascot, Tenn., 900....C10, m14 83
Mascota, Mex., 5,674....m11 34
Mascouche, Que., Can., 8,812....D4 42
Mascoutah, Ill., 5,045....E4 58
Mashhad (Meshed), Iran, 409,616....B6 15
Masindi, Ug., 1,571....H4 23
Masisea, Peru, 1,742....C3 31
Masjed, Soleymān, Iran, 64,488....C4 15
Maskinongé, Que., Can., 893....C4 42
Maskinongé, co., Que., Can., 21,466....C4 42
Mason, Mich., 5,468....F6 66
Mason, Ohio, 5,677....C1, n13 78
Mason, Tex., 1,806....D3 84
Mason, W. Va., 1,319....B2 87
Mason, co., Ill., 16,161....C4 58
Mason, co., Ky., 17,273....B6 62
Mason, co., Mich., 22,612....D4 66
Mason, co., Tex., 3,356....D3 84
Mason, co., Wash., 20,918....B2 86
Mason, co., W. Va., 24,306....C3 87
Mason City, Ill., 2,611....C4 58
Mason City, Iowa, 30,379....A4 60
Masontown, Pa., 4,226....G2 81
Masontown, W. Va., 868....B5 87
Mass, Mich., 500....B1, m12 66
Massa, It., 62,400 (*137,000)....B3 9
Massac, co., Ill., 13,889....F5 58
Massachusetts, state, U.S., 5,822,000.... 65
Massaemett, mtn., Mass....A2 65
Massafra, It., 22,500....D6 9
Massa Marittima, It., 5,700....C3 9
Massanutten, mtn., Va....B4 85

Moncton, N.B., Can.,
47,891 (*71,416).....C5 43
Mondoñedo, Sp., 9,153...A2 8
Mondoví, It., 8,800......B1 9
Mondovi, Wis., 2,338.....D2 88
Monessen, Pa., 15,216....F2 81
Monett, Mo., 5,937......E4 69
Monette, Ark., 1,076.....B5 49
Monfalcone, It., 27,900..B4 9
Monforte de Lemos, Sp.,
13,502................A2 8
Monfort Heights, Ohio,
8,000................*C1 78
Monghyr, India, 102,474
(*164,205).........C8 20
Mong Mit, Bur., 5,000...D10 20
Mongolia, country, Asia,
1,375,000...........B4 17
Moniquirá, Col., 4,882...B3 32
Moniteau, co., Mo.,
10,742..............C5 69
Monmouth, Ill., 11,022....C3 58
Monmouth, Oreg.,
5,237............C3, k11 80
Monmouth, co., N.J.,
461,849.............C4 74
Monmouth, co., Wales,
461,670.............*E5 4
Monmouth, mtn., B.C.,
Can.................D6 37
Monmouth, peak, Oreg....C3 80
Monmouth Beach, N.J.,
2,042...............C5 74
Monmouth Junction,
N.J., 950............C3 74
Mono, co., Calif., 4,016...D4 50
Monon, Ind., 1,548......C4 59
Monona, Iowa, 1,395.....A6 60
Monona, Wis., 10,420....E4 88
Monona, co., Iowa, 12,069.B1 60
Monongah, W. Va.,
1,194............B4, k10 87
Monongahela, Pa., 7,113..F2 81
Monongalia, co., W. Va.,
63,714..............B4 87
Monopoli, It., 27,000.....D6 9
Monor, Hung., 14,830....B4 10
Monóvar, Sp., 9,933.....C5 8
Monponsett, Mass., 600...B9 65
Monreale, It., 20,500.....E4 9
Monroe, Conn., 760......D3 52
Monroe, Ga., 8,071......C3 55
Monroe, Iowa, 1,389.....C4 60
Monroe, La., 56,374
(*105,000)...........B3 63
Monroe, Mich., 23,894
(*56,100)............G7 66
Monroe, N.Y.,
4,439............D6, m14 75
Monroe, N.C., 11,282....C2 76
Monroe, Ohio, 3,492.....*C1 78
Monroe, Utah, 918.......B5 72
Monroe, Va., 800........C3 85
Monroe, Wash., 2,687.....B4 86
Monroe, Wis., 8,654.....F4 88
Monroe, co., Ala., 20,883.D2 46
Monroe, co., Ark., 15,657.C4 49
Monroe, co., Fla., 52,586..G5 54
Monroe, co., Ga., 10,991..D3 55
Monroe, co., Ill., 18,831...E3 58
Monroe, co., Ind., 84,849..F4 59
Monroe, co., Iowa, 9,357..D5 60
Monroe, co., Ky., 11,642..D4 62
Monroe, co., Mich.,
119,172.............G7 66
Monroe, co., Miss., 34,043.B5 68
Monroe, co., Mo., 9,542..B5 69
Monroe, co., N.Y., 711,917.B3 75
Monroe, co., Ohio, 15,739..C4 78
Monroe, co., Pa., 45,422..D11 81
Monroe, co., Tenn.,
23,475..............D9 83
Monroe, co., W. Va.,
11,272..............D4 87
Monroe, co., Wis., 31,610..E3 88
Monroe City, Mo., 2,456..B6 69
Monroeville, Ala., 4,846...D2 46
Monroeville, Ind., 1,353...C8 59
Monroeville, Ohio, 1,455..A3 78
Monroeville, Pa., 29,011..*E1 81
Monrovia, Calif., 30,562..m13 50
Monrovia, Lib., 80,992....G2 22
Mons, Bel., 28,877
(*169,000)..........B5 5
Monson, Maine, 500
(669 ▲)..............C3 64
Monson, Mass., 1,110
(7,355 ▲)............B2 65
Montague, Calif., 890.....B2 50
Montague, P.E.I., Can.,
1,608...............C7 43
Montague, Mass., 600
(8,451 ▲)............A2 65
Montague, Mich., 2,396...E4 66
Montague, co., Tex.,
15,326..............C4 84
Montague City, Mass.,
700.................A2 65

Mont Alto, Pa., 1,532.....G6 81
Montalvo, Calif..........*E4 50
Montana, state, U.S.,
726,000.............. 70
Montánchez, Sp., 4,190...C2 8
Montargis, Fr., 18,225
(*45,000)............D5 5
Montauban, Que., Can.,
623.................C5 42
Montauban, Fr., 34,513...E4 5
Montauk, N.Y., 600......m17 75
Monta Vista, Calif.,
1,000...............*D3 50
Monta Vista, Wash.,
1,500...............*B3 86
Montbéliard, Fr., 23,908
(*115,000)...........D7 5
Mont Belvieu, Tex.,
1,144............E5, r15 84
Montbrison, Fr., 9,449.....E6 5
Montcalm, co., Que.,
Can., 19,260.........C3 42
Montcalm, co., Mich.,
39,660..............E5 66
Mont-Carmel, Que.,
Can., 895............B8 42
Montceau-les-Mines, Fr.,
27,421 (*50,000).......D6 5
Montchanin [-les-Mines],
Fr., 6,408............D6 5
Montclair (Monte Vista),
Calif., 22,546........m13 50
Montclair, N.J., 44,043....B4 74
Mont Clare, Pa., 1,274....o19 81
Montcoal, W. Va.,
275...............D3, n12 87
Mont-De-Marsan, Fr.,
24,458..............F3 5
Montebello, Calif.,
42,807..............m12 50
Montebello, Que., Can.,
1,486...............D3 42
Monte Caseros, Arg.,
12,930..............A5 28
Montecelio, It., 5,000.....g9 9
Montecristi, Dom. Rep.,
8,300...............E8 35
Montefrío, Sp., 5,137.....D3 8
Montego Bay, Jam.,
42,800..............E5 35
Montegut, La., 700......E5 63
Monteith, mtn., B.C.,
Can.................B6 38
Montélimar, Fr., 26,748...E6 5
Montellano, Sp., 9,334....D3 8
Montello, Wis., 1,082.....E4 88
Montemorelos, Mex.,
18,642..............B5 34
Montemor-o-Novo, Port.,
5,047...............C1 8
Montenegro, Braz.,
21,497..............D2 30
Montenegro (Crna Gora),
rep., Yugo., 471,894...*D4 10
Monte Plata, Dom. Rep.,
3,600...............E9 35
Montepulciano, It.,
3,400...............C3 9
Montereau, Fr., 14,121....C5 5
Monterey, Calif., 26,302
(*127,100)...........D3 50
Monterey, Ohio, 1,500....*C1 78
Monterey, Tenn., 2,351...C8 83
Monterey, co., Calif.,
247,450.............D3 50
Monterey Park, Calif.,
49,166..............m12 50
Montería, Col., 90,000
(161,300▲)..........B2 32
Monteros, Arg., 11,968....E2 29
Monterotondo, It., 9,340...g9 9
Monterrey, Mex., 858,107
(*1,200,000).........B4 34
Montesano, Wash., 2,847..C2 86
Monte Sant' Angelo, It.,
20,100..............D5 9
Montes Claros, Braz.,
81,572..............B4 30
Monte Sereno, Calif.,
3,089...............*D3 50
Montevallo, Ala., 3,719....B3 46
Montevarchi, It., 9,100....C3 9
Montevideo, Minn., 5,661.F3 67
Montevideo, Ur.,
1,325,000 (*1,525,000)...E1 30
Montevideo, dept., Ur.,
1,158,632...........*E1 30
Monte Vista, Colo., 3,909..D4 51
Montezuma, Ga., 4,125...D2 55
Montezuma, Ind., 1,192...C3 59
Montezuma, Iowa, 1,353..C5 60
Montezuma, co., Colo.,
12,952..............D2 51
Montfort, Wis., 518......F3 88
Montgomery, Ala., 133,386
(*188,000)...........C3 46
Montgomery, Ill.,
3,278............B5, k8 58

Montgomery, La., 923.....C3 63
Montgomery, Minn.,
2,281...............F5 67
Montgomery, N.Y., 1,533..D6 75
Montgomery, Ohio,
5,683...............*C1 78
Montgomery, Pa., 1,902..D8 81
Montgomery, W. Va.,
2,525............C3, m13 87
Montgomery, co., Ala.,
167,790.............C3 46
Montgomery, co., Ark.,
5,821...............C2 49
Montgomery, co., Ga.,
6,099...............D4 55
Montgomery, co., Ill.,
30,260..............D4 58
Montgomery, co., Ind.,
33,930..............D4 59
Montgomery, co., Iowa,
12,781..............C2 60
Montgomery, co., Kans.,
39,949..............E8 61
Montgomery, co., Ky.,
15,364..............B6 62
Montgomery, co., Md.,
522,809.............B3 53
Montgomery, co., Miss.,
12,918..............B4 68
Montgomery, co., Mo.,
11,000..............C6 69
Montgomery, co., N.Y.,
55,883..............C6 75
Montgomery, co., N.C.,
19,267..............B3 76
Montgomery, co., Ohio,
608,413.............C1 78
Montgomery, co., Pa.,
623,956.............F11 81
Montgomery, co., Tenn.,
62,721..............A4 83
Montgomery, co., Tex.,
49,479..............D5 84
Montgomery, co., Va.,
47,157..............C2 85
Montgomery, co., Wales,
43,110..............*D5 4
Montgomery City, Mo.,
2,187...............C6 69
Monticello, Ark., 5,085....D4 49
Monticello, Fla., 2,473....B3 54
Monticello, Ga., 2,132....C3 55
Monticello, Ill., 4,130.....C5 58
Monticello, Ind., 4,869....C4 59
Monticello, Iowa, 3,509...B6 60
Monticello, Ky., 3,618....D5 62
Monticello, Maine, 600
(1,072 ▲)............B5 64
Monticello, Minn., 1,636..E5 67
Monticello, Miss., 1,790...D3 68
Monticello, N.Y., 5,991...D6 75
Monticello, Utah, 1,431...C7 72
Monticello, Wis., 870.....F4 88
Montigny [-lès-Metz], Fr.,
24,520..............C5 5
Montijo, Port., 17,751...C1, f10 8
Montijo, Sp., 14,961.....C2 8
Montilla, Sp., 19,755.....D3 8
Montivilliers, Fr., 8,910...C4 5
Mont-Joli, Que., Can.,
6,698...............G20 36
Mont-Laurier, Que., Can.,
8,240...............C2 42
Montluçon, Fr., 57,871....D5 5
Montmagny, Que.,
Can., 12,432.........C7 42
Montmagny, co., Que.,
Can., 26,751.........C7 42
Montmartre, Sask., Can.,
482.................G4 39
Montmorenci, S.C., 900...D4 82
Montmorency, Que.,
Can., 4,949........C6, n17 42
Montmorency, Fr.,
18,691..............g10 5
Montmorency, co., Mich.,
5,247...............C6 66
Montmorency No. 1, co.,
Que., Can., 20,680....B6 42
Montmorency No. 2, co.,
Que., Can., 5,268.....C7 42
Montmorillon, Fr., 4,766..D4 5
Montoro, Sp., 14,950....C3 8
Montour, co., Pa., 16,508.D8 81
Montour Falls, N.Y.,
1,534...............C4 75
Montoursville, Pa., 5,985..D8 81
Montpelier, Idaho, 2,604..G7 57
Montpelier, Ind., 2,093...C7 59
Montpelier, Ohio, 4,184...A1 78
Montpelier, Vt., 8,609....C2 73
Montpellier, Fr., 161,910..F5 5
Montréal, Que., Can.,
1,214,352
(*2,743,208)...D4, q19 42
Montreal, Wis., 877......B3 88
Montréal West, Que.,
Can., 6,368.........*D4 42

Montreuil-sous-Bois, Fr.,
95,714..............C5 5
Montreux, Switz., 20,700..E3 6
Mont-Rolland, Que., Can.,
1,503...............D3 42
Montrose, Ala., 500......E2 46
Montrose, Calif., 6,000...*E4 50
Montrose, B.C., Can., 862.E9 37
Montrose, Colo., 6,496...C3 51
Montrose, Iowa, 735.....D6 60
Montrose, Mich., 1,789...E7 66
Montrose, Pa., 1,100.....*F10 81
Montrose, Pa., 2,058....C10 81
Montrose, Scot., 10,091...B5 4
Montrose, co., Colo.,
18,366..............C2 51
Montrose Hill, Pa., 2,400..*E1 81
Montrouge, Fr., 44,922...g10 5
Mont-Royal, Que., Can.,
21,561..............p19 42
Montserrat, Br. dep.,
N.A., 14,800.........H13 35
Montvale, N.J., 7,327.....g8 74
Montville, Conn., 1,688...D8 52
Montville, N.J., 2,500....B4 74
Monument, peak, Idaho...G4 57
Monument Beach, Mass.,
1,000...............C6 65
Monywa, Bur., 26,172...D10 20
Monza, It., 105,400......B2 9
Monzón, Peru, 514......C2 31
Moodus, Conn., 1,352....D7 52
Moody, Tex., 1,286......D4 84
Moody, co., S. Dak., 7,622.F9 77
Mooers, N.Y., 536......f11 75
Moonachie, N.J., 2,951...*B4 74
Moon Crest, Pa., 1,000...*E1 81
Moon Run, Pa., 700.....k13 81
Moonta, Austl., 1,578....F6 25
Moora, Austl., 1,423.....F2 25
Moorcraft, Wyo., 981....B8 89
Moore, Okla., 18,761....B4 79
Moore, co., N.C., 39,048..B3 76
Moore, co., Tenn., 3,568..B5 83
Moore, co., Tex., 14,060..B2 84
Moorefield, W. Va., 2,124..B6 87
Moore Haven, Fla., 974..F5 54
Mooreland, Okla., 1,196...A2 79
Moorestown, N.J., 15,577.D3 74
Mooresville, Ind., 5,800...E5 59
Mooresville, N.C., 8,808..B2 76
Moorhead, Minn., 29,687..D2 67
Moorhead, Miss., 2,284...B3 68
Mooringsport, La., 830....B2 63
Moorpark, Calif., 3,380...E4 50
Moose, mtn., Sask., Can...H4 39
Mooseheart, Ill., 1,200..B5, k8 58
Moose Jaw, Sask., Can.,
31,854...........G3, n7 39
Moose Lake, Minn.,
1,400...............D6 67
Moosic, Pa., 4,273......m18 81
Moosic, mts., Pa.........m18 81
Moosomin, Sask., Can.,
2,407...............G5 39
Moosonee, Ont., Can.,
1,793...............o19 41
Moosup, Conn., 3,376....C9 52
Mopti, Mali, 32,000.....F4 22
Moquegua, Peru, 7,700...E3 31
Moquegua, dept., Peru,
41,072..............E3 31
Mor, Hung., 11,482.....B4 10
Mora, Minn., 2,582......E5 67
Mora, N. Mex., 400......B6 48
Mora, Sp., 10,657.......C4 8
Mora, Swe., 17,462.....G6 11
Mora, co., N. Mex., 4,673..A6 48
Morada, Calif., 2,936....*D3 50
Morādābād, India, 258,590,
(*272,652)..........C6 20
Moraine, Ohio, 4,898....*C1 78
Moramanga, Mad.,
5,700...............D9 24
Moran, Kans., 550......E8 61
Morant Bay, Jam., 7,800..F5 35
Moratalla, Sp., 5,879....C5 8
Moratuwa, Sri Lanka,
77,600..............*G6 20
Moravia, Iowa, 699.....D5 60
Moravia, N.Y., 1,642....C4 75
Moravia (Morava), reg.,
Czech., 3,738,035....D4 7
Moray, co., Scot., 52,329.*B5 4
Morbihan, dept., Fr.,
540,474............*D2 5
Morden, Man., Can.,
3,266...............E2 40
Moreauville, La., 807....C4 63
Moree, Austl., 9,114....E8 25
Morehead, Ky., 7,191....B6 62
Morehead City, N.C.,
5,233...............C6 76
Morehouse, par., La.,
32,463..............B4 63
Morehouse, Mo., 1,332..E8 69
Moreland Hills, Ohio,
2,952...............*A4 78

Mulgrave, N.S., Can.,
1,145................D8 43
Mulhacén, mtn., Sp.,...D4 8
Mülheim an der Ruhr,
Ger., Fed. Rep. of,
191,807...............C3 6
Mulhouse, Fr., 116,336
(*200,000)............D7 5
Mullan, Idaho, 1,279....B3 57
Mullens, W. Va., 2,967...D3 87
Mullewa, Austl., 874....E2 25
Mullica Hill, N.J., 550..D2 74
Mullingar, Ire., 6,790...D3 4
Mullins, S.C., 6,006.....C9 82
Multān, Pak., 520,000
(*544,000)............B5 20
Multnomah, co., Oreg.,
554,668...............B4 80
Mulvane, Kans., 3,185...E6 61
Muna, Mex., 5,491......C7 34
München, see Munich, Ger.,
Fed. Rep. of
Munchŏn, Kor., 12,005...G3 18
Muncie, Ind., 69,082
(*122,300)............D7 59
Muncy, Pa., 2,872.......D8 81
Mundare, Alta., Can., 603.C4 38
Munday, Tex., 1,726.....C3 84
Mundelein, Ill., 16,128.A5, h9 58
Münden, Ger., Fed. Rep.
of, 27,497.............C4 6
Munford, Tenn., 1,281...B2 83
Munfordville, Ky., 1,233..C4 62
Mungindi, Austl., 848....E8 25
Munhall, Pa., 16,574....k14 81
Munich (München), Ger.,
Fed. Rep. of, 1,338,924
(*1,885,000)..........D5 6
Munising, Mich., 3,677...B4 66
Munroe Falls, Ohio,
3,794................*A4 78
Munsan, Kor., 5,000.....H3 18
Munsey Park, N.Y.,
2,980................*E7 75
Munster, Fr., 4,888......C7 5
Munster, Ind., 16,514....A2 59
Münster [in Westfalen],
Ger., Fed. Rep. of,
200,509 (*255,000)......C3 6

Munster, prov., Ire.,
859,334..............*D2 4
Muntenia, prov., Rom.,
4,991,289............*C8 10
Muntenia, reg., Rom......C7 10
Muntok, Indon., 6,929....F3 19
Muong Hou Nua, Laos,
10,000...............*D11 20
Muong Sing, Laos,
10,000................D11 20
Murakami, Jap., 32,549...G9 18
Murcia, Sp., 160,000
(243,687 ▲)...........C5 8
Murcia, reg., Sp.,
1,200,100.............C5 8
Murfreesboro, Ark., 1,350..C2 49
Murfreesboro, N.C.,
3,508.................A5 76
Murfreesboro, Tenn.,
26,360................B5 83
Murgon, Austl., 2,479....E9 25
Muriae, Braz., 34,118....C4 30
Murmansk, Sov. Un.,
309,000...............C15 11
Murom, Sov. Un.,
99,000................D13 12
Muroran, Jap., 162,059
(*210,000)............E10 18
Muroto, Jap., 27,445....J7 18
Murphy, Mo., 800.......g13 69
Murphy, N.C., 2,082.....F8 76
Murphysboro, Ill., 10,013..F4 58
Murray, Iowa, 620.......C4 60
Murray, Ky., 13,537......f9 62
Murray, Utah,
21,206.............A6, C2 72
Murray, co., Ga., 12,986...B2 55
Murray, co., Minn.,
12,508................F3 67
Murray, co., Okla., 10,669.C4 79
Murray, riv., Austl.......G7 25
Murray Bridge, Austl.,
7,400.................G6 25
Murray City, Ohio, 562...C3 78
Murrells Inlet, S.C., 700..D9 82
Murrysville, Pa., 2,600...k15 81
Murud, India, 9,744.....E5 20
Murwāra, India, 54,864
(*86,535).............D7 20

Murwillumbah, Austl.,
7,374................D9 26
Mürzzuschlag, Aus.,
11,494................E7 6
Muş, Tur., 23,058......C13 14
Musala, peak, Bul.......D6 10
Musan, Kor., 20,717.....E4 18
Musashino, Jap.,
136,959..............*I9 18
Muscat, Om., 6,000.....D2 20
Muscat & Oman, see Oman,
country, Asia
Muscatine, Iowa,
22,405................C6 60
Muscatine, co., Iowa,
37,181................C6 60
Muscle Shoals, Ala.,
6,907.................A2 46
Musclow, mtn., B.C.,
Can...................C4 37
Muscoda, Wis., 1,099....E3 88
Musconetcong, mtn.,
N.J...................B2 74
Muse, Pa., 1,358........F1 81
Musgravetown, Newf.,
Can., 597.............D5 44
Mushin, Nig., 145,976....*G5 22
Mushketovo, Sov. Un.,
10,000................r20 12
Muskego, Wis.,
11,573.............F5, n11 88
Muskegon, Mich., 44,631
(*178,400)............E4 66
Muskegon, co., Mich.,
157,426...............E4 66
Muskegon Heights, Mich.,
17,304................E4 66
Muskingum, co., Ohio,
77,826................B3 78
Muskö, Swe............u36 11
Muskogee, Okla., 37,331..B6 79
Muskogee, co., Okla.,
59,542................B6 79
Muskoka, dist., Ont.,
Can., 27,691..........B5 41
Musquash, mtn., Maine...C5 64
Musquodoboit Harbour,
N.S., Can., 654........E6 43

Musselburgh, Scot.,
16,903................C5 4
Musselshell, co., Mont.,
3,734.................D8 70
Mustafakemalpaşa, Tur.,
25,684................B7 14
Muswellbrook, Austl.,
8,082.................F9 25
Mutanchiang, China,
251,000...............C10 17
Mutsu, Jap., 41,134....F10 18
Mutton, mts., Oreg......C5 80
Muttontown, N.Y.,
2,081................*E7 75
Muzaffarnagar, India,
114,783..............*C6 20
Muzaffarpur, India,
126,379...............C8 20
Muzambinho, Braz.,
6,731.................k8 30
Muztagh Ata, mtn.,
China.................A7 20
Mwanza, Tan., 19,877....I4 23
Myaungmya, Bur.,
20,770...............*E9 20
Myers, S.C., 950.......k12 82
Myerstown, Pa., 3,645...F9 81
Myingyan, Bur., 36,536..D10 20
Myitkyina, Bur., 12,833..C10 20
Myjava, Czech., 9,935....D4 7
Myrtle Beach, S.C.,
9,035.................D10 82
Myrtle Creek, Oreg.,
2,733.................D3 80
Myrtle Grove, Fla.,
16,186...............u14 54
Myrtle Point, Oreg.,
2,511.................D2 80
Mysen, Nor., 2,525.....p29 11
Myślenice, Pol., 12,100...D5 7
Mysłowice, Pol., 44,700..g10 7
Mysore, India, 355,685...F6 20
Mysore, see Karnataka,
state, India
Mystic, Conn., 4,850....D9 52
Mystic, Iowa, 696.......D5 60
My Tho, Viet, 62,700....C3 19
Mytishchi, Sov. Un.,
119,000..............n17 12

N

Naalehu, Haw., 1,014....D6 56
Nabadwip, India, 94,204.*D8 20
Nabeul, Tun., 14,047.....A7 22
Nabnasset, Mass., 2,700..A5 65
Nābulus, Jordan,
44,223.............B3, g5 15
Naches, Wash., 666......C5 86
Náchod, Czech., 19,019...C4 7
Nacogdoches, Tex.,
22,544................D5 84
Nacogdoches, co., Tex.,
36,362................D5 84
Nacozari [de García],
Mex., 2,976...........A3 34
Nadiād, India, 108,269..*D5 20
Nădlac, Rom., 12,284....B5 10
Nadvornaya, Sov. Un.,
16,000................G5 12
Naesong, Kor., 5,000.....H4 18
Naestved, Den., 22,900
(*33,000).............J4 11
Naga, Phil., 79,846......C6 19
Nagaland, state, India,
516,449..............*C9 20
Nagano, Jap., 215,000
(285,355 ▲)...........H9 18
Nagano, pref., Jap.,
1,956,917............*H9 18
Nagaoka, Jap., 162,262..*H9 18
Nāgappattinam, India,
68,026 (*74,019)......F6 20
Nagasaki, Jap., 421,114..J4 18
Nagasaki, pref., Jap.,
1,570,245............*J4 18
Nāgercoil, India,
141,288...............G6 20
Nagoya, Jap., 2,075,249
(*3,450,000)........J8, n15 18
Nāgpur, India, 866,076
(*950,000)............D6 20
Nags Head, N.C., 414....B7 76
Nagua, Dom. Rep., 13,900.E9 35
Nagykanizsa, Hung.,
39,411................B3 10

Nagykőrös, Hung.,
20,503 (25,785 ▲).....B4 10
Naha, Jap., 276,380.....F10 17
Nahant, Mass., 4,119....g10 65
Nahariyya, Isr., 24,000...A3 15
Nahunta, Ga., 974.......E5 55
Naicam, Sask., Can., 672..E3 39
Nairn, Scot., 5,367......B5 4
Nairn, co., Scot., 8,304..*B5 4
Nairobi, Ken., 478,000...I5 23
Najin, Kor., 34,338......E5 18
Nakaminato, Jap., 32,873.m19 18
Nakamura, Jap., 33,573...J6 18
Nakatsu, Jap., 43,000
(57,461 ▲)............J5 18
Nakhichevan [na Arakse],
Sov. Un., 33,000......F7 16
Nakhon Ratchasima,
Thai., 66,071.........C2 19
Nakina, Ont., Can., 673..o18 41
Nakło, Pol., 16,800......B4 7
Nakskov, Den., 16,639...J4 11
Nakuru, Ken., 38,181....I5 23
Nakusp, B.C., Can., 1,163.D9 37
Nalchik, Sov. Un.,
146,000..............*E7 13
Namcha Barwa, mtn.,
China.................F4 17
Namangan, Sov. Un.,
175,000...............E10 12
Nambour, Austl., 6,744...E9 25
Nam Dinh, Viet, 86,132...A3 19
Namibia, see South West
Africa, country, Afr.
Namiquipa, Mex., 4,874..B3 34
Nampa, Idaho, 20,768....F2 57
Nampo (Chinnampo),
Kor., 82,162..........G2 18
Nampula, Moz...........D7 24
Namur, Bel., 32,194
(*88,000).............B6 5
Namur, prov., Bel.,
382,500..............*B6 5

Namwŏn, Kor., 32,000
(46,532 ▲)............I3 18
Nanaimo, B.C., Can.,
14,948 (*38,760)....E5, f12 37
Nanakuli, Haw.,
6,506..............B3, g9 56
Nanam, Kor., 21,258.....F4 18
Nanao, Jap., 37,500
(47,855 ▲)............H8 18
Nance, co., Nebr., 5,142..C7 71
Nanchang, China,
520,000...............F8 17
Nanchung, China,
164,700...............E6 17
Nancy, Fr., 123,428
(*260,000)............C7 5
Nanda Devi, peak, India..B7 20
Nanded, India, 126,538..*E6 20
Nānga Parbat, peak, Pak..A5 20
Nanhai (Fatshan), China,
120,000..............*G7 17
Nanju, Kor., 15,000......I3 18
Nanking (Nanching), China,
1,750,000.............E8 17
Nanning, China, 264,000..G6 17
Nanping, China, 29,000...F8 17
Nanterre, Fr., 90,332.....g9 5
Nantes, Fr. 259,208
(*400,000)............D3 5
Nanticoke, Md., 600.....D6 53
Nanticoke, Pa.,
14,632............D10, n16 81
Nanton, Alta., Can.,
1,054.................D4 38
Nantucket, Mass., 2,461..D7 65
Nantucket, co., Mass.,
3,774.................D7 65
Nantung, China,
240,000..............*E9 17
Nanty Glo, Pa., 4,298....F4 81
Nanuet, N.Y., 10,447....g12 75
Nanyang, China, 50,000...E7 17
Naoma, W. Va., 500.....n13 87
Naousa, Grc., 17,375.....B4 14

Napa, Calif., 35,978.....C2 50
Napa, co., Calif., 79,140..C2 50
Napanee, Ont., Can.,
4,638.................C8 41
Napanoch, N.Y., 950....D6 75
Naperville, Ill.,
22,617.............B5, k8 58
Napier, N.Z., 41,400
(*91,500)............M16 26
Napierville, Que., Can.,
1,987.................D4 42
Napierville, co., Que.,
Can., 11,822..........D4 42
Naples, Fla., 12,042.....F5 54
Naples (Napoli), It.,
1,276,800 (*1,920,000)...D5 9
Naples, N.Y., 1,324......C3 75
Naples, Tex., 1,726......C5 84
Napo, riv., Ec., Peru.....B2 31
Napoleon, N. Dak., 1,036..D6 77
Napoleon, Ohio, 7,791....A1 78
Napoleonville, La.,
1,008..............E4, k9 63
Napoli, see Naples, It.
Nappanee, Ind., 4,159....B5 59
Naqadeh, Iran, 10,801...D15 14
Nara, Jap., 208,266.....o14 18
Naracoorte, Austl., 4,399..G7 25
Naranja, Fla., 2,900...G6, s13 54
Nārāyanganj, Bngl.
125,792...............D9 20
Narberth, Pa., 5,151..F11, o20 81
Narbonne, Fr., 38,441....F5 5
Nardó, It., 23,700.......D7 9
Nariño, dept., Col.,
757,600...............C2 32
Narita, Jap., 25,500
(42,514 ▲)...........n19 18
Narmada, riv., India.....D6 20
Narodnaya, mtn.,
Sov. Un...............C9 13
Naro-Fominsk, Sov. Un.,
49,000...............D11 12
Narol, Man., Can., 592...D3 40

New-Nog 165

New Freedom, Pa., 1,495..G8 81
New Germany, N.S., Can., 623..............E5 43
New Glarus, Wis., 550.....F4 88
New Glasgow, N.S., Can., 10,849 (*23,435).......D7 43
New Gretna, N.J., 550....D4 74
New Guinea, isl., Oceania..G6 2
New Guinea, Territory of, Austl. trust., Oceania 1,955,000.............h12 25
Newgulf, Tex., 900.......*E5 84
Newhall, Calif., 7,000.....E4 50
Newhall, Iowa, 701.......C6 60
New Hamburg, Ont., Can., 3,008 (*10,010)...D4 41
New Hampshire, state, U.S., 788,000............ 73
New Hampton, Iowa, 3,621.................A5 60
New Hanover, co., N.C., 82,996.................C5 76
New Harbour, Newf., Can., 756..............E5 44
New Harmony, Ind., 971..H2 59
New Hartford, Conn. 1,076.................B5 52
New Hartford, Iowa, 690..B5 60
New Hartford, N.Y., 2,433.................*B5 75
New Haven, Conn., 137,707 (*493,400)......D5 52
New Haven, Ill., 606......F5 58
New Haven, Ind., 5,728...B7 59
New Haven, Ky., 977.....C4 62
New Haven, Mich., 1,855..F8 66
New Haven, Mo., 1,474...C6 69
New Haven, W. Va., 1,538.................C3 87
New Haven, co., Conn., 744,948...............D4 52
New Hebrides, Br. and Fr. dep., Oceania, 88,000...H8 2
New Holland, Ga., 800....B3 55
New Holland, Ohio, 796...C2 78
New Holland, Pa., 3,971...F9 81
New Holstein, Wis., 3,012..............E5, k9 88
New Hope, Ala., 1,300....A3 46
New Hope, Minn., 23,180.*E5 67
New Hope, Pa., 978......F12 81
New Hudson, Mich., 600..o14 66
New Hyde Park, N.Y., 10,116..............G2 52
New Iberia, La., 30,147...D4 63
Newington, Conn., 26,037..C6 52
New Jersey, state, U.S., 7,361,000............... 74
New Kensington, Pa., 20,312...........E2, h14 81
New Kent, co., Va., 5,300..C6 85
Newkirk, Okla., 2,173.....A4 79
New Knoxville, Ohio, 852..B1 78
New Kowloon, Hong Kong, 1,479,417..............*G7 17
Newland, N.C., 524...A1, e11 76
New Lebanon, Ohio, 4,248................*C1 78
New Lenox, Ill., 2,855.............B6, k9 58
New Lexington, Ohio 4,921.................C3 78
New Lisbon, Wis., 1,361...E3 88
New Liskeard, Ont., Can., 5,488.................p20 41
New London, Conn., 31,630 (*238,700)......D8 52
New London, Iowa, 1,900..D6 60
New London, Minn., 736..E4 67
New London, Mo., 967....B6 69
New London, N.H., 1,347..E4 73
New London, Ohio, 2,336..A3 78
New London, Wis., 5,801..D5 88
New London, co., Conn., 230,654...............C8 52
New Madison, Ohio, 959..C1 78
New Madrid, Mo., 2,719...E8 69
New Madrid, co., Mo., 23,420................E8 69
New Malden, Eng., 46,587..............m11 4
Newman, Calif., 2,505.....D3 50
Newman, Ill., 1,018.......D6 58
Newman Grove, Nebr., 863..................C8 71
Newmanstown, Pa., 1,532..F9 81
Newmarket, Ont., Can., 18,941................C5 41
New Market, Ind., 640....E4 59
Newmarket, N.H., 2,645...E6 73
New Market, N.J........*B4 74
New Market, Va., 718.....B4 85
New Martinsville, W. Va., 6,528..................B4 87
New Matamoras, Ohio, 940..................C4 78
New Meadows, Idaho, 605..................E2 57
New Mexico, state, U.S., 1,090,000................ 48
New Miami, Ohio, 3,273............C1, n12 78
New Milford, Conn., 4,606.C3 52
New Milford, N.J., 19,149..h8 74
New Milford, Ohio.......A4 78
New Milford, Pa., 1,143..C10 81
New Monmouth, N.J......C4 74
Newnan, Ga., 11,205......C2 55
New Norfolk, Austl., 6,893..................o15 25
New Orleans, La., 593,471 (*1,052,500).......E5, h11 63
New Oxford, Pa., 1,495...G7 81
New Palestine, Ind., 863...E6 59
New Paltz, N.Y., 6,058....D6 75
New Paris, Ind., 1,080.....B6 59
New Paris, Ohio, 1,692....C1 78
New Philadelphia, Ohio, 15,184................B4 78
New Philadelphia, Pa., 1,528...................E9 81
New Plymouth, Idaho, 986.F2 57
New Plymouth, N.Z., 35,100 (*39,700)......M15 26
Newport, Ark., 7,725......B4 49
Newport, Del., 1,366......A6 53
Newport, Eng., 21,870.....E6 4
New Port, Ind., 708.......E3 59
Newport, Ky., 25,998...........A5, h14 62
Newport, Maine, 1,588....D3 64
Newport, Mich., 650......G7 66
Newport, Minn., 2,922....n13 67
Newport, N.H., 3,296.....E3 73
Newport, N.J., 400........E2 74
New Port, N.Y., 908.......B5 75
Newport, N.C., 1,735......C6 76
Newport, Ohio, 700.......C4 78
Newport, Oreg., 5,188.....C2 80
Newport, Pa., 1,747.......F7 81
Newport, R.I., 34,562 (*76,400).............D11 52
Newport, Tenn., 7,328...D10 83
Newport, Vt., 4,664.......B3 73
Newport, Wales, 111,810 (*315,000).............E5 4
Newport, Wash., 1,418....A8 86
Newport, co., R.I., 94,228...............C11 52
Newport Beach, Calif., 49,582............F5, n13 50
Newport News (Independent City), Va., 138,177 (*296,800)........D6, k15 85
New Port Richey, Fla., 6,098.................D4 54
Newportville, Pa., 1,300.*F11 81
New Prague, Minn., 2,680..F5 67
New Providence, N.J., 13,796.................B4 74
New Providence, isl., Ba..............B5, m17 35
Newquay, Eng., 13,220....E4 4
New Richland, Minn., 1,113..................G5 67
New Richmond, Que., Can., 3,957............A4 43
New Richmond, Ohio, 2,650..................D1 78
New Richmond, Wis., 3,707..................C1 88
New Road, N.S., Can., 1,109..................E6 43
New Roads, La., 3,945....D4 63
New Rochelle, N.Y., 75,385..........h13, n15 75
New Rockford, N. Dak., 1,969..................C6 77
Newry, N. Ire., 11,393....C3 4
Newry, S.C., 750.........B2 82
New Salem, N. Dak., 943..D4 77
New Salem, Pa., 384.....*G2 81
New Sarpy, La., 1,643....k11 63
New Sharon, Iowa, 944....C5 60
New Shrewsbury, N.J., 8,395..................C4 74
New Smyrna Beach, Fla., 10,580................C6 54
New South Wales, state, Austl., 4,780,000........F8 25
New Straitsville, Ohio, 947.C3 78
New Tazewell, Tenn., 1,192..................C10 83
Newton, Ala., 1,865.......D4 46
Newton, Ill., 3,024........E5 58
Newton, Iowa, 15,619......C4 60
Newton, Kans., 15,439............D6, f12 61
Newton, Mass., 91,263............B5, g11 65
Newton, Miss., 3,556......C4 68
Newton, N.J., 7,297.......A3 74
Newton, N.C., 7,857......B1 76
Newton, Tex., 1,529.......D6 84
Newton, co., Ark., 5,844...B2 49
Newton, co., Ga., 26,282...C3 55
Newton, co., Ind., 11,606..B3 59
Newton, co., Miss., 18,983................C4 68
Newton, co., Mo., 32,901..E3 69
Newton, co., Tex., 11,657..D6 84
Newton Falls, N.Y., 750................A6, f9 75
Newton Falls, Ohio, 5,378..A5 78
Newtonville, N.Y., 1,500..*C7 75
Newtown, Newf., Can., 585..................D5 44
Newtown, Conn., 1,963....D3 52
New Town, N. Dak., 1,428..................C3 77
Newtown, Ohio, 2,038.............C1, o13 78
Newtown, Pa., 2,216......F12 81
Newtown [& Llanllwchaiarn], Wales, 5,621...........D5 4
Newtownards, N. Ire., 15,387................C4 4
Newtown Square, Pa., 11,081................p20 81
New Ulm, Minn., 13,051..F4 67
New Vienna, Ohio, 849....C2 78
Newville, Pa., 1,631.......F7 81
New Washington, Ohio, 1,251..................B3 78
New Waterford, N.S., Can., 9,579.............C9 43
New Waterford, Ohio, 735..B5 78
New Westminster, B.C., Can., 42,835.......E6, f13 37
New Whiteland, Ind., 4,200..................E5 59
New Wilmington, Pa., 2,721..................D1 81
New Windsor, Ill., 723....B3 58
New Windsor, Md., 788...A3 53
New Windsor, N.Y., 8,803..................*D6 75
New York, N.Y., 7,895,563 (*17,326,600)......E7, h13 75
New York, co., N.Y., 1,539,233.............k13 75
New York, state, U.S., 18,292,000............. 75
New York Mills, Minn., 791...................D3 67
New York Mills, N.Y., 3,805.................*B5 75
New Zealand, country, Oceania, 2,985,000....N15 26
Nezhin, Sov. Un., 56,000..F8 12
Nez Perce, Idaho, 555.....C2 57
Nez Perce, co., Idaho, 30,376..................C2 57
Ngaoundéré, Cam........G7 22
Nha Trang, Viet., 59,600..C3 19
Niagara, Wis., 2,347......C6 88
Niagara, co., Ont. Can....D5 41
Niagara, co., N.Y., 235,720................B2 75
Niagara Falls, Ont., Can., 67,163................D5 41
Niagara Falls, N.Y., 85,615................B1 75
Niagara-on-the-Lake, Ont., Can., 12,552...........D5 41
Niagara University, N.Y., 2,000................*B1 75
Niamey, Niger, 60,000.....F5 22
Niantic, Conn., 4,000.....D8 52
Niantic, Ill., 705..........D4 58
Nicaragua, country, N.A., 2,100,000..............E7 34
Nicaragua, lake, Nic.......E7 34
Nicastro (Lamezia Terme), It., 26,700 (55,700▲)....E6 9
Nice, Fr., 322,442 (*400,000)..............F7 5
Niceville, Fla., 4,155......u15 54
Nichinan, Jap., 39,000 (53,288▲)..............K5 18
Nicholas, co., Ky., 6,508...B5 62
Nicholas, co., W. Va., 22,552..................C4 87
Nicholasville, Ky., 5,829...C5 62
Nicholls, Ga., 1,150.......E4 55
Nichols, N.Y., 638........C4 75
Nichols, S.C., 549.........C9 82
Nichols Hills, Okla., 4,478..B4 79
Nicholson, Pa., 877......C10 81
Nickerson, Kans., 1,187....D5 61
Nicolet, Que., Can., 4,714..C5 42
Nicolet, co., Que., Can., 30,829..................C5 42
Nicollet, Minn., 618.......F4 67
Nicollet, co., Minn., 24,518..................F4 67
Nicoma Park, Okla., 2,560.B4 79
Nicosia (Levkosía), Cyp., 48,000 (*106,000)......A4 23
Nicosia, It., 17,600........F5 9
Nicotera, It., 9,143........E5 9
Nicoya, C.R., 3,196........E7 34
Niedersachsen (Lower Saxony), state, Ger., Fed. Rep. of, 7,270,000......*B4 6
Nienburg, Ger., Fed. Rep. of, 22,283..............B4 6
Nievre, dept., Fr., 247,702.*D5 5
Niğde, Tur., 26,936......D10 14
Niger, country, Afr., 4,340,000..............F6 22
Niger, riv., Afr............F5 22
Nigeria, country, Afr., 60,260,000.............G6 22
Nigríta, Grc., 7,301........B4 14
Niigata, Jap., 383,919.....H9 18
Niigata, pref., Jap., 2,360,982.............*H9 18
Niihama, Jap., 126,033....J6 18
Niihau, isl., Haw..........B1 56
Niimi, Jap., 30,966........I6 18
Níjar, Sp., 2,052..........D4 8
Nijmegen, Neth., 149,205 (*209,164)..............B6 5
Nikitovka, Sov. Un., 10,000..................q21 12
Nikko, Jap., 28,502.......H9 18
Nikolayev, Sov. Un., 331,000..................H9 12
Nikopol, Sov. Un., 125,000..................H10 12
Niland, Calif., 950........F6 50
Nile, riv., Afr............C4 23
Niles, Ill., 31,432..........h9 58
Niles, Mich., 12,988.......G4 66
Niles, Ohio, 21,581.......A5 78
Nimes, Fr., 123,292.......F6 5
Ninette, Man., Can., 673...E2 40
Ninety Six, S.C., 2,166....C3 82
Ningan, China, 40,000....D4 18
Ninghsien, China, 5,000...D6 17
Ningpo, China, 280,000....F9 17
Ningsia, see Yinchuan, China
Ningsia Hui, auton. reg., China, 1,810,000.......D6 17
Ningte, China, 30,000.....F8 17
Ninh Binh, Viet., 25,000..A3 19
Niobrara, Nebr., 602......B7 71
Niobrara, co., Wyo., 2,924.C8 89
Niort, Fr., 53,394.........D3 5
Niota, Tenn., 629.........D9 83
Nipawin, Sask., Can., 4,057..................D3 39
Nipigon, lake, Ont., Can..o17 41
Nipissing, dist., Ont., Can., 73,533...........A5 41
Nipomo, Calif., 3,642......E3 50
Niquero, Cuba, 11,300 (36,500▲)..............D5 35
Nirasaki, Jap., 14,100 (27,267▲)...............n17 18
Nis, Yugo., 127,178.......D5 10
Nisa, Port., 5,617.........C2 8
Nishinomiya, Jap., 377,043.*I7 18
Nishio, Jap., 57,000 (75,193▲)..............o16 18
Nisko, Pol., 8,312.........C7 7
Nisswa, Minn., 1,011......D4 67
Niterói, Braz., 291,970.C4, h6 30
Nitra, Czech., 43,596......D5 7
Nitro, W. Va., 8,019......C3 87
Niue, N.Z., dep., Oceania, 4,900................*H9 2
Nivelles, Bel., 16,433......B6 5
Nivernais, former prov., Fr.D5 5
Niverville, Man., Can., 474..................E3 40
Nixa, Mo., 1,636..........D4 69
Nixon, N.J...............B4 74
Nixon, Tex., 1,925.....E4, k8 84
Nizāmābād, India, 115,640..............*E6 20
Nizhneudinsk, Sov. Un., 40,000..............D12 13
Nizhneye, Sov. Un., 10,000..................q21 12
Nizhniy Tagil, Sov. Un., 378,000..................D9 13
Nkangsamba, Cam.......H6 22
Noank, Conn., 1,371......D9 52
Nobel, Ont., Can., 693....B4 41
Nobeoka, Jap., 128,292....J5 18
Noble, Ill., 719............E5 58
Noble, Okla., 2,241........B4 79
Noble, co., Ind., 31,382....B7 59
Noble, co., Ohio, 10,428...C4 78
Noble, co., Okla., 10,043..A4 79
Nobles, co., Minn., 23,208..G3 67
Noblesville, Ind., 7,548....D6 59
Noboribetsu, Jap., 46,526.E10 18
Nocatee, Fla., 900........E5 54
Nochixtán, Mex., 3,235...o15 34
Nocona, Tex., 2,871.......C4 84
Nodaway, co., Mo., 22,467..................A3 69
Noel, Mo., 924............E3 69
Nogales, Ariz., 8,946......D3 48
Nogales, Mex., 52,108....A2 34
Nogales, Mex., 14,254....n15 34

North Sydney, N.S., Can., 8,604.............C9 43
North Syracuse, N.Y., 8,687.............B4 75
North Tarrytown, N.Y., 8,334......g13, m15 75
North Terre Haute, Ind., 2,500.............E3 59
North Tewksbury, Mass., 900.............A5 65
North Tonawanda, N.Y., 36,012.............B2 75
North Troy, Vt., 774......B3 73
North Turlock, Calif.....*D3 50
North Turner, mtn., Mass.............C4 65
Northumberland, Pa., 4,102.............E8 81
Northumberland, co., N.B., Can., 51,711.....B3 43
Northumberland, co., Ont., Can., 45,074.....C6 41
Northumberland, co., Eng., 795,850.........*C6 4
Northumberland, co., Pa., 99,190.............D8 81
Northumberland, co., Va., 9,239.............C6 85
North Uxbridge, Mass., 1,960.............B4 65
Northvale, N.J., 5,177.....g9 74
North Valley Stream, N.Y., 14,881.......*E7 75
North Vancouver, B.C., Can., 31,847.......E6, f12 37
North Vandergrift, Pa., 1,000.............*E2 81
North Vassalboro, Maine, 800.............D3 64
North Vernon, Ind., 4,582..F6 59
Northville, Mich., 5,400...p15 66
Northville, N.Y., 1,192.....B6 75
North Wales, Pa., 3,911...F11 81
North Walsham, Eng., 6,490.............D7 4
North Warren, Pa., 1,360..C3 81
Northwest Park, Md., 4,000.............*B3 53
North Westport, Mass.....C5 65
North West River, Newf., Can., 753........B1, h9 44
Northwest Territories, ter., Can., 40,000.....C10 36
North Wilbraham, Mass...B3 65
North Wildwood, N.J., 3,914.............E3 74
North Wilkesboro, N.C., 3,357.............A1 76
Northwood, Iowa, 1,950...A4 60
Northwood, Mich., 1,500.............*E5 66
Northwood, N.H., 350.....E5 73
Northwood, N. Dak., 1,189.............C8 77
Northwoods, Mo., 4,611...*C7 69
North York, Pa., 2,032....G8 81
North York, Ont., Can., 504,150.........D5, k15 41
Norton, N.S., Can., 846...D4 43
Norton, Kans., 3,627.....C4 61
Norton, Mass., 2,073.....C5 65
Norton, Ohio, 12,308.....A4 78
Norton (Independent City), Va., 4,172.......f9 85
Norton, co., Kans., 7,279..C4 61
Norton Shores, Mich., 22,271.............E4 66

Nortonville, Kans., 727.............C8, k15 61
Nortonville, Ky., 699......C2 62
Norvelt, Pa., 1,500........*F2 81
Norwalk, Calif., 91,827...n12 50
Norwalk, Conn., 79,288...E3 52
Norwalk, Iowa, 1,745..C4, f8 60
Norwalk, Ohio, 13,386....A3 78
Norwalk, Wis., 432........E3 88
Norway, Iowa, 554........C6 60
Norway, Maine, 2,430 (3,595 ▲).............D2 64
Norway, Mich., 3,033.....C3 66
Norway, S.C., 579........E5 82
Norway, country, Eur., 3,980,000.............E5 11
Norway House, Man., Can., 494...........C3 40
Norwayne, Mich.........*F7 66
Norwell, Mass., 600 (7,796 ▲).............h12 65
Norwich, Ont., Can., 1,703.............E4 41
Norwich, Conn., 41,739....C8 52
Norwich, Eng., 120,740 (*197,000).............D7 4
Norwich, N.Y., 8,843.....C5 75
Norwood, Ont., Can., 1,060.............C7 41
Norwood, Mass., 30,815.............B5, h11 65
Norwood, Minn., 1,058....F5 67
Norwood, N.J., 4,398......h9 74
Norwood, N.Y., 2,098.....f10 75
Norwood, N.C., 1,896......B2 76
Norwood, Ohio, 30,420....o13 78
Norwood, Pa., 7,229......p20 81
Norwood, Tenn., 400.....*D10 83
Norwottock, mtn., Mass...B2 65
Noshiro, Jap., 44,000 (59,795▲)............F10 18
Nossa Senhora das Dores, Braz., 5,674.........*E7 27
Notch, mtn., Mass........A3 65
Noto, It., 20,700.........F5 9
Notodden, Nor., 13,600...H3 11
Notre Dame, Ind., 8,100..*A5 59
Notre-Dame-de-Lourdes, Man., Can., 511......E2 40
Notre Dame du Lac, Que., Can., 2,107......B9 42
Notre-Dame-du-Laus, Que., Can., 565........C2 42
Nottingham, Eng., 296,750 (*650,000).....D6 4
Nottingham, Pa., 3,200...*F11 81
Nottingham, co., Eng., 972,130.............*D6 4
Nottoway, co., Va., 14,260.............C4 85
Nouadhibou, Maur., 5,283..D4 21
Nouakchott, Maur., 16,000.E1 22
Nouméa, N. Cal., 34,990..*H8 2
Nova Cruz, Braz., 8,533...*D7 27
Nova Friburgo, Braz., 65,732.............C4, h6 30
Nova Iguaçu, Braz., 331,457.............h6 30
Nova Lima, Braz., 27,386.............C4 30
Nova Lisboa, Ang., 38,745.............C3 24
Novara, It., 98,900.......B2 9
Nova Scotia, prov., Can., 810,000.............D6 43
Novato, Calif., 31,006.....C2 50

Nova Varos, Yugo., 3,186.............D4 10
Novaya Ladoga, Sov. Un., 25,000.............A9 12
Novaya Zemlya, is., Sov. Un.............B8 16
Nova Zagora, Bul., 19,258.............D8 10
Nové Zámky, Czech., 24,628.............E5 7
Novgorod, Sov. Un., 128,000.............B8 12
Novgorod-Severskiy, Sov. Un., 11,249.......E9 12
Novi, Mich., 9,668.......p15 66
Novigrad, Yugo., 531.....C2 10
Novi Ligure, It., 32,700...B2 9
Novi Pazar, Bul., 5,461...D8 10
Novi Pazar, Yugo., 29,072.............D5 10
Novi Sad, Yugo., 141,712..C4 10
Novoaydar, Sov. Un., 10,000.............G12, q21 12
Novocherkassk, Sov. Un., 162,000.............H13 12
Novoekonomicheskoye, Sov. Un., 31,000......q20 12
Novogrudok, Sov. Un., 25,000.............E5 12
Novo-Kazalinsk, Sov. Un., 19,499.......E9 16
Novokuznetsk, Sov. Un., 499,000.............D11 13
Novomoskovsk, Sov. Un., 61,000.............G10 12
Novomoskovsk, Sov. Un., 134,000 (*340,000)....D12 12
Novorossiysk, Sov. Un., 133,000.............I11 12
Novoshakhtinsk, Sov. Un., 102,000.......H12 12
Novosibirsk, Sov. Un., 1,180,000 (*1,285,000)..D11 13
Novosil, Sov. Un., 20,000.............E11 12
Novoukrainka, Sov. Un., 20,000.............G8 12
Nový Bohumín, Czech., 13,104.............D5 7
Nový Bydžov, Czech., 6,120.............C3 7
Nový Jičín, Czech., 19,740.............D5 7
Novyye Senzhary, Sov. Un.............G10 12
Novyy Oskol, Sov. Un., 10,000.............F11 12
Nowa Sól, Pol., 33,300....C3 7
Nowata, Okla., 3,679.....A6 79
Nowata, co., Okla., 9,773.............A6 79
Nowra-Bomaderry, Austl., 12,866.............G8 26
Nowshera, Pak., 21,516 (*43,757).............B5 20
Nowy Dwór, Pol., 16,900..k13 7
Nowy Sącz, Pol., 41,100...D6 7
Nowy Targ, Pol., 21,900...D6 7
Noxen, Pa., 822......D9, m16 81
Noxubee, co., Miss., 14,288.............B5 68
Noya, Sp., 4,236.........A1 8
Noyon, Fr., 11,603.......C5 5
Nsawam, Ghana, 20,200...G4 22
Ñuble, prov., Chile, 329,100.............B2 28

Nuckolls, co., Nebr., 7,404.............D7 71
Nucla, Colo., 949........C2 51
Nueces, co., Tex., 237,544..F4 84
Nueva Atzacoalco, Mex., 57,456.............*D5 34
Nueva Casas Grandes, Mex., 20,023.........A3 34
Nueva Ecija, prov., Phil., 608,362.............*C6 19
Nueva Esparta, state Ven., 89,492.........A5 32
Nueva Gerona, Cuba, 17,200 (20,100 ▲).....D2 35
Nueva Imperial, Chile, 6,400.............B2 28
Nueva Rosita, Mex., 34,706.............B4 34
Neuva San Salvador, Sal., 35,106.............*E7 34
Nueva Vizcaya, prov., Phil., 138,090.........*B6 19
Nueve de Julio, Arg., 17,768.............B4 28
Nuevitas, Cuba, 20,700 (21,500 ▲).............D5 35
Nuevo Laredo, Mex., 148,867.............B5 34
Nuevo León, state, Mex., 1,290,500.............B5 34
Nukualofa, Tonga, 15,545.............*H9 2
Nules, Sp., 8,460........C5 8
Numazu, Jap., 189,038 (*375,000).........I9, n17 18
Nu Mine, Pa., 475........E3 81
Nunda, N.Y., 1,254......C3 75
Nungan, China, 35,000...C10 17
Nuoro, It., 28,800.......D2 9
Nuquí, Col., 1,500.......C3 27
Nuremberg, Pa., 800.....E9 81
Nuri, Mex., 1,887........B3 34
Nürnberg (Nuremberg), Ger., Fed. Rep. of, 514,976 (*850,000).............D5 6
Nushki, Pak., 2,142......C4 20
Nutley, N.J., 31,913....B4, h8 74
Nutter Fort, W. Va., 2,379.............B4, k10 87
Nutting Lake, Mass., 1,500.............f10 65
Nuwara Eliya, Sri Lanka, 16,347.............G7 20
Nyack, N.Y., 6,659...D7, m15 75
Nyamandhlovu, Rh., 350..D5 24
Nyandoma, Sov. Un., 23,000.............A13 12
Nyasa, lake, Afr..........C6 24
Nybro, Swe., 15,317......I6 11
Nye, co., Nev., 5,599.....B3 72
Nyíregyháza, Hung., 55,805 (70,640 ▲).....B5 10
Nykøbing Falster, Den., 23,000.............A1 7
Nykøbing Mors, Den., 9,326.............I3 11
Nykoping, Swe., 37,175.............H7, u34 11
Nyland Acres, Calif., 1,200.............*E4 50
Nymburk, Czech., 13,139.............C3, n19 7
Nynäshamn, Swe., 11,416.............H7, u35 11
Nyngan, Austl., 2,478.....F8 25
Nysa, Pol., 31,800.......C4 7
Nyssa, Oreg., 2,620......D10 80

O

Oahu, isl., Haw........B4, g9 56
Oak Bay, B.C., Can., 18,426.............h12 37
Oak Bluffs, Mass., 1,385..D6 65
Oakbrook Terrace, Ill., 1,126.............*F2 58
Oak Creek, Colo., 492.....A4 51
Oak Creek, Wis., 13,928..n12 88
Oakdale, Calif., 6,594....D3 50
Oakdale, La., 7,301......D3 63
Oakdale, Mass., 500......B4 65
Oakdale, N.Y., 7,334.....n16 75
Oakdale, Pa., 2,136......k13 81
Oakes, N. Dak., 1,742....D7 77
Oakfield, Maine, 500 (836 ▲).............B4 64

Oakfield, N.Y., 1,964.....B2 75
Oakford, Pa., 1,500..F12, o22 81
Oak Forest, Ill., 17,870...k9 58
Oak Grove, Ga., 3,500...*C2 55
Oak Grove, La., 1,980....B4 63
Oak Grove, Oreg., 6,000.............B4, h12 80
Oakharbor, Ohio, 2,807...A2 78
Oak Harbor, Wash., 9,167.............A3 86
Oak Hill, Fla., 747......D6 54
Oak Hill, Mich., 900.....D4 66
Oak Hill, Ohio, 1,642....D3 78
Oak Hill, Tenn.........*A5 83
Oak Hill, W. Va., 4,738.............D3, n13 87

Oakhurst, N.J., 4,600.....C4 74
Oakhurst, Okla., 1,800....A5 79
Oakland, Calif., 361,561.............D2, h8 50
Oakland, Ill., 1,012......D5 58
Oakland, Iowa, 1,603.....C2 60
Oakland, Maine, 2,261....D3 64
Oakland, Md., 1,786.....m12 53
Oakland, Mo., 1,609.....*C7 69
Oakland, Nebr., 1,355....C9 71
Oakland, N.J., 14,420....A4 74
Oakland, Oreg., 1,010....D3 80
Oakland, Pa., 2,303......*D1 81
Oakland, co., Mich., 907,871.............F7 66

Oakland City, Ind., 3,289.............H3 59
Oaklandon, Ind., 1,000...k11 59
Oakland Park, Fla., 16,261.............F6, r13 54
Oak Lawn, Ill., 60,305.............B6, k9 58
Oaklawn, Kans., 5,000....B5 61
Oakley, Idaho, 656.......G5 57
Oakley, Kans., 2,327.....C3 61
Oakley Park, Mich., 36,762.............*F7 66
Oaklyn, N.J., 4,626......*D2 74
Oakman, Ala., 853.......B2 46
Oakmont, Pa., 7,550..E2, h14 81
Oak Park, Ill., 62,511..B6, k9 58

Ontario, co., N.Y., 78,849..C3 75
Ontario, prov., Can., 7,990,000............... 41
Onteniente, Sp., 18,787....C5 8
Ontonagon, Mich., 2,432............B1, m12 66
Ontonagon, co., Mich., 10,548..............m12 66
Oolitic, Ind., 1,155.......G4 59
Oostburg, Wis., 1,309.....E6 88
Oostende, Bel., 71,575 (*81,000)..............B5 5
Ootacamund, India, 63,310................F6 20
Oot Park, N.Y., 2,000....*B4 75
Opal Cliffs, Calif., 3,825..*D2 50
Opa-Locka, Fla., 11,902...s13 54
Opatów, Pol., 5,636.......C6 7
Opava, Czech., 47,909....D4 7
Opelika, Ala., 19,027......C4 46
Opelousas, La., 20,387.....D3 63
Opochka, Sov. Un., 10,000...............C7 12
Opoczno, Pol., 12,100.....C6 7
Opole, Pol., 86,500.......C4 7
Opole Lubelskie, Pol., 3,746.................C6 7
Opp, Ala., 6,493..........D3 46
Oppdal, Nor..............F3 11
Oppeln see Opole, Pol.
Oppland, co., Nor., 170,900..............*G4 11
Opportunity, Wash., 16,604............B8, g14 86
Oquawka, Ill., 1,352......C3 58
Oradea, Rom., 122,500 (134,900 ▲)............B5 10
Oradell, N.J., 8,903.......h8 74
Oran (Ouahran), Alg., 328,257 (*369,462)......A4 22
Oran, Mo., 1,226.........D8 69
Oran, dept., Alg., 1,990,729..............*B5 22
Orange, Austl., 23,143.....F8 25
Orange, Calif., 77,365.....n13 50
Orange, Conn., 13,524....D4 52
Orange, Fr., 18,616.......E6 5
Orange, Mass., 3,847 (6,104▲)...............A3 65
Orange, N.J., 32,566......B4 74
Orange, Ohio, 2,112.....*A4 78
Orange, Tex., 24,457......D6 84
Orange, Va., 2,768........B4 85
Orange, co., Calif., 1,421,233..............F5 50
Orange, co., Fla., 344,311...............D5 54
Orange, co., Ind., 16,968..G4 59
Orange, co., N.Y., 221,657................D6 75
Orange, co., N.C., 57,707..A3 76
Orange, co., Tex., 71,170..D6 84
Orange, co., Vt., 17,676...D3 73
Orange, co., Va., 13,792...B4 85
Orange, riv., Afr..........F3 24
Orangeburg, N.Y., 3,500................*D6 75
Orangeburg, S.C., 13,252..E6 82
Orangeburg, co., S.C., 69,789.................E6 82
Orange City, Fla., 1,777...D5 54
Orange City, Iowa, 3,572.................A1 60
Orange Cove, Calif., 3,392................*D4 50
Orange Free State, prov., S. Afr., 1,860,000.......F5 24
Orange Grove, Tex., 1,075..................F4 84
Orange Park, Fla., 7,619..............B5, m8 54
Orangevale, Calif., 8,000..................*C3 50
Orangeville, Ont., Can., 8,074..................D4 41
Oranienburg, Ger. Dem. Rep., 20,600...........B6 6
Oras, Phil., 4,863........*C7 19
Orăstie, Rom., 10,488.....C6 10
Oravița, Rom., 8,175......C5 10
Orchard Avenue, Wash....*B8 86
Orchard Beach, Md., 1,700.................*B4 53
Orchard Homes, Mont., 3,500.................D2 70
Orchard Lake, Mich., 1,487..................*F7 66
Orchard Park, N.Y., 3,732.................C2 75
Orchard Valley, Wyo., 1,015..................E8 89
Orchards, Wash., 9,500....D3 86
Orcotuna, Peru, 3,400.....D2 31
Orcutt, Calif., 1,500.......E3 50
Ord, Nebr., 2,439.........C7 71
Ordenes, Sp., 1,311.......A1 8
Ordu, Tur., 38,483.......B11 14
Orduña, Sp., 5,950........A4 8
Ordville, Nebr...........*C2 71
Ordway, Colo., 1,017......C7 51
Ordzhonikidze, Sov. Un., 236,000.......E7 13
Örebro, Swe., 115,827.H6, t33 11
Örebro, co., Swe., 273,200 ....*H6 11
Oregon, Ill., 3,539........A4 58
Oregon, Mo., 789.........B2 69
Oregon, Ohio, 16,563..A2, e7 78
Oregon, Wis., 2,553.......F4 88
Oregon, co., Mo., 9,180....E6 69
Oregon, state, U.S., 2,227,000................ 80
Oregon City, Oreg., 9,176..............B4, h12 80
Orekhov, Sov. Un., 10,000...............H10 12
Orekhovo-Zuyevo, Sov. Un., 120,000 (*180,000).......D12, n18 12
Orel, Sov. Un., 232,000...E11 12
Oreland, Pa., 9,000.....*F11 81
Orem, Utah, 25,729.......A6 72
Orenburg, Sov. Un., 344,000......D8 13
Orense, prov., Sp., 445,600..............*A2 8
Orestes, Ind., 519.........D6 59
Orestiás, Grc., 10,727......B6 14
Orford, mtn., Que., Can...D5 42
Orfordville, Wis., 888......F4 88
Orgeyev, Sov. Un., 25,800.................H7 12
Orick, Calif., 900.........B1 50
Orient, Ill., 502...........F5 58
Orient, N.Y., 600........m16 75
Oriental, N.C., 445.......B6 76
Oriente, prov., Cuba, 1,797,606..............D6 35
Orihuela, Sp., 15,873 (44,830 ▲).............C5 8
Orillia, Ont., Can., 24,040.................C5 41
Orinda, Calif., 18,700....*D2 50
Orinoco, river, Ven........B5 32
Orion, Ill., 1,801..........B3 58
Oriskany, N.Y., 1,627......B5 75
Oriskany Falls, N.Y., 927..C5 75
Orissa, state, India, 21,944,615.............E7 20
Oristano, It., 19,800.......E2 9
Orizaba, Mex., 92,517 (*210,000)..D5, n15 34
Orkney, co., Scot., 17,137.................*A5 4
Orkney, isl., Scot.........*A5 4
Orland, Calif., 2,884......C2 50
Orlando, Fla., 99,006 (*363,700)..............D5 54
Orland Park, Ill., 6,391....k9 58
Orleanais, former prov., Fr.D4 5
Orleans, Calif., 600.......B2 50
Orléans, Ont., Can., 2,810.................h12 41
Orléans, Fr., 95,828 (*170,000)...............D4 5
Orleans, Ind., 1,834.......G5 59
Orleans, Mass., 950 (3,055 ▲)................C7 65
Orleans, Nebr., 592.......D6 71
Orleans, Vt., 1,138........B3 73
Orleans, co., N.Y., 37,305..................B2 75
Orleans, co., Vt., 20,153...B3 73
Orleans, par., La., 593,471...................E6 63
Orléansville, see El Asnam, Alg.
Orlovista, Fla., 4,700.....*D5 54
Ormoc, prov., Phil., 13,640.................*C6 19
Ormond Beach, Fla., 14,063.................C5 54
Ormstown, dept., Que., Can., 1,527............D3 42
Orne, dept., Fr., 288,524.................*C3 5
Örnsköldsvik, Swe., 36,336.F8 11
Orocué, Col., 1,600.......C3 32
Orofino, Idaho, 3,883......C2 57
Oro Grande, Calif., 700....E5 50
Oromocto, N.B., Can., 11,427..................D3 43
Orono, Ont., Can., 964....D6 41
Orono, Maine, 9,989......D4 64
Orono, Minn., 6,787.....*E5 67
Oronogo, Mo., 492.......D3 69
Oroquieta, Phil., 4,265...*D6 19
Orosháza, Hung., 29,146 (33,346 ▲)..............B5 10
Oroville, Calif., 7,536......C3 50
Oroville, Wash., 1,555.....A6 86
Orpington, Eng., 81,600..m13 4
Orrick, Mo., 883..........B3 69
Orrville, Ohio, 7,408.......B4 78
Orsainville, Que., Can., 12,520..................n17 42
Orsha, Sov. Un., 101,000..D8 12
Orsk, Sov. Un., 225,000...D8 13
Orsova, Rom., 6,527.......C6 10
Orthez, Fr., 5,125.........F3 5
Ortigueria, Sp., 1,590......A2 8
Orting, Wash., 1,643......B3 86
Ortiz, Mex., 1,133........B2 34
Ortona a Mare, It., 10,700..................C5 9
Ortonville, Mich., 983.....F7 66
Ortonville, Minn., 2,665...E2 67
Oruro, Bol., 90,100.......C2 29
Oruro, dept., Bol., 270,500.................C2 29
Orvieto, It., 9,500........C4 9
Orwell, Ohio, 965.........A5 78
Orwigsburg, Pa., 2,661....E9 81
Oryakhovo, Bul., 6,972....D6 10
Osage, Iowa, 3,815.......A5 60
Osage, co., Kans., 13,352..D8 61
Osage, co., Mo., 10,994....C6 69
Osage, co., Okla., 29,750.................A4 79
Osage Beach, Mo., 1,091..C5 69
Osage City, Kans., 2,600...D8 61
Ōsaka, Jap., 2,841,937 (*14,175,000).......I7, o14 18
Osaka, Jap..............n16 18
Ōsaka, pref., Jap., 7,620,480...............*I7 18
Osakis, Minn., 1,306......E3 67
Osawatomie, Kans., 4,294..................D9 61
Osborne, Kans., 1,980.....C5 61
Osborne, co., Kans., 6,416..................C5 61
Osbornsville, N.J., 800...*C4 74
Osburn, Idaho, 2,248......B3 57
Osceola, Ark., 7,204.......B6 49
Osceola, Ind., 1,572.......A5 59
Osceola, Iowa, 3,124......C4 60
Osceola, Mo., 874.........C4 69
Osceola, Nebr., 923.......C8 71
Osceola, Wis., 1,152.......C1 88
Osceola, co., Fla., 25,267...E5 54
Osceola, co., Iowa, 8,555..................A2 60
Osceola, co., Mich., 14,838..................E5 66
Osceola Mills, Pa., 1,671...E5 81
Oschatz, Ger. Dem. Rep., 15,500..................C6 6
Oschersleben, Ger. Dem. Rep., 19,100..............B5 6
Oscoda, Mich., 2,170......D7 66
Oscoda, co., Mich., 4,726..................D6 66
Osgoode, Ont., Can., 823..B9 41
Osgood, Ind., 1,346.......F7 59
Osh, Sov. Un., 120,000...E10 13
Oshamambe, Jap.........E10 18
Oshawa, Ont., Can., 91,587 (*120,318).......D6 41
Oshkosh, Nebr., 1,067.....C3 71
Oshkosh, Wis., 53,082 (*70,100)....D5, h8 88
Oshogbo, Nig., 208,966....G5 22
Osijek, Yugo., 93,912......C4 10
Osinniki, Sov. Un., 62,000................*D11 13
Oskaloosa, Iowa 11,224...C5 60
Oskaloosa, Kans., 955...............C8, k15 61
Oskarshamm, Swe., 22,096 (27,412 ▲)..............I7 11
Oslo, Nor., 487,000 (*715,000).........G4, p28 11
Oslo, co., Nor., 487,600...............*H4 11
Osmaniye, Tur., 46,355..................D11 14
Osmond, Nebr., 883.......B8 71
Osnabrück, Ger., Fed. Rep. of, 163,984 (*255,000)...B4 6
Osorno, Chile, 55,091......C2 28
Osorno, prov., Chile, 170,400..................C2 28
Osoyoos, B.C., Can., 1,022...................E8 37
Osprey, Fla., 1,115.......E4 54
Oss, Neth., 42,753........B6 5
Ossa, mtn., Austl.........o15 25
Osseo, Minn., 2,908......m12 67
Osseo, Wis., 1,356........D2 88
Ossian, Ind., 1,538........C7 59
Ossian, Iowa, 847........A6 60
Ossining, N.Y., 21,659..............D7, m15 75
Ostashkov, Sov. Un., 23,000..................C9 12
Osteen, Fla., 550.........D5 54
Östergötland, co., Swe., 372,500................*H6 11
Östersund, Swe., 44,491....F6 11
Osterville, Mass., 1,286....C7 65
Östfold, co., Nor., 216,800................*H4 11
Ostrava, Czech., 278,737 (*670,000).....D5 7
Ostróda, Pol., 21,300......B5 7
Ostrogozhsk, Sov. Un., 30,000.................F12 12
Ostrołęka, Pol., 17,100.....B6 7
Ostrov, Czech., 19,313.....C2 7
Ostrov, Sov. Un., 10,000...C7 12
Ostrowiec [Swietokrzyski], Pol., 49,900............C6 7
Ostrów Mazowiecka, Pol., 15,000..................B6 7
Ostrów Wielkopolski, Pol., 49,500............C4 7
Ostrzeszów, Pol., 7,357....C4 7
Ostuni, It., 25,400........D6 9
Ōsuka, Jap................o16 18
Osuna, Sp., 19,569........D3 8
Oswego, Ill., 1,862.....B5, k8 58
Oswego, Kans., 2,200......E8 61
Oswego, N.Y., 20,913......B4 75
Oswego, co., N.Y., 100,897.B4 75
Oswestry, Eng., 11,215....D5 4
Oświecim, Pol., 39,600............C5, g10 7
Ota, Jap., 98,257.......*m18 18
Otaki, Jap................n19 18
Otaré, mtn., Col..........C3 32
Otaru, Jap., 191,856.....E10 18
Otavalo, Ec., 8,630.......A2 31
Otay, Calif., 3,500.......*F5 50
Oteen, N.C., 2,000........f10 76
Otego, N.Y., 956..........C5 75
Otero, co., Colo., 23,523...D7 51
Otero, co., N. Mex., 41,097..................C6 48
Othello, Wash., 4,122.....C6 86
Otho, Iowa, 581..........B3 60
Otis Orchards, Wash., 1,200..................g14 86
Otisville, Mich., 724.......E7 66
Otisville, N.Y., 933......*D6 75
Otoe, co., Nebr., 15,576...D9 71
Otsego, Mich., 3,957.......F5 66
Otsego, co., Mich., 10,422..C6 66
Otsego, co., N.Y., 56,181...C5 75
Ōtsu, Jap., 171,777.......o14 18
Otsuki, Jap., 36,858.......n17 18
Ottawa, Ont., Can., 302,341 (*602,510)..B9, h12 41
Ottawa, Ill., 18,716.......B5 58
Ottawa, Kans., 11,036.....D8 61
Ottawa, Ohio, 3,622.......A1 78
Ottawa, co., Kans., 6,183..C6 61
Ottawa, co., Mich., 128,181..................F4 66
Ottawa, co., Ohio, 37,099..A2 78
Ottawa, co., Okla., 29,800..................A7 79
Ottawa, river, Ont., Que., Can............E18 36
Ottawa-Carleton, co., Ont., Can., 471,931......B9 41
Ottawa Hills, Ohio, 4,270..............A2, e6 78
Otterbien, Ind., 899.......D3 59
Otter Lake, Mich., 551....E7 66
Otter River, Mass., 600....A3 65
Otter Tail, co., Minn., 46,097..................D3 67
Otterville, Ont., Can., 725..................E4 41
Ottoville, Ohio, 914.......B1 78
Ottumwa, Iowa, 29,610....C5 60
Otuzco, Peru, 3,534.......C2 31
Otwell, Ind., 600.........H3 59
Otwock, Pol., 39,800.....m14 7
Ouachita, co., Ark., 30,896..................D3 49
Ouachita, par., La., 115,387..................B3 63
Ouachita, river, U.S.......D8 45
Ouagadougou, Upper Volta, 77,500...........F4 22
Ouahigouya, Upper Volta, 10,000...........F4 22
Ouargla, Alg., 18,206......B6 22
Oudtshoorn, S. Afr., 26,525..................G4 24
Ouezzane, Mor., 33,267....B3 22
Ouidah, Dah., 14,000......G5 22
Oujda, Mor., 175,532......C5 21
Oullins, Fr., 26,604.......E6 5
Oulu, Fin., 86,880 ....E11 11
Oulu, prov., Fin., 422,700................*E11 11
Ouray, Colo., 741.........C3 51
Ouray, co., Colo., 1,546...C3 51
Ourinhos, Braz., 40,733....C3 30
Ouro Fino, Braz., 9,122..............C3, m8 30
Ouro Prêto, Braz., 24,050..C4 30
Outagamie, co., Wis., 119,398..................D5 88
Outes, Sp., 869...........A1 8

P

Q

Quilpie, Austl., 747......E7 25
Quilpué, Chile, 26,588...A2 28
Quimper, Fr., 52,496.....C2 5
Quimperlé, Fr., 10,698...D2 5
Quincy, Calif., 2,500....C3 50
Quincy, Fla., 8,334......B2 54
Quincy, Ill., 45,288......D2 58

Quincy, Mass., 87,966.B5, h11 65
Quincy, Mich., 1,540.....G6 66
Quincy, Wash., 3,237.....B6 86
Qui Nhon, Viet., 50,000...C3 19
Quinnville, R.I., 400.....B11 52
Quintana de la Serena, Sp., 7,861.....C3 8

Quintanar, Sp., 9,483....C4 8
Quintana Roo, Ter., Mex., 69,800.....D7 34
Quinter, Kans., 930......C3 61
Quinton, Okla., 1,262....B6 79
Quiroga, Sp., 8,380......A2 8
Quitman, Ga., 4,818......F3 55

Quitman, Miss., 2,702....C5 68
Quitman, Tex., 1,494.....C5 84
Quitman, co., Ga., 2,180..E1 55
Quitman, co., Miss., 15,888.....A3 68
Quito, Ec., 496,400......B2 31
Quixadá, Braz., 16,905...*D7 27

R

Raba, Indon., 29,881.....G5 19
Rabat, Mor., 367,620 (*540,000).....B3 22
Rabaul, N. Gui., 10,600..h13 25
Rabun, Ala., 200.....D2 46
Rabun, co., Ga., 8,327....B3 55
Raceland, Ky., 1,857.....B7 62
Raceland, La., 4,880..E5, k10 63
Rach Gia, Viet., 56,000..*C2 19
Racibórz, Pol., 40,400....C5 7
Racine, Wis., 95,162 (*132,300).....F6, n12 88
Racine, co., Wis., 170,838..F5 88
Radauti, Rom., 15,949....B7 10
Radcliff, Ky., 7,881......C4 62
Radeberg, Ger. Dem. Rep., 38,588.....C6 6
Radford (Independent City), Va., 11,596...C2 85
Radiant Valley, Md., 1,500.....C4 53
Radnor, Pa., 1,000......*G11 81
Radnor, co., Wales, 18,270.....*D5 4
Radom, Pol., 158,600.....C6 7
Radomir, Bul., 5,778.....D6 10
Radomsko, Pol., 31,100...C5 7
Radville, Sask., Can., 1,024.....H3 39
Radzionków, Pol., 27,800..g9 7
Rãe Bareli, India, 38,765..C7 20
Raeford, N.C., 3,180.....C3 76
Rafaela, Arg., 43,000.....A4 28
Rafah, Gaza Strip, 49,812..C2 15
Ragland, Ala., 1,239.....B3 46
Ragunda, Swe.....F7 11
Ragusa, It., 52,900......F5 9
Rahīmyār-Khān, Pak., 14,919.....C5 20
Rahway, N.J., 29,114..B4, k7 74
Rāichūr, India, 79,831....E6 20
Raigarh, India, 46,745...D7 20
Rainbow City, Ala., 3,107.....*A3 46
Rainbow City, C.Z., 2,375.....*B2 32
Rainier, Oreg., 1,731.....A4 80
Rainier, mtn., Wash.....C4 86
Rains, co., Tex., 3,752....C5 84
Rainsville, Ala., 2,099...A4 46
Rainy River, Ont., Can., 1,196.....*o16 41
Rainy River, dist., Ont., Can., 25,816.....o16 41
Raipur, India, 174,518 (*205,986).....D7 20
Rājahmundry, India, 165,912 (*188,805)...E7 20
Rajapalaiyam, India, 86,952.....*G6 20
Rājasthān, state, India, 25,765,806.....C5 20
Rājkot, India, 300,612....D5 20
Rājshāhi, Bngl., 56,885...D8 20
Rakovník, Czech., 12,927..C2 7
Rakvere, Sov. Un., 18,000.....B6 12
Raleigh, N.C., 123,793 (*216,900).....B4 76
Raleigh, W. Va., 800.....n13 87
Raleigh, co., W. Va., 70,080.....D3 87
Ralls, Tex., 1,962......C2 84
Ralls, co., Mo., 7,764....B6 69
Ralston, Nebr., 4,731....g12 71
Rām Allāh, Jordan, 14,759.....C3 15
Ramat Gan, Isr., 120,100..B2 15
Ramat HaSharon, Isr., 20,100.....*B2 15
Rambervillers, Fr., 7,042..C7 5
Ramea, Newf., Can., 970..E3 44
Ramenskoye, Sov. Un., 61,000.....D12, n18 12
Ramla, Isr., 34,100......C2 15
Ramleh, Eg., 52,000.....*G8 14

Ramona, Calif., 3,554....F5 50
Rāmpur, India, 161,417...C6 20
Ramsay, Mich., 1,068....n12 66
Ramseur, N.C., 1,328.....B3 76
Ramsey, N.J., 12,571.....A4 74
Ramsey, co., Minn., 476,255.....E5 67
Ramsey, co., N. Dak., 12,915.....B7 77
Ramsgate, Eng., 39,770...E7 4
Rancagua, Chile, 53,318...A2 28
Ranches of Taos, N. Mex., 1,600.....A6 48
Rānchī, India, 175,934 (*255,551).....D8 20
Rancho Cordova, Calif., 35,300.....*C3 50
Rand, W. Va., 2,600.....m12 87
Randall, co., Tex., 53,885..B2 84
Randallstown, Md., 15,000.B4 53
Randers, Den., 42,000 (*57,500).....I4 11
Randers, co., Den., 184,000.....*I4 11
Randleman, N.C., 2,312...B3 76
Randolph, Maine, 1,741...D3 64
Randolph, Mass., 27,035.....B5, h11 65
Randolph, Nebr., 1,130...B8 71
Randolph, Vt., 2,115.....D2 73
Randolph, Wis., 1,582....E4 88
Randolph, co., Ala., 18,331.....B4 46
Randolph, co., Ark., 12,645.....A4 49
Randolph, co., Ga., 8,734.....E2 55
Randolph, co., Ill., 31,379.E4 58
Randolph, co., Ind., 28,915.....D7 59
Randolph, co., Mo., 22,434.....B5 69
Randolph, co., N.C., 76,358.....B3 76
Randolph, co., W. Va., 24,596.....C5 87
Randolph Hills, Md., 4,500.....*B3 53
Rangely, Colo., 1,591....A2 51
Ranger, Tex., 3,094......C3 84
Rangoon, Bur., 821,800...E10 20
Rangpur, Bngl., 31,759...C8 20
Rāniganj, India, 40,104...D8 20
Rankin, Pa., 3,704......k14 81
Rankin, Tex., 1,105......D2 84
Rankin, co., Miss., 43,933..C4 68
Ranlo, N.C., 2,092......*B1 76
Ranshaw, Pa., 950.....*E9 81
Ransom, co., N. Dak., 7,102.....D8 77
Ranson, W. Va., 2,189....B7 87
Rantoul, Ill., 25,562.....C5 58
Rapallo, It., 25,300......B2 9
Rapid City, S. Dak., 43,836 (*59,800).....F2 77
Rapides, par., La., 118,078.....C3 63
Rappahannock, co., Va., 5,199.....B4 85
Raritan, N.J., 6,691.....B3 74
Raseiniai, Sov. Un., 6,181..A7 7
Rashīd (Rosetta), Eg., 36,711.....G8 14
Rasht, Iran, 143,557.....A7 23
Rasskazovo, Sov. Un., 40,000.....E13 12
Rastatt, Ger., Fed. Rep. of, 37,032.....D4 6
Rat Buri, Thai., 32,271...C1 19
Rathenow, Ger. Dem. Rep., 31,841.....B6 6
Ratibor, see Raciborz, Pol.
Ratlām, India, 106,666 (*119,247).....*D6 20
Ratnāgiri, India, 37,551...E5 20
Raton, N. Mex., 6,962....A6 48

Rauch, Arg., 6,953......B5 28
Rauma, Fin., 26,520.....G9 11
Raurkela, India, 90,287...*D7 20
Ravalli, co., Mont., 14,409.....D2 70
Rava-Russkaya, Sov. Un., 10,000.....F4 12
Raven, Va., 1,819......e10 85
Ravena, N.Y., 2,797.....C7 75
Ravenna, It., 82,500 (130,100▲).....B4 9
Ravenna, Ky., 784......C6 62
Ravenna, Nebr., 1,356...C7 71
Ravenna, Ohio, 11,780...A4 78
Ravensburg, Ger., Fed. Rep. of, 35,525.....E4 6
Ravenswood, W. Va., 4,240.....C3 87
Rāwalpindi, Pak., 197,370 (*340,175).....B5 20
Rawa Mazowiecka, Pol., 10,700.....C6 7
Rawdon, Que., Can., 2,740.....C4 42
Rawicz, Pol., 14,100....C4 7
Rawlins, Wyo., 7,855....E5 89
Rawlins, co., Kans., 4,393..C2 61
Ray, Ariz.....C3, D3 48
Ray, N. Dak., 776......B2 77
Ray, co., Mo., 17,599....B3 69
Raybon, Ga.....E5 55
Raychikhinsk, Sov. Un., 30,000.....B4 18
Raymond, Alta., Can., 2,156.....E4 38
Raymond, Miss., 1,620...C3 68
Raymond, Wash., 3,126...C2 86
Raymond Terrace, Austl., 6,001.....F8 26
Raymondville, Tex., 7,987.F4 84
Rayne, La., 9,510......D3 63
Raynham Center, Mass., 800.....C5 65
Rayong, Thai, 9,701.....*C2 19
Raytown, Ga.....C5 55
Raytown, Mo., 33,306....h11 69
Rayville, La., 3,962.....B4 63
Razgrad, Bul., 26,289....D8 10
Razlog, Bul., 6,857.....E6 10
Reading, Eng., 133,360 (*195,000).....E6 4
Reading, Mass., 22,539.....A5, f11 65
Reading, Mich., 1,125....G6 66
Reading, Ohio, 14,617.....C1, o13 78
Reading, Pa., 87,643 (*204,100).....F10 81
Reagan, co., Tex., 3,239..D2 84
Real, co., Tex., 2,013....E3 84
Ream, Camb., 5,000.....*C2 19
Ream, W. Va.....*D3 87
Reamstown, Pa., 1,050...F9 81
Recanati, It., 6,288.....C4 9
Rechitsa, Sov. Un., 48,000.....E8 12
Recife (Pernambuco), Braz., 1,060,752 (*1,750,000)...D7 27
Recklinghausen, Ger., Fed. Rep. of, 124,907.....C3 6
Reconquista, Arg., 21,000..E4 29
Rector, Ark., 1,990.....A5 49
Red, riv., U.S.....D8 45
Red, sea, Afr.....D9 21
Red, sea, Asia.....D9 21
Red Bank, N.J., 12,847...C4 74
Red Bank, Tenn., 12,715.....D8 83
Red Bay, Ala., 2,464....A1 46
Red Bluff, Calif., 7,676...B2 50
Red Boiling Springs, Tenn., 726.....C8 83
Red Bud, Ill., 2,559.....E4 58
Redcliff, Alta., Can., 2,255.....D5 38
Red Cloud, Nebr., 1,531..D7 71

Red Deer, Alta., Can., 27,674.....C4, g8 38
Reddell, La., 250......D3 63
Redding, Calif., 16,659...B2 50
Redfield, Iowa, 921.....C3 60
Redfield, S. Dak., 2,943...F7 77
Redford Township, Mich., 71,901.....p15 66
Red Hill, Pa., 1,201.....*F11 81
Red Hook, N.Y., 1,680....D7 75
Redington Beach, Fla., 1,583.....*E4 54
Redington Shores, Fla., 1,733.....*E4 54
Red Jacket, W. Va., 850...D2 87
Red Key, Ind., 1,667....D7 59
Red Lake, Ont., Can., 2,155.....o16 41
Red Lake, co., Minn., 5,388.....C2 67
Red Lake Falls, Minn., 1,740.....C2 67
Redlands, Calif., 36,355...E5 50
Red Lion, Pa., 5,645....G8 81
Red Lodge, Mont., 1,844..E7 70
Redmond, Oreg., 3,721...C5 80
Redmond, Wash., 11,020..e11 86
Red Oak, Ga., 1,200.....h7 55
Redon, Fr., 9,363......D3 5
Redondela, Sp., 3,261....A1 8
Redondo Beach, Calif., 57,451.....n12 50
Redore, Minn.....C6 67
Red River, co., Tex., 14,298.....C5 84
Red River, par., La., 9,226.....B2 63
Red Springs, N.C., 3,383..C3 76
Redstone, Colo., 150.....B3 51
Red Tank, C.Z., 1,949....*B2 32
Redtop, Mo.....D4 69
Redwater, Alta., Can., 1,135.....C4 38
Red Willow, co., Nebr., 12,191.....D5 71
Red Wing, Minn., 10,441..F6 67
Redwood, co., Minn., 20,024.....F3 67
Redwood City, Calif., 55,686.....D2, k8 50
Redwood Estates, Calif., 1,100.....*D3 50
Redwood Falls, Minn., 4,774.....F3 67
Reed City, Mich., 2,286...E5 66
Reedley, Calif., 8,131....D4 50
Reedsburg, Wis., 4,585...E3 88
Reeds Lake, Mich.....*F5 66
Reedsport, Oreg., 4,039..D2 80
Reedsville, Pa., 950.....E6 81
Reese Village, Tex., 2,545.....*C2 84
Reeves, co., Tex., 16,526..o13 84
Reform, Ala., 1,893.....B1 46
Refuge, Tex.....D5 84
Refugio, co., Tex., 9,494..E4 84
Regensburg, Ger., Fed. Rep. of, 133,501 (*182,000).....D6 6
Reggio di Calabria, It., 138,600 (164,800▲)...E5 9
Reggio nell 'Emilia, It., 98,600 (126,900▲).....B3 9
Reghin, Rom., 18,091....B7 10
Regina, Sask., Can., 139,469 (*140,734)..G3, n8 39
Region Occidental (Chaco), dept., Par., 54,277.....*D3 29
Regla, Cuba, (part of Havana).....C2 35
Rehoboth Beach, Del., 1,614.....C7 53
Reẖovot, Isr., 39,200....C2 15
Reichenbach, Ger. Dem. Rep., 27,832.....C6 6

S

Salavat, Sov. Un., 114,000 .*D8 13
Salaverry, Peru, 3,403.....C2 31
Salcedo, Ec., 3,442.......B2 31
Saldanha, S. Afr., 4,916...G3 24
Saldus, Sov. Un., 10,000...C4 12
Sale, Austl., 10,404......I6 26
Salé, Mor., 155,557.....B3 22
Salekhard, Sov. Un.,
  22,000...............C9 13
Salem, Ill., 6,187.......E5 58
Salem, India, 308,716.....F6 20
Salem, Ind., 5,041......G5 59
Salem, Mass., 40,556..A6, f12 65
Salem, Mo., 4,363.......D6 69
Salem, N.H., 10,000.....F5 73
Salem, N.J., 7,648......D2 74
Salem, N.Y., 1,025......B7 75
Salem, Ohio, 14,186.....B5 78
Salem, Oreg., 68,480
  (*141,300)......C4, k12 80
Salem, S. Dak., 1,391......G8 77
Salem, Utah, 1,081.......D2 72
Salem, Va. (Independent
  City), 21,982........C2 85
Salem, W. Va., 2,597..B4, k9 87
Salem, co., N.J., 60,346...D2 74
Salem Depot, N.H........F5 73
Salem Heights, Oreg.....*C4 80
Salemi, It., 13,300.......F4 9
Salerno, It., 148,100
  (*220,000)..........D5 9
Salford, Eng., 131,330....D5 4
Salgótarján, Hung., 37,212.A4 10
Salida, Calif., 1,109.....*D3 50
Salida, Colo., 4,355.......C5 51
Salies-de-Béarn, Fr.,
  2,859...............F3 5
Salihli, Tur., 34,478.....*C7 14
Salin, Bur., 5,000.......*D9 20
Salina, Kans., 37,714
  (*41,300)...........D6 61
Salina, Okla., 1,024......A6 79
Salina, Utah, 1,494.......B6 72
Salinas, Calif., 58,896
  (*78,200)...........D3 50
Salinas, P.R., 3,666.....*G11 35
Salina Springs, Ariz......A4 48
Saline, Mich., 4,811......F7 66
Saline, co., Ark., 36,107...C3 49
Saline, co., Ill., 25,721...F5 58
Saline, co., Kans., 46,592..D6 61
Saline, co., Mo., 24,837...B4 69
Saline, co., Nebr., 12,809..D8 71
Salineville, Ohio, 1,686...B5 78
Salisbury, Eng., 35,500...E6 4
Salisbury, Md., 15,252...D6 53
Salisbury, Mass., 1,500...A6 65
Salisbury, Mo., 1,960.....B5 69
Salisbury, N.C., 22,515
  (*54,700)...........B2 76
Salisbury, Rh., 210,000
  (*380,000)..........D6 24
Salisbury West, N.C......*B2 76
Sallisaw, Okla., 4,888.....B7 79
Salmon, Idaho, 2,910.....D5 57
Salmon Arm, B.C., Can.,
  1,981...............D8 37
Salmon Falls, N.H........E6 73
Salo, Fin., 11,000.......G10 11
Salon-de-Provence, Fr.,
  25,174..............F6 5
Salonta, Rom., 16,276.....B5 10
Salsk, Sov. Un., 50,000...H13 12
Salsomaggiore, It., 8,600...B2 9
Salta, Arg., 172,000......D2 29
Salta, prov., Arg., 412,854.D2 29
Saltillo, Mex., 161,114.....B4 34
Salt Lake, co., Utah,
  458,607.............A5 72
Salt Lake City, Utah,
  175,885 (502,900)...A6, C2 72
Salto, Braz., 19,060......m8 30
Salto, Ur., 57,714.......E1 30
Salto, dept., Ur., 92,216..*E1 30
Saltpond, Ghana, 9,900...G4 22
Salt River, Ky., 400......C4 62
Saltsburg, Pa., 1,037.....F3 81
Salt Springs, Fla., 900....C5 54
Saltville, Va., 2,527......f10 85
Saluda, S.C., 2,442......D4 82
Saluda, co., S.C., 14,528...C4 82
Saluda Gardens, S.C.....*D5 82
Sālūr, India, 30,929......E7 20
Saluzzo, It., 11,100......B1 9
Salvador, Braz., 1,007,744
  (*1,020,000)........E7 27
Salvatierra, Mex.,
  18,975..............m13 34
Salween, riv., Asia......D10 20
Salyersville, Ky., 1,196...C6 62
Salzburg, Aus., 127,455
  (*150,000)..........E6 6
Salzburg, state, Aus.,
  388,600.............E6 6
Salzgitter, Ger., Fed. Rep.
  of, 117,640..........B5 6
Salzwedel, Ger. Dem. Rep.,
  20,890..............B5 6

Samani, Jap...........E11 18
Samaniego, Col., 3,181....C2 32
Samar, prov., Phil.,
  867,994............C7 19
Samar, isl., Phil.........C7 19
Samarinda, Indon.,
  137,521.............F5 19
Samarkand, Sov. Un.,
  267,000.............F9 13
Sāmarrā', Iraq, 24,746....E14 14
Sambalpur, India, 64,675..D7 20
Sambas, Indon., 12,000....E3 19
Sambhal, India, 86,323...*C6 20
Sambor, Sov. Un., 29,000.G4 12
Samchŏk, Kor., 28,500
  (38,815 ▲)...........H4 18
Samchonpo, Kor., 33,000
  (54,945 ▲)...........I4 18
Samokov, Bul., 21,611....D6 10
Samos, prov., Grc.,
  41,687.............*D6 14
Samoset, Fla., 4,070.....q10 54
Sampson, co., N.C.,
  44,954..............B4 76
Samson, Ala., 2,257......D3 46
Samsun, Tur., 134,061....B11 14
Samtown, La., 3,750......*C3 63
San'ā, Yemen, 89,000.....F3 15
San Agustín, Col., 3,250...C2 32
Sanandaj, Iran, 54,748.....B4 15
San Andreas, Calif., 1,800..C3 50
San Andrés de Giles, Arg.,
  5,392...............g7 28
San Andrés Tuxtla, Mex.,
  24,267..............D5 34
San Angelo, Tex., 63,884
  (*65,900)...........D2 84
San Anselmo, Calif.,
  13,031.............h7 50
San Antonio, Chile, 26,917.A2 28
San Antonio, Tex.,
  654,153 (*835,200)...E3, k7 84
San Antonio de Areco,
  Arg., 9,249.........g7 28
San Antonio de los Baños,
  Cuba, 25,300 (30,000 ▲).C2 35
San Antonio Heights,
  Calif., 2,000.......*E5 50
San Augustine, Tex.,
  2,539..............D5 84
San Augustine, co., Tex.,
  7,858..............D5 84
San Bartolomeo
  [in Galdo], It., 8,767....D5 9
San Benedetto del Tronto,
  It., 35,600..........C4 9
San Benito, Tex., 15,176...F4 84
San Benito, co., Calif.,
  18,226.............D3 50
San Bernardino, Calif.,
  104,251 (*577,000).E5, m14 50
San Bernardino, co.,
  Calif., 682,233......E5 50
San Bernardo, Chile,
  45,207.............A2 28
Sanborn, Iowa, 1,456.....A2 60
Sanborn, co., S. Dak.,
  3,697..............G7 77
San Bruno, Calif.,
  36,254...........D2, h8 50
San Carlos, Arg., 809.....C2 28
San Carlos, Calif., 26,053..k8 50
San Carlos, Chile, 16,097..B2 28
San Carlos, Phil., 23,633
  (90,058 ▲)..........o13 19
San Carlos, Ur., 13,695...E2 30
San Carlos [de Bariloche],
  Arg., 23,000........C2 28
San Cataldo, It., 22,500...F4 9
Sanch'ung, Tai., 166,300..*G9 17
San Clemente, Calif.,
  17,063.............F5 50
San Clemente, Sp., 6,948..C4 8
San Cristóbal, Dom. Rep.,
  25,800.............E8 35
San Cristóbal, Ven.,
  152,239.............B3 32
San Cristóbal Las Casas,
  Mex., 25,700........D6 34
Sancti-Spíritus, Cuba,
  57,700 (66,500 ▲).....D4 35
Sanda, Jap., 33,090......o14 18
Sandakan, Mala., 42,413...D5 19
Sandefjord, Nor., 7,000...p28 11
Sanders, co., Mont., 7,093..C1 70
Sandersville, Ga., 5,546...D4 55
Sandia, Peru, 1,482......D4 31
San Diego, Calif., 697,027
  (*1,206,800)...F5, o15 50
San Diego, Tex., 4,490....F3 84
San Diego, co., Calif.,
  1,357,854...........F5 50
Sandikli, Tur., 11,056....C8 14
Sandīla, India, 22,365....C7 20
San Dimas, Calif., 15,692.*F4 50
Sandoa, Zaire...........B4 24
Sandomierz, Pol., 16,800...C6 7
Sandoná, Col., 6,776.....C2 32

San Donà di Piave, It.,
  18,500.............B4 9
Sandoval, Ill., 1,332......E4 58
Sandoval, co., N. Mex.,
  17,492.............B5 48
Sandpoint, Idaho, 4,144...A2 57
Sandspit, B.C., Can., 466..C2 37
Sands Point, N.Y., 2,916..*G2 52
Sand Springs, Okla.,
  10,565.............A5 79
Sandstone, Minn., 1,641...D6 67
Sandusky, Mich., 2,071...E8 66
Sandusky, Ohio, 32,674...A3 78
Sandusky, co., Ohio,
  60,983.............A2 78
Sandusky South, Ohio,
  4,724..............*A3 78
Sandviken, Swe., 43,489...G7 11
Sandwich, Ill., 5,056......B5 58
Sandwich, Mass., 1,305...C7 65
Sandy, Oreg., 1,544......B4 80
Sandy, Pa., 2,000.......*D4 81
Sandy, Utah, 6,438.......D2 72
Sandy Beach, N.Y., 1,691.*C2 75
Sandy Hook, Conn., 900..D3 52
Sandy Springs, Ga.,
  16,000.............h8 55
San Elizario, Tex., 950...o11 84
San Estanislao, Par.,
  10,948.............D4 29
San Felipe, Chile, 19,048..A2 28
San Felipe, N. Mex.,
  1,187............B5, D6 48
San Felipe, Ven., 43,801...A4 32
San Felipe de Jesus, Mex.,
  59,932.............*D5 34
San Felíu de Guixols, Sp.,
  10,307.............B7 8
San Fernando, Arg.,
  119,565..........A5, g7 28
San Fernando, Calif.,
  16,571.............m12 50
San Fernando, Chile,
  21,774.............A2 28
San Fernando, Phil.,
  11,084...........B6, n13 19
San Fernando, Phil.,
  33,335.............o13 19
San Fernando, Sp.,
  57,235.............D2 8
San Fernando, Trin.,
  37,313 (*68,000).......A5 32
San Fernando de Apure,
  Ven., 38,960........B4 32
San Fernando de Atabapo,
  Ven., 898...........C4 32
Sanford, Fla., 17,393.....D5 54
Sanford, Maine, 10,457....E4 64
Sanford, N.C., 11,716....B3 76
San Francisco, Arg.,
  44,000.............A4 28
San Francisco, Calif.,
  715,674
  (*4,274,800).......D2, h8 50
San Francisco, Col.,
  1,248..............C2 32
San Francisco del Oro,
  Mex., 12,315........B3 34
San Francisco del Rincón,
  Mex., 27,079........m13 34
San Francisco de Macorís,
  Dom. Rep., 43,900...E8 35
San Gabriel, Calif.,
  29,336.............m12 50
San Gabriel, Ec., 6,803....A2 31
San Gabriel Chilac,
  Mex., 6,707.......D5, n15 34
Sangamon, co., Ill.,
  161,335.............D4 58
Sanger, Calif., 10,088.....D4 50
Sanger, Tex., 1,603......C4 84
Sangerhausen, Ger. Dem.
  Rep., 32,084........C5 6
San Germán, P.R.,
  11,613 (27,990 ▲).....*G11 35
San Gil, Col., 18,518.....B3 32
San Giovanni in Fiore, It.,
  17,400.............E6 9
Sangju, Kor., 28,000
  (52,504 ▲)..........H4 18
Sāngli, India, 115,138
  (*201,597)..........*E5 20
San Gorgonio, mtn.,
  Calif...............E5 50
San Ignacio, Par., 6,116...E4 29
Sanilac, co., Mich.,
  35,181.............E8 66
San Isidro, Arg., 250,008..g7 28
San Jacinto, Calif., 4,385..F5 50
San Jacinto, co., Tex.,
  6,702..............D5 84
San Javier, Chile, 8,500...B2 28
Sanjo, Jap., 77,814......H9 18
San Joaquin, co., Calif.,
  291,073.............C3 50
San Jose, Ariz., 100......C4 48
San Jose, Calif.,
  446,537...........D3, k9 50

San José, C.R., 201,100
  (*385,000)..........F8 34
San Jose, Ill., 681......C4 58
San José, Ur., 21,200....E1 30
San José, dept., Ur.,
  77,300.............*E1 30
San José, prov., C.R.,
  563,800.............*F8 34
San José de Feliciano,
  Arg., 3,721.........A5 28
San José de los Molinos,
  Peru, 1,221.........D2 31
San Juan, Arg., 112,500
  (*210,000)..........A3 28
San Juan, Colo., 100.....D6 51
San Juan, Dom. Rep.,
  32,200.............E8 35
San Juan, P.R., 452,749
  (*936,693)........*G11 35
San Juan, Tex., 5,070....G2 84
San Juan, co., Colo., 831..D3 51
San Juan, co., N. Mex.,
  52,517.............A4 48
San Juan, co., Utah,
  9,606..............C6 72
San Juan, co., Wash.,
  3,856..............A2 86
San Juan, prov., Arg.,
  352,387.............A3 28
San Juan Bautista, Calif.,
  1,164.............*D3 50
San Juan Bautista, Par.,
  6,457..............E4 29
San Juan Capistrano,
  Calif., 3,781........F5 50
San Juan de los Lagos,
  Mex., 19,570........m12 34
San Juan de los Morros,
  Ven., 37,817........B4 32
San Juan del Río, Mex.,
  15,422.............m13 34
San Julián, Arg., 3,649...D3 28
San Justo, Arg., 659,193..*B5 28
Sankt Gallen, Switz.,
  80,500 (*114,000).....E4 6
Sankt Gallen, canton,
  Switz., 381,000......*E4 6
Sankt Pölten, Aus.,
  50,144.............D7 6
Sankt Veit an der Glan,
  Aus., 11,058........E7 6
San Leandro, Calif.,
  68,698.............h8 50
San Lorenzo, Arg., 28,000.A4 28
San Lorenzo, Calif.,
  27,000.............*D2 50
San Lorenzo, P.R.,
  7,702 (27,755 ▲).....*G12 35
San Lorenzo del
  Escorial, Sp., 7,965..B3, o16 8
Sanlúcar, Sp., 32,580
  (40,335 ▲)..........D2 8
San Luis, Arg., 50,000....A3 28
San Luis, Colo., 781.....D5 51
San Luis, Cuba, 17,400
  (35,000 ▲)..........D6 35
San Luis, prov., Arg.,
  174,316.............A3 28
San Luis de la Paz,
  Mex., 12,654........m13 34
San Luis Obispo, Calif.,
  28,036.............E3 50
San Luis Obispo, co.,
  Calif., 105,690......E3 50
San Luis Potosí, Mex.,
  230,039.........C4, k13 34
San Luis Potosí, state,
  Mex., 1,145,900....C4, k13 34
San Manuel, Ariz.,
  4,332.............*C3 48
San Marco [in Lamis], It.,
  19,014.............D5 9
San Marcos, Tex.,
  18,860...........E4, h8 84
San Marino, Calif.,
  14,177.............m12 50
San Marino, country, Eur.,
  20,000.............C4 9
San Martín (General
  San Martín), Arg.,
  278,751.............g7 28
San Martín, Calif.,
  1,162.............*D3 50
San Martín, dept., Peru,
  120,913.............C2 31
San Mateo, Calif., 78,991..h8 50
San Mateo, Ven., 1,849...B5 32
San Mateo, co., Calif.,
  556,605.............D2 50
San Miguel, Sal., 59,304...E7 34
San Miguel, co., Colo.,
  1,949..............D2 51
San Miguel, co., N. Mex.,
  21,951.............B6 48
San Miguel de Allende,
  Mex., 24,286........m13 34

Southgate, Mich., 33,909 ..p15 66
South Glastonbury, Conn.,
  1,600................C6 52
South Glens Falls, N.Y.,
  4,013...............*B7 75
South Grafton, Mass.,
  3,000................B4 65
South Greensburg, Pa.,
  3,288...............*F2 81
South Greenwood, S.C....C3 82
South Hackensack, N.J.,
  2,412...............*B4 74
South Hadley, Mass.,
  6,000................B2 65
South Hadley Falls, Mass.,
  9,000................B3 65
South Hamilton,
  Mass., 3,500......A6, f12 65
South Hanover, Mass.,
  900.................h12 65
South Harriman, Tenn...*D9 83
South Harwich, Mass.,
  600.................C7 65
South Haven, Mich.,
  6,471................F4 66
South Hempstead, N.Y.,
  3,000...............*E7 75
South Henderson, N.C.,
  1,843...............*A4 76
South Hill, Va., 3,858....D4 85
South Holland, Ill.,
  23,931...............k9 58
South Holland
  (Zuid-Holland), prov.,
  Neth., 2,943,600......*A6 5
South Hooksett, N.H.,
  1,200................D4 73
South Houston, Tex.,
  11,527..............r14 84
South Huntington, N.Y.,
  9,115...............*D3 75
South Hutchinson, Kans.,
  1,879................f11 61
Southington, Conn.,
  16,000...............C5 52
South International Falls,
  Minn., 2,116.........B5 67
South Jacksonville, Ill.,
  2,950................D3 58
South Jordan, Utah,
  2,942...............*A6 72
Southkent, Mich......*F5 66
South Laguna, Calif.,
  2,000...............*F5 50
Southlake, Tex., 2,031...*C4 84
South Lake Tahoe, Calif.,
  21,921...............C4 50
South Lancaster, Mass.,
  2,679................B4 65
Southland, Mich.,
  2,000...............*F6 66
Southlawn, Ill., 3,000...*D4 58
South Lebanon, Ohio,
  3,014................C1 78
South Lyon, Mich.,
  2,675............F7, p14 66
South Mansfield, La., 439..B2 63
South Miami, Fla.,
  11,780...........G6, s13 54
South Milwaukee,
  Wis., 23,297......F6, n12 88
South Modesto, Calif.,
  9,000...............*D3 50
South Monroe, Mich.,
  1,200...............*G7 66
Southmont, N.C., 600....B2 76
Southmont, Pa., 2,653...*F4 81
South Montrose, Pa.,
  500.................C10 81
South Mt. Vernon, Ohio,
  1,044...............*B3 78
South Nelson, N.S., Can.,
  792.................*C4 43
South Nelson Village,
  B.C., Can., 939.......*E9 37
South New Castle, Pa.,
  940.................*D1 81
South Nyack, N.Y.,
  3,435................g9 75
South Ogden, Utah,
  9,991............A6, C2 72
Southold, N.Y., 2,030...m16 75
South Orange, N.J.,
  16,971...............B4 74
South Oroville, Calif.,
  3,704...............*C3 50
South Paris, Maine,
  2,315................D2 64
South Park, Ill., 2,500...*B5 58
South Pasadena, Calif.,
  22,979..............*E4 50
South Patrick Shores,
  Fla., 10,313.........D6 54
South Pekin, Ill., 955....C4 58
South Pittsburg, Tenn.,
  3,613................D8 83
South Plainfield, N.J.,
  21,142...............B4 74

South Point, Ohio, 2,243..D3 78
South Porcupine, Ont.,
  Can., 4,843.........o19 41
Southport, Austl., 66,558...E9 25
Southport, Eng., 84,870...D5 4
Southport, Fla., 1,560....u16 54
Southport, Ind.,
  2,342............E5, m10 59
Southport, N.Y., 8,685...*C4 75
Southport, N.C., 2,220....D4 76
South Portland, Maine,
  23,267...........E2, g7 64
South Pottstown, Pa.,
  800................*F10 81
South Range, Mich., 898..A2 66
South Renovo, Pa., 662...D6 81
South Revelstoke, B.C.,
  Can., 737...........D8 37
South River, Ont., Can.,
  1,044................B5 42
South River, N.J.,
  15,428...............C4 74
South Rockwood, Mich.,
  1,477...............*F7 66
South Roxana, Ill.,
  2,241...............*E4 58
South Russell, Ohio,
  2,673...............*A4 78
South St. Paul, Minn.,
  25,016...........F5, n12 67
South Salisbury, N.C.,
  2,199...............*B2 76
South Salt Lake, Utah,
  7,810................C2 72
South San Francisco,
  Calif., 46,646.......h8 50
South San Gabriel,
  Calif., 26,213......*F4 50
South Shields, Eng.,
  100,220..............C6 4
South Shore, Mo., 200...f12 69
Southside Estates, Fla...*B5 54
South Side Place, Tex.,
  1,466...............r14 84
South Sioux City, Nebr.,
  7,920................B9 71
South Stickney, Ill......k9 58
South Streator, Ill.,
  1,869...............*B5 58
South Swansea, Mass.,
  1,500................C5 65
South Taft, Calif.,
  1,910...............*E4 50
South Temple, Pa.,
  1,600...............*F10 81
South Toms River, N.J.,
  3,981................D4 74
South Torrington, Wyo.,
  250.................D8 89
South Trail, Fla........q10 54
South Tucson, Ariz.,
  6,220................C3 48
South Uniontown, Pa.,
  3,546...............*G2 81
South Walpole, Mass.,
  600.................h10 65
South Waverly, Pa.,
  1,307................C8 81
South Webster, Ohio,
  825.................D3 78
Southwest, Pa., 700.....F2 81
South West, div., Ice.,
  77,976..............n22 11
South West Africa
  (Namibia), country,
  Afr., 800,000........E3 24
South Westbury, N.Y.,
  10,978..............*E7 75
Southwest Dillon, S.C...*C9 82
Southwestern, mts., Va...B4 85
South West Fargo, N. Dak.D9 77
Southwest Greensburg,
  Pa., 3,186..........*F2 81
Southwest Harbor, Maine,
  900.................D4 64
South Whitley, Ind.,
  1,632................B6 59
Southwick, Mass., 1,263...B2 65
South Williamson, Ky.,
  700.................C7 62
South Williamsport, Pa.,
  7,153................D7 81
South Wilmington, Ill.,
  725.................B5 58
South Windermere, S.C...*F8 82
South Windham, Maine,
  1,453............E2, g7 64
South Windsor, Conn.,
  10,200...............B6 52
Southwood Acres, Conn.,
  10,000..............*B6 52
South Yarmouth, Mass.,
  5,380................C7 65
South Zanesville, Ohio,
  1,436................C3 78
Sovetsk (Tilsit), Sov. Un.,
  38,000...............A6 7

Sovetskaya Gavan, Sov.
  Un., 28,000.........E17 13
Soviet Union (U.S.S.R.),
  country, Eur., Asia,
  251,050,000............ 13
Spa, Bel., 9,557........B6 5
Spain, country, Eur.,
  34,905,000............. 8
Spalding, Eng., 16,970...D6 4
Spalding, Nebr., 676.....C7 71
Spalding, co., Ga., 39,514..C2 55
Spanaway, Wash., 5,768...B3 86
Spangler, Pa., 3,109.....E4 81
Spaniard's Bay, Newf.,
  Can., 1,764..........E5 44
Spanish Fork, Utah,
  7,284............A6, D2 72
Spanish Ont., Can., 1,257.A2 41
Spanish Sahara, dep.,
  Afr., 106,000........D2 22
Spanish Town, Jam.,
  41,600...............F5 35
Sparkill, N.Y., 1,200....*D6 75
Sparkman, Ark., 663.....D3 49
Sparks, Ga., 1,337......E3 55
Sparks, Nev., 24,187....B2 72
Sparlingville, Mich.,
  1,845...............*F8 66
Sparrows Point, Md.,
  2,750................B5 53
Sparta, Ga., 2,172......C4 55
Sparta, Ill., 4,307......E4 58
Sparta, Mich., 3,094....E5 66
Sparta, N.J., 6,262......A3 74
Sparta, N.C., 1,304......A1 76
Sparta, Tenn., 4,930....D8 83
Sparta, Wis., 6,258......E3 88
Sparta, mtn., N.J........B3 74
Spartanburg, S.C.,
  44,546 (*125,000)....B4 82
Spartanburg, co., S.C.,
  173,631..............B3 82
Sparti (Sparta), Grc.,
  10,549 (*13,432)......D4 14
Spassk-Dalniy, Sov. Un.,
  45,000..............E16 13
Spearfish, S. Dak., 4,661..F2 77
Spearman, Tex., 3,435...A2 84
Spearville, Kans., 738....E4 61
Speed, Ind., 640........H6 59
Speedway, Ind.,
  14,649...........E5, k10 59
Speers, Pa., 1,408......*F2 81
Speight, Ky., 230.......C7 62
Spenard, Alsk........*C10 47
Spencer, Ind., 2,553....F4 59
Spencer, Iowa, 10,278...A2 60
Spencer, Mass., 5,895....B4 65
Spencer, Nebr., 606.....B7 71
Spencer, N.Y., 854......C4 75
Spencer, N.C., 3,075....B2 76
Spencer, Ohio, 758......A3 78
Spencer, Okla., 3,714....*B4 79
Spencer, W. Va., 2,271...C3 87
Spencer, Wis., 1,181....D3 88
Spencer, co., Ind., 17,134..H4 59
Spencer, co., Ky., 5,488...B4 62
Spencerport, N.Y., 2,929..B3 75
Spencerville, Ohio, 2,241..B1 78
Sperry, Okla., 1,123.....A6 79
Speyer, Ger., Fed. Rep. of,
  43,415..............D4 6
Spiceland, Ind., 957.....E7 59
Spinazzola, It., 10,850...D6 9
Spindale, N.C., 3,848....B1 76
Spink, co., S. Dak., 10,595.F7 77
Spirit Lake, Idaho, 622...B3 57
Spirit Lake, Iowa, 3,014...A2 60
Spirit River, Alta., Can.,
  1,091................B1 38
Spiro, Okla., 2,057......B7 79
Spišská Nová Ves, Czech.,
  22,554...............D6 7
Spittal an der Drau, Aus.,
  12,556...............E6 6
Split, Yugo., 151,875....D3 10
Spokane, Wash., 170,516
  (*259,000)......B8, g14 86
Spokane, co., Wash.,
  287,487..............B8 86
Spoleto, It., 26,300.....C4 9
Spooner, Wis., 2,444....C2 88
Spotswood, N.J., 7,891...C4 74
Spotsylvania, co., Va.,
  16,424...............B5 85
Sprague, W. Va., 1,500...n13 87
Spray, N.C............A3 76
Spreckels, Calif., 750....*D3 50
Spreckelsville, Haw., 120..*C5 56
Spremberg, Ger. Dem.
  Rep., 22,900.........C7 6
Spring, Tex., 950.......q14 84
Spring Arbor, Mich., 1,832.F6 66
Springboro, Ohio, 2,799...C1 78
Spring City, Pa., 3,578...F10 81
Spring City, Tenn., 1,756..D9 83
Springdale, Ark., 16,783...A1 49

Springdale, Newf., Can.,
  3,224................D3 44
Springdale, Ohio, 8,127...n13 78
Springdale, Pa., 5,202.E2, h14 81
Springdale, S.C., 2,638...*D5 82
Springer, N. Mex., 1,574...A6 48
Springfield, Colo., 1,660...D8 51
Springfield, Fla., 5,949...v16 54
Springfield, Ill., 91,753
  (*137,400)...........D4 58
Springfield, Ky., 2,961....C4 62
Springfield, Mass., 163,905
  (*500,000)..........B2 65
Springfield, Minn., 2,530..F4 67
Springfield, Mo., 120,096
  (*151,400)..........D4 69
Springfield, Nebr.,
  795.................C9, g12 71
Springfield, N.J., 15,740...B4 74
Springfield, Ohio, 81,941..C2 78
Springfield, Oreg., 27,047..C4 80
Springfield, Pa., 29,006..*B11 81
Springfield, S.C., 724....E5 82
Springfield, S. Dak.,
  1,566................H8 77
Springfield, Tenn., 9,720...A5 83
Springfield, Vt., 5,632....E3 73
Springfield, Va., 11,613...g12 85
Springfield Place, Mich...*B5 54
Spring Glen, Fla........*B5 54
Spring Green, Wis., 1,199..E3 88
Spring Grove, Minn.,
  1,290................G7 67
Spring Grove, Pa., 1,669...G8 81
Springhill, N.S., Can.,
  5,262................D6 43
Spring Hill, Kans., 1,186..D9 61
Springhill, La., 6,496....A2 63
Spring Hill, Pa., 500....*F4 81
Spring Hope, N.C., 1,334..B4 76
Spring Lake, Mich., 3,034..E4 66
Spring Lake, N.J., 3,896...C4 74
Spring Lake, N.C., 3,968...B3 76
Spring Lake Heights, N.J.,
  4,602................C4 74
Spring Lake Park, Minn.,
  6,411...............*E5 67
Springlee, Ky., 583......*H6 62
Spring Mills, S.C., 900...*B6 82
Springmont, Pa., 600....*F10 81
Springport, Mich., 723...F6 66
Springs, S. Afr., 99,047...*F5 24
Springsure, Aust., 820....B8 25
Springvale, Maine, 2,914..E2 64
Spring Valley, Calif.,
  34,400..............o16 50
Spring Valley, Ill., 5,605..B4 58
Spring Valley, Minn.,
  2,572................G6 67
Spring Valley, N.Y.,
  18,112..............g12 75
Spring Valley, Ohio, 667..C1 78
Spring Valley, Tex.,
  3,170...............*E5 84
Springville, Iowa, 970....B6 60
Springville, N.Y., 4,350...C2 75
Springville, Utah,
  8,790............A6, D2 72
Spruce Knob, mtn.,
  W. Va...............C5 87
Spruce Pine, N.C., 2,333...f10 76
Spur, Tex., 1,747.......C2 84
Squamish, B.C., Can.,
  1,597................E6 37
Squatteck, Que., Can.,
  1,088................B9 42
Squaw Lake, Minn., 113...C4 67
Squaw Rapids, Sask.,
  Can., 1,024..........D4 39
Srbobran, Yugo., 14,150...C4 10
Sredne-Kolymsk, Sov.
  Un., 2,500..........C18 13
Sremska Mitrovica, Yugo.,
  31,921...............C4 10
Sretensk, Sov. Un.,
  13,900..............D14 13
Sri Lanka, country, Asia,
  13,065,000...........G7 20
Srinagar, India, 403,413
  (*415,271)..........B6 20
Ssuping (Szeping), China,
  130,000..............C9 17
Staatsburg, N.Y., 800....D7 75
Stade, Ger., Fed. Rep. of,
  40,687...............B4 6
Stafford, Eng., 54,120....D5 4
Stafford, Kans., 1,414....E5 61
Stafford, Tex., 2,906....*E5 84
Stafford, co., Eng.,
  1,860,200...........*D5 4
Stafford, co., Kans.,
  5,943................D5 61
Stafford, co., Va., 24,587..B5 85
Stafford Springs, Conn.,
  3,339................B7 52
Staffordsville, Ky., 700...C7 62
Staines, Eng., 56,370....m11 4
Stains, Fr., 32,169......g10 5

T

Toledo, prov., Sp., 490,000 *C3 8
Toler, Ky., 500 C7 62
Tolima, dept., Col., 879,800 C2 32
Tolland, co., Conn., 103,440 B7 52
Tolleson, Ariz., 3,881 D1 48
Tolmin, Yugo., 1,638 B1 10
Tolna, Hung., 8,748 B4 10
Tolna, co., Hung., 259,267 *B4 10
Tolono, Ill., 2,027 D5 58
Tolosa, Sp., 16,281 A4 8
Toluca, Ill., 1,319 B4 58
Toluca [de Lerdo], Mex., 114,079 D5, n14 34
Tolyatti, Sov. Un., 251,000 *D7 13
Tomah, Wis., 5,647 E3 88
Tomahawk, Wis., 3,419 C4 88
Tomakomai, Jap., 101,573 E10 18
Tomakovka, Sov. Un., 10,000 H10 12
Tomar, Port., 8,034 C1 8
Tomari, Sov. Un., 16,100 E17 13
Tomaszow Lubelski, Pol., 12,300 C7 7
Tomaszow Mazowiecki, Pol., 54,900 C6 7
Tomball, Tex., 2,734 D5 84
Tombouctou (Timbuktu), Mali, 9,000 E4 22
Tombstone, Ariz., 1,241 D4 48
Tomé, Chile, 26,942 B2 28
Tomelloso, Sp., 27,815 C4 8
Tom Green, co., Tex., 71,047 D2 84
Tomkins Cove, N.Y., 800 D7, m14 75
Tommot, Sov. Un., 6,600 D15 13
Tompkins, co., N.Y., 77,064 C4 75
Tompkinsville, Ky., 2,207 D4 62
Tom Price, Austl., 3,370 D2 25
Tomsk, Sov. Un., 338,000 D11 13
Toms River, N.J., 7,303 D4 74
Tonalá, Mex., 15,611 D6 34
Tonasket, Wash., 951 A6 86
Tonawanda, N.Y., 21,898 B2 75
Tondano, Indon., 22,678 E6 19
Tønder, Den., 7,192 A4 6
Tønder, co., Den., 43,200 *J3 11
Tonga, Br. dep., Oceania, 95,000 H9 2
Tonganoxie, Kans., 1,717 C8, k15 61
Tonk, India, 55,866 C6 20
Tonka Bay, Minn., 1,397 *F5 67
Tonkawa, Okla., 3,337 A4 79
Tonkin, reg., Viet., 11,000,000 A3 19
Tonopah, Nev., 1,716 B3 72
Tönsberg, Nor., 11,400 (*34,500) H4, p28 11
Tooele, Utah, 12,539 A5, D2 72
Tooele, co., Utah, 21,545 A5 72
Toole, co., Mont., 5,839 B5 70
Toombs, co., Ga., 19,151 D4 55
Toowoomba, Austl., 59,476 E9 25
Topanga, Calif., 1,800 *F4 50
Topeka, Kans., 125,011 (*151,900) C8, k13 61
Topol'čany, Czech., 12,757 D5 7
Topolovgrad, Bul., 6,591 D8 10
Toppenish, Wash., 5,744 C5 86
Topsfield, Mass., 2,200 A6 65
Topsham, Maine, 2,700 E3, g8 64
Topton, Pa., 1,744 F10 81
Torbay, Newf., Can., 2,090 E5 44
Torez, Sov. Un., 93,000 (*275,000) q21 12
Torhout, Bel., 15,413 B5 5
Toride, Jap., 40,287 n19 18
Torino, see Turin, It.
Toro, Sp., 10,218 B3 8
Törökszentmiklós, Hung., 20,988 (24,229 ▲) B5 10
Toronto, Ont., Can., 712,786 (*2,628,043) D5, m15 41
Toronto, Ohio, 7,705 B5 78
Toropets, Sov. Un., 17,000 C8 12
Torquay (Torbay), Eng., 105,050 E5 4
Torrance, Calif., 134,968 n12 50
Torrance, co., N. Mex., 5,290 B5 48
Torre Annunziata, It., 63,100 D5 9
Torre del Greco, It., 80,100 D5 9
Torredonjimeno, Sp., 14,204 D4 8
Torrelavega, Sp., 13,612 A3 8
Torremaggiore, It., 17,318 D5 9
Torrens, lake, Austl. F6 25
Torrente, Sp., 24,042 C5 8
Torreón, Mex., 223,104 (*410,000) B4 34
Torre Pacheco, Sp., 9,541 D5 8
Torres Novas, Port., 7,291 C1 8
Torrevieja, Sp., 9,234 D5 8
Torrington, Conn., 31,952 B4 52
Torrington, Wyo., 4,237 D8 89
Torrox, Sp., 7,384 D4 8
Tortilla Flat, Ariz., 15 C3 48
Tortona, It., 23,000 B2 9
Tortosa, Sp., 18,674 (43,267 ▲) B6 8
Toruń, Pol., 129,100 B5 7
Torzhok, Sov. Un., 46,000 C10 12
Toscana, pol. dist., It., 3,286,160 *C3 9
Tosno, Sov. Un., 20,000 C10 12
Tosya, Tur., 16,698 B10 14
Totana, Sp., 9,949 D5 8
Totkomlós, Hung., 8,122 B5 10
Totonicapán, Guat., 8,727 D6 34
Totowa, N.J., 11,580 B4 74
Tottori, Jap., 113,151 I7 18
Tottori, pref., Jap., 568,777 *I7 18
Totz, Ky., 350 D6 62
Toubkal, Jbel, mtn., Mor. B3 22
Tougaloo, Miss., 1,300 C3 68
Touggourt, Alg., 26,486 (50,159 ▲) B6 22
Toul, Fr., 14,780 (*20,000) C3 68
Toulon, Fr., 174,746 (*340,000) F6 5
Toulon, Ill., 1,207 B4 58
Toulouse, Fr., 370,796 (*440,000) F4 5
Toungoo, Bur., 31,589 E10 20
Touraine, former prov., Fr. D4 5
Tourcoing, Fr., 98,755 B5 5
Tourlaville, Fr., 12,062 C3 5
Tours, Fr., 128,120 (*205,000) D4 5
Towaco, N.J., 1,400 B4 74
Towanda, Kans., 1,190 E7, k12 61
Towanda, Pa., 4,224 C9 81
Tower City, Pa., 1,774 E8 81
Town and Country, Mo., 2,645 *C7 69
Towner, N. Dak., 870 B5 77
Towner, co., N. Dak., 4,645 B6 77
Townley, Ala., 500 B2 46
Town of Pines, Ind., 1,007 *A4 59
Town of Tonawanda, N.Y., 86,302 *B2 75
Towns, co., Ga., 4,565 B3 55
Townsend, Mass., 1,329 A4 65
Townsend, Mont., 1,371 D5 70
Townsville, Austl., 71,109 C8 25
Towson, Md., 80,000 B4, g11 53
Toyama, Jap., 269,276 H8 18
Toyama, pref., Jap., 1,029,695 *H8 18
Toyohashi, Jap., 258,547 I8, o16 18
Toyokawa, Jap., 85,860 *I8 18
Toyonaka, Jap., 368,498 o14 18
Toyota, Jap., 197,193 n16 18
Tozeur, Tun., 11,820 B6 22
Trabzon, Tur., 80,795 B12 14
Tracadie, N.B., Can., 2,222 B5 43
Tracy, Calif., 14,724 D3, h10 50
Tracy, Minn., 2,516 F3 67
Tracy City, Tenn., 1,388 D7 83
Traer, Iowa, 1,682 B5 60
Trafford, Pa., 4,383 k14 81
Traiguén, Chile, 10,000 B2 28
Trail, B.C., Can., 11,149 (*17,177) E9, o19 37
Trail Creek, Ind., 2,697 A4 59
Trailer Estates, Fla., 1,759 *E4 54
Traill, co., N. Dak., 9,571 C8 77
Trainer, Pa., 2,336 *G11 81
Tralee, Ire., 12,287 D2 4
Tranås, Swe., 18,959 H6 11
Trani, It., 41,500 D6 9
Transilvania, prov., Rom., 3,420,859 *B6 10
Transvaal, prov., S. Afr., 8,000,000 E5 24
Transylvania, co., N.C., 19,713 f10 76
Transylvania, reg., Rom. B6 10
Trapani, It., 66,700 E4 9
Trappe, Pa., 1,676 *F11 81
Traralgon, Austl., 14,624 I6 26
Trás-os-Montes, reg., Port., 582,800 B2 8
Trás-os-Montes e Alto Douro, prov., Port., 639,846 *B2 8
Traunstein, Ger., Fed. Rep. of, 15,079 E6 6
Travelers Rest, S.C., 2,241 B3 82
Traverse, co., Minn., 6,254 E2 67
Traverse City, Mich., 18,048 D5 66
Travis, co., Tex., 295,516 D4 84
Travnik, Yugo., 12,977 C3 10
Treasure, co., Mont., 1,069 D9 70
Treasure Island, Fla., 6,120 *E4 54
Třebíč, Czech., 21,417 D3 7
Trebinje, Yugo., 4,072 D4 10
Trebišov, Czech., 11,142 D6 7
Trego, co., Kans., 4,436 D4 61
Treinta y Tres, Ur., 21,035 E2 30
Treinta y Tres, dept., Ur., 43,623 *E2 30
Trélazé, Fr., 11,664 D3 5
Trelew, Arg., 21,000 C3 28
Trelleborg, Swe., 29,038 J5 11
Tremont, Ill., 1,942 C4 58
Tremont, Pa., 1,833 E9 81
Tremonton, Utah, 2,794 A5 72
Trempealeau, co., Wis., 23,344 D2 88
Trenčín, Czech., 28,746 (*39,000) D5 7
Trenggauu, state, Mala., 346,000 *D2 19
Trenque Lauquén, Arg., 13,263 B4 28
Trentino-Alto-Adige, pol. dist., It., 785,967 *A3 9
Trento, It., 88,500 A3 9
Trenton, N.S., Can., 3,331 D7 43
Trenton, Ont., Can., 14,589 (*28,650) C7 41
Trenton, Fla., 1,074 C4 54
Trenton, Ga., 1,523 B1 55
Trenton, Ill., 2,328 E4 58
Trenton, Mich., 24,127 F7, p15 66
Trenton, Mo., 6,063 A4 69
Trenton, Nebr., 770 D4 71
Trenton, N.J., 104,786 C3 74
Trenton, Ohio, 5,278 C1 78
Trenton, Tenn., 4,226 B3 83
Trentwood, Wash., 1,800 *B8 86
Tres Arroyos, Arg., 37,000 B4 28
Tresckow, Pa., 1,146 E10 81
Trés Coraçoes, Braz., 25,707 C3 30
Três Lagoas, Braz., 40,137 C2 30
Treutlen, co., Ga., 5,647 D4 55
Treviglio, It., 21,600 B2 9
Treviso, It., 88,100 B4 9
Trevorton, Pa., 2,196 E8 81
Trevose, Pa., 7,000 *F12 81
Trevose Heights, Pa., 3,000 *F12 81
Treynor, Iowa, 472 C2 60
Trezevant, Tenn., 877 A3 83
Triangle, Va., 3,021 B5 85
Tribbett, Miss., 90 B3 68
Tribune, Kans., 1,013 D2 61
Trichinopoly, see Tiruchchirāppalli, India
Trichūr, India, 76,241 F6 20
Trier, Ger., Fed. Rep. of, 102,752 D3 6
Trieste, It., 279,400 B4 9
Trigg, co., Ky., 8,620 D2 62
Triglav, mtn., Yugo. B1 10
Trigueros, Sp., 6,454 D2 8
Trikkala, Grc., 34,794 C3 14
Trikkala, prov., Grc., 131,820 *C3 14
Tri Lakes, Ind., 1,193 *B7 59
Trimble, co., Ky., 5,349 B4 62
Trimont, Minn., 835 G4 67
Trincomalee, Sri Lanka, 41,784 G7 20
Tring-Jonction, Que., Can., 1,283 C6 42
Trinidad, Bol., 16,800 B3 29
Trinidad, Colo., 9,901 D6 51
Trinidad, Cuba., 31,500 (37,000 ▲) D4 35
Trinidad, Tex., 1,079 C4 84
Trinidad, Ur., 16,599 E1 30
Trinidad & Tobago, country, N.A., 1,110,000 A5 32
Trinité, Mart., 3,631 I14 35
Trinity, Tex., 2,512 D5 84
Trinity, co., Calif., 7,615 B2 50
Trinity, co., Tex., 7,628 D5 84
Trinity, mts., Calif. B2 50
Trino, It., 8,100 B2 9
Trion, Ga., 1,965 B1 55
Tripoli, Iowa, 1,345 B5 60
Tripolis, Grc., 20,209 D4 14
Tripoli (Tarābulus), Leb., 157,320 f5 15
Tripoli (Tarābulus), Libya, 157,320 B7 22
Tripp, S. Dak., 851 G8 77
Tripp, co., S. Dak., 8,171 G6 77
Tripura, state, India, 1,556,342 D9 20
Tristate Village, Ill., 1,700 *B5 58
Triumph, La., 1,600 E6 63
Trivandrum, India, 409,627 G6 20
Trnava, Czech., 38,634 (*46,000) D4 7
Trois-Pistoles, Que., Can., 4,678 A8 42
Trois-Rivières, Que., Can., 55,869 (*97,930) C5 42
Troitsk, Sov. Un., 85,000 D9 13
Trollhättan, Swe., 48,840 H5 11
Troms, co., Nor., 135,900 *C8 11
Tromsö, Nor., 37,200 C8 11
Trona, Calif., 1,500 E5 50
Trondheim, Nor., 123,600 F4 11
Troodos, mtn., Cyp. E9 14
Tropea, It., 6,702 E5 9
Trotwood, Ohio, 6,997 C1 78
Troup, Tex., 1,668 C5 84
Troup, co., Ga., 44,466 C1 55
Trousdale, co., Tenn., 5,155 A5 83
Trouville, Fr., 6,429 (*15,000) C3 5
Trowbridge, Eng., 19,380 E5 4
Troy, Ala., 11,482 D4 46
Troy, Ill., 2,144 E4 58
Troy, Kans., 1,047 C8 61
Troy, Mich., 39,419 o15 66
Troy, Mo., 2,538 C7 69
Troy, N.Y., 62,918 C7 75
Troy, N.C., 2,429 B3 76
Troy, Ohio, 17,186 B1 78
Troy, Pa., 1,315 C8 81
Troyes, Fr., 74,898 (*115,000) C6 5
Trubchevsk, Sov. Un., 10,000 E9 12
Trucial States, see United Arab Emirates, country, Asia
Trucksville, Pa., 2,200 *D10 81
Trujillo, Peru, 127,535 C2 31
Trujillo, Sp., 13,326 C3 8
Trujillo, Ven., 25,921 B3 32
Trujillo, state, Ven., 326,634 B3 32
Truman, Minn., 1,137 G4 67
Trumann, Ark., 6,023 B5 49
Trumansburg, N.Y., 1,803 C4 75
Trumbull, Conn., 31,394 E4 52
Trumbull, co., Ohio, 232,579 A5 78
Truro, N.S., Can., 13,047 (*24,914) D6 43
Truro, Eng., 15,100 E4 4
Trussville, Ala., 2,985 B3, f7 46
Truth or Consequences, N. Mex., 4,656 C5 48
Trutnov, Czech., 24,666 C3 7
Tryon, N.C., 1,951 f10 76
Trysil, Nor., 787 G5 11
Tsangwu, see Wuchou, China
Tselinograd, Sov. Un., 180,000 D10 13
Tsinan (Chinan), China, 882,000 D8 17
Tsinghai (Chinghai), prov., China, 2,050,000 D8 17
Tsingtao (Chingtao), China, 1,350,000 D9 17
Tsingyuan, see Paoting, China
Tskhinvali, Sov. Un., 30,000 A14 14
Tsu, Jap., 125,203 I8, o15 18
Tsuchiura, Jap., 89,958 H10, m19 18
Tsuni, China, 200,000 F6 17
Tsun Wan, Hong Kong, 267,670 *G7 17
Tsuruga, Jap., 56,445 I8, n15 18
Tsuruoka, Jap., 74,000 (95,136 ▲) G9 18
Tsushima, Jap., 51,441 n15 18
Tsuyama, Jap., 54,000 (76,368 ▲) I7 18
Tubarão, Braz., 51,121 D3 30

Tübingen, Ger., Fed. Rep. of, 69,261...........D4 6
Ţubruq, (Tobruk), Libya, 15,900...............B2 23
Tuchola, Pol., 8,114.......B4 7
Tuckahoe, N.Y., 6,236...h13 75
Tucker, Ga., 12,500.....h8 55
Tucker, co., W. Va., 7,447................B5 87
Tuckerman, Ark., 1,731...B4 49
Tuckerton, N.J., 1,926...D4 74
Tucson, Ariz., 262,933 (*325,000)..........C3 48
Tucumán, Arg., 280,000...E2 29
Tucumán, prov., Arg., 773,972..............E2 29
Tucumcari, N. Mex., 7,189................B7 48
Tudela, Sp., 16,456......A5 8
Tuguegarao, Phil., 14,116.B6 19
Tuktoyaktuk, N.W. Ter., Can., 596.............C7 36
Tukwila, Wash., 3,509....f11 86
Tula, Sov. Un., 462,000 (*545,000)..........D11 12
Tulancingo, Mex., 35,799.............C5, m14 34
Tulare, Calif., 16,235....D4 50
Tulare, co., Calif., 188,322..............D4 50
Tularosa, N. Mex., 2,851..C5 48
Tulcán, Ec., 20,300......A2 31
Tulcea, Rom., 35,600....C9 10
Tuléar, Mad., 40,400....E8 24
Tulelake, Calif., 857.....B3 50
Tulia, Tex., 5,294.......B2 84
Ţūlkarm, Jordan, 15,275...B3 15
Tullahoma, Tenn., 15,311..............B5 83
Tullamore, Ire., 6,809...D3 4
Tulle, Fr., 20,016.......E4 5
Tullytown, Pa., 2,194....*F12 81
Tulsa, Okla., 330,350 (*460,300)..........A6 79
Tulsa, co., Okla., 400,709.B6 79
Tuluá, Col., 59,300......C2 32
Tulufan (Turfan), China, 25,000.............C2 17
Tulun, Sov. Un., 49,000..D13 13
Tulungagung, Indon., 68,899..............G4 19
Tumaco, Col., 25,145....C2 32
Tumbarumba, Austl., 1,511...............G7 26

Tumbes, Peru, 32,972.....B1 31
Tumen, China, 28,000....C10 17
Tumkūr, India, 70,476....F6 20
Tumuti, Austl., 5,525....*G8 25
Tumwater, Wash., 5,373..B3 86
Tunbridge Wells, Eng., 44,610..............E7 4
Tunchi, China, 50,000...*F8 17
Tunghsien, China, 55,000.............*D8 17
Tunghua, China, 129,100..F2 18
Tungliao, China, 40,000..C9 17
Tungurahua, prov., Ec., 245,600............B2 31
Tunhua, China, 35,000...C10 17
Tunica, Miss., 1,685.....A3 68
Tunica, co., Miss., 11,854..A3 68
Tunis, Tun., 469,997 (*685,000).........A7 22
Tunisia, country, Afr., 5,575,000..........A6 22
Tunja, Col., 40,451......B3 32
Tunkhannock, Pa., 2,251.............C10 81
Tuntutuliak, Alsk., 158...C7 47
Tuolumne, Calif., 1,365..D3 50
Tuolumne, co., Calif., 32,169.............C4 50
Tupelo, Miss., 20,471....A5 68
Tupper Lake, N.Y., 4,584............A6, f10 75
Tupungato, mtn., Arg...A3 28
Tura, Sov. Un., 2,000....C13 13
Turbaco, Col., 14,255....A2 32
Turčiansky Svaty Martin, Czech., 22,400.......D5 7
Turda, Rom., 42,300 (*69,800)...........B6 10
Turek, Pol., 18,500......B5 7
Turfan, see Tulufan, China
Turgay, Sov. Un., 5,800..E9 13
Turgovishte, Bul., 25,502..D8 10
Turgutlu, Tur., 40,986...C6 14
Turin (Torino), It., 1,177,000 (*1,560,000)........B1 9
Turka, Sov. Un., 10,000..G4 12
Turkestan, Sov. Un., 54,000.............E9 13
Túrkeve, Hung., 10,103 (11,415 ▲)..........B5 10
Turkey, Tex., 680.......B2 84
Turkey, country, Asia, Eur., 38,355,000......C9 14

Turkmen, S.S.R., rep., Sov. Un., 2,330,000...*F8 16
Turks & Caicos Islands, Br. dep., N.A., 6,000...D8 35
Turku (Åbo), Fin., 155,497 (*204,000)....G10 11
Turku-Pori, prov., Fin., 678,000............*G10 11
Turley, Okla., 6,300.....A6 79
Turlock, Calif., 13,992...D3 50
Turner, Kans..........B8 61
Turner, co., Ga., 8,790...E3 55
Turner, co., S. Dak., 9,872.G8 77
Turners Falls, Mass., 4,470.A2 65
Turner Valley, Alta., Can., 702...............D3 38
Turnhout, Bel., 38,194....B6 5
Turnov, Czech., 13,077...C3 7
Turnovo, Bul., 37,269...D7 10
Turnu Măgurele, Rom., 18,055.............D7 10
Turnu Severin, Rom., 45,400.............C6 10
Turquino, peak, Cuba....D5 35
Turtkul, Sov. Un., 19,000..E9 13
Turtle Creek, Pa., 8,308..k14 81
Turukhansk, Sov. Un., 5,000..............C11 13
Tuscaloosa, Ala., 65,773 (*98,200)..........B2 46
Tuscaloosa, co., Ala., 116,029............B2 46
Tuscany, reg., It.......C3 9
Tuscarawas, co., Ohio, 77,211.............B4 78
Tuscola, Ill., 3,917......D5 58
Tuscola, co., Mich., 48,285.............E7 66
Tusculum College, Tenn., 1,180.............*C5 83
Tuscumbia, Ala., 8,828...A2 46
Tuskegee, Ala., 11,028...C4 46
Tuskegee Institute, Ala....C4 46
Tustin, Calif., 21,178....*F5 50
Tuticorin, India, 155,310 (*181,913).........G6 20
Tutrakan, Bul., 7,203....C8 10
Tuttlingen, Ger., Fed. Rep. of, 32,212..........E4 6
Tutwiler, Miss., 1,103...A3 68
Tuxedo, Md., 1,000.....C4 53
Tuxedo Park, N.Y., 861...............D6, m14 75

Tuxpan, Mex., 20,322...........C3, m11 34
Tuxpan, Mex., 14,693....n12 34
Tuxpan de Rodriguez Cano, Mex., 33,901.......C5, m15 34
Tuxtla Gutiérrez, Mex., 66,857.............D6 34
Tuy, Sp., 2,779.........A1 8
Tuyün, China, 60,000...F6 17
Tuzla, Yugo., 53,825....C4 10
Tweed, Ont., Can., 1,738..............C7 41
Twenty-Nine Palms, Calif., 5,667..............E5 50
Twig, Minn., 175.......D6 67
Twiggs, co., Ga., 8,222...D3 55
Twillingate, Newf., Can., 1,437..............D4 44
Twin City, Ga., 1,119...D4 55
Twin Falls, Idaho, 21,914..G4 57
Twin Falls, co., Idaho, 41,807............G4 57
Twin Lakes, Calif., 2,300..............*D2 50
Twin Lakes, Ohio, 1,200..*A4 78
Twin Lakes, Wis., 2,276...........F5, n11 88
Twin Oaks, Pa., 1,600...*G11 81
Twin Orchards, N.Y., 1,500.............*C15 75
Twin Rocks, Pa., 700....F4 81
Twinsburg, Ohio, 6,432...A4 78
Two Harbors, Minn., 4,437..............C7 67
Two Rivers, Wis., 13,553...........D6, h10 88
Tyler, Minn., 1,069.....F2 67
Tyler, Tex., 57,770 (*77,100)......C5 84
Tyler, co., Tex., 12,417...D5 84
Tyler, co., W. Va., 9,929..B4 87
Tyler Park, Va., 1,650...*B5 85
Tylertown, Miss., 1,736...D3 68
Tyndall, S. Dak., 1,245...H8 77
Tynemouth, Eng., 68,740..C6 4
Tyre, see Sūr, Leb.
Tyrrell, co., N.C., 3,806...B6 76
Tyrone, Pa., 7,072......E5 81
Tyrone, co., N. Ire., 138,975............*C3 4
Tyumen, Sov. Un., 269,000............D9 13
Tzukung, China, 280,000..F5 17

U

Ubá, Braz., 29,025.....C4, g6 30
Ube, Jap., 152,935 (*203,000)..........J5 18
Ubeda, Sp., 28,956.....C4 8
Uberaba, Braz., 108,576..B3 30
Uberlândia, Braz., 110,463.B3 30
Ubon Ratchathani, Thai., 40,650.............B2 19
Uccle, Bel., 79,225.....B6 5
Udaipur, India, 161,278...D5 20
Uddevalla, Swe., 47,306...H4 11
Udine, It., 95,700 (*115,000)..........A4 9
Udon Thani, Thai., 56,218.............B2 19
Ueda, Jap., 93,198...H9, m17 18
Uelen, Sov. Un., 800....C21 13
Uelkal, Sov. Un., 800....C21 13
Uelzen, Ger., Fed. Rep. of, 37,819............B5 6
Ueno, Jap., 41,000 (57,666 ▲)..........o15 18
Ufa, Sov. Un., 771,000...D8 13
Uganda, country, Afr., 10,940,000.........H4 23
Uglegorsk (Esutoru), Sov. Un., 20,000......B11 18
Uglich, Sov. Un., 35,000.............C12 12
Uherské Hradiště, Czech., 15,796 (*32,000)......D4 7
Uhrichsville, Ohio, 5,731..B4 78
Ŭijongbu, Kor., 94,518....H3 18
Uinta, co., Wyo., 7,100...E2 89
Uintah, co., Utah, 12,684..B7 72
Uitenhage, S. Afr., 69,048.............G5 24
Uji, Jap., 103,497.....*o14 18

Ujjain, India, 203,278 (*208,561).........D6 20
Ujung Pandang, Indon., 434,766............G5 19
Ukhta, Sov. Un., 63,000..C8 13
Ukiah, Calif., 10,095....C2 50
Ukraine (S.S.R.), rep., Sov. Un., 48,810,000...*E6 16
Ulan Bator (Urga), Mong., 262,600............B6 17
Ulan-Ude, Sov. Un., 254,000............D13 13
Ulhasnagar, India, 168,462............*E5 20
Ulla, Sov. Un., 10,000....D7 12
Ulm, Ger., Fed. Rep. of, 93,407 (*200,000)....D4 6
Ulman, Mo., 100.......C5 69
Ulsan, Kor., 108,000 (159,340 ▲).........I4 18
Ulster, co., N.Y., 141,241..D6 75
Ulster, prov., Ire., 208,303.............*C3 4
Ulugh Muztagh, mtn., China..............A8 20
Ulverston, Eng., 12,010...C5 4
Ulyanovsk, Sov. Un., 351,000............D7 13
Ulysses, Kans., 3,779....E2 61
Uman, Sov. Un., 63,000..G8 12
Umatilla, Fla., 1,600....D5 54
Umatilla, co., Oreg., 44,923.............B7 80
Umbria, pol. dist., It., 794,745...........*C4 9
Umbria, reg., It., 783,200..C4 9
Umeå, Swe., 57,898......F9 11
Umm Durmān, see Omdurman, Sud.

Umm Ruwābah, Sud., 7,805..............F4 23
'Umrān, Yemen, 20,000...F3 15
Umtali, Rh., 50,000 (*54,000)..........D6 24
Umvuma, Rh., 1,750....D6 24
Una, S.C., 2,000.......*B4 82
Unadilla, Ga., 1,457....D3 55
Unadilla, N.Y., 1,489....C5 75
'Unayzah, Sua., Ar., 50,000.............D3 15
Uncasville, Conn., 1,350..D8 52
Uncompahgre, mts., Colo..C3 51
Underwood, N. Dak., 781..C4 77
Unecha, Sov. Un., 22,000..E9 12
Unggi, Kor., 20,882.....E5 18
Unicoi, co., Tenn., 15,254.............C11 83
Unidad de San Juan de Aragón, Mex., 61,525..*D5 34
Union, Miss., 1,856......C4 68
Union, Mo., 5,183......C6 69
Union, N.J., 53,077.....B4 74
Union, Ohio, 3,654.....C1 78
Union, Oreg., 1,531.....B9 80
Union, S.C., 10,775.....B4 82
Union, co., Ark., 45,428..D3 49
Union, co., Fla., 8,112...B4 54
Union, co., Ga., 6,811...B2 55
Union, co., Ill., 16,071...F4 58
Union, co., Ind., 6,582...E8 59
Union, co., Iowa, 13,557..C3 60
Union, co., Ky., 15,882...C1 62
Union, co., Miss., 19,096..A4 68
Union, co., N.J., 543,116..B4 74
Union, co., N. Mex., 4,925..............A7 48
Union, co., N.C., 54,714.............*B2 76

Union, co., Ohio, 23,786.............B2 78
Union, co., Oreg., 19,377.............B8 80
Union, co., Pa., 28,603...E7 81
Union, co., S.C., 29,133..B4 82
Union, co., S. Dak., 9,643..............H9 77
Union, co., Tenn., 9,072.............C10 83
Union, par., La., 18,447.............B3 63
Union Beach, N.J., 6,472..C4 74
Union City, Calif., 14,724..h8 50
Union City, Ga., 3,031...C2 55
Union City, Ind., 3,995...D8 59
Union City, Mich., 1,740..F5 66
Union City, N.J., 57,305..h8 74
Union City, Ohio, 1,808...B1 78
Union City, Pa., 3,638...C2 81
Union City, Tenn., 11,925..A2 83
Uniondale, N.Y., 22,400..*G2 52
Unión de Reyes, Cuba, 7,000 (9,200 ▲).....C3 35
Union Gap, Wash., 2,040..C5 86
Union Grove, Wis., 2,703...........F5, n11 88
Union Lake, Mich., 9,000.............*F7 66
Union of Soviet Socialist Republics, country, Europe, Asia, 251,050,000...13
Union Park, Fla., 3,166...*D5 54
Union Point, Ga., 1,624...C3 55
Union Springs, Ala., 4,324..............C4 46
Union Springs, N.Y., 1,183..............C4 75
Uniontown, Ala., 2,133...C2 46

V

Volusia, co., Fla., 169,487 ..C5 54
Volzhskiy, Sov. Un.,
142,000................G15 12
Voorheesville, N.Y.,
2,826.................*C7 75
Vorarlberg, state, Aus.,
508,200...............E4 6
Vordingborg, Den.,
11,780.................A1 7
Vorkuta, Sov. Un.,
90,000................C9 13

Voronezh, Sov. Un.,
660,000..............F12 12
Voroshilovgrad (Lugansk),
Sov. Un., 383,000 .G12, q22 12
Vosges, dept., Fr.,
388,201.................*C7 5
Votkinsk, Sov. Un.,
74,000.................*D8 13
Voznesensk, Sov. Un.,
36,000................H8 12
Vranje, Yugo., 25,685...D5 10

Vratsa, Bul., 39,091.......D6 10
Vratsa, co., Bul., 308,852..D6 10
Vršac, Yugo., 34,231....C5 10
Vsetín, Czech., 22,092....D5 7
Vukovar, Yugo., 30,149...C4 10
Vulcan, Alta., Can.,
1,310.................D4 38
Vulcan, Mo., 100.........D7 69
Vung Tau, Viet., 54,200..*C3 19
Vyazma, Sov. Un.,
44,000...............D10 12

Vyazniki, Sov. Un.,
43,000................C14 12
Vyborg, Sov. Un.,
65,000.................A7 12
Vyksa, Sov. Un.,
46,000................D14 12
Vyshniy Volochek,
Sov. Un., 74,000......C10 12
Vysoké Tatry, Czech......D6 7
Vytegra, Sov. Un.,
11,800...............A11 12

W

Wabana (Bell Island),
Newf., Can., 5,421.....E5 44
Wabash, Ind., 13,379.....C6 59
Wabash, co., Ill., 12,841...E6 58
Wabash, co., Ind., 35,553..C6 59
Wabasha, Minn., 2,371..F6 67
Wabasha, co., Minn.,
17,224................F6 67
Wabasso, Fla., 600.......E6 54
Wabaunsee, co., Kans.,
6,397.................D7 61
Wacissa, Fla., 300........B3 54
Waco, Tex., 95,326
(*127,700).............D4 84
Waconia, Minn., 2,445....F5 67
Waddington, B.C., Can....F8 36
Waddington, N.Y., 955.....f9 75
Wadena, Sask., Can.,
1,311.................F4 39
Wadena, Minn., 4,640...D3 67
Wadena, co., Minn.,
12,412................D4 67
Wadesboro, N.C., 3,977...C2 76
Wadley, Ga., 1,989.......D4 55
Wad Madani, Sud., 63,700.F4 23
Wadsworth, Ohio, 13,142..A4 78
Waelder, Tex., 1,138......E4 84
Wagga Wagga, Austl.,
28,814................G8 25
Wagner, S. Dak., 1,655...G7 77
Wagoner, Okla., 4,959....B6 79
Wagoner, co., Okla.,
22,163................B6 79
Wagon Mound, N. Mex.,
630...................B6 48
Wągrowiec, Pol., 15,600..B4 7
Wah Cantonment, Pak.,
109,000...............*B5 20
Wahiawa, Haw.,
17,598..............B3, f9 56
Wahkiakum, co., Wash.,
3,592.................C2 86
Wahneta, Fla., 2,733.....*E5 54
Wahoo, Nebr., 3,835..C9, g11 71
Wahpeton, N. Dak., 7,076..D9 77
Waialua, Haw., 4,047..B3, f9 56
Waianae, Haw., 3,302..B3, g9 56
Waikabubak, Indon.,
3,934.................G5 19
Wailua, Haw., 1,379......A2 56
Wailuku, Haw., 7,979.....C5 56
Waimanalo, Haw.,
2,081..............B4, g11 56
Waimea, Haw., 1,569.....B2 56
Waimea, Haw., 756........f9 56
Wainwright, Alta., Can.,
3,872.................C5 38
Waipahu, Haw., 22,798.B3, g9 56
Waipio Acres, Haw.,
2,146.................g9 56
Waite Park, Minn., 2,824..E4 67
Waitsburg, Wash., 953...C7 86
Wajima, Jap., 18,500
(33,652 ▲).............H8 18
Wakarusa, Ind., 1,160....A5 59
Wakaw, Sask., Can., 974..E3 39
Wakayama, Jap.,
365,267.........I7, o14 18
Wakayama, pref., Jap.,
1,042,736.............*I7 18
Wake, co., N.C., 228,453..B4 76
WaKeeney, Kans., 2,334...C4 61
Wakefield, Mass.,
25,402.............B5, f11 65
Wakefield, Mich., 2,757..n12 66
Wakefield, Nebr., 1,160...B9 71
Wakefield, R.I., 3,300...D11 52
Wakefield, Va., 942.......D6 85
Wake Forest, N.C., 3,148..B4 76
Wakkanai, Jap., 54,493..D10 18
Wakulla, co., Fla., 6,308..B2 54
Walbridge, Ohio, 3,208....e6 78

Wałbrzych, Pol., 125,000
(*160,000).............C4 7
Walden, N.Y., 5,277......D6 75
Waldo, Ark., 1,658.......D2 49
Waldo, co., Maine,
28,328................D3 64
Waldorf, Md., 6,000......C4 53
Waldron, Ark., 2,132.....C1 49
Waldwick, N.J., 12,313....A4 74
Wales, reg., U.K.,
2,775,000..............D5 4
Walhalla, N. Dak., 1,471..A8 77
Walhalla, S.C., 3,662.....B1 82
Walker, La., 1,363.......g10 63
Walker, Mich., 11,492....E5 66
Walker, Minn., 1,073.....C4 67
Walker, co., Ala., 56,246..B2 46
Walker, co., Ga., 50,691..B1 55
Walker, co., Tex., 27,680..D5 84
Walkersville, Md., 1,269..B3 53
Walkerton, Ont., Can.,
4,479.................C3 41
Walkerton, Ind., 2,006...B5 59
Walkertown, N.C., 1,652..A2 76
Walkerville, Mont., 1,097..D4 70
Wall, Pa., 1,265.........*F2 81
Wallace, Idaho, 2,206.....B3 57
Wallace, N.C., 2,095.....C4 76
Wallace, co., Kans., 2,215..D2 61
Wallaceburg, Ont., Can.,
10,550................E2 41
Wallasey, Eng., 97,470...D5 4
Walla Walla, Wash.,
23,619................C7 86
Walla Walla, co., Wash.,
42,176................C7 86
Walled Lake, Mich.,
3,759................o15 66
Waller, Tex., 1,123.......D5 84
Waller, co., Tex., 14,285..E4 84
Wallingford, Conn.,
35,714................D5 52
Wallingford, Vt., 800.....E2 73
Wallington, Eng.,
32,500...............m12 4
Wallington, N.J., 10,284..h8 74
Wallis, Tex., 1,033.......E4 84
Wallkill, N.Y., 1,849......D6 75
Wallowa, Oreg., 811.....B9 80
Wallowa, co., Oreg., 6,247..B9 80
Wallsend, Eng., 45,950...C6 4
Walnut, Calif., 5,992.....*F4 50
Walnut, Ill., 1,295.......B4 58
Walnut Cove, N.C., 1,213..A2 76
Walnut Creek, Calif.,
39,844................h8 50
Walnut Heights, Calif.,
700..................*D2 50
Walnut Park, Calif.,
8,925................*F4 50
Walnutport, Pa., 1,942...E10 81
Walnut Ridge, Ark., 3,800..A5 49
Walpole, Mass., 8,500.B5, h10 65
Walsall, Eng., 184,380.....D6 4
Walsenburg, Colo., 4,329..D6 51
Walsh, co., N. Dak.,
16,251................B8 77
Walterboro, S.C., 6,257...F6 82
Walters, Okla., 2,611.....C3 79
Walthall, co., Miss.,
12,500................D3 68
Waltham, Mass.,
61,582.............B5, g11 65
Walthill, Nebr., 897.......B9 71
Walton, Ind., 1,054......C5 59
Walton, Ky., 1,801...B5, k13 62
Walton, N.Y., 3,744......C5 75
Walton, co., Fla., 16,087.u15 54
Walton, co., Ga., 23,404...C3 55
Walton Hills, Ohio,
2,508................*A4 78
Walvisbaai, S. Afr., 21,725.E2 24

Walworth, Wis., 1,637.....F5 88
Walworth, co., S. Dak.,
7,842.................E5 77
Walworth, co., Wis.,
63,444................F5 88
Wamac, Ill., 1,347.......E4 58
Wamego, Kans., 2,507...C7 61
Wampum, Pa., 1,189....E1 81
Wanamassa, N.J., 4,000..C4 74
Wanaque, N.J., 8,636....A4 74
Wanganui, N.Z., 35,750
(*38,000).............M15 26
Wangaratta, Austl.,
15,535................H6 26
Wangching, China.......C10 17
Wanhsien, China, 90,000..E6 17
Wankie, Rh., 23,000......D5 24
Wantagh, N.Y., 22,300...G2 52
Wapakoneta, Ohio, 7,324..B1 78
Wapato, Wash., 2,841....C5 86
Wapello, Iowa, 1,873.....C6 60
Wapello, co., Iowa, 42,149.C5 60
Wappingers Falls, N.Y.,
5,607.................D7 75
War, W. Va., 2,004.......D3 87
Warangal, India, 207,520..E6 20
Ward, W. Va., 125.......m13 87
Ward, co., N. Dak., 58,560..B4 77
Ward, co., Tex., 13,019...D1 84
Warden, Wash., 1,254....C6 86
Ward Ridge, Fla., 8......*C1 54
Wardville, La., 1,087.....*C3 63
Ware, Mass., 6,509.......B3 65
Ware, co., Ga., 33,525....E4 55
Wareham, Mass., 2,024...C6 65
Warehouse Point, Conn.,
700..................B6 52
Waren, Ger. Dem. Rep.,
19,700................B6 6
Ware Shoals, S.C., 2,480..C3 82
Warfield, B.C., Can.,2,132.E9 37
Warner Robins, Ga.,
33,491................D3 55
Warr Acres, Okla., 9,887..B4 79
Warragul, Austl., 7,103...*G8 25
Warren, Ark., 6,433.......D3 49
Warren, Ill., 1,523.......A4 58
Warren, Ind., 1,229......C7 59
Warren, Mass., 1,688....B3 65
Warren, Mich.,
179,260.........F7, p16 66
Warren, Minn., 1,999....B2 67
Warren, Ohio, 63,494....A5 78
Warren, Pa., 12,998......C3 81
Warren, R.I., 10,523.....C11 52
Warren, co., Ga., 6,669...C4 55
Warren, co., Ill., 21,595..C3 58
Warren, co., Ind., 8,705..D3 59
Warren, co., Iowa, 27,432..C4 60
Warren, co., Ky., 57,432..C3 62
Warren, co., Miss., 44,981..C3 68
Warren, co., Mo., 9,699...C6 69
Warren, co., N.J., 73,960..B3 74
Warren, co., N.Y., 49,402..B7 75
Warren, co., N.C., 15,810..A4 76
Warren, co., Ohio, 85,505..C1 78
Warren, co., Pa., 47,682..C3 81
Warren, co., Tenn.,
26,972................D8 83
Warren, co., Va., 15,301..B4 85
Warrensburg, Mo., 13,125.C4 69
Warrensburg, N.Y., 2,743.B7 75
Warrensville Heights,
Ohio, 18,925..........h9 78
Warrenton, Ga., 2,073....C4 55
Warrenton, Mo., 2,057....C6 69
Warrenton, N.C., 1,035...A4 76
Warrenton, Oreg., 1,825..A3 80
Warrenton, Va., 4,027....B5 85
Warrenville, Ill., 3,281...k8 58
Warrenville, S.C., 1,059..D4 82
Warri, Nig., 55,254......G6 22

Warrick, co., Ind., 27,972..H3 59
Warrington, Eng.,
67,890 (*135,000)......D5 4
Warrington, Fla., 15,848..u14 54
Warrior, Ala., 2,621......B3 46
Warrnambool, Austl.,
18,663.............G7, n14 25
Warroad, Minn., 1,086...B3 67
Warsaw, Ill., 1,758......C2 58
Warsaw, Ind., 7,506.....B6 59
Warsaw, Mo., 1,423.....C4 69
Warsaw, N.Y., 3,619.....C2 75
Warsaw, N.C., 2,701....B4 76
Warsaw (Warszawa),
Pol., 1,308,100
(*1,760,000).......B6, m14 7
Warson Woods, Mo.,
2,544................*C7 69
Warwick, Que., Can.,
2,847.................D6 42
Warwick, Eng., 18,040...D6 4
Warwick, N.Y.,
3,604............D6, m14 75
Warwick, R.I., 83,694...C10 52
Warwick, co., Eng.,
2,081,690.............*D6 4
Wasatch, co., Utah, 5,863..A6 72
Wasco, Calif., 8,269......E4 50
Wasco, co., Oreg., 20,133.B5 80
Waseca, Minn., 6,789....F5 67
Waseca, co., Minn.,
16,663................F5 67
Washabaugh, co., S. Dak.,
1,389.................G4 77
Washakie, co., Wyo.,
7,569.................C5 89
Washburn, Ill., 1,173....C4 58
Washburn, Maine, 1,098..B4 64
Washburn, Wis., 1,957...B3 88
Washburn, co., Wis.,
10,601................C2 88
Washington, D.C.,
756,510
(*2,964,500).......C3, f8 53
Washington, Ga., 4,094...C4 55
Washington, Ill., 6,790...C4 58
Washington, Ind., 11,358.G3 59
Washington, Iowa, 6,317..C6 60
Washington, Kans., 1,584..C6 61
Washington, La., 1,473...D3 63
Washington, Mo., 8,499...C6 69
Washington, N.J., 5,943..B3 74
Washington, N.C., 8,961..B5 76
Washington, Pa., 19,827..F1 81
Washington, co., Ala.,
16,241................D1 46
Washington, co., Ark.,
77,370................A1 49
Washington, co., Colo.,
5,550.................B7 51
Washington, co., Fla.,
11,453...............u16 54
Washington, co., Ga.,
17,480................C3 55
Washington, co., Idaho,
7,633.................E2 57
Washington, co., Ill.,
13,780................E4 58
Washington, co., Ind.,
19,278................G5 59
Washington, co., Iowa,
18,967................C6 60
Washington, co., Kan.,
9,249.................C6 61
Washington, co., Ky.,
10,728................C4 62
Washington, co., Maine,
27,859................D5 64
Washington, co., Md.,
103,829...............A2 53
Washington, co., Minn.,
82,948................E6 67

X

Y

Z